Biochemical Actions of Hormones

Volume X

Contributors

Evelyn R. Barrack

Ralph A. Bradshaw

Juan Casanova

Donald S. Coffey

Herbert W. Dickerman

Kevin P. Dolan

Howard J. Eisen

Philip Feigelson

Mark Feldman

David L. Gasser

Allen S. Goldman

Rita R. Hannah

Harriette Haubenstock

Vincent P. Hollander

Zebulun D. Horowitz

Tamiko Kano-Sueoka

S. Anand Kumar

Yannick Laperche

Wendell W. Leavitt

Catherine Legraverend

Kevin R. Lynch

Richard G. MacDonald

Margaret McLaughlin

Hira L. Nakhasi

Daniel W. Nebert

Allan B. Okey

William C. Okulicz

Bruce M. Raaka

Rosemary Reinke

Herbert H. Samuels

Lawrence E. Shapiro

Frederick Stanley

John Stevens

Yee-Wan Stevens

Jir S. Tsai

Ronald Unterman

Albert Volchek

Franz Waldhauser

Richard J. Wurtman

Barry M. Yaffe

Biochemical Actions of Hormones

Edited by GERALD LITWACK

Fels Research Institute and Department of Biochemistry
Temple University, School of Medicine
Philadelphia, Pennsylvania

VOLUME X

1983

ACADEMIC PRESS

A Subsidiary of Harcourt Brace Jovanovich, Publishers

New York   London

Paris   San Diego   San Francisco   São Paulo   Sydney   Tokyo   Toronto

ACADEMIC PRESS, INC.
111 Fifth Avenue, New York, New York 10003

United Kingdom Edition published by
ACADEMIC PRESS, INC. (LONDON) LTD.
24/28 Oval Road, London NW1 7DX

Liorary of Congress Cataloging in Publication Data
Main entry under title:

Biochemical actions of hormones.

Includes bibliographies.
1. Hormones--Collected works. I. Litwack, Gerald, ed.
II. Axelrod, Julius, Date. [DNLM: 1. Hormones.
2. Physiology. WK102 B615]
QP571.B56   574.19'27   70-107567
ISBN 0-12-452810-4 (v. 10)

Contents

1. The Application of Recombinant Techniques to the Study of the Control of α_{2u} Globulin Gene Expression

Kevin P. Dolan, Rosemary Reinke, Kevin R. Lynch, Margaret McLaughlin, Ronald Unterman, Hira L. Nakhasi, Yannick Laperche, and Philip Feigelson

2. The Role of the Nuclear Matrix in Steroid Hormone Action

Evelyn R. Barrack and Donald S. Coffey

3.   Nerve Growth Factor and Related Hormones

Ralph A. Bradshaw

4.   Hormonal Regulation of Growth Hormone Synthesis in Cell Cultures: Role of Thyroid and Glucocorticoid Hormone Receptors

Herbert H. Samuels, Juan Casanova, Zebulun D. Horowitz, Bruce M. Raaka, Lawrence E. Shapiro, Frederick Stanley, Jir S. Tsai, and Barry M. Yaffe

5.   Factors Affecting Mammary Cells in Culture

Tamiko Kano-Sueoka

10. Hormonal Regulation of Estrogen and Progesterone Receptor Systems

Wendell W. Leavitt, Richard G. MacDonald, and William C. Okulicz

11. Genetic and Biochemical Studies on Glucocorticoid-Induced Cleft Palate

David L. Gasser and Allen S. Goldman

12. Molecular Basis of Glucocorticoid Resistance in Experimental and Human Leukemia

John Stevens, Yee-Wan Stevens, and Harriette Haubenstock

Contributors

Numbers in parentheses indicate the pages on which the author's contributions begin.

Evelyn R. Barrack (23), The James Buchanan Brady Urological Institute of the Department of Urology, Department of Pharmacology and Experimental Therapeutics, The Johns Hopkins Oncology Center, Johns Hopkins University School of Medicine, Baltimore, Maryland 21205

Ralph A. Bradshaw* (91), Department of Biological Chemistry, Washington University School of Medicine, St. Louis, Missouri 63110

Juan Casanova (115), Division of Molecular Endocrinology, The Rose F. Tishman Laboratories for Geriatric Endocrinology, Department of Medicine, New York University Medical Center, New York, New York 10016

Donald S. Coffey (23), The Department of Urology, The Johns Hopkins University School of Medicine, Baltimore, Maryland 21205

Herbert W. Dickerman (259), Department of Biochemistry, Albany Medical College, Albany, New York 12201

Kevin P. Dolan (1), The Institute of Cancer Research, Department of Biochemistry, College of Physicians and Surgeons, Columbia University, New York, New York 10032

Howard J. Eisen (227), Developmental Pharmacology Branch, National Institute of Child Health and Human Development, National Institutes of Health, Bethesda, Maryland 20205

* Present address: Department of Biological Chemistry, University of California—Irvine, California College of Medicine, Irvine, California 92717.

Philip Feigelson (1), The Institute of Cancer Research, Department of Biochemistry, College of Physicians and Surgeons, Columbia University, New York, New York 10032

Mark Feldman (303), Department of Surgery and Neoplastic Diseases, Mount Sinai School of Medicine, New York, New York 10029

David L. Gasser (357), Department of Human Genetics, University of Pennsylvania School of Medicine, Philadelphia, Pennsylvania 19104

Allen S. Goldman (357), Division of Human Genetics and Teratology, The Children's Hospital of Philadephia, Philadelphia, Pennsylvania 19104

Rita R. Hannah (227), Developmental Pharmacology Branch, National Institute of Child Health and Human Development, National Institutes of Health, Bethesda, Maryland 20205

Harriette Haubenstock (383), Department of Neoplastic Diseases, Mount Sinai School of Medicine, New York, New York 10029

Vincent P. Hollander (303), Department of Surgery and Neoplastic Diseases, Mount Sinai School of Medicine, New York, New York 10029

Zebulun D. Horowitz (115), Division of Molecular Endocrinology, The Rose F. Tishman Laboratories for Geriatric Endocrinology, Department of Medicine, New York University Medical Center, New York, New York 10016

Tamiko Kano-Sueoka (163), Department of Molecular, Cellular, and Developmental Biology, University of Colorado, Boulder, Colorado 80309

S. Anand Kumar* (259), Department of Chemistry, State University of New York at Albany, Albany, New York 12201

Yannick Laperche (1), The Institute of Cancer Research, Department of Biochemistry, College of Physicians and Surgeons, Columbia University, New York, New York 10032

Wendell W. Leavitt (323), Worcester Foundation for Experimental Biology, Shrewsbury, Massachusetts 01545

* Present address: Center for Laboratories and Research, New York State Department of Health, Empire State Plaza, Albany, New York 12201.

Catherine Legraverend (227), Developmental Pharmacology Branch, National Institute of Child Health and Human Development, National Institutes of Health, Bethesda, Maryland 20205

Kevin R. Lynch (1), The Institute of Cancer Research, Department of Biochemistry, College of Physicians and Surgeons, Columbia University, New York, New York 10032

Richard G. MacDonald (323), Worcester Foundation for Experimental Biology, Shrewsbury, Massachusetts 01545

Margaret McLaughlin (1), The Institute of Cancer Research, Department of Biochemistry, College of Physicians and Surgeons, Columbia University, New York, New York 10032

Hira L. Nakhasi* (1), The Institute of Cancer Research, Department of Biochemistry, College of Physicians and Surgeons, Columbia University, New York, New York 10032

Daniel W. Nebert (227), Developmental Pharmacology Branch, National Institute of Child Health and Human Development, National Institutes of Health, Bethesda, Maryland 20205

Allan B. Okey (227), Department of Pediatrics, Division of Clinical Pharmacology, The Hospital for Sick Children, Toronto, Canada M5G 1X8

William C. Okulicz (323), Worcester Foundation for Experimental Biology, Shrewsbury, Massachusetts 01545

Bruce M. Raaka (115), Division of Molecular Endocrinology, The Rose F. Tishman Laboratories for Geriatric Endocrinology, Department of Medicine, New York University Medical Center, New York, New York 10016

Rosemary Reinke (1), The Institute of Cancer Research, Department of Biochemistry, College of Physicians and Surgeons, Columbia University, New York, New York 10032

Herbert H. Samuels (115), Division of Molecular Endocrinology, The Rose F. Tishman Laboratories for Geriatric Endocrinology,

---

* Present address. Laboratory of Pathophysiology, National Cancer Institute, National Institutes of Health, Bethesda, Maryland 20205.

Department of Medicine, New York University Medical Center, New York, New York 10016

Lawrence E. Shapiro (115), Department of Medicine, Division of Endocrinology and Metabolism, Montefiore Medical Center and the Albert Einstein College of Medicine, Bronx, New York 10467

Frederick Stanley (115), Division of Molecular Endocrinology, The Rose F. Tishman Laboratories for Geriatric Endocrinology, Department of Medicine, New York University Medical Center, New York, New York 10016

John Stevens (383), Research Department, American Cancer Society, New York, New York 10017

Yee-Wan Stevens (383), Memorial Sloan-Kettering Cancer Center, New York, New York 10021

Jir S. Tsai (115), Endocrine Division, Department of Medicine, New York University Medical Center, New York, New York 10016

Ronald Unterman (1), The Institute of Cancer Research, Department of Biochemistry, College of Physicians and Surgeons, Columbia University, New York, New York 10032

Albert Volchek (303), Department of Surgery and Neoplastic Diseases, Mount Sinai School of Medicine, New York, New York 10029

Franz Waldhauser* (187), Laboratory of Neuroendocrine Regulation, Massachusetts Institute of Technology, Cambridge, Massachusetts 02139

Richard J. Wurtman (187), Laboratory of Neuroendocrine Regulation, Massachusetts Institute of Technology, Cambridge, Massachusetts 02139

Barry M. Yaffe (115), Division of Molecular Endocrinology, The Rose F. Tishman Laboratories for Geriatric Endocrinology, Department of Medicine, New York University Medical Center, New York, New York 10016

---

* Present address: Universitäts-Kinderklinik, Waehringer Guertel 74-76, Vienna A-1090, Austria.

Preface

Two important areas have had impact on biochemical endocrinology recently, one of which is the application of recombinant DNA technology to genes for hormones. New information on the genetic regulation of these genes can be expected. Another exciting development is that the nuclear matrix may represent a preferred acceptor site for certain steroid hormone receptor complexes. These two advances are highlighted in two contributions to this volume, the first as approached by the Feigelson group for the α_{2u} globulin gene and its regulation by several hormones, and the second by the Coffey laboratory reviewing their observations on the nuclear matrix. An excellent model for determining the roles of various receptors operating at the genetic level has embodied the use of cells in culture derived from the anterior pituitary. These cells are capable of secreting hormones in response to the stimuli of releasing factors as well as other hormones and have retained capacity for feedback inhibition. Progress along these lines is reported in a contribution from the Samuels laboratory. Future volumes can be expected to concentrate on similar models. Since certain polypeptide hormones apparently share ancestral, closely related genes and consequently various aspects of their structures, Bradshaw summarizes this conceptual advance by reviewing the nerve growth factor and related hormones. Also, many of the polypeptide hormones have come to be recognized as growth factors for cells in culture. Kano-Sueoka reviews her work in this area and related studies on factors affecting the growth of mammary cells in culture. Some new insights into the pineal hormone, melatonin, have appeared. These are summarized in a timely article from Wurtman's laboratory.

The remainder of the topics covered here deal with more specific subjects. Recent studies in the Nebert laboratory on the *Ah* receptor have produced a great deal of information on a specific carcinogen receptor which seems to be analogous in many respects to a steroid receptor. This interesting subject appears here for the benefit of endocrinologists who may not be fully aware of this fascinating system. The remaining five chapters center around various aspects of steroid receptors. Current interest has been expressed in specific acceptor sites in genes and their flanking sequences.

Therefore, the work taking place in Dickerman's laboratory on synthetic oligonucleotide acceptors for steroid receptor complexes is reviewed. With this interesting introduction it is to be hoped that future treatises in this series will review the developing work on identifying gene sequences involved in high-affinity binding sites for steroid receptor complexes. Hollander's laboratory reviews mammary tumor growth and response to ovariectomy, which is of particular interest with respect to specific alterations in the estradiol receptor. Leavitt's laboratory reviews the hormonal regulation of estrogen and progesterone receptors. The genesis of cleft palate provides an experimental model which may lead to an understanding of the genetic regulation of factors involved in the expression of activities of the glucocorticoid receptor and possibly to specific chromosomal assignment of these functions. This subject is emphasized in a contribution from Gasser and Goldman. Finally, the Stevens group brings us up to date on the mechanisms of glucocorticoid resistance in leukemia cells and discusses the possibility of two apparently different steroid receptors which could result from the occurrence of separate gene products.

Modern endocrinology is developing very rapidly at the experimental level and is overlapping other disciplines, particularly molecular biology. I will attempt to keep abreast of these developments in future volumes of this publication.

Gerald Litwack

Biochemical Actions of Hormones

Volume X

CHAPTER 1

The Application of Recombinant Techniques to the Study of the Control of α_{2u} Globulin Gene Expression

Kevin P. Dolan, Rosemary Reinke,
Kevin R. Lynch, Margaret McLaughlin,
Ronald Unterman, Hira L. Nakhasi,
Yannick Laperche, and Philip Feigelson

I. INTRODUCTION

α_{2u} Globulin is a small (M_r 18,700, pI 5.1–5.5) protein synthesized predominantly in the liver and excreted in the urine of male rats (Roy and Neuhaus, 1966a; Roy *et al.*, 1966). It was first described by Roy *et al.*, who found it in the urine of male but not female rats and demonstrated that in order to excrete normal levels of α_{2u} globulin an adult male rat requires androgen, glucocorticoid, growth hormone, thyroxine, and insulin

BIOCHEMICAL ACTIONS OF HORMONES, VOL. X

(Roy and Neuhaus, 1967; Roy, 1973a,b; Roy and Leonard, 1973). Female rats will excrete α_{2u} globulin in response to androgen only if they are first ovariectomized (Sippel *et al.*, 1975); α_{2u} globulin excretion is drastically reduced in male animals by estrogen treatment (Roy *et al.*, 1975).

Glucocorticoids have been shown to act directly on hepatocyte suspensions *in vitro* to elevate α_{2u} globulin synthesis and secretion and this induction was shown to be α-amanitin sensitive (Chen and Feigelson, 1978, 1980). It should be noted, however, that the stimulatory effects of androgen, thyroid hormone, growth hormone, and insulin, as well as the suppressive effect of estrogen, have only been convincingly demonstrated *in vivo*. The possibility exists that certain of these latter hormones may elicit their hepatic α_{2u} globulin responses indirectly, e.g., estrogen via prolactin, thyroid hormone via growth hormone, and insulin and growth hormone via somatomedin. Thus, α_{2u} globulin synthesizing hepatocytes might be directly responding to a smaller set of hormones.

In addition to the complex hormonal control of α_{2u} globulin synthesis in adult male rats, its synthesis also follows a distinct developmental pattern. α_{2u} globulin is undetectable in the urine of male rats until the onset of puberty (about 31 days of age) (Roy, 1973b). From this point until adulthood the amount of α_{2u} globulin excreted increases reaching the mature level of approximately 20 mg/day at about 50 days of age. α_{2u} Globulin is excreted in this quantity throughout the life of the adult male rat, decreasing again to nearly undetectable levels in senescence (Roy and Neuhaus, 1966b; Roy *et al.*, 1974). Prior to the onset of puberty, administration of androgen will not induce α_{2u} globulin excretion (Roy, 1973b). Rats castrated before puberty, however, respond to androgen administration after 50 days of age by excreting α_{2u} globulin at near normal levels. It therefore appears that androgen is not required for the development of the competence to synthesize this protein. Conversely, hypophysectomy does prevent the development of this competence. Male rats hypophysectomized after puberty respond to injections of androgen, growth hormone, glucocorticoid, and thyroxine by excreting approximately normal levels of α_{2u} globulin, while animals hypophysectomized before puberty and treated similarly with these hormones at 65 days of age excrete only about 10% the normal levels (Lynch *et al.*, 1982) (Fig. 1). These results suggest that a hormone provided or directed by the pituitary is responsible for the development of the competence of the mature male liver to respond normally to androgen.

Further interest in the control of α_{2u} globulin synthesis is based on the finding that several transplantable hepatomas have lost the ability to synthesize this protein although the livers of the host rats continue to do so normally (Sippel *et al.*, 1976; Feigelson and DeLap, 1977). Thus, it is evident that understanding the control of α_{2u} globulin synthesis has the potential to provide useful insights into basic biological questions including the mechanisms responsible for tissue specific differentiation, the mode of actions of polypeptide, steroid, and other hormones, and the basis for altered gene expression consequent to neoplastic transformation. Considerable effort has, therefore, been focused on the elucidation of the biochemical processes underlying this complex hormonal and developmental control.

In order to determine whether the altered rates of α_{2u} globulin synthesis were due to fluctuations in the level of its mRNA, the hepatic levels of functional α_{2u} globulin mRNA were measured. These experiments involved the translation, in a heterologous cell-free system, of the mRNA isolated from the livers or tumors of rats in different hormonal states. The α_{2u} globulin synthesized *in vitro* under the direction of this mRNA was precipitated with monospecific antibody to α_{2u} globulin, separated on sodium dodecyl sulfate (SDS)–polyacrylamide gels, and quantified. In every case of endocrine (Kurtz *et al.*, 1976a,b; Roy and Dowbenko, 1977; Lynch *et al.*, 1982; Roy, 1973a,b; Roy and Leonard, 1973; Roy *et al.*, 1976a,b; Feigelson and Kurtz, 1978; Chen and Feigelson, 1980), developmental (Chatterjee and Roy, 1980), and neoplastic control (Sippel *et al.*, 1976; Feigelson and DeLap, 1977; Nakhasi *et al.*, 1982), the enrichment of the hepatic mRNA, measured by *in vitro* translation, paralleled exactly its *in vivo* rate of synthesis and the level of α_{2u} globulin excreted by the animal. A representative experiment of this type is shown in Figs. 1B and 5C. The coordinate rise in α_{2u} globulin synthesis and in its hepatic mRNA makes it likely that the site of developmental, neoplastic, and endocrine action is prior to the appearance of functional cytoplasmic α_{2u} globulin mRNA. For reviews of this work see Kurtz and Feigelson (1978) and Roy (1979). While transcription is a likely site of control (Chan *et al.*, 1978), processing of the gene transcript, transport of the mRNA to the cytoplasm, and the stability of each of the processing intermediates are all potential sites of regulation. To distinguish between these alternatives a specific probe capable of hybridizing with α_{2u} globulin sequences was required.

II. CLONING

We prepared and cloned α_{2u} globulin cDNA using standard technology (Unterman *et al.*, 1981). A cDNA copy was made from oligo(dT)-primed mature male liver RNA using reverse transcriptase to synthesize the first strand (Kacian and Myers, 1976) and DNA polymerase I for the second strand (Seeburg *et al.*, 1977). The double-stranded cDNA was inserted in the *Pst*I site of pBR322 by the G–C tailing method and transformed into

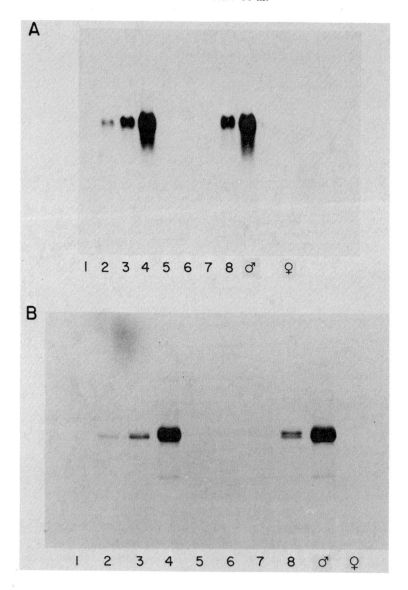

Fig. 1. Amount of α_{2u} globulin RNA present in the livers of hormone-treated hypophysectomized rats. (A) The autoradiograph depicted was generated by electrophoresis of 30 μg of
total RNA extracted from the livers of prepubescently hypophysectomized (lanes 5, 6, 7, and
8) or postpubescently hypophysectomized (lanes 1, 2, 3, and 4) rats through a 1.75% denaturing
agarose gel, after which the RNA was blotted onto nitrocellulose paper and hybridized to ^{32}P-
labeled α_{2u} globulin cDNA. The rats were treated with one of the following hormonal regimens
for 12 days: no hormones (lanes 1 and 5); dihydrotestosterone, L-thyroxine, and hydrocortisone

Escherichia coli strain HB101 (Roychoudhury *et al.*, 1976; Wensink *et al.*, 1974). A cDNA has also been prepared using linkers to adapt cDNA for insertion into plasmid (Kurtz and Nicodemus, 1981).

Clones containing α_{2u} globulin cDNA inserts were selected by taking advantage of the fact that no α_{2u} globulin mRNA could be detected in female rat liver by *in vitro* translation (Kurtz *et al.*, 1976b). *Escherichia coli* colonies containing adult male hepatic cDNA sequences were screened in duplicate with ^{32}P-labeled single-stranded cDNA reverse transcribed from male and female hepatic poly(A$^+$) RNA. A typical set of filters is shown in Fig. 2. The arrows indicate colonies scored as male specific. From a total of 800 colonies, 20 were found to hybridize to male but not to female cDNA sequences. Nineteen of these later proved to be α_{2u} globulin cDNA clones.

Our general strategy, cloning from unfractionated male poly(A$^+$) mRNA and screening with male and female sequences, is ideal for systems where the sequence(s) of interest are in relatively high abundance and represent a difference between closely related phenotypes. This procedure minimizes manipulation of the RNA, thereby reducing degradation and loss of RNA during purification. As the abundance of the sequence decreases, the use of unfractionated RNA for cloning becomes unwieldy simply due to the number of clones that must be screened. Screening can be simplified by first enriching the mRNA of interest prior to preparation of its cDNA by sucrose gradient or agarose gel fractionation or immunochemical isolation of polysomes. These techniques are especially useful for RNAs whose sizes are unusual in the population (Parnes *et al.*, 1981; Gray *et al.*, 1982; Lynch *et al.*, 1979). Glucose-6-phosphate dehydrogenase, whose mRNA represents less than 0.01% of the total mRNA in human fibroblasts, has been cloned in this manner (Persico *et al.*, 1981).

The sequences of interest need not represent absolute differences in phenotype. By carefully standardizing duplicate filters containing cDNA clones the relative abundance of a particular sequence in different popu-

---

acetate (lanes 2 and 6); dihydrotestosterone, L-thyroxine, hydrocortisone acetate, and 12 hours growth hormone (lanes 3 and 7); or dihydrotestosterone, L-thyroxine, hydrocortisone acetate, and 12 days growth hormone (lanes 4 and 8). Lanes 9 and 10 are RNA from intact adult male and female rats, respectively. Each lane contains RNA pooled from at least three rats. Radiographic time was 11 hours. (B) This fluorograph represents the amount of α_{2u} globulin synthesized *in vitro* in response to the RNA's described in (A). Total liver RNA was used to program a reticulocyte lysate-based system; ^{35}S-labeled α_{2u} globulin was isolated by immunoprecipitation and the dissolved immunoprecipitates were subjected to electrophoresis through a denaturing 12.5% acrylamide gel. The gel was treated for fluorography, dried, and allowed to expose X-ray film for 3 days. At this time it is uncertain whether the doublet in lane 8 represents different forms of α_{2u} globulin (K. R. Lynch and P. Feigelson, unpublished data). The lane designations are analogous to those in (A).

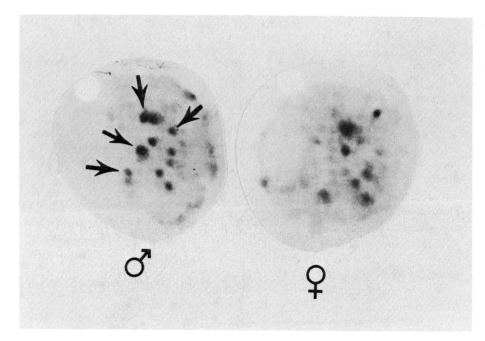

FIG. 2. Comparative colony hybridization. This autoradiogram shows two duplicate colony hybridizations of 60 adult male liver cDNA clones (colony positions are congruent). One filter (♂) was hybridized to ³²P-labeled cDNA prepared by reverse transcription of adult male liver poly(A⁺) RNA, and the other filter (♀) was hybridized to the corresponding female cDNA probe. Arrows indicate male-specific clones, i.e., those that hybridized to the male probe but not to the female probe.

lations of RNA can be determined. This can be done by hybridizing the filters to labeled RNA or first strand cDNA and comparing the intensity of hybridization of the duplicate colonies (Laskey *et al.*, 1980). Grunstein and Hogness (1975) have provided a valuable discussion of the kinetics of hybridization to sequences immobilized on filters.

The identity of the selected male-specific clones was confirmed by demonstrating that RNA that hybridized to DNA from these clones directed the synthesis of only one peptide in a heterologous cell-free protein synthesizing system and that this peptide was of the expected size and was immunoprecipitated by anti-α_{2u} globulin (Unterman *et al.*, 1981) (Fig. 3). Several of these clones were sequenced, revealing one open reading frame which specified the amino acid sequence of α_{2u} globulin (Fig. 4). This sequence was in agreement with the partial N-terminal amino acid sequence derived by sequential Edman degradation of purified urinary α_{2u} globulin. α_{2u} globulin was found to have a hydrophobic amino terminal leader sequence typical of secreted proteins. This leader sequence is processed

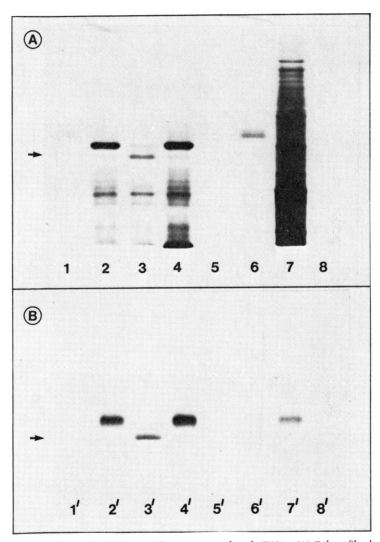

FIG. 3. Translation of mRNAs complementary to cloned cDNAs. (A) Gel profile showing the translation products of rat liver mRNAs complementary to several cloned cDNAs. Lanes 2 and 4, proteins derived from two of the selected male-specific clones; lane 1, protein derived from a control clone that was not male specific; lane 6, protein derived from clone p41, previously shown to contain a male cDNA that is not α_{2u} globulin; lane 3, translation product derived when canine pancreatic microsomes are included in the lane 2 translation reaction; lane 5, control demonstrating the lack of specific hybridization to the plasmid vector pBR322; lane 7, total translation products from poly(A^+) male liver RNA; lane 8, endogenous activity of the wheat germ system. Arrow indicates the mobility of purified urinary α_{2u} globulin. (B) Lanes 1'–8', the corresponding peptide products, if any, immunoprecipitable with anti-α_{2u} globulin. Those in lanes 2'–4' are immunologically identical to α_{2u} globulin, and those in lanes 1' and 6' are antigenically unrelated to α_{2u} globulin.

```
-15                                                              -1 +1
leu leu leu cys leu gly leu thr leu leu val cys gly his ala glu glu ala ser ser thr arg gly asn leu asp val ala
CTG CTG CTG TGT CTG GGC CTG ACA CTG CTG GTG TGT GGC CAT GCA GAA GAA GCT AGT TCC ACA AGA GGG AAC CTC GAT GTG GCT

                                                                                          40
lys leu asn gly asp trp phe ser ile val ala ser asn lys arg glu lys ile glu glu ser met arg val phe
AAG CTC AAT GGG GAT TGG TTT TCT ATT GTC GTG GCC TCT AAC AAA AGA GAA AAG ATA GAA GAG AAT GGC AGC ATG AGA GTT TTT
                                20

                                                      60
met gln his ile asp val leu glu asn ser leu gly phe lys phe arg ile lys glu ile lys glu gly asn gly leu tyr leu
ATG CAG CAC ATC GAT GTC TTG GAG AAT TCC TTA GGC TTC AAG TTC CGT ATT AAG GAA ATT AAG GAA GGA GAG CTA TAT TTG

                                                            80
val ala tyr lys thr pro glu asp gly glu tyr phe val glu tyr asp gly gly asn thr phe thr ile leu lys thr asp tyr
GTT GCC TAC AAA ACG CCA GAA GAT GGC GAA TAT TTT GTT GAG TAT GAC GGA GGG AAT ACA TTT ACT ATA CTT AAG ACA GAC TAT

                                                                                    120
asp arg tyr val met his leu asn ile lys phe ala lys lys leu cys glu thr phe gln leu met val leu gly arg thr lys asp
GAC AGA TAT GTC ATG CAT CTC ATT AAG TTC GCA AAG AAG CTC TGT GAG ACC TTC CAG CTG ATG GTG CTC GGC AGA ACA AAG GAT
        100

                                                            140
leu ser ser asp ile lys glu lys phe ala lys cys glu leu thr arg asp asn ile ile asp leu thr lys
CTG AGT TCA GAC ATC AAG GAA AAG TTT GCA AAA CTA TGT GAG CTG ACT AGG GAC AAT ATC ATT GAT CTA ACC AAG

thr asp arg cys leu gln ala arg gly ***
ACT GAT CGC TGT CTC CAG GCC CGA GGA TGA  AGAAAGGCCTGAGCCTCCAGTGCTGAGTGGAGACTTCTCACCAGGACTCTAGCATCACCATTTCCTGTCC
        160

ATGGAGCATCCTGAGACAAATTCTGCGATCTGATTTCCATCCTCGTCTTCTCCAGCATCTTCCCTAGTTACCAGGACAACACATCGA

GAATTAAAGCTTTCTTAAATTTCTCTTGGCCCCACCCATGATCATTCCGCACAAATATCTTGCTCTTGCCTTGCAGTTCAATAAATGATTACCCTTGCACTT poly(A)
```

FIG. 4. α_{2u} Globulin cDNA and amino acid sequences. The nucleotide sequences as determined by the procedures of Maxam and Gilbert (1977) and the deduced amino acid sequence are shown. Position 1 indicates the NH-terminal amino acid of mature α_{2u} globulin. Positions −1 through −15 define the amino acids of the hydrophobic signal peptide. Amino acid residues that were independently determined by sequential Edman degradation of the purified protein are underlined. The probable site of glycosylation (Asn-Gly-Ser) is indicated by a dot. The two alternative polyadenylation/transcription termination sites (AATTAAA and AATAAA) are underlined. The termination codon (TGA) is starred.

cotranslationally by dog pancreatic microsomes to a polypeptide which co-migrates with authentic α_{2u} globulin (Fig. 3). One unusual observation is that all of the six leucine residues contained in the signal sequence are coded by only one (CTG) of the five possible leucine codons. This is the only significant divergence from the normal codon usage distribution. Whether this is coincidental, a mechanism providing for the subcellular localization of this mRNA, or a possible mechanism for translational control of this secreted protein is unknown.

Most known poly(A^+) mRNA species contain the hexanucleotide sequence (AAUAAA) 15–20 bases 5' to the poly(A) tail. Two cases have been reported where the sequence is modified to the heptanucleotide (AAUUAAA) (MacDonald *et al.*, 1980; Hobart *et al.*, 1980). It is thought that these nucleotides provide the signal for cleavage of the gene transcript and poly(A) addition (Proudfoot and Brownlee, 1976). At least four species of dihydro-folate reductase mRNA's that appear to differ only in the length of their 3' untranslated regions have been reported. These different RNA precursors have apparently arisen by the addition of poly(A) tails at different poly(A) addition signal sites in the transcribed dihydrofolate reductase transcript (Setzer *et al.*, 1980). We found that the α_{2u} globulin cDNA sequence contains both an AAUAAA sequence at the expected location 18 base pairs (bp) 5' of poly(A) addition and the heptanucleotide AAUUAAA about 75 bp further 5' but still in the noncoding portion of the RNA. Three of the four otherwise identical cDNA clones sequenced in this region have poly(A) tracts whose addition appears to have been directed by the more common AAUAAA sequence while the fourth mRNA species is 74 bp shorter and appears to have had its polyadenylation directed by the more 3' AAUUAAA sequence. Since these clones are otherwise identical we consider these cDNA's to represent two classes of mRNA, generated from a single gene by differential processing at their polyadenylation sites. It would also appear from this very limited sample that AAUAAA directed polyadenylation is preferred.

A glycosylated form of α_{2u} globulin has been reported which contains *N*-acetylglucosamine as its only amino sugar (Roy *et al.*, 1966; Haars and Pitot, 1980). The linkage of *N*-acetylglucosamine to proteins requires the sequence Asn-X-Ser or Asn-X-Thr where the glycosyl moiety is linked to the asparagine residue (Neuberger *et al.*, 1972). Only one such sequence is present in α_{2u} globulin; therefore, we postulate that the glycosylation site is located at asparagine 35 of the mature protein (Unterman *et al.*, 1981) (Fig. 4). The amino acid sequence specified by the nucleotide sequence of the α_{2u} globulin cDNA has been compared with other previously determined protein sequences stored at the National Biomedical Research Foundation (Georgetown University Medical Center, Washington, D.C.) (Schwartz and

Dayhoff, 1978). This comparison, aided by a computerized alignment procedure (Cohn *et al.*, 1979), indicates that α_{2u} globulin has a significant homology to several proteins from various sources. One of the most interesting of these is bovine β-lactoglobulin (alignment score of 10.3, equivalent to a $p < 10^{-23}$). Bovine β-lactoglobulin is, like α_{2u} globulin, a 162 amino acid secreted protein; it is synthesized in the lactating mammary gland of ruminants (Braunitzer *et al.*, 1973). The complex hormonal control of mammary gland development and lactation is reminiscent of the control of hepatic α_{2u} globulin synthesis. That these proteins may share a common hormonally controlled ancestral gene is an interesting possibility.

The α_{2u} globulin cDNA was further used to determine whether the levels of functional mRNA assayed by *in vitro* translation accurately reflected the levels of α_{2u} globulin RNA sequences present in animals under various hormonal and developmental conditions. In these studies the concentration of α_{2u} globulin RNA sequences was measured by R_0t analysis and the sizes of this RNA and its precursor were measured by Northern blots. A representative set of experiments is shown in Fig. 5. In the cases of developmental and hormonal controls, the amount of translationally active mRNA was paralleled by the concentration of total α_{2u} globulin RNA sequences. Furthermore, we detected no change in the precursor pattern of the α_{2u} globulin RNAs under any hormonal or developmental condition. Thus, the site of control of α_{2u} globulin expression appears to precede the appearance of α_{2u} globulin RNA sequences.

Neoplasia presents a somewhat different picture. In Morris hepatoma 7793, neither α_{2u} globulin RNA sequences nor its functional mRNA are detectable. In hepatoma 5123D, however, we detect a low level of α_{2u} globulin RNA sequences, but no α_{2u} globulin could be translated from this mRNA *in vitro*, although the ability of this mRNA to direct global protein synthesis was unimpaired (Nakhasi *et al.*, 1982a). When comparable amounts of liver RNA were translated we readily detected the translation product. These data indicate that in hepatoma 7793 the α_{2u} globulin genes cease being transcribed, whereas hepatoma 5123D is characterized by a diminished synthesis of an apparently translationally inactive α_{2u} globulin RNA species.

III. THE α_{2u} GLOBULIN GENE

The α_{2u} globulin cDNA previously described was used to identify and isolate α_{2u} globulin genes from a gene library constructed in λ phage (Sargent *et al.*, 1979). For a thorough explanation of the use of λ as a gene cloning

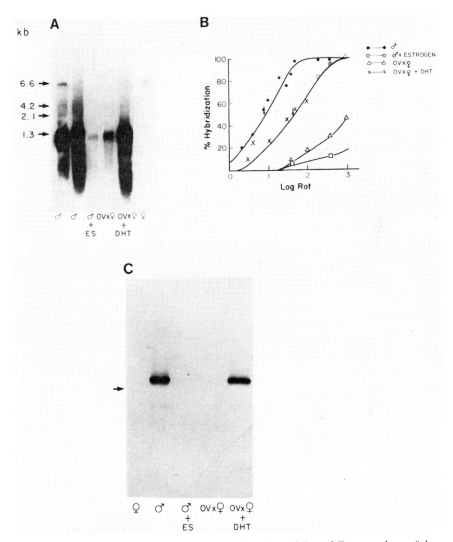

FIG. 5. The three panels in this figure report data derived from different analyses of the same preparation of RNA isolated from animals treated as indicated. (A) A Northern blot run as described in the legend to Fig. 1. (B) R_0t curves carried out in RNA excess using a cloned α_{2u} cDNA (α 7) as tracer. (C) A fluorogram of the *in vitro* translation products of this RNA immunoprecipitated and electrophoresed as described in the legend to Fig. 3. Indicated animals were ovariectomized (OVX) 10 days prior to the beginning of the hormone treatment. Treated animals were injected daily with either estradiol (ES; 5 μg/100 gm body weight) or dihydrotestosterone (DHT; 30 μg/100 gm body weight).

Kevin P. Dolan et al.

vector, see Enquist and Sternberg (1979). This library was constructed in such a way that it is expected to contain six to eight copies of each unique genomic fragment. Screening approximately half the library with α_{2u} globulin cDNA yielded more than 60 phage-containing α_{2u} globulin genomic sequences. While several interpretations of these data are possible, they suggest that rather than being coded for by a unique gene, α_{2u} globulin is encoded by a moderately large family of genes. The complexity of the banding pattern (Fig. 6), which was visualized when alpha α_{2u} globulin cDNA was hybridized to Southern blots of restriction enzyme-digested genomic DNA, further supported this concept. The plaque-purified α_{2u} globulin genomic clones were digested with various restriction enzymes and compared with digests of total genomic cDNA. Phage 207 yielded a restriction pattern indicating that it is one of the major α_{2u} globulin genes. This gene was, therefore, selected for detailed characterization. To facilitate the analysis a 7-kb *Bam*HI fragment containing the gene was subcloned into pBR322. We have shown that this gene covers about 4 kb of genomic information from the beginning of the transcription of the major transcript to the poly(A) addition site(s) (Fig. 7) and is interrupted by six intervening

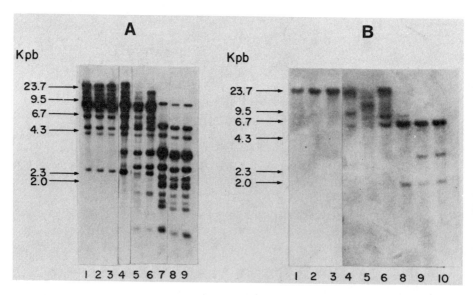

FIG. 6. Autoradiogram of a Southern blot of high-molecular-weight DNA from normal male rat liver and hepatomas 5123D and 7793. (A) 20 μg of DNA was digested either with *Bam*HI/ *Hpa*II (lanes 4–6) or *Bam*HI/*Msp*I alone (lanes 1–3) or with *Bam*HI (lanes 7–9). DNA samples in lanes 1, 4, and 7 are from adult Buffalo male rat liver; lanes 2, 5, and 8 are from hepatoma 5123D; lanes 3, 8, and 9 are from hepatoma 7793. (B) Duplicate Southern blot hybridized to hp 22 cDNA. Radiograph exposure time was 24 hours; Kpb, kilobase pairs.

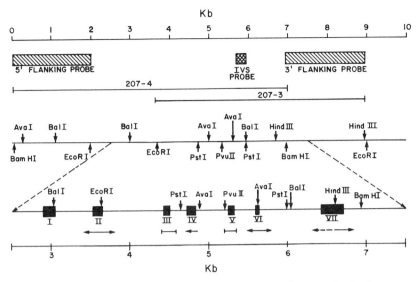

Fig. 7. The restriction map of the α_{2u} globulin clone was determined. The bottom two lines represent structure of the α_{2u} globulin gene and the corresponding scale. Coding sequence is indicated (■) and exons are numbered with Roman numerals proceeding 3′ from the 5′-most exon of the mature mRNA. Arrows under exons indicate sequencing strategy and method (Maxam and Gilbert,→) (Sanger-M13,⊢). Solid lines indicate sequencing of both strands while broken lines report a sequence read several times from the same strand. The line above, drawn to the scale indicated at the top, reports a more extensive restriction map which allows us to indicate the subclones (207-3 and 207-4) actually sequenced and from which probes were prepared.

sequences. The size of the gene and its restriction map eliminate the possibility that the complex genomic restriction pattern is due to a very large gene and confirmed our suspicion that α_{2u} globulin is encoded by a family of genes. Estimates derived from solution hybridization experiments place the number of α_{2u} globulin genes at 18 to 20 (Kurtz, 1981a).

When the exons of this gene were sequenced we found that the RNA sequence it encodes was very similar, but not identical, to the sequence of the cDNA which had previously been determined. The gene sequence contained appropriate splice signals (Lerner et al., 1980) at each intron/exon boundary and no frame shift mutations or premature terminations which would prevent it from coding for α_{2u} globulin. The total sequence homology between the cDNA and gene 207 was greater than 98% throughout the 3′ noncoding as well as the coding regions. We have now sequenced two other variant α_{2u} globulin cDNAs, bringing to four the different α_{2u} globulin sequences which we have determined in whole or in part (three from cDNAs and one from a gene). These sequences are clearly different from each other, having at least two single base changes. The four sequences differ, however, by less than 2% in overall sequence. These data clearly suggest that more than one α_{2u} globulin gene is expressed and that at least some of the α_{2u} globulin genes are very closely related.

One of the problems encountered in analyzing these data is the possibility that the differences we are detecting are actually artifacts of cloning or sequencing. This seems unlikely since the cDNAs were all cloned using the same preparation of poly(A^+) RNA as template. While this RNA was prepared from two animals, it seems unlikely that three different alleles are being expressed in two Sprague–Dawley rats. The α_{2u} globulin cDNA sequences discussed above represent classes of RNAs. Three individual members of the most abundant class have been sequenced. These three clones are of different lengths and, therefore, do not represent duplicate bacterial colonies containing the progeny of a single cDNA. If errors were to be introduced randomly during a polymerization step at a rate of 1–2% it would be unlikely for us to have found 3 of 5 cDNA species to be absolutely identical over 400 to 500 nucleotides (Unterman *et al.*, 1981). This observation also argues against sequencing errors. Furthermore, all sequences included in this calculation were determined by sequencing both complementary strands. Another argument against a cloning artifact is that a genomic fragment that was cloned in λ phage without reverse transcription yields the same 98% degree of homology with the cDNAs as they do with each other. In this case the sequence derived by the method of Maxam and Gilbert was confirmed using the phage M13/dideoxynucleotide procedure of Messing and Sanger (Messing *et al.*, 1977; Sanger *et al.*, 1977). We therefore are convinced that the approximately 98% homology which we detect between some α_{2u} globulin clones accurately reflects the highly conserved homology between members of the α_{2u} globulin gene family. We have also demonstrated that a probe prepared from the intervening sequence region of genomic clone 207 yields hybridization patterns with restriction enzyme-digested genomic DNA which are not simpler than those observed with probes containing coding sequences. Thus, the high homology between these genes seems to extend into the intervening sequences.

The mouse synthesizes a urinary protein called major urinary protein (MUP) (Finlayson *et al.*, 1965; Szoka and Paigen, 1978), which is the mouse homologue of α_{2u} globulin. This protein is also encoded by a large gene family which is under multihormonal control (Hastie *et al.*, 1979; Hastie and Held, 1978). It seems likely that the duplication that generated these extensive families took place once prior to the speciation of mice and rats about 10 million years ago. Calculations based on the assumption of Gilbert (1978) predict that the mouse and rat genes should have diverged by about

10%. Thermal melt studies between α_{2u} globulin and MUP sequences indicate a total nonhomology of about 10% (Laird *et al.*, 1969), confirming this estimate. In the absence of a mechanism which would correct the α_{2u} family we would, therefore, expect at least 10% divergence among members of this family. The degree of nonhomologies could be even greater if the duplication took place a significant time before speciation. Our sequence data clearly indicate that the α_{2u} globulin gene family is much more closely related than 10% and suggests that a mechanism exists which "corrects" mutations in this gene.

One possibility for preservation of high homology between the various α_{2u} globulin genes is that the intron and 3' noncoding regions serve an important role and that selective pressures operate to preserve these essential sequences. Another mechanism that might function, without selective pressure, to correct the α_{2u} gene family is homologous recombination between tandemly repeated genes. It has been proposed that by placing upper and lower limits on the copy number of any tandemly repeated sequence, homologous recombination will tend to make all the copies of the sequence the same in any individual breeding group (Smith, 1973). This mechanism would allow for the accumulation of mutations in genetically isolated populations while tending to keep the family members within each population similar. Such a mechanism is compatible with the numerous bands visualized when α_{2u} globulin cDNA probes are hybridized to Southern blots of restriction enzyme-digested genomic DNA. This model also predicts that the extent of homology will be similar throughout the gene without regard to function, that the genes exist as tandem repeats, and that divergence between different genetically isolated populations of rats will be greater than differences within a breeding population. We have not examined the α_{2u} globulin genes of different strains of rats, and it is not established that the α_{2u} gene family exists as a set of tandem repeats. *In situ* hybridization studies have been reported (Kurtz, 1981b) and indicate that the only chromosomal hybridization to α_{2u} globulin probes is a single region on chromosome 5. Although these results do not demonstrate the existence of tandem repeats, they do indicate that many of the α_{2u} genes are clustered. If the genes are tandemly repeated the repeat unit is greater than 15 kb since we have detected no λ clones containing even partial copies of two α_{2u} globulin genes. Our sequencing data reveal no bias in the frequency of mutations in coding and noncoding portions of α_{2u} globulin genes. Furthermore, intervening sequence probes reveal a hybridization pattern just as complex as that seen when coding probes are hybridized to Southern blots of genomic DNA. These data all support the belief that homology has been preserved without preference for coding sequences.

This does not rule out the possibility that regions of the α_{2u} globulin gene that do not code for the protein are important for expression and so their homology is conserved by classical selection.

The homologous recombination and selection models discussed above are not the only possible explanations for the apparent correction mechanism operative in the α_{2u} globulin gene family. Several reports indicate that "gene conversion" in yeast may take place between copies of genes that are far removed from each other, even located on different chromosomes (Klein and Petes, 1981; Scherer and Davis, 1980). The homologous recombination model discussed above requires crossing-over between different tandemly repeated members of the gene family. This crossover must be unequal resulting in differences in gene dosage. The gene conversion model allows for correction without a change in copy number on either chromatid. For recent reviews of this topic see Baltimore (1981) and Egel (1981).

Our characterization of this gene has also revealed that one of the introns interrupts the 3' noncoding region of the mRNA. It has been suggested that exons code for functional domains which can be rearranged during evolution (Gilbert, 1978). The idea that this 3' exon may represent a domain that is important for the expression of α_{2u} globulin is an interesting hypothesis, the testing of which awaits further study.

IV. DNA METHYLATION

Methylation has been shown to correlate with gene expression for several genes in expressing and nonexpressing tissues (Mandel and Chambon, 1979; McGhee and Ginder, 1979; Van der Ploeg *et al.*, 1980; Guntaka *et al.*, 1980; Sutter and Doerfler, 1980; Desrosiers *et al.*, 1979) and in neoplastic tissues (Holiday, 1979; Nakhasi *et al.*, 1981; Tantravahi *et al.*, 1981). Our studies of the methylation pattern have revealed that the α_{2u} globulin gene undergoes marked changes in its methylation pattern which correlates with the onset of its expression at puberty (Nakhasi *et al.*, 1982b). These experiments take advantage of the fact that there exist pairs of restriction enzymes (isoschizomers) which recognize the same sequence. In some cases one of the isoschizomeric pair will digest regardless of methylation within the restriction site while the other is inhibited by methylation. Differences in the banding pattern visualized by Southern blotting genomic DNA digested by such a pair of enzymes are, therefore, attributed to methylation. *Msp*I and *Hpa*II are such an isoschizomeric pair; *Msp*I digests regardless of methylation while *Hpa*II is inhibited by the presence of 5-methylcytosine at the internal C of the CCGG restriction site (Bird and Southern, 1978; Waalwjik and Flavel, 1978). This pair is especially valuable for studies on eukaryotic DNA since eukaryotic methylation typically takes place at the C residue of CG base pairs.

Our initial studies compared the α_{2u} globulin gene in normal liver and several hepatomas. These studies showed a generally lower degree of methylation in the nonexpressing hepatoma than in α_{2u} globulin expressing adult liver (Nakhasi *et al.*, 1982a) (Fig. 6). We then examined the DNA of young (14 days postpartum) and mature rat liver in which the α_{2u} globulin genes are untranscribed and transcribed, respectively. In these studies DNA was first digested with *Bam*HI and then with *Msp*I or *Hpa*II. We noted a distinct, methylation-dependent band which was absent in young (nonexpressing) animals but was present in genomic digests from mature (expressing) animals. Further examination of hepatic genomic DNA from male animals of various ages revealed that the methylation event occurs at the onset of puberty (31 days of age) and therefore coincides with the expression of α_{2u} globulin. This band appears not only in the liver but in several nonexpressing tissues (brain, lung, heart, and testis) at this age. To determine whether the appearance of this band could be prevented, animals were hypophysectomized before puberty (21 days) and sacrificed at 65 days of age. In these animals the α_{2u} globulin methylation pattern remained characteristic of the immature liver. These data suggest that the methylation event is subject to hormonal manipulation. This methylation event does not occur in the female at puberty but can be induced by ovariectomizing the adult animal and treating her with dihydrotestosterone, a treatment that changes the level of methylation of the α_{2u} globulin DNA and induces hepatic α_{2u} globulin mRNA synthesis. We have localized the site of this methylation event toward the 5' end of the gene by hybridizing with probes derived from different areas of the cDNA probe.

The banding pattern generated when genomic DNA is hybridized to an α_{2u} globulin cDNA probe is too complex to determine whether the change in methylation pattern is due to methylation or demethylation. It must also be pointed out that this technique is only capable of assaying 1–2% of the total C residues present in the genome and about 10% of the possible methylation sites. The location of the specific methylation site assayed above cannot necessarily be assumed to be a physiologically significant methylation site. It is, however, indicative of the methylation status in the region. It is clear from these data that a DNA methylation event, marked by the appearance of a hybridizing band on Southern blots, correlates with the expression of α_{2u} globulin. The event normally takes place in nonexpressing, as well as expressing, tissues at puberty in the male rat but can be prevented by hypophysectomy. In female rats this event does not take place at puberty but can be induced in the liver only by ovariectomy followed by androgen administration, a treatment that induces the expression of α_{2u} globulin. We feel that this gene methylation event may be a necessary although insufficient condition for the expression of α_{2u} globulin genes and that it may be typical of the type of genomic changes that take place at major developmental junctures such as puberty.

V. SALIVARY GLAND α_{2u} GLOBULIN SYNTHESIS

α_{2u} Globulin has also been reported to be present in the kidney and submaxillary gland of adult male rats. In both cases it was assumed that the protein was present as a result of its removal from circulation (Roy and Neuhaus, 1966a; Roy and Byrd, 1976). In the kidney this is indeed the case, but in the salivary gland we have detected significant levels of functional α_{2u} globulin mRNA sequences as well as α_{2u} globulin (Laperche *et al.*, 1982). Surprisingly, we detected α_{2u} globulin RNA sequences in the salivary glands of young as well as adult animals of both sexes. Neither hypophysectomy nor streptozotocin-induced diabetes, both of which dramatically lower hepatic α_{2u} globulin mRNA levels, exert a detectable effect on the α_{2u} globulin mRNA levels in the salivary gland. Salivary gland α_{2u} globulin RNA is the same size as that of the liver and remains hybridized under stringent conditions (i.e., washed in $0.1 \times$ SSC at 65°C) to the liver cDNA. The protein synthesized *in vitro* under the direction of this RNA is also identical in size to the liver and urinary protein. Like its hepatic counterpart this salivary gland α_{2u} globulin can be processed cotranslationally by dog pancreatic microsomes to a smaller form which is identical in size to the liver and urinary protein. The salivary gland contains about one-third the amount of α_{2u} globulin RNA as the liver measured on a per microgram RNA basis (Laperche *et al.*, 1982).

The salivary forms of α_{2u} globulin can be distinguished from the liver forms by their isoelectric points. We have analyzed the *in vitro* translation products of both salivary and liver forms of α_{2u} globulin mRNA on isoelectric focusing gels. Both the liver and salivary gland appear to synthesize multiple forms of α_{2u} globulin as predicted by the sequencing data discussed above. The salivary family, however, is significantly more acidic than the liver family. Whether this difference is due to the expression of a different set of α_{2u} globulin genes or due to a different processing pathway of the same set of transcripts is as yet unknown. This aspect of α_{2u} globulin synthesis appears to provide a valuable model for understanding tissue-specific differences in gene expression. The salivary gland apparently is a tissue that does not modulate α_{2u} expression in response to those hormonal stimuli that do control α_{2u} globulin RNA levels and synthesis in the liver.

In many aspects the α_{2u} globulin system seems to provide an ideal paradigm for examining some of the most important questions in gene regulation. The mechanism of action of glucocorticoids seems to be the closest to resolution. Several genes including α_{2u} globulin (Kurtz, 1981a) have been reported to be controlled by glucocorticoids when transferred into TK⁻ mouse L cells. In addition, mouse mammary tumor virus has been shown to contain sequences responsible for its glucocorticoid-regulated transcription (Ucker *et al.*, 1981). It was recently reported that the glucocorticoid receptor binds specifically to several regions of the MMTV genome, including the region just 5′ to the beginning of transcription (Payvar *et al.*, 1981). Similar results have been reported for the binding of progesterone receptor to the ovalbumin gene (Mulvihill *et al.*, 1982). It was recently reported that the metallothionine gene (Brinster *et al.*, 1982) can be microinjected into germinal vessicles, which were subsequently reimplanted and grew into normal animals containing the gene. This may provide a general method to study the way by which different tissues control transferred genes at different times during development. The combination of direct receptor binding experiments and gene transfer should provide the tools to understand the mechanisms that underlie the control of gene expression by hormones.

The techniques of molecular biology in concert with the binding studies and receptor characterizations carried out over the past 20 years have now provided further tools to explore the mechanism by which this gene family is controlled by its many hormonal effectors. In addition to the use of α_{2u} globulin as a model system for hormone action it also provides a valuable model for development, differentiation, and transformation. We have obviously just begun to understand α_{2u} globulin gene control. We have no doubt that an understanding of this system will clarify some of the fundamental biological questions currently being posed.

ACKNOWLEDGMENTS

These studies were supported in part by the National Institutes of Health, National Cancer Institute (CA-22376), Postdoctorate Fellowship (CA-06514) to K. P. D., and Training Grant (AM 07328) to K. R. L.

REFERENCES

Baltimore, D. (1981). *Cell* **24**, 592.
Bird, A. P., and Southern, E. M. (1978). *J. Mol. Biol.* **118**, 27.
Braunitzer, G., Chen, B., Schiank, B., and Stangel, A. (1973). *Hoppe-Seyler's Physiol. Chem.* **354**, 867.

Brinster, R. L., Chen, H. Y., Trumbauer, M., Senear, A. W., Warren, R., and Palmiter, R. D. (1982). *Cell* **27**, 223.

Chan, K-M., Kurtz, D. T., and Feigelson, P. (1978). *Biochemistry* **17**, 3092.

Chatterjee, B., and Roy, A. K. (1980). *J. Biol. Chem.* **255**, 1607.

Chen, C-L. C., and Feigelson, P. (1978). *Biochemistry* **17**, 5308.

Chen, C-L. C., and Feigelson, P. (1980). *Ann. N. Y. Acad. Sci.* **349**, 28.

Cohn, D. V., Smardo, F. L., and Morrissey, J. J. (1979). *Proc. Natl. Acad. Sci. U.S.A.* **76**, 1469.

Desrosiers, R. C., Mulder, C., and Fleckenstein, B. (1979). *Proc. Natl. Acad. Sci. U.S.A.* **76**, 3839.

Egel, R. (1981). *Nature (London)* **290**, 191.

Enquist, L., and Sternberg, N. (1979). *In* "Methods in Enzymology" (R. Wu, ed.), Vol. 68, p. 281. Academic Press, New York.

Feigelson, P., and DeLap, L. (1977). "Morris Hepatomas: Mechanisms of Regulation." Plenum, New York.

Feigelson, P., and Kurtz, D. T. (1978). *Adv. Enzymol. Relat. Areas Mol. Biol.* **47**, 275.

Finlayson, J. S., Asofsky, R., Potter, M., and Runner, C. C. (1965). *Science* **149**, 981.

Gilbert, W. (1978). *Nature (London)* **271**, 501.

Gray, P. W., Leung, D. W., Pennica, D., Yelverton, E., Najarian, R., Simonsen, C. C., Derynck, R., Sherwood, P. J., Wallace, D. M., Berger, S. L., Levinson, A. D., and Goeddel, D. V. (1982). *Nature (London)* **295**, 503.

Grunstein, M., and Hogness, D. S. (1975). *Proc. Natl. Acad. Sci. U.S.A.* **72**, 3961.

Guntaka, R. V., Rao, P. Y., Mitsialis, S. A., and Katz, R. (1980). *J. Virol.* **34**, 569.

Haars, L. J., and Pitot, H. C. (1980). *Arch. Biochem. Biophys.* **201**, 556.

Hastie, N. D., and Held, W. A. (1978). *Proc. Natl. Acad. Sci. U.S.A.* **75**, 1217.

Hastie, N. D., Held, W. A., and Toole, J. J. (1979). *Cell* **17**, 449.

Hobart, P., Crawford, R., Shen, L. P., Pictet, R., and Rutter, W. J. (1980). *Nature (London)* **288**, 137.

Holliday, R. (1979). *Br. J. Cancer* **40**, 513.

Kacian, D. L., and Myers, J. C. (1976). *Proc. Natl. Acad. Sci. U.S.A.* **73**, 2191.

Klein, H. L., and Petes, T. D. (1981). *Nature (London)* **289**, 144.

Kurtz, D. T. (1981a). *Nature (London)* **291**, 629.

Kurtz, D. T. (1981b). *J. Mol. App. Gen.* **1**, 29.

Kurtz, D. T., and Feigelson, P. (1978). *In* "Biochemical Actions of Hormones" (G. Litwack, ed.), Vol. V, p. 433. Academic Press, New York.

Kurtz, D. T., and Nicodemus, C. F. (1981). *Gene* **13**, 145.

Kurtz, D. T., Sippel, A. E., and Feigelson, P. (1976a). *Biochemistry* **15**, 1031.

Kurtz, D. T., Sippel, A. E., Ansah-Yiadom, R., and Feigelson, P. (1976b). *J. Biol. Chem.* **251**, 3594.

Laird, C. D., McConaughy, B. L., and McCarthy, B. J. (1969). *Nature (London)* **224**, 149.

Laperche, Y., Lynch, K. R., Dolan, K. P., and Feigelson, P. (1982). *J. Biol. Chem.* (submitted).

Lasky, L. A., Lev, Z., Xin, J-H., Britten, R. J., and Davidson, E. H. (1980). *Proc. Natl. Acad. Sci. U.S.A.* **77**, 5317.

Lerner, M. R., Boyle, J. A., Mount, S. M., Wolin, S. L., and Steitz, J. A. (1980). *Nature (London)* **283**, 220.

Lynch, K. R., Pennica, D., Ennis, H. L., and Cohen, P. S. (1979). *Virology* **98**, 251.

Lynch, K. R., Dolan, K. P., Nakhasi, H. L., Unterman, R., and Feigelson, P. (1982). *Cell* **28**, 185.

MacDonald, R. J., Crerar, M. M., Swain, W. F., Picket, R. L., Thomas, G., and Rutter, W. J. (1980). *Nature (London)* **287**, 117.

McGhee, J. D., and Ginder, G. D. (1979). *Nature (London)* **280**, 419.

Mandel, J. L., and Chambon, P. (1979). *Nucleic Acids Res.* **7**, 2081.

Maxam, A. M., and Gilbert, W. (1977). *Proc. Natl. Acad. Sci. U.S.A.* **74**, 560.

Messing, J., Gronenborn, B., Muller-Hill, B., and Hofschneider, P. H. (1977). *Proc. Natl. Acad. Sci. U.S.A.* **74**, 3642.

Mulvihill, E. R., LePennec, J.-P., and Chambon, P. (1982). *Cell* **28**, 621.

Nakhasi, H. L., Lynch, K. R., Dolan, K. P., Unterman, R. D., and Feigelson, P. (1981). *Proc. Natl. Acad. Sci. U.S.A.* **78**, 834.

Nakhasi, H. L., Lynch, K. R., Dolan, K. P., Unterman, R., Antakly, T., and Feigelson, P. (1982). *J. Biol. Chem.* **257**, 2726.

Neuberger, A., Gottschalk, A., Marshall, R. D., and Spiro, R. G. (1972). *In* "Glycoproteins: Their Composition, Structure, and Function" (A. Guttschalk, ed.), p. 450. Elsevier, New York.

Parnes, J. R., Velan, B., Felsenfeld, A., Ramanathan, L., Ferrini, U., Appella, E., and Seidman, J. G. (1981). *Proc. Natl. Acad. Sci. U.S.A.* **78**, 2253.

Payvar, F., Wrange, O., Carlstedt-Duke, J., Olket, S., Gustafsson, J.-A., and Yamamoto, K. R. (1981). *Proc. Natl. Acad. Sci. U.S.A.* **78**, 6628.

Persico, M. G., Toniolo, D., Nobile, C., D'Urso, M., and Luzzatto, L. (1981). *Nature (London)* **294**, 778.

Proudfoot, N. J., and Brownlee, G. G. (1976). *Nature (London)* **263**, 211.

Roy, A. K. (1973a). *J. Endocrinol.* **56**, 265.

Roy, A. K. (1973b). *Endocrinology (Baltimore)* **92**, 957.

Roy, A. K. (1979). *In* "Biochemical Actions of Hormones" (G. Litwack, ed.), Vol. VI, p. 481. Academic Press, New York.

Roy, A. K., and Byrd, J. G. (1976). *J. Endocrinol.* **71**, 265.

Roy, A. K., and Dowbenko, D. J. (1977). *Biochemistry* **16**, 3918.

Roy, A. K., and Leonard, S. (1973). *J. Endocrinol.* **57**, 327.

Roy, A. K., and Neuhaus, O. W. (1966a). *Proc. Soc. Exp. Biol. Med.* **121**, 894.

Roy, A. K., and Neuhaus, O. W. (1966b). *Biochim. Biophys. Acta* **127**, 82.

Roy, A. K., and Neuhaus, O. W. (1967). *Nature (London)* **214**, 618.

Roy, A. K., Neuhaus, O. W., and Harmison, C. R. (1966). *Biochim. Biophys. Acta* **127**, 72.

Roy, A. K., Milin, B. S., and McMinn, D. M. (1974). *Biochim. Biophys. Acta* **354**, 213.

Roy, A. K., McMinn, D. M., and Biswas, N. M. (1975). *Endocrinology (Baltimore)* **97**, 1505.

Roy, A. K., Schiop, M. J., and Dowbenko, D. J. (1976a). *FEBS Lett.* **64**, 396.

Roy, A. K., Schiop, M. J., and Dowbenko, D. J. (1976b). *FEBS Lett.* **70**, 137.

Roychoudhury, R., Jay, H., and Wu, R. (1976). *Nucleic Acids Res.* **3**, 863.

Sanger, F., Nicklen, S., and Coulson, A. R. (1977). *Proc. Natl. Acad. Sci. U.S.A.* **74**, 5463.

Sargent, T. D., Wu, J.-R., Sala-Trepat, J. M., Wallace, R. B., Reyes, A. A., and Bonner, J. (1979). *Proc. Natl. Acad. Sci. U.S.A.* **76**, 3256.

Scherer, S., and Davis, R. W. (1980). *Science* **209**, 1380.

Schwartz, R. M., and Dayhoff, M. O. (1978). *In* "Atlas of the Protein Sequence and Structure" (M. O. Dayhoff, ed.), Suppl. 3, Vol. 5, p. 353. Natl. Biomed. Found., Washington, D.C.

Seeburg, P. H., Shine, J., Martial, J. A., Baxter, J. D., and Goodman, H. M. (1977). *Nature (London)* **270**, 486.

Setzer, D. R., McGrogan, M., Nunberg, J. H., and Schimke, R. T. (1980). *Cell* **22**, 361.

Sippel, A. E., Feigelson, P., and Roy, A. K. (1975). *Biochemistry* **14**, 825.

Sippel, A. E., Kurtz, D. T., Morris, H. P., and Feigelson, P. (1976). *Cancer Res.* **36**, 3588.

Smith, G. P. (1973). *Cold Spring Harbor Symp. Quant. Biol.* **38**, 507.

Sutter, D., and Doerfler, W. (1980). *Proc. Natl. Acad. Sci. U.S.A.* **77**, 253.

Szoka, P. R., and Paigen, K. (1978). *Genetics* **90**, 597.

Tantravahi, U., Guntaka, R. V., Erlanger, B. F., and Miller, O. J. (1981). *Proc. Natl. Acad. Sci. U.S.A.* **78**, 489.

Ucker, D. S., Ross, S. R., and Yamamoto, K. R., (1981). *Cell* **27**, 257.

Unterman, R. D., Lynch, K. R., Nakhasi, H. L., Dolan, K. P., Hamilton, J. W., Cohen, D. V., and Feigelson, P. (1981). *Proc. Natl. Acad. Sci. U.S.A.* **78**, 3478.

Van der Ploeg, L. H. T., and Flavell, R. A. (1980). *Cell* **19**, 947.

Waalwijk, C., and Flavell, R. A. (1978). *Nucleic Acids Res.* **5**, 4631.

Wensink, P. C., Finnegan, D. J., Donelson, J. E., and Hogness, D. S. (1974). *Cell* **3**, 315.

CHAPTER 2

The Role of the Nuclear Matrix in Steroid Hormone Action

Evelyn R. Barrack and Donald S. Coffey

23

BIOCHEMICAL ACTIONS OF HORMONES, VOL. X

I. INTRODUCTION

A. OVERVIEW

The importance of cellular structural elements in the regulation of bio-logical function is becoming increasingly appreciated (see reviews by Shaper *et al.*, 1979; Porter and Tucker, 1981; Isaacs *et al.*, 1981). One of these structural components is the nuclear matrix, which is an insoluble, skeletal framework of the nucleus. The nuclear matrix may be defined as a residual nuclear scaffolding system with dynamic properties that provides functional organization for the DNA. The nuclear matrix may provide a direct pas-sageway from the interior of the nucleus to the pore complexes. During mitosis, the peripheral lamina components of the matrix depolymerize, and the matrix proteins at the points of attachment of the DNA loops appear to condense to form the core scaffolding of the metaphase chromosomes.

We will review briefly some aspects of the isolation and characterization of the nuclear matrix, as well as some of the observations that have been made in this and other laboratories which support the concept that the nuclear matrix plays a functional and dynamic role in many important biological processes, such as DNA synthesis, RNA synthesis, processing and transport, and hormone action. We will focus primarily on our studies on the interaction of sex steroid hormones with the nuclear matrix (Barrack *et al.*, 1977, 1979; Barrack and Coffey, 1980).

B. THE CYTOSKELETON

A major change in the understanding of cellular structure was obtained in the 1970's with the identification of an elaborate structural network within the cytoplasm or ground substance of the cell that has been termed the cytoskeleton or microtrabecular lattice. These earlier observations of intracellular structural proteins (see early reviews of Goldman and Knipe, 1972; Pollard and Weihing, 1973) were confirmed when fluorescent actin antibodies revealed an elaborate actin network within a variety of nonmuscle cells (Lazarides and Weber, 1974). It now appears that an even more elaborate and dynamic protein cytoskeleton is formed from several components including actin filaments, microtubules, and intermediate filaments (Lazarides, 1981; Schliwa and Van Blerkom, 1981). This cytoskeleton system appears to form a microtrabecular lattice or network in whole cells when viewed by stereophotography utilizing high-voltage electron microscopy (Porter and Tucker, 1981; Henderson and Weber, 1979). This cytoskeleton system had also been observed earlier in detergent-washed cells after extraction of the plasma membrane phospholipid and many of the soluble cellular proteins (Osborn and Weber, 1977; Lenk *et al.*, 1977).

Many investigators now believe that most of the soluble proteins comprising the cytosol may not, in fact, be soluble in the cell but are actually associated with the microtrabecular lattice and are extracted by the specific buffers and salts in the homogenizing media and in the wash solutions (Porter and Tucker, 1981). As will be discussed later, this may have important implications with regard to our concepts of soluble steroid hormone receptors.

In summary, the old concept of defining the cytoplasm as a sol–gel state is slowly being replaced by the more modern concept of a dynamic filamentous and trabecular system that orders and directs the function of the cytoplasmic compartment (Table I). The older concept that macromolecules, such as proteins, RNA, and receptor molecules, freely diffuse toward a random collision with an acceptor site appears now to require some reevaluation.

TABLE I

CONCEPTS OF THE GROUND SUBSTANCE OF THE CELL

Concept	Nomenclature	Intracellular macromolecular transport	Determination of cell shape and motility
Sol–gel	Protoplasm Cytoplasm Nucleoplasm	Primarily by diffusion	Interconversion of sol to gel states
Fibrillar–trabecular	Cytoskeleton Microtrabecular lattice Nuclear matrix	Directed by filaments and microtrabeculae	Polymerization or chemomechanical interaction of fibrillar components

C. The Nuclear Matrix

As the cytoplasm was being redefined in terms of residual structural elements, so were the nucleus and its nucleoplasm and chromatin fractions undergoing conceptual revision. Studies of the nuclear matrix (nuclear skeleton) (Berezney and Coffey, 1974, 1976, 1977) actually preceded those of the cytoskeleton, but the full acceptance of the nuclear matrix has been slower due to the difficulties in developing specific fluorescent antibodies to the nuclear matrix and due to the very insoluble nature of these proteins which have been most difficult to characterize. Such insoluble proteins raise justified questions concerning denaturation artifacts. Our studies have concentrated not on circumventing this issue, but rather on determining if the nuclear matrix is associated with important biological properties that would indicate whether it was worthy of additional study. Since the isolated nuclear matrix contains approximately 10% of the original nuclear proteins and is essentially devoid of histones and phospholipids, it represents only a fraction of the original nuclear mass. In contrast, the nuclear matrix structure is very highly enriched with >90% of the total newly synthesized DNA, as well as heterogeneous nuclear RNA. Moreover, the nuclear matrix represents a major site of steroid hormone binding in the nucleus. These and many other important biological functions reported to be associated with the nuclear matrix are summarized in Table II. Additional details

TABLE II
BIOLOGICAL FUNCTIONS ASSOCIATED WITH THE NUCLEAR MATRIX (1974–1981)

The nuclear matrix contains structural elements of the pore complex, lamina, internal network, and nucleolus	Berezney and Coffey (1974, 1976, 1977), Comings and Okada (1976), Wunderlich and Herlan (1977), Hodge *et al.* (1977); also see Table IV
DNA binding proteins in the nuclear matrix	
DNA is tightly attached to the nuclear matrix	Berezney and Coffey (1975, 1976, 1977), Pardoll *et al.* (1980)
Tenacious binding of DNA to specific nuclear matrix proteins	Bowen *et al.* (1980), Razin *et al.* (1981)
Mouse liver nuclear matrix proteins have a high affinity for DNA and show a preference for binding single-stranded DNA, AT-rich DNA and poly(dT)	Comings and Wallack (1978)

(continued)

TABLE II *(continued)*.

Role in DNA organization

DNA is organized in the nucleus in the form of supercoiled loops, each containing 60,000–100,000 bp per loop. These loops are anchored at their base to the nuclear matrix — Vogelstein *et al*. (1980), Georgiev *et al*. (1978), Cook *et al*. (1976), Razin *et al*. (1979)

In bovine kidney cells, 60% of the tightly attached matrix-associated DNA is tandemly repeated satellite DNA — Matsumoto (1981)

Role in DNA replication

Newly replicated DNA is associated preferentially with the nuclear matrix — Berezney and Coffey (1975, 1976), Dvorkin and Vanyushin (1978), Dijkwel *et al*. (1979), Pardoll *et al*. (1980), Vogelstein *et al*. (1980), McCready *et al*. (1980), Hunt and Vogelstein (1981), Berezney and Buchholtz (1981a,b)

The nuclear matrix contains fixed sites of DNA replication — Pardoll *et al*. (1980), Vogelstein *et al*. (1980), Hunt and Vogelstein (1981), Berezney and Buchholtz (1981a)

DNA polymerase α is tightly bound to the nuclear matrix of actively replicating liver, but not of normal liver — Smith and Berezney (1980)

Enrichment of certain actively transcribed genes with the nuclear matrix

Ribosomal RNA genes are enriched at least six-fold in the residual DNA associated with liver nuclear matrix — Pardoll and Vogelstein (1980)

SV40 sequences are enriched four- to seven-fold in nuclear matrix-associated DNA of SV40-transformed 3T3 cells — Nelkin *et al*. (1980)

The transcriptionally active ovalbumin gene is preferentially associated with the nuclear matrix in hen oviduct, whereas the inactive β-globin gene is not enriched on the oviduct nuclear matrix — Robinson *et al*. (1982)

Association of hnRNA with the nuclear matrix

RNP particles are a component of the internal network of the nuclear matrix — Berezney and Coffey (1974, 1976, 1977), Miller *et al*. (1978a), Berezney (1979, 1980), Steele and Busch (1966), Pogo (1981)

Essentially all of the hnRNA and snRNA are associated exclusively with the nuclear matrix — Miller *et al*. (1978a,b), Herman *et al*. (1978), Long *et al*. (1979), van Eekelen and van Venrooij (1981), Jackson *et al*. (1981)

Globin RNA, containing introns, is tightly associated with the nuclear matrix of chicken erythroblasts — Ross (1980)

(continued)

TABLE II *(continued)*

Precursor mRNAs for ovomucoid and ovalbumin are on the nuclear matrix of hen oviduct	Ciejek *et al.* (1981)
hnRNA is attached to the nuclear matrix via two of the major hnRNP proteins	van Eekelen and van Venrooij (1981)
RNA is synthesized at fixed transcription complexes on the nuclear matrix	Jackson *et al.* (1981)
Nascent RNA is attached at the 5′ cap, and perhaps also at the 3′ end, to the nuclear matrix	Jackson *et al.* (1981)

Interaction with viruses

Certain SV40-specific proteins are associated exclusively with the nuclear matrix of infected HeLa cells	Deppert (1978)
Significant amounts of polyoma T-antigen and intact viral genomes are associated with the nuclear matrix of lytically infected 3T6 cells; implication of the nuclear matrix as a site of viral DNA replication	Buckler-White *et al.* (1980)

Phosphorylation of matrix and lamina proteins

Increased phosphorylation of specific rat liver nuclear matrix proteins occurs just prior to the onset of DNA synthesis in regenerating rat liver	Allen *et al.* (1977)
Phosphorylation of specific proteins of clam nuclear lamina–pore complex fraction by endogenous nuclear envelope-associated enzymes	Maul and Avdalović (1980)
Protein phosphokinase activity in the pore complex-lamina fraction of rat liver phosphorylates endogenous pore complex-lamina proteins	Steer *et al.* (1980), Lam and Kasper (1979a)
The three major nuclear lamina proteins of the matrix are phosphoproteins and are phosphorylated to a greater extent prior to or during mitosis than in interphase. Phosphorylation of the major lamina proteins is probably involved in the reversible depolymerization of the lamina during cell division	Gerace and Blobel (1980)
Phosphorylation of nuclear matrix proteins of sea urchin embryos by endogenous matrix kinase activity *in vitro;* more phosphorylation in blastula than pluteus stage	Sevaljević *et al.* (1981)

Reversible expansion/contraction of the matrix

The nuclear matrix isolated from *Tetrahymena* macronuclei reversibly contracts when Ca^{2+} and Mg^{2+} concentrations are decreased to 5 mM or increased to 125 mM	Wunderlich and Herlan (1977)

(continued)

TABLE II *(continued)*

Modulation of nuclear membrane lipid fluidity by internal components of the nuclear matrix	
Lipid fluidity is higher in isolated nuclear membrane ghosts than in intact nuclei	Giese and Wunderlich (1980), Wunderlich *et al.* (1978)
Contains binding sites for steroid hormones, epidermal growth factor, lectins, and polyribonucleotides	
Specific, high-affinity, tissue- and steroid-specific binding sites for androgens and estrogens on the nuclear matrix of target tissues (rat uterus, chicken liver, rat prostate)	Barrack *et al.* (1977, 1979), Barrack and Coffey (1980), Agutter and Birchall (1979)
Lentil binding sites on nuclear matrix of sea urchin embryos	Sevaljević *et al.* (1981)
Binding of wheat germ agglutinin to the internal structure and binding of concanavalin A to the periphery of HeLa cell nuclear scaffolds	Hozier and Furcht (1980)
Binding of poly(A) to lamina	McDonald and Agutter (1980)
Binding sites for epidermal growth factor in chromatin-depleted nuclei	Johnson *et al.* (1980)
Preferential binding of carcinogens to the nuclear matrix	
Benzo[*a*]pyrene binding to nuclear matrix of rat lung, rat liver, and thymocytes	Hemminki and Vainio (1979), Blazsek *et al.* (1979), Ueyama *et al.* (1981)
Retinol markedly inhibits binding of benzo[*a*]pyrene to DNA and protein of the rat liver nuclear matrix but has little or no effect on binding of benzo[*a*]pyrene to bulk DNA and protein in chromatin	Nomi *et al.* (1981)
Heat-shock proteins become associated with the nuclear matrix	
Heat-shock proteins may be structural components of the nucleus, serving to protect the cell from effects of heat shock	Levinger and Varshavsky (1981), Sinibaldi and Morris (1981)

regarding the properties of the nuclear matrix are also presented in several reviews (Berezney and Coffey, 1976; Shaper *et al.*, 1979; Berezney, 1979; Agutter and Richardson, 1980; Isaacs *et al.*, 1981). A wealth of evidence, therefore, indicates that the nuclear matrix may be involved directly in many fundamental nuclear processes such as DNA replication, RNA synthesis, processing and transport, as well as hormone action. The possibility that these observations are the results of nonspecific adsorption, macromolecular aggregation, and denaturation must be considered as alternative explanations. However, although these arguments cannot be eliminated completely, many attempts to assess these difficult problems by a variety of mixing experiments have all tended to diminish this possibility. In summary, the increasing evidence for an important role for the nuclear matrix in biological processes reported by numerous investigators over the past several years (Table II) indicates that this matrix structure merits continued study.

II. ISOLATION AND CHARACTERIZATION OF THE NUCLEAR MATRIX

A. Early Studies of Residual Nuclear Structures

The isolation of residual nuclear protein fractions originated with the work of Mayer and Gulick (1942) and Mirsky and Ris (1951), who treated isolated nuclei with high concentrations of salt and nucleases and found residual chromosomal proteins. The appearance of these residual fractions by light and electron microscopy was not studied until several years later. The laboratories of Zbarsky and Georgiev reported that after extraction of nuclei with 1 to 2 M NaCl solutions, residual nuclear structures were still observed (Zbarsky and Georgiev, 1959; Georgiev and Chentsov, 1962; Zbarsky *et al.*, 1962). Although the majority of the DNA, RNA, and protein had been extracted, histochemical staining revealed residual nucleoli closely associated with residual chromosome structures. Electron microscopy of this material, which was referred to as a nucleonemata, showed a nuclear membrane surrounding fibrillar structures and ribonucleoprotein (RNP) particles. Following these earlier studies, Busch and his colleagues reported a more detailed electron microscopic study of this type of structure which they termed the nuclear ribonucleoprotein network. This network was observed to extend from an intact nuclear envelope to the nucleolus (Smetana *et al.*, 1963; Shankar Narayan *et al.*, 1967). A comprehensive study was made by Steele and Busch (1966) of the RNA associated with this residual nucleus.

B. The Nuclear Matrix

The residual nuclear structures referred to above were complex structures composed of intact nuclear envelopes, residual nucleoli, and considerable amounts of RNP particles. Based on these previous observations, experiments were carried out in this laboratory to determine whether a fundamental constitutive framework structure was present in the cell nucleus.

Our approach was to remove as many of the nuclear components as possible, including the lipid of the membrane, without destroying nuclear spheres, and thereby isolate the minimal residual components required for maintaining the basic structure of the nucleus. The progressive removal of various nuclear components was monitored biochemically (Table III), and light and electron microscopic observations were made to monitor the integrity of nuclear structure. We succeeded in removing 98% of both the phospholipid and RNA of the rat liver nucleus as well as 99.9% of the DNA and 90% of the total nuclear proteins, thus yielding what appears to be the fundamental structural framework of the nucleus (Berezney and Coffey, 1974, 1976, 1977). The resulting constitutive structure, which we termed the nuclear protein matrix, is composed primarily of protein. The four major steps in the procedure for the isolation of the matrix involve sequential extractions of isolated nuclei with buffers of low ionic strength and high ionic strength, nonionic detergent, and nuclease treatment. These are shown in Table III, along with the cumulative percentages of total nuclear constituents remaining after each step.

A detailed electron microscopic analysis of the nuclear protein matrix has been described by Berezney and Coffey (1974, 1976, 1977). Three major structural components of the nuclear matrix can be resolved (e.g., see Fig. 1):

1. The residual elements of the nuclear envelope and nuclear lamina that form a continuous structure surrounding the nuclear sphere. Tangential sections through this residual nuclear envelope reveal the presence of annular structures characteristic of the nuclear pore complexes which form an integral part of the intact nuclear envelope.

2. Highly condensed residual nucleoli.

3. An extensive granular and fibrous interchromatinic matrix structure which extends throughout the interior of the nuclear sphere.

The nuclear matrix appears to be a universal feature of eukaryotic nuclei. Such residual structures have now been isolated from a wide variety of mammalian and nonmammalian sources (Table IV), and there appear to be numerous similarities in their protein constituents. Some of the different terms that have been used to describe these residual nuclear structures include nuclear matrix, nuclear framework structure, nuclear skeleton (Miller *et al.*, 1978a), nuclear ghost (Riley *et al.*, 1975), nuclear scaffold (Adolph, 1980), chromatin-depleted nuclei (Herman *et al.*, 1978), and nuclear cage (McCready *et al.*, 1980).

One should distinguish between the *nuclear matrix* and the *nuclear protein matrix* (Table III). The nuclear matrix, as originally defined, represents a DNase-, Triton-, and 2 *M* NaCl-resistant structure that retains

TABLE III

STEPS IN THE ORIGINAL PROCEDURE FOR ISOLATION OF THE NUCLEAR MATRIX FROM RAT LIVER NUCLEI[a,b]

Step	Consecutive extractions	Resultant nuclear sphere	Extraction medium (0°C)	Number of extractions	Centrifugation time at 770g (minutes)	Recovery from starting nuclei (%)			
						Protein	DNA	RNA	Phospholipid
0	Untreated control nuclei	Intact nucleus (N)	Isolated through 2.2 M sucrose, 5 mM MgCl$_2$, 10 mM Tris, pH 7.4	—	—	100	100	100	100
1	Low magnesium treatment (0.2 mM MgCl$_2$)	Low Mg^{2+} sphere (LM)	0.2 mM MgCl$_2$, 10 mM Tris, pH 7.4	3	30	48.0 ± 1.23	24.2 ± 2.78	80.3 ± 1.83	97.5 ± 2.13
2	High salt treatment (2 M NaCl)	High salt sphere (HS)	2 M NaCl, 0.2 mM MgCl$_2$, 10 mM Tris, pH 7.4	3	60	16.3 ± 1.17	2.40 ± 0.21	34.0 ± 1.64	93.6 ± 1.65
3	Detergent treatment (1% Triton X-100)	Nuclear matrix (NM)	1% (w/v) Triton X-100, 5 mM MgCl$_2$, 10 mM Tris, pH 7.4	1	30	10.0 ± 0.57	2.3 ± 0.21	29.0 ± 1.68	2.2 ± 0.51
4	Nuclease treatment (DNase, RNase)	Nuclear protein matrix (NPM)	200 μg DNase I/ml plus 200 μg RNase A/ml in 5 mM MgCl$_2$, 10 mM Tris, pH 7.4, 1 hour at 22°C	1	30	9.8 + 0.55	<0.01	3.0 ± 0.12	2.0 ± 0.47

[a] See method of Berezney and Coffey (1977).
[b] See text for special considerations. This general procedure has been modified, as described in the text and in the legend to Fig. 1.

32

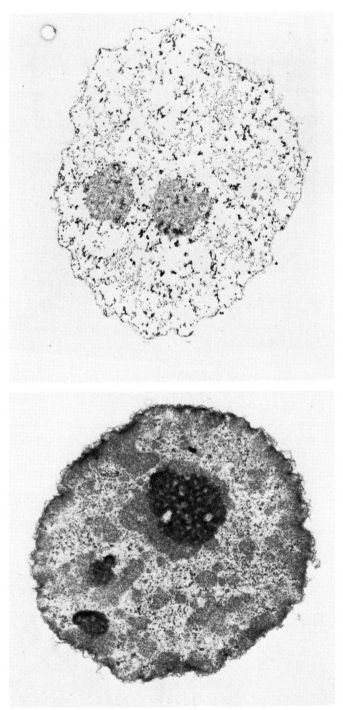

Fig. 1. Transmission electron micrographs of thin sections of an isolated rat liver nucleus (left panel) and of an isolated rat liver nuclear matrix (right panel). The nuclear matrix is isolated from highly purified nuclei by a modification of the original method of Berezney and Coffey (1977). Freshly prepared nuclei are extracted sequentially with 1% Triton X-100 [4°C, 10 minutes, in 0.25 M sucrose containing TM buffer (10 mM Tris, pH 7.4, at 22°C, 5 mM MgCl$_2$)]; pancreatic DNase I (electrophoretically purified by Worthington, Freehold, New Jersey; 10–20 μg/ml in TM buffer, 4°C, 30 minutes; 0.2 mM MgCl$_2$, 10 mM Tris, pH 7.4 (LM buffer), 4°C, 15 minutes; 2 M NaCl in LM buffer obtained by increasing gradually the concentration of NaCl from 0 to 2 M (two extractions, 4°C, 30 minutes); and finally washed and resuspended in 0.2 mM MgCl$_2$, 10 mM Tris, pH 7.4. Phenylmethylsulfonyl fluoride (PMSF), at a final concentration of 1 mM, is generally added to all buffers used in the isolation and extraction of nuclei. Centrifugation of samples is carried out at 750g for 15 minutes (following Triton X-100 and DNase I treatments) or 1500g for 30–40 minutes (following subsequent extractions). $\times$14,400.

33

TABLE IV

EUKARYOTIC SYSTEMS FROM WHICH A RESIDUAL NUCLEAR MATRIX STRUCTURE HAS
BEEN ISOLATED

Source of nuclei	Reference
Rat liver	Berezney and Coffey (1974, 1977), Miller *et al.* (1978a,b), Agutter and Birchall (1979), Berezney (1980), Kaufmann *et al.* (1981), Zbarsky (1981), Kuzmina *et al.* (1981), Matsuura *et al.* (1981)
Mouse liver	Comings and Okada (1976)
Rat uterus	Barrack *et al.* (1977), Agutter and Birchall (1979)
Rat lung	Hemminki and Vainio (1979), Agutter and Birchall (1979)
Rat ventral prostate	Barrack and Coffey (1980)
Chick liver	Barrack *et al.* (1979), Barrack and Coffey (1980)
Chick oviduct	Ciejek *et al.* (1981)
HeLa cells	Riley *et al.* (1975), Riley and Keller (1976), Hodge *et al.* (1977), Herman *et al.* (1978), Adolph (1980), Bouvier *et al.* (1980), van Eekelen and van Venrooij (1981)
SV-40 infected HeLa cells	Deppert (1978)
Hepatoma	Berezney *et al.* (1979), Kuzmina *et al.* (1980), Zbarsky (1981)
Human lymphocytes and granulocytes	Shaper *et al.* (1979)
Erythroleukemia cells	Long *et al.* (1979)
Bovine lymphocytes	Nakayasu and Ueda (1981)
Rabbit granulocytes	Eastment *et al.* (1981)
Bovine kidney cells	Matsumoto (1981)
Mouse spermatocytes and spermatids	Ierardi *et al.* (1981)
3T6 fibroblasts	Buckler-White *et al.* (1980)
Xenopus laevis liver	Snead *et al.* (1979)
Xenopus laevis spermatogonia and spermatocytes	Gambino *et al.* (1981)
Sea urchin embryos	Poznanović and Sevaljević (1980), Sevaljević *et al.* (1980)
Drosophila melanogaster cells	Levinger and Varshavsky (1981), Sinibaldi and Morris (1981)
Physarum polycephalum	Mitchelson *et al.* (1979), Hunt and Vogelstein (1981)
Tetrahymena pyriformis	Wunderlich and Herlan (1977), Herlan *et al.* (1979), Wolfe (1980)

the spherical integrity of the nucleus, but which contains only 10% of the protein, 2% of the DNA, 30% of the RNA, and 2% of the phospholipid of the nucleus (see Table III). Since the original objective had been to describe the minimal residual components of the nucleus responsible for maintaining nuclear spherical integrity (Berezney and Coffey, 1974, 1976, 1977), additional attempts were made to fully digest the remaining nucleic acid constituents using high concentrations of DNase I and RNase A (Table III); the resultant structure was called the *nuclear protein matrix*.

C. Considerations in the Isolation of the Nuclear Matrix

Many factors are important in the nuclear matrix isolation process which can affect the nature of the final product (Table V). Although most investigators use a similar approach to obtain the nuclear matrix, in that they employ detergent, hypotonic and high-salt extractions, and nuclease treatments, the specific details are frequently different (Table V; see also Shaper *et al.*, 1979). For example, rat liver nuclei contain an endogenous magnesium-activated DNase, the activity of which facilitates the extraction of DNA at low magnesium ion concentrations (0.2 mM) and high ionic strength (2 M NaCl) (see Table III, steps 1 and 2). Without the endogenous DNase activity, these extractions may yield large gelatinous aggregates that inter-

TABLE V

Variations in Extraction Procedures Reported for Isolating Nuclear Matrix Preparations[a]

General scheme
    Detergents
    Hypotonic solutions
    Hypertonic solutions
    Nuclease treatment

Variables
    Source and purity of nuclei
    Nature and purity of detergent (Triton X-100; NP-40; peroxide contaminants)
    High salt (0.4–2.0 M NaCl, KCl, or ammonium sulfate)
    Magnesium concentration (0, 0.2 mM, 5 mM, or 0.5 M)
    Chelating agents (EDTA; citric acid)
    Inhibitors of proteolysis (PMSF; sodium tetrathionate)
    Sulfhydryl reagents (β-mercaptoethanol, dithiothreitol)
    State of sulfhydryl oxidation
    DNase (type, amount, time, temperature; protease and RNase contaminants)
    RNase A, RNase T$_1$
    Endogenous nuclease activity
    Protease activity (endogenous; contaminants)
    Extraction temperature ($-20°$ to $+37°$C), pH (7.2–8.5)
    Order of extractions (also number, duration)
    Centrifugation conditions (g force, duration)
    Fixatives and methods of observing (thin sections, whole mounts)

[a] See Shaper *et al.* (1979).

fere with the subsequent isolation of the nuclear matrix. Since nuclei from different tissues contain varying amounts of endogenous DNase activity, the problem of gel formation can be circumvented by carrying out an initial brief digestion of the nuclei with low concentrations of DNase I, followed by the hypotonic and hypertonic extraction steps as described in the legend to Fig. 1. (Compare these modifications with the original procedure described in Table III which was applied to liver nuclei that had undergone endogenous nuclease digestion during an overnight incubation.)

Other important factors that can affect the isolation of the nuclear matrix include endogenous protease activities, the state of oxidation of the nuclear protein sulfhydryl groups, and the order of the extraction steps (also see Table V). Matrix structures of varying morphology and that retain variable amounts of the internal network and residual nucleolus can be obtained by manipulating these variables. Specific details of these effects have been reported for rat liver nuclei (Shaper *et al.*, 1979; Kaufmann *et al.*, 1981). Of particular interest is the observation that if DNase and RNase treatments are applied after the salt extraction, an extensive internal fibrogranular network is retained (Table III), whereas digestion of nuclei with both DNase I and RNase A prior to extraction with 2 *M* NaCl often leads to the disruption of the internal network structure of nuclear matrix spheres (Kaufmann *et al.*, 1981; Herman *et al.*, 1978; Giese and Wunderlich, 1979; Adolph, 1980; Barrack and Coffey, 1980). Other factors (e.g., see Table V; also see Kaufmann *et al.*, 1981) may contribute to these observations, however, since the internal network of the nuclear matrix is not universally found to be sensitive to this latter treatment regimen (Wunderlich and Herlan, 1977; Miller *et al.*, 1978a; Wolfe, 1980).

Perhaps as a result of the variables shown in Table V, extraction of nuclei by what appear to be similar methods frequently leads to the extraction of intranuclear components and isolation of only the residual pore complex-lamina component of the nuclear matrix. A pore complex-lamina has been isolated from many types of nuclei (Aaronson and Blobel, 1975; Dwyer and Blobel, 1976; Shelton *et al.*, 1980; Maul and Avdalović, 1980; Krohne *et al.*, 1981).

These considerations are discussed further in Section VII,A.

D. THE PROTEINS OF THE NUCLEAR MATRIX

The nuclear matrix represents about 10–20% of the total nuclear protein mass and is composed of nonhistone proteins. The matrix proteins are primarily, but not exclusively, in the molecular weight range of 55,000–75,000 (Berezney and Coffey, 1974, 1977; Comings and Okada, 1976; Riley *et al.*, 1975; Hodge *et al.*, 1977; Cobbs and Shelton, 1978; Peters and Comings,

1980; Comings and Peters, 1981). Three of the major polypeptide fractions of MW 62,000–70,000 appear to be associated with the pore complex-lamina component of the matrix (Aaronson and Blobel, 1975; Dwyer and Blobel, 1976; Gerace *et al.*, 1978; Krohne *et al.*, 1978). Some of these matrix proteins appear, by tryptic peptide mapping analysis, to be related in sequence (Shaper *et al.*, 1979; Cochran *et al.*, 1979; Shelton *et al.*, 1980) and may form oligomers by disulfide bridge cross-linking (Cobbs and Shelton, 1978; Shelton and Cochran, 1978; Lam and Kasper, 1979b; S. H. Kaufmann and J. H. Shaper, manuscript in preparation). These three lamina protein fractions have recently been termed lamin A, lamin B, and lamin C, and appear to be phosphorylated at the time of disassembly of the nuclear envelope during mitosis (Gerace and Blobel, 1980).

Peters and Comings (1980) have made a detailed analysis by two-dimensional polyacrylamide gel electrophoresis of the rat liver nuclear proteins, and conclude that 80% of the mass of the nonhistone chromosomal proteins of unextracted nuclei are contained in the nuclear matrix and hnRNP fractions. They point out that the three lamin protein bands (A, B, C) of MW 60,000–75,000 are themselves composed of three distinct subsets comprising a group of several isomers. They also conclude that approximately one-third of the nuclear matrix proteins consist of hnRNP proteins and that actin is also present in the matrix. Peters and Comings (1980) point out that the residual nucleolar matrix is made up of proteins that are different from those of the lamina or intranuclear network of the nuclear matrix (see also Todorov and Hadjiolov, 1979; Franke *et al.*, 1981; Comings and Peters, 1981).

At present, antibodies have been made only against the matrix proteins of MW 62,000–70,000 that are associated with the lamina component of the nuclear matrix (Krohne *et al.*, 1978; Gerace *et al.*, 1978; Stick and Hausen, 1980; Jost and Johnson, 1981).

III. THE ROLE OF THE NUCLEAR MATRIX IN DNA REPLICATION

Work in this laboratory has demonstrated the possible role of the nuclear matrix in DNA replication (see also Table II). Berezney and Coffey (1975, 1976) reported that newly synthesized DNA is tightly associated with the nuclear matrix. At the earliest time intervals after injecting [^{3}H]thymidine into the hepatic portal vein of partially hepatectomized rats, nuclear matrix fractions were obtained which contained tightly attached DNA that was highly enriched in label. At later times after the injection, the specific activity of the matrix-associated DNA decreased, while that of the easily extracted bulk DNA increased (Berezney and Coffey, 1975, 1976). They concluded that the newly synthesized DNA is associated with the nuclear matrix and is subsequently transported off of the matrix (Berezney and Coffey, 1975, 1976). Further insight into nuclear matrix-associated DNA replication was obtained from studies carried out by Pardoll *et al.* (1980) using 3T3 cells in culture. From a detailed analysis of the kinetics of pulse–chase labeling studies, Pardoll *et al.* (1980) proposed a fixed site model of DNA replication in which DNA replication complexes are anchored to the nuclear matrix, and that loops of DNA are reeled through these fixed complexes as they are replicated. Autoradiograms of pulse-labeled, matrix-associated DNA indicate that the replication sites are distributed throughout the interior network of the nuclear matrix (Pardoll *et al.*, 1980). Experiments using synchronized *Physarum polycephalum* provide additional evidence that is consistent with this model of DNA synthesis (Hunt and Vogelstein, 1981).

According to the model proposed by Pardoll *et al.* (1980) (see Fig. 2),

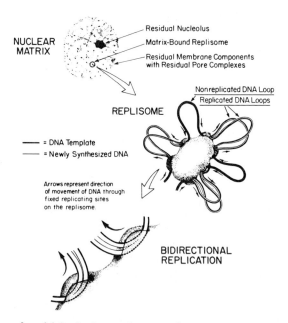

FIG. 2. Proposed model for fixed sites of DNA replication on the nuclear matrix. The top drawing is a schematic representation of a nuclear matrix. The middle drawing shows a cluster of fixed replication complexes forming a replisome. DNA is bound via the replication complexes in alternating replicated and nonreplicated loops. The bottom drawing shows one fixed replication complex with the DNA being reeled through as it is replicated. The process shown would result in a bidirectionally replicated section of DNA with the origin of replication at the center of the replicated loop. For details of evidence for this model consult Pardoll *et al.* (1980) and Vogelstein *et al.* (1980).

multiple loops (approximately 20,000/cell) of DNA are attached at their base to the nuclear matrix. The two sites of attachment for each loop contain a fixed site for DNA replication. During replication each DNA loop moves downward through each of the two fixed replicating complexes. As the parent DNA loop passes through the fixed replication sites, two new loops are formed and the old loop disappears. Each of the new loops contains one single strand of the parent DNA combined with a single strand of newly synthesized DNA (see Fig. 2). This model fulfills many of the earlier experimental observations related to DNA synthesis; these are summarized in Table VI. The aspect of the new model of Pardoll *et al.* (1980) that fits each observation is given within parentheses following each of the earlier observations (Table VI).

Recently, it has become possible to directly visualize the loops of supercoiled DNA attached to the matrix, and to monitor the movement of newly synthesized DNA within these loops (Vogelstein *et al.*, 1980).

There have been several additional recent studies of DNA synthesis associated with the nuclear matrix (Dijkwel *et al.*, 1979; McCready *et al.*, 1980; Berezney and Buchholtz, 1981a,b). Models have been proposed which are essentially similar in nature to the one described above, but which

TABLE VI

PREVIOUS OBSERVATIONS OF DNA SYNTHESIS THAT ARE SATISFIED BY THE PROPOSED MODEL OF FIXED REPLICATION SITES[a]

Loop domains of DNA are often observed in interphase nuclei and may be maintained even in metaphase chromosomes. (These loops are attached at their base to the nuclear matrix.)

A replicating point moves outward forming two replicating forks moving in opposite directions. An "eye" pattern of newly synthesized DNA is formed. (Pattern also consistent with fixed site model.)

DNA is synthesized in replication units. (A replicon = one DNA loop.)

Replicons are approximately 50,000–100,000 bp in length. (Corresponds to the length of a loop of DNA attached to the matrix at its base.)

An individual replicon is synthesized in approximately 30 minutes. (Time of loop synthesis derived from kinetic analyses is 30 minutes.)

Replicons are often synthesized in tandem. (Coupled loop movements on replisome; see Fig. 2.)

Origin of DNA synthesis is never next to a terminus of DNA synthesis. (Origin starts at bottom of loop, and after DNA replication is found at top of new loop next to another origin.)

Many enzymes are required for DNA synthesis and they may be combined into a large complex at the replicating fork. (Size more compatible with fixed site of DNA synthesis.)

New and old strands of DNA are combined following DNA replication.

The vast amount of DNA must be ordered so that there is no entanglement during or following DNA replication. (DNA ordered by loop attachment to matrix.)

[a] See Pardoll *et al.* (1980).

differ with respect to the questions of whether the origin of DNA replication remains attached to the nuclear matrix throughout DNA replication (Dijkwel *et al.*, 1979), and whether the matrix-bound replication complexes slide along the DNA (Berezney and Buchholtz, 1981a) or remain fixed with respect to the movement of the DNA loops through these sites (Pardoll *et al.*, 1980; See Fig. 2).

Many more studies will be required to resolve the many complex aspects of DNA synthesis, and to test and resolve the fine features of the loop model and the fixed site model of DNA replication. Nevertheless, the proposal that the DNA of the eukaryotic nucleus is organized in the form of supercoiled loops that are attached to the nuclear matrix (Vogelstein *et al.*, 1980), and that during DNA replication these loops of DNA are reeled through fixed replication sites on the nuclear matrix (Pardoll *et al.*, 1980), provides an attractive explanation for the mechanism by which an enormous length of DNA must be ordered spatially during replication such that the daughter strands remain untangled yet coupled in a precise fashion for later entry into mitosis.

IV. THE ASSOCIATION OF RNA WITH THE NUCLEAR MATRIX

Earlier studies had recognized that RNA was an important component of the residual nucleus (Georgiev and Chentsov, 1962; Zbarsky *et al.*, 1962; Steele and Busch, 1966; Shankar Narayan *et al.*, 1967; Busch and Smetana, 1970). Busch and his colleagues (Steele and Busch, 1966; Busch and Smetana, 1970) analyzed the specific RNA's associated with the ribonucleoprotein network of the nucleus, and found that 20 minutes after a pulse of [^{32}P]orthophosphate to rats, the specific activity of the residual liver nuclear RNA was threefold higher than that of the RNA associated with the chromatin. The highest specific activity was with the high-molecular-weight RNA >45 S. These observations were confirmed and extended by Faiferman and Pogo (1975). In addition, several investigators have observed that nuclear RNP particles are associated with the nuclear matrix (Berezney and Coffey, 1974, 1976, 1977; Miller *et al.*, 1978a; Berezney, 1979, 1980; Pogo, 1981). Since the nuclear matrix provides a continuous structure directly linking residual nuclear components with the nuclear pore complexes, it was suggested by Berezney and Coffey (1976) that the nuclear matrix might provide a structural passageway for RNA transport. This concept may be feasible since essentially all of the hnRNA and snRNA molecules are associated with the nuclear matrix (Miller *et al.*, 1978a,b; Herman *et al.*, 1978; Long *et al.*, 1979; van Eekelen and van Venrooij, 1981; Jackson *et al.*, 1981). Recently, it has been reported that the pre-mRNA for globin, containing the introns, is tightly associated with the nuclear matrix isolated from chicken erythroblasts (Ross, 1980). Similarly, when chicken oviduct nuclei were fractionated into matrix and nonmatrix components, virtually all the precursor to ovomucoid and ovalbumin mRNA were observed to be bound to 7% of the total nuclear protein that represented the nuclear matrix fraction (Ciejek *et al.*, 1981). They suggested that, following synthesis, the precursor to mRNA is integrated into the structure of the nuclear matrix. Several investigators have proposed that the matrix is either the site for RNA processing or is involved in a structural sense with the processing of RNA precursors (Herman *et al.*, 1978; Ross, 1980; van Eekelen and van Venrooij, 1981; Jackson *et al.*, 1981; Ciejek *et al.*, 1981).

Recently, insight has been gained into the site of attachment of the hnRNP particles to the nuclear matrix (van Eekelen and van Venrooij, 1981). These investigators demonstrated that ultraviolet irradiation resulted in the cross-linking of two of the major hnRNP proteins of MW 41,500 and 43,000 to the hnRNA. These same proteins became cross-linked to the hnRNA when either intact cells (HeLa S3) or the isolated nuclear matrix were irradiated. Since these proteins were found to be components of the nuclear matrix, it was suggested that the hnRNA is bound to the matrix via these proteins (van Eekelen and van Venrooij, 1981). In addition, there is a wide variety of stable small-molecular-weight RNAs associated with the nuclear matrix that may provide attachment sites for hnRNA (Miller *et al.*, 1978b).

In the previous section related to DNA synthesis on the nuclear matrix, evidence was presented that DNA loops are reeled through fixed replication sites that are attached to the nuclear matrix (Pardoll *et al.*, 1980). Recently, a similar mechanism has been proposed in which transcription also occurs as DNA passes through transcription complexes that are fixed to the nuclear matrix (Jackson *et al.*, 1981). In addition, these authors report that the nascent RNA is attached to the matrix at the 5′ cap and perhaps also at the 3′ end.

V. REGULATION OF DNA STRUCTURE ON THE MATRIX

All the models in which DNA moves through fixed sites attached to the matrix require special considerations of the topological constraints that arise from the supercoiling of DNA; clearly, these constraints would have to be relieved by topoisomerase-like activities (Feinberg and Coffey, 1982; B. Vogelstein and D. M. Pardoll, unpublished results). Recently, it has been proposed that chick oviduct progesterone receptor subunit A, by virtue of its preferential binding to single-stranded DNA, may be active in DNA helix destabilization (Hughes *et al.*, 1981). It is also noteworthy that proteins with DNA unwinding activity are induced in the prostate by androgen treatment (Rennie *et al.*, 1975; Mainwaring *et al.*, 1976).

Several investigators have reported that certain active genes are in relatively close proximity to the nuclear matrix DNA attachment points (Pardoll and Vogelstein, 1980; Nelkin *et al.*, 1980; Robinson *et al.*, 1982; Bekhor and Mirell, 1979; Gates and Bekhor, 1980; Norman and Bekhor, 1981). Studies cited by Bekhor and his colleagues were carried out on salt-resistant components of chromatin; these components appear to be related to the nuclear matrix proteins but as yet this has not been proved. The implication of these data is that the nuclear matrix structural components may play a critical role in the regulation of gene function.

In summary, there is increasing evidence that the nuclear matrix may play a major role in the transcription, processing, and transport of nuclear RNA, and in DNA replication and differentiation. Elements of the nuclear matrix may order the DNA both in the interphase nucleus and become part of the core scaffold of the metaphase chromosomes (Basler *et al.*, 1981). If the nuclear matrix possesses chemomechanical properties such as those observed in the condensation of chromosomes, similar properties may also be utilized in the transport of macromolecules within the interphase nucleus.

The control of DNA replication, gene expression, and RNA processing and transport remain at the frontier of our knowledge in cell biology. It is of interest that each of these biological processes appears to be associated with the nuclear matrix. Since hormones initiate these functions it seemed only logical to determine whether and how hormones might interact in a specific manner with the nuclear matrix.

VI. THE INTERACTION OF STEROID HORMONES
WITH THE NUCLEAR MATRIX

A. INTRODUCTION

The interaction of steroid hormones and their specific receptor proteins with the nucleus of target tissues is an essential step in the mechanism by which these hormones modulate nuclear events such as gene expression (see reviews by Gorski and Gannon, 1976; Thrall *et al.*, 1978; Jensen, 1979; Liao *et al.*, 1979). The hormone–receptor complex is presumed to bind to specific regulatory sites near the genes they regulate, but the precise identification of these binding sites and the mechanism for specific recognition and regulation of these sites remain an enigma. Numerous efforts to identify and localize these nuclear "acceptor" sites to which the steroid–receptor complex binds have attributed this property to basic nuclear proteins (Puca *et al.*, 1975), DNA (Yamamoto and Alberts, 1976), ribonucleoprotein particles (Liao *et al.*, 1973), chromatin (Thrall *et al.*, 1978; Jensen, 1979), nucleosomes (Senior and Frankel, 1978; Rennie, 1979), nonhistone proteins (Thrall *et al.*, 1978), nuclear membrane (Jackson and Chalkley, 1974; Lefebvre and Novosad, 1980; Smith and von Holt, 1981), or salt-insoluble nuclear fractions (see Section VI,B). Although the possibility should be considered that each of these putative acceptor sites may be involved in different aspects of the mechanism of hormone action, an alternative explanation is that they represent operationally defined components of the same overall system (see also Sections VII,F and VIII,C).

We have focused our attention on the identification of specific steroid binding sites associated with the nuclear matrix, and will present evidence that the nuclear matrix is a major site of steroid hormone binding in the nucleus. While it might appear that this only adds to the apparently confusing array of potential nuclear targets for steroid hormone action, there is increasing evidence that the nuclear matrix provides an organizational and structural framework on which nuclear events are regulated (see Table II). It thus provides a potential link between nuclear structure and function.

B. Identification of Hormone Binding to Salt-Resistant Nuclear Components

Nuclear steroid receptors are often characterized by their extraction from nuclei with 0.3–0.6 *M* KCl or NaCl (Jensen *et al.*, 1968; Puca and Bresciani, 1968; Bruchovsky and Wilson, 1968). However, in many different target tissue systems a significant amount of steroid binding activity remains resistant to solubilization by salt (Fang *et al.*, 1969; DeHertogh *et al.*, 1973, Lebeau *et al.*, 1973; Mester and Baulieu, 1975; Klyzsejko-Stefanowicz *et al.*, 1976; Nyberg and Wang, 1976; Clark and Peck, 1976; Barrack *et al.*, 1977, 1979, 1983; Honma *et al.*, 1977; Boesel *et al.*, 1977; Davies *et al.*, 1977; Ruh and Baudendistel, 1977; Snow *et al.*, 1978; Gschwendt and Schneider, 1978; Danzo and Eller, 1978; Kaufman *et al.*, 1978; Wang, 1978; Franceschi and Kim, 1979; Sanborn *et al.*, 1979; Sato *et al.*, 1979; Barrack and Coffey, 1980; Cidlowski and Munck, 1980; Tsai *et al.*, 1980; Brown *et al.*, 1981).

A number of attempts have been made to characterize these salt-resistant steroid binding sites further and the work of several investigators has provided evidence that salt-resistant nuclear steroid receptors represent a physiologically meaningful compartment of nuclear receptors. For example, DeHertogh *et al.* (1973) proposed, on the basis of *in vivo* infusion studies of [^{3}H]estradiol labeling of rat uterine nuclei, that the salt-resistant nuclear fraction represented the ultimate site of hormone localization in the nucleus. Clark and Peck (1976) later demonstrated that estrogen-induced long-term growth of the rat uterus, which involves both hypertrophy and hyperplasia, depends on the specific interaction of estradiol–receptor complexes with nuclear salt-resistant binding components. Using an *in vitro* [^{3}H]estradiol exchange assay (Anderson *et al.*, 1972a) to quantitate the amount of hormone that had become bound to these sites as a result of *in vivo* processes of hormone–receptor complex translocation, Clark and Peck (1976) observed that the number of salt-resistant nuclear estradiol receptors was identical with the number of receptors required for maximal uterine growth, and they proposed that these binding sites represent specific nuclear acceptor sites. Similar observations were made by Ruh and Baudendistel (1977), who in addition observed that treatment of immature rats with estradiol results in the appearance of both salt-extractable and salt-resistant nuclear estradiol receptors in the uterus, whereas treatment with antiestrogens, which stimulate only limited uterine growth, results in the appearance of only salt-extractable uterine nuclear receptors. Ruh and Baudendistel (1978) concluded that the salt-resistant nuclear estradiol binding sites may be involved primarily in events that result in the replenishment and processing of receptors, an event required for continued growth response to estrogen stimulation.

Nuclear salt-resistant steroid hormone receptors have also been implicated in the mechanism of induction by estrogens of Leydig cell tumors in mice, since in strains that are susceptible to tumor induction, the Leydig cells contain salt-resistant nuclear receptors, whereas Leydig cells of resistant mice contain only salt-extractable nuclear estradiol receptors (Sato *et al.*, 1979). The presence of nuclear salt-resistant receptors for glucocorticoids in dexamethasone-sensitive mouse myeloid leukemic cells, but not in certain clones of dexamethasone-resistant cells (Honma *et al.*, 1977), further suggests that nuclear salt-resistant steroid hormone receptors may be involved in the responsiveness of normal and neoplastic cells to specific steroid hormones.

Additional evidence that nuclear salt-resistant hormone binding sites play an important role in the mechanism of action of hormones has come from a different approach. In cell-free binding experiments, high affinity, tissue-specific nuclear acceptor sites for isolated steroid hormone–receptor complexes have been described in residual fractions of chromatin that resist dissociation by 0.5–2 M NaCl or 4–5 M GuHCl. These salt-resistant acceptor sites have been characterized for androgen receptors in the rat prostate (Wang, 1978), testis (Klyzsejko-Stefanowicz *et al.*, 1976), Sertoli cell (Tsai *et al.*, 1980), and for progesterone receptors in the chick oviduct (Thrall *et al.*, 1978).

Thus, by three different experimental approaches, i.e., labeling *in vivo*, exchange *in vitro*, and cell-free reconstitution, biological functions have been ascribed to nuclear salt-resistant hormone binding activities.

Some have questioned the evidence for a salt-resistant class of nuclear receptors (Juliano and Stancel, 1976; Traish *et al.*, 1977; Müller *et al.*, 1977). Following the incubation of rat uteri *in vitro* in the presence of 10 nM [³H]estradiol (Müller *et al.*, 1977), approximately 100 fmol/uterus, or 10% of the nuclear bound radioactivity, is resistant to repeated extractions with 0.6 M KCl. Wotiz and his colleagues concluded that this is an insignificant percentage and probably represents nuclear receptors entrapped in the gelatinous DNA pellet that results when uterine nuclei are exposed to high concentrations of salt (Traish *et al.*, 1977). It is important to recognize, however, that only about 10–20% of the maximum number of estrogen receptors that can be translocated to the nucleus following treatment of rats with pharmacological doses (1–2.5 µg) of estradiol exhibit long-term retention in the nucleus, which is a requirement for the stimulation of true uterine growth (Anderson *et al.*, 1972b, 1975; Clark and Peck, 1976). Moreover, this limited number of nuclear estradiol binding sites is salt resistant (Clark and Peck, 1976). It is important to note that although the *percentage* of nuclear receptors which are salt resistant varies with the dose of estradiol given *in vivo* (20% following 2.5 µg estradiol versus 60% following 0.1 µg estradiol), maximal uterine growth is obtained with both doses, and the *number* of salt-resistant receptors is the same (Clark and Peck, 1976).

Therefore, although Wotiz and colleagues (Traish *et al.*, 1977; Müller *et al.*, 1977) measured steroid binding directly (via 1 µg [³H]estradiol *in vivo* or 10 nM [³H]estradiol *in vitro* with intact uteri) while Clark and co-workers (Anderson *et al.*, 1972b, 1975; Clark and Peck, 1976) measured receptors by an *in vitro* exchange assay (following 0.1–2.5 µg unlabeled estradiol *in vivo*), a significant number of salt-resistant estradiol receptors (1500–3000 molecules/nucleus) can be detected by these three different approaches. Conflicting results, however, have been obtained by Juliano and Stancel (1976), who injected a physiological dose (0.1 µg) of [³H]estradiol into rats and found essentially no salt-resistant nuclear radioactivity.

Additional insight into this controversy has been obtained from experiments carried out in this laboratory (Barrack *et al.*, 1977, 1979). Our analysis of several different protocols has revealed that methodological differences may account, in large part, for the divergent interpretations related to the measurement of nuclear salt-resistant steroid receptors. Some of these experiments are summarized in Table VII. Studies *in vivo* were carried out in which immature female rats were given a physiological dose (0.1 μg) of estradiol, either unlabeled or radiolabeled. One hour later, uterine nuclei were isolated and estradiol binding to the total, salt-extractable, and salt-resistant nuclear fractions was quantitated. Following the administration of unlabeled steroid, specific estradiol binding sites were quantitated by

TABLE VII

COMPARISON OF DIFFERENT METHODS USED TO STUDY SUBNUCLEAR DISTRIBUTION OF ESTRADIOL BINDING SITES IN IMMATURE RAT UTERI[a]

	Specific estradiol binding (fmol/uterus)		
Method	Total nuclei	Salt extractable	Salt resistant
I. *In vivo* studies[b]			
A. Unlabeled E_2 (0.1 μg)			
1. *In vitro* exchange, then extract	483 ± 19	269 ± 33	220 ± 10
2. Extract, then exchange	—	181 ± 20	210 ± 17
B. [³H]E_2 (0.1 μg)			
1. Count fractions directly	210 ± 15	214 ± 18	22 ± 4
2. *In vitro* exchange assay	—	—	199 ± 20
II. *In vitro* studies[c]			
A. Unlabeled E_2 (20 nM)			
In vitro exchange, then extract	826 ± 179	551 ± 139	233 ± 63
B. [³H]E_2 (20 nM)			
Count fractions directly	1137 ± 131	865 ± 179	204 ± 55

[a] Data from Barrack *et al.* (1977, 1979).

[b] Immature female Sprague–Dawley rats (21–25 days old) were given a single subcutaneous injection of either 0.1 μg [³H]17β-estradiol (90–102 Ci/mmol) (I,B) or 0.1 μg unlabeled 17β-estradiol (I,A) in 0.5 ml of 0.9% NaCl. One hour later, the uteri were homogenized in 10 mM Tris, pH 7.4, 1.5 mM EDTA, and a crude nuclear myofibrillar pellet was prepared, as described by Anderson *et al.* (1972a). Where indicated, the *in vitro* exchange assay (Anderson *et al.*, 1972a) was carried out at 37°C, 30 minutes in the presence of 14 nM [³H]estradiol without (to measure total binding) or with excess unlabeled estradiol (1.4 μM; to measure nonspecific binding). Only specific binding data (total minus nonspecific binding) are shown (mean ± SD). Samples were pelleted at 4°C, washed three times with Tris–EDTA buffer to remove unbound steroid, and then either dissolved in tissue solubilizer or extracted with ethanol and counted; or extracted with 0.6 M KCl and 10 mM Tris, pH 8.0, before counting. Where extraction with KCl preceded the exchange assay, the binding reactions for the soluble salt extracts were terminated by the addition of hydroxyapatite, washing, and extraction of bound radioactivity with ethanol.

[c] Uteri obtained from untreated immature female rats were placed into Eagle's HeLa medium containing 20 nM ³H-labeled or unlabeled estradiol and incubated at 37°C for 1 hour under an atmosphere of 95% O_2–5% CO_2. Nuclei were isolated and extracted with KCl as described above.

the *in vitro* [³H]estradiol exchange assay method described by Anderson *et al*. (1972a). Approximately 50% (220 fmol/uterus) of the total nuclear estradiol binding capacity was resistant to solubilization by 0.6 *M* KCl (Table VII, part I,A), in agreement with the findings of Clark and Peck (1976). Comparable results were obtained whether binding was quantitated before or after salt extraction.

In contrast, when the same dose of *radiolabeled* estradiol (0.1 μg) was administered *in vivo* and bound estradiol was quantitated by direct counting of the nuclear fractions before and after salt extraction, 22 fmol/uterus or less than 10% of the total nuclear label was salt resistant (Table VII, part I,B,1). A similar observation was made by Juliano and Stancel (1976). However, when we further subjected this salt-resistant pellet to an *in vitro* binding assay in the presence of [³H]estradiol, 200 fmol of specific estradiol binding was detected (Table VII, part I,B,2). Thus, 0.1 μg labeled estradiol injected *in vivo* is not recovered with the salt-resistant sites, though these binding sites can be revealed when the isolated fractions are subjected to an exchange assay *in vitro*.

Total nuclear estradiol binding sites measured by the exchange assay were 2.3-fold more numerous than those found after injection of 0.1 μg labeled estradiol *in vivo* (Table VII, part I,A versus I,B). This increase is accounted for by the ability of the exchange assay to detect salt-resistant sites *in vitro* which are not labeled by the *in vivo* approach (Table VII, part I,B). In contrast, labeling of the salt-extractable receptors is equally efficient by both methods (Table VII, part I,A and B).

The results of incubating intact uteri *in vitro* at 37°C for 1 hour in the presence of labeled or unlabeled estradiol (20 n*M*) are also shown in Table VII. Incubation with unlabeled estradiol, followed by quantitation of nuclear estradiol receptors by the *in vitro* exchange assay, results in higher levels of total nuclear and salt-extractable receptors than are obtained 1 hour after the injection of 0.1 μg unlabeled estradiol *in vivo* (Table VII, part I,A versus II,A). This is probably due to a dose-dependent translocation of cytoplasmic receptors into the nucleus, since the level of estradiol to which the uteri are continuously exposed during an *in vitro* incubation is likely to be greater than that which follows a single injection of 0.1 μg estradiol *in vivo*. Evidence for dose-related translocation was also obtained by Clark and Peck (1976) who observed much greater levels of nuclear estradiol receptors 1 hour following the administration of a pharmacological dose (2.5 μg) of estradiol than following a physiological dose (0.1 μg).

As shown in Table VII (parts I,A and II,A), the number of nuclear salt-resistant estradiol binding sites is the same following incubation of intact uteri *in vitro* or the injection of unlabeled estradiol *in vivo*. This is in agreement with the observation by Clark and Peck (1976) of similar numbers of nuclear salt-resistant estradiol binding sites following either low (0.1 µg) or high (2.5 µg) doses of estradiol.

Table VII also shows that whereas only about 5–10% of the nuclear salt-resistant sites can be labeled by injecting 0.1 µg [³H]estradiol *in vivo* (Table VII, part I,B,1), virtually all these sites can be labeled by incubating intact uteri *in vitro* with [³H]estradiol, despite the fact that this salt-resistant binding represents less than 20% of the total nuclear binding measured under these conditions (Table VII, part II,B). Similar results were obtained whether the uteri were homogenized in the presence or absence of a hundredfold excess (2 µM) of unlabeled estradiol, indicating that the binding did not merely occur during cell disruption. Coincubation of uteri with [³H]estradiol and 2 µM unlabeled estradiol greatly diminished the amount of [³H]estradiol bound to all fractions. We conclude that nuclear salt-resistant sites in the intact cell are accessible to estradiol, though the degree of occupancy of these sites may be dose related.

It is important to account for the observation that 0.1 µg [³H]estradiol *in vivo* does not appear to label nuclear salt-resistant binding sites (Table VII), yet this dose is capable of stimulating true uterine growth (Anderson *et al.*, 1972b, 1975). Several possible explanations might be considered.

1. If nuclear salt-resistant binding sites can be demonstrated only by subjecting isolated nuclei to an *in vitro* labeling method, one might question whether the *in vitro* exchange assay conditions are measuring or exposing binding sites that do not bind estradiol under *in vivo* conditions. However, salt-resistant sites can become occupied by steroid when intact uteri are incubated with [³H]estradiol *in vitro* (Table VII, part II,B).

2. Alternatively, one might infer that the *in vitro* exchange reaction is capable of detecting both occupied and unoccupied sites, whereas the *in vivo* labeling method measures only unoccupied sites. This would imply that the salt-resistant sites were already occupied by endogenous estrogen *in vivo;* however, if this were the case, one would have to explain why the immature uterus is not already maximally stimulated.

3. The inability to recover label with the nuclear salt-resistant sites following an *in vivo* pulse may be due to a more rapid dissociation of [³H]estradiol from salt-resistant sites than from salt-extractable sites during the nuclear isolation procedure. Yet, when salt-resistant sites are labeled by the exchange assay *in vitro*, the [³H]estradiol remains bound throughout extensive washing procedures to remove unbound steroid. However, there is no way of knowing whether subtle changes in binding parameters might be induced during *in vitro* manipulations.

4. Another explanation is that partial occupancy of salt-resistant sites by estradiol *in vivo*, following the administration of 0.1 µg estradiol, may be

all that is required for maximal growth stimulation. Thus, estradiol may induce an increase in the number of salt-resistant sites to a level of approximately 200 fmol/uterus, but most of these may represent spare receptors. Alternatively, the mechanism by which salt-resistant sites may be related to growth may not necessarily involve or require bound estradiol, at least during the time frame of these experiments.

C. Estradiol Binding Sites on the Nuclear Matrix of Rat Uterus

We set out to determine whether the nuclear salt-resistant estradiol receptors of the rat uterus were in fact associated with the nuclear matrix, since the salt-resistant nuclear fraction still contained the nuclear envelope and most of the nuclear DNA and RNA. One hour after the injection of 0.1 μg unlabeled estradiol into immature female rats, uterine nuclei were isolated and extracted sequentially with 1% Triton X-100, DNase I, low magnesium hypotonic buffer, 2 M NaCl, and Tris–EDTA buffer. The residual nuclear matrix fraction contained only 1% of the total nuclear DNA. Specific estradiol binding sites on the nuclear matrix were quantitated *in vitro*. As shown in Fig. 3, the nuclear matrix contains saturable, high-

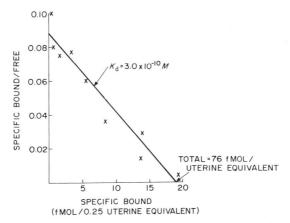

FIG. 3. Binding of estradiol to rat uterine nuclear matrix. One hour after the injection of 0.1 μg unlabeled estradiol to immature female rats, uterine nuclei were isolated. The nuclear matrix was obtained as described in Fig. 1, but in the absence of protease inhibitors. The final nuclear matrix pellet was washed in 10 mM Tris, pH 7.4, 1.5 mM EDTA; estradiol binding was measured *in vitro* by saturation analysis in the presence of increasing concentrations of [³H]estradiol (70 pM to 14 nM) without (total binding) or with a 100-fold excess of unlabeled estradiol (nonspecific binding). Specific binding was calculated by subtracting nonspecific from total binding, and plotted by the method of Scatchard (1949).

affinity, specific estradiol binding sites. Quantitation of specific, high-affinity estradiol binding to unextracted uterine nuclei is shown for comparison in Fig. 4. The nuclear matrix, which remains after the removal of most of the nuclear phospholipid, DNA, RNA, and protein, retains 22% of the total nuclear specific estradiol binding capacity, a significant enrichment. It is important to note that these calculations underestimate binding recovery since they do not take into account the less than quantitative recovery of matrix spheres from the starting nuclear spheres.

Several additional points are worth noting. It had been argued by Traish *et al.* (1977) that salt-resistant binding merely represents incomplete extraction of nuclear salt-extractable receptors that have become entrapped in the gelatinous DNA pellet that is obtained when nuclei are incubated

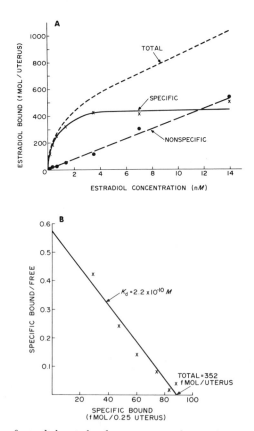

Fig. 4. Binding of estradiol to isolated rat uterine nuclei. Nuclei were isolated from uteri of estradiol-treated rats, and were subjected to saturation analysis *in vitro* as described in the legend to Fig. 3. (A) Total (- - -), nonspecific (————), and specific (×———×) binding are plotted. (B) Scatchard plot of specific binding.

in concentrated salt solutions. This is not the case, however, since we can demonstrate significant amounts of specific steroid binding activity in the nuclear matrix fraction, which routinely contains much less than 5% of the total nuclear DNA. The isolation of nuclear matrix spheres involves an initial brief digestion of the nuclei with DNase I, which allows the subsequent solubilization of chromatin by low magnesium and 2 M NaCl solutions and prevents the formation of a gelatinous pellet.

1. Tissue and Steroid Specificity

Other important features of the estradiol binding sites associated with the uterine nuclear matrix are their steroid specificity and tissue specificity. In competitive binding assays carried out *in vitro*, only estrogens are capable of inhibiting the binding of [³H]estradiol to specific, high-affinity binding sites (Table VIII). With regard to tissue specificity, nuclear matrix spheres isolated from livers of immature female rats that had received 0.1 μg estradiol *in vivo* contained no detectable high-affinity, saturable estradiol binding activity (Barrack *et al.*, 1977). It is important to note, however, that rat liver is an estrogen responsive tissue, but the translocation of cytoplasmic estradiol receptors to the liver nucleus occurs only following treatment of animals with very large doses of estrogens (Aten *et al.*, 1978). It appears that the requirement for a high dose of estrogen to affect liver responsiveness is due to rapid metabolism by the liver which greatly reduces

TABLE VIII

STEROID-SPECIFIC INHIBITION OF [³H]ESTRADIOL BINDING
TO RAT UTERINE NUCLEAR MATRIX[a]

Hormone	Relative binding affinity (%)
Estradiol	100
Estrone	51
Estriol	32
Testosterone	4
Dihydrotestosterone	9
Progesterone	23
Cortisol	18

[a] The nuclear matrix fraction from uteri of immature female rats, given 0.1 μg unlabeled estradiol 1 hour prior to sacrifice, was incubated *in vitro* in the presence of [³H]estradiol (12 nM) with or without increasing concentrations of unlabeled steroids (120–1200 nM). The relative binding affinity equals (the concentration of unlabeled estradiol required to inhibit [³H]estradiol binding to specific sites by 50%) divided by (the concentration of other competitors required to produce the same amount of inhibition), multiplied by 100%.

the concentration of estradiol in the cell that is available for binding to receptors and translocation into the nucleus (Dickson *et al.*, 1980; Dickson and Eisenfeld, 1981). Recently, Agutter and Birchall (1979) have confirmed that the rat uterine nuclear matrix contains specific estradiol binding sites and have shown in addition that the rat lung nuclear matrix contains none.

2. Relationship to Type II Receptors

Clark and his colleagues have recently demonstrated that rat uterine nuclei contain, in addition to the well-known high-affinity (Type I, $K_d \sim$ 1 nM) estradiol receptors, low-affinity (Type II, $K_d \sim$ 30 nM) specific estradiol binding sites (Markaverich *et al.*, 1980; Clark *et al.*, 1980). They find that under certain conditions of hormone administration to rats, the sum of the number of Type II sites measured independently in the salt-extractable and salt-resistant fractions is much greater than the number of Type II sites detected in unextracted isolated nuclei. In other words, extraction of rat uterine nuclei with KCl exposes estradiol binding sites in the salt-resistant fraction that were not originally accessible to estradiol in the intact nucleus (Markaverich *et al.*, 1980; Clark *et al.*, 1980). This is in marked contrast to the situation we observe for the high-affinity ($K_d \sim$ 1 nM, equivalent to the Type I sites, according to the terminology of Clark and colleagues) estradiol binding sites that are associated with the nuclear matrix. As shown in Table VII and Fig. 3, high-affinity binding in the salt-extractable and salt-resistant nuclear fractions accounts for essentially all the binding observed in unextracted nuclei. It is important to keep in mind, however, that the experiments described in Table VII and Figs. 3 and 4 were carried out under conditions in which *only* high-affinity (Type I) steroid–receptor interactions would be detected. In order to measure low-affinity binders, saturation analysis must be performed over a wide range of [³H]estradiol concentrations, up to 80 nM (Eriksson *et al.*, 1978; Markaverich *et al.*, 1980; Clark *et al.*, 1980). It remains to be seen whether the salt-resistant low-affinity Type II nuclear estradiol binding sites are also associated with the uterine nuclear matrix.

3. Additional Considerations

The uterine nuclear matrix fractions used for the estradiol binding studies discussed in this section were not pure, since it is difficult to isolate in high yield uterine nuclei that are free of myofibrillar components. Thus, we could not be certain whether the salt-resistant estradiol binding sites were associated with the nuclear matrix or with contaminating nonnuclear structures.

For example, one should consider potential contamination of nuclei with plasma membrane fragments and/or microsomal membranes, both of which have been shown to contain specific, high-affinity estradiol binding sites (Szego and Pietras, 1981; Nenci *et al.*, 1981; Parikh *et al.*, 1980). Contamination of uterine nuclear matrix preparations with plasma membrane-associated estradiol binding sites is not considered likely for at least two reasons. According to Szego and Pietras (1981), the method of tissue homogenization that we have used for the isolation of uterine nuclear matrix would probably have disrupted the plasma membranes into fragments that do not pellet with the nuclei. Secondly, plasma membrane-associated estradiol binding sites are extracted by Triton X-100 (Szego and Pietras, 1981), whereas nuclear matrix-associated estradiol binding sites are resistant to Triton X-100 (Barrack *et al.*, 1977, 1979).

Estradiol binding sites associated with the nuclear matrix also appear to be distinct from microsomal estradiol binding sites in that binding to microsomes is increased by 40% following extraction with 1.5 M KCl (Parikh *et al.*, 1980), whereas the high-affinity binding sites on the nuclear matrix was unaffected by 2 M NaCl (Barrack *et al.*, 1977, 1979).

D. IDENTIFICATION AND CHARACTERIZATION OF ESTRADIOL BINDING SITES ON THE NUCLEAR MATRIX OF AVIAN LIVER

In order to circumvent the potential problem of impure nuclear preparations, we chose to study hormone interactions in a target tissue from which nuclei can be isolated in good yield and with a high degree of purity. For this purpose, the estrogen-sensitive avian liver offers many advantages.

The estrogen-dependent regulation of vitellogenin synthesis in the liver of hens and estrogen-treated immature chicks or roosters is a well-characterized model for studying the modulation of specific gene expression by steroid hormones (Deeley *et al.*, 1977; Tata, 1978). Increased nuclear binding of estradiol has been correlated with the stimulation of the biological response (Snow *et al.*, 1978; Lazier, 1975), and, in addition, it has been reported that a large proportion (40–80%) of the estrogen receptors in these liver nuclei is resistant to salt extraction (Lebeau *et al.*, 1973; Snow *et al.*, 1978; Gschwendt and Schneider, 1978).

The nuclear matrix fraction was isolated from purified liver nuclei of diethylstilbestrol (DES)-treated chicks. Extraction of these nuclei with Triton X-100, DNase I, low magnesium, and high-salt buffers results in the removal of most of the total nuclear DNA, protein, phospholipid, and RNA. Examination of the residual pellet of nuclear matrix by phase contrast microscopy reveals intact spheres of low refractivity that have retained the

major nuclear landmarks: a distinct peripheral boundary (lamina) and residual nucleoli. Electron microscopy reveals, in addition, remnants of an
internal fibrogranular network. Saturation analysis of the binding of
[³H]estradiol to this isolated liver nuclear matrix was determined by an
exchange assay *in vitro,* and the results are shown in Fig. 5. Specific binding
of estradiol to the matrix is saturable and high affinity, with an apparent
equilibrium dissociation constant, K_d, of 0.5 nM (Fig. 5). Furthermore,
there appears to be only a single class of high-affinity estradiol binding sites
associated with the nuclear matrix. In an assay that contained 165 μg of
nuclear matrix protein the total number of specific estradiol binding sites
was 210 fmol, or 127 fmol/100 μg matrix protein (Table IX). Since 165 μg
of matrix protein was obtained from a starting amount of nuclei equivalent

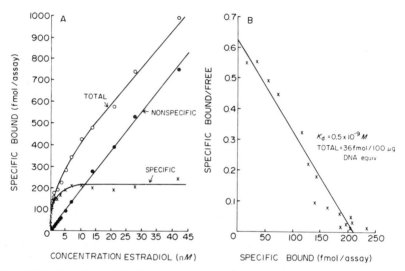

FIG. 5. Binding of estradiol to liver nuclear matrix of DES-treated chicks. Immature chicks
were treated with diethylstilbestrol (25 mg/kg) and killed 20 hours later. Livers were perfused
with 0.9% NaCl, and purified nuclei were isolated by centrifugation through 2.2 M sucrose,
10 mM Tris, pH 7.4, 5 mM $MgCl_2$, as described by Berezney and Coffey (1977). Nucleated
erythrocytes were a minor contaminant (1–2%). The nuclear matrix was isolated from these
purified liver nuclei as described in Fig. 1, and estradiol binding was quantitated by an *in
vitro* assay (4°C, 20–24 hours), as described by Snow *et al.* (1978). Each assay tube contained
165 μg nuclear matrix protein which was derived from an amount of nuclei equivalent to 580
μg of starting nuclear DNA. (A) Total binding (O——O) was measured in the presence of
[³H]estradiol alone (70 pM to 42 nM). Nonspecific binding (●——●) was measured in the
presence of [³H]estradiol plus unlabeled estradiol (0.7 μM). Specific binding (×——×) is the
difference between total and nonspecific binding. (B) Scatchard plot of specific binding
(×——×) in (A). Total binding capacity of the nuclear matrix was 210 fmol/assay. From
Barrack and Coffey (1980).

TABLE IX

COMPARISON OF SPECIFIC ESTRADIOL BINDING IN CHICK LIVER NUCLEI AND
NUCLEAR MATRIX[a]

	Recovery (% of total nuclear)		Specific binding of estradiol			
Isolate	Protein	DNA	fmol/100 μg protein in fraction	fmol/100 μg starting DNA equivalents	Binding sites per nucleus	K_d (nM)
Total nuclei[b]	100	100	24.2 (1.0)[c]	59.2 (1.0)	850[d]	0.9
Nuclear matrix[e]	7	2	127.3 (5.3)	36.2 (0.61)	520	0.5

[a] Liver nuclei and nuclear matrix were isolated from immature chicks 20 hours following a single injection of DES, as described earlier (Barrack and Coffey, 1980). Specific estradiol binding capacities and dissociation constants were derived from Scatchard analyses. From Barrack and Coffey (1980).

[b] Aliquots of nuclei containing 255 μg DNA and 625 μg total nuclear protein were assayed for estradiol binding by saturation analysis. Total specific binding, derived from a Scatchard plot, was 151 fmol/assay.

[c] Numbers in parentheses indicate values relative to intact nuclei.

[d] Based on a value of 2.4 pg DNA per nucleus (Lebeau et al., 1973) and on the assumption that all nuclei have the same binding capacity.

[e] Estradiol binding to liver nuclear matrix is described in the legend to Fig. 5.

to 580 μg of DNA, we can also express the binding data as 36 fmol/100 μg starting nuclear DNA equivalents. This corresponds to approximately 520 sites/nucleus, based on a value of 2.4 pg of DNA per intact nucleus, and on the assumption that all nuclei have the same binding capacity. For comparison, the specific binding of estradiol to intact liver nuclei from DES-treated chicks is 24.2 fmol/100 μg total nuclear protein, or 59.2 fmol/ 100 μg nuclear DNA (Table IX). Therefore, 61% of the total specific estradiol binding capacity of unextracted nuclei is associated with the nuclear matrix (Table IX). In contrast, only 7% of the total nuclear protein and 2% of the DNA are recovered with the nuclear matrix. Thus, there is a fivefold enrichment of nuclear estradiol binding sites on the nuclear matrix when expressed per unit amount of protein (Table IX).

The high-affinity binding sites on the liver nuclear matrix of estrogen treated chicks are specific for estrogens (Fig. 6). In a competitive binding assay, the binding of [3H]estradiol can be inhibited equally efficiently by the simultaneous addition of unlabeled estradiol or diethylstilbestrol, and less well by estriol. In contrast, the binding of [3H]estradiol is virtually unaffected by the addition of even very high concentrations of unlabeled dihydrotestosterone, cortisol, or progesterone (Fig. 6). This steroid specificity is characteristic of estrogen receptors.

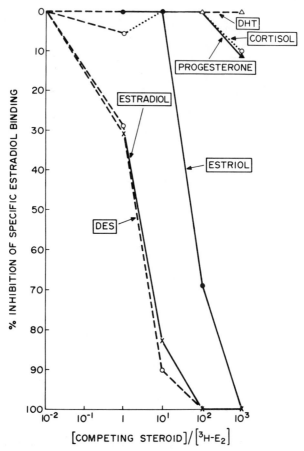

FIG. 6. Steroid-specific inhibition of estradiol binding to chick liver nuclear matrix. Liver nuclear matrix, isolated from the liver nuclei of DES-treated chicks, was incubated *in vitro* (4°C, 24 hours) in the presence of [³H]estradiol (7 nM) alone (total binding) or with increasing concentrations of unlabeled steroids (7 nM to 7 μM; nondisplaceable binding). Specific binding of [³H]estradiol measured in the presence and absence of a 100-fold excess of unlabeled estradiol (0.7 μM) was set equal to 100%. DHT, 5α-dihydrotestosterone; DES, diethylstilbestrol. From Barrack and Coffey (1980).

Correlation with Hormonal Status

To determine whether the levels of nuclear matrix-associated estradiol binding reflect the hormonal status of the animal, we examined the binding of estradiol to the liver nuclear matrix of egg-laying hens and of adult roosters. The binding of estradiol to the liver nuclear matrix of hens is shown in Fig. 7. Since untreated roosters are not under estrogen stimulation

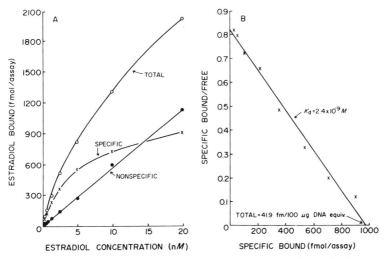

FIG. 7. Binding of estradiol to liver nuclear matrix of egg-laying hens. The liver nuclear matrix was isolated from egg-laying hens and assayed *in vitro* for specific [³H]estradiol binding activity, as described in the legend to Fig. 5.

and do not produce vitellogenin, they represent a control situation that offers an ideal opportunity to investigate the relationship between steroid binding sites and biological responsiveness. The liver nuclear matrix of hens and roosters were subjected individually to saturation analysis under exchange conditions *in vitro*, and a composite of the Scatchard plots of specific estradiol binding is presented in Fig. 8. The liver nuclear matrix of the vitellogenin-producing hen can bind approximately 42 fmol of estradiol/100 μg starting nuclear DNA equivalents, or 600 molecules/nucleus. In contrast, the liver nuclear matrix of untreated roosters, which do not produce yolk proteins, contains only one-eighth as many specific binding sites for estradiol (5.5 fmol/100 μg nuclear DNA equivalents) as that of the laying hen (Fig. 8). However, the administration of pharmacological doses of estrogen (diethylstilbestrol, 25 mg/kg) to roosters results in a stimulation of vitellogenin mRNA synthesis (Deeley *et al.*, 1977) and a marked increase (12-fold) in the number of nuclear matrix-associated specific estradiol binding sites (65 fmol/100 μg nuclear DNA equivalents; Fig. 9). The recoveries of matrix spheres (>70%) and nuclear protein (8–12%) from all groups of animals were approximately similar, and therefore indicate that the different binding capacities observed in Figs. 8 and 9 are not the result of variable recoveries of nuclear matrix. Therefore, the appearance of specific estradiol binding sites on the liver nuclear matrix occurs in response to an appropriate hormonal stimulus, not indiscriminately.

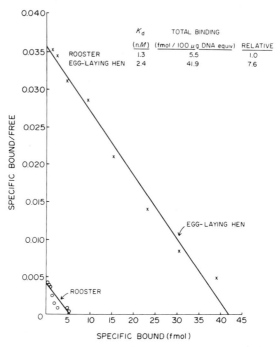

FIG. 8. Specific binding of estradiol to liver nuclear matrix of adult roosters and egg-laying hens. Scatchard plots are presented of specific binding of [³H]estradiol to the liver nuclear matrix fractions isolated from purified liver nuclei of untreated roosters (O———O) and hens (×———×). Saturation analyses were carried out in the presence of 0.15–20 nM [³H]estradiol alone or together with 1 μM unlabeled estradiol. Specific binding results have been normalized to fmol/100 μg starting nuclear DNA equivalents. From Barrack and Coffey (1980).

E. IDENTIFICATION AND CHARACTERIZATION OF ANDROGEN BINDING SITES ON THE NUCLEAR MATRIX OF RAT PROSTATE

The binding of steroids to the nuclear matrix appears to be a general property of the interactions of both estrogens and androgens with their respective target tissues. As a model of androgen target tissue interactions we have studied the rat ventral prostate, the growth and functions of which are androgen dependent. Since 5α-dihydrotestosterone (DHT) is the major active androgen metabolite in the nucleus of the prostate (Bruchovsky and Wilson, 1968; Fang *et al.*, 1969), we have used [³H]DHT to measure specific androgen binding sites on the nuclear matrix of the adult male rat ventral prostate. Specific binding of [³H]DHT to the ventral prostate nuclear matrix (Fig. 10), quantitated by an *in vitro* exchange assay, is saturable and high affinity (K_d = 1.6 nM). The total specific binding capacity of the matrix for

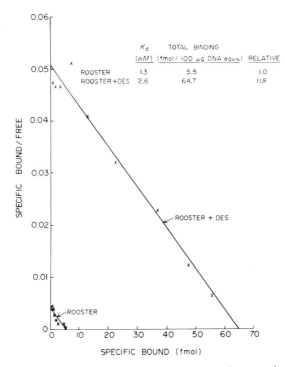

FIG. 9. Specific binding of estradiol to liver nuclear matrix of untreated and estrogenized roosters. Scatchard plots are presented of specific binding of estradiol to liver nuclear matrix fractions isolated from adult untreated roosters (*———*), and roosters given two daily injections of DES (25 mg/kg) (×———×). Saturation analyses were carried out over a concentration range of 0.15–20 nM [³H]estradiol alone and together with 1 μM unlabeled estradiol. Specific binding data have been normalized to fmol/100 μg starting nuclear DNA equivalents. Phenylmethyl-sulfonyl fluoride was added at each step of the isolation and assay procedures. From Barrack and Coffey (1980).

DHT is approximately 100 fmol/100 μg starting nuclear DNA equivalents, or 7200 molecules of DHT/nucleus. We have looked, in addition, for low-affinity ($K_d \sim$ 30 nM; Type II) binding of [³H]DHT to the nuclear matrix of these prostates by carrying out the saturation analysis in the presence of concentrations of [³H]DHT ranging from 0.1 to 80 nM but find only a single class of specific, high-affinity (K_d = 2–3 nM) DHT binding sites which become saturated by 10–20 nM [³H]DHT.

Table X shows the subnuclear distribution of specific DHT binding in the ventral prostates of intact adult rats. Only about 50% of the total nuclear binding can be extracted with salt. Salt-resistant nuclear matrix binding sites comprise approximately 50% of the total nuclear binding; yet the nuclear matrix contains only 10–15% of the total nuclear protein and about

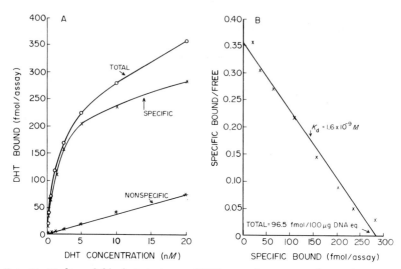

FIG. 10. Binding of dihydrotestosterone (DHT) to nuclear matrix of ventral prostates of intact adult rats. The nuclear matrix was isolated (see Figs. 1 and 14) from ventral prostate nuclei that had been purified by the method of Chung and Coffey (1971). [³H]Dihydrotestosterone binding to the nuclear matrix was assayed *in vitro* as described for estradiol binding in Fig. 5. Each assay tube contained nuclear matrix derived from nuclei equivalent to 295 μg nuclear DNA. Phenylmethylsulfonyl fluoride was added at all steps. (A) O———O, total binding in the presence of [³H]DHT only; *———*, nonspecific binding in the presence of [³H]DHT with unlabeled DHT; ×———×, specific binding represents the difference between total and non-specific binding. (B) Scatchard plot of specific binding (×———×) in (A). From Barrack and Coffey (1980).

1–2% of the DNA. The sum of the binding activities in these two fractions accounts for almost all (90%) of the binding to unextracted nuclei.

Similar levels of [³H]DHT binding are observed whether samples are dissolved in tissue solubilizer or the radioactivity is extracted into ethanol. This indicates that the nuclease-, detergent-, and salt-resistant binding of steroid to the nuclear matrix is not the result of a covalent interaction. In addition, no significant metabolism of [³H]dihydrotestosterone occurs during the time interval of the binding assay *in vitro* (4°C, 20–24 hours), since greater than 95% of the radioactivity that is recovered from prostate nuclei, salt extracts, or nuclear matrix can be identified as DHT. Dihydrotestosterone is also the predominant androgen in the nucleus *in vivo* (Bruchovsky and Wilson, 1968; Fang *et al.*, 1969). In contrast, however, it is of interest to note that salt-resistant nuclear glucocorticoid receptors in the rat mammary gland are associated predominantly with an acylated form of corticosterone, whereas the precursor, corticosterone, is found associated primarily with salt-extractable glucocorticoid receptors (Hampel *et al.*, 1978).

TABLE X

SPECIFIC BINDING OF DIHYDROTESTOSTERONE IN RAT VENTRAL PROSTATES OF INTACT
ADULT RATS: SUBNUCLEAR DISTRIBUTION[a]

Isolate	Specific binding of DHT[b]			
	fmol/100 μg starting DNA equivalents	Binding sites/nucleus	Relative	Number of experiments
Total nuclei[c]	286 ± 35[d]	20,600[e] ± 2,520	1.00	8
Salt extractable[f]	130 ± 25	9,360 ± 1,800	0.45	10
Nuclear matrix[g]	128 ± 23	9,220 ± 1,660	0.45	13

[a] From Barrack and Coffey (1980).

[b] Binding assays were carried out in the presence of 20 nM [^{3}H]DHT with and without 2 μM unlabeled DHT. Specific binding was calculated by subtracting nonspecific from total binding. Phenylmethylsulfonyl fluoride was added at all steps.

[c] Binding assays were carried out with purified ventral prostate nuclei. Nuclear pellets were washed, solubilized, and counted.

[d] Mean ± SD.

[e] Based on a value of 12 pg DNA per nucleus (DeKlerk *et al.*, 1976; Van Doorn *et al.*, 1976).

[f] Salt extracts were obtained by incubating nuclei with DNase I and extracting once with 2 M NaCl in buffer. Extracts obtained following an exchange assay of nuclei were counted directly. Alternatively, nuclei were first extracted and binding activity of the salt extract was assayed. Assays were terminated by the addition of either dextran-coated charcoal (an aliquot of the supernatant was then counted) or hydroxyapatite (the precipitate was washed and an ethanol extract was counted). Results were similar for the different methods.

[g] Binding assays were carried out with isolated nuclear matrix.

1. Sensitivity to Proteolysis

It is essential to add inhibitors of proteolysis such as phenylmethylsulfonyl fluoride (PMSF), at a final concentration of 1 mM, to all buffers used in the isolation of prostate nuclei and nuclear matrix. In the absence of such protease inhibitors, the amount of specific DHT binding to the nuclear matrix is 20 to 50 times lower (Table XI). The specific binding of DHT to whole nuclei also is lower when PMSF is omitted from the homogenization buffer, although the yield of nuclei from prostate tissue is not affected. The amount or binding in the salt-extractable nuclear fraction is the same in the presence or absence of PMSF; in contrast, the salt-resistant DHT binding activity is markedly reduced in the absence of the inhibitor (Table XI). The greatly lowered binding of DHT to the nuclear matrix in the absence of PMSF is accompanied by a severely reduced recovery of matrix spheres and matrix protein from nuclei. The structural protein components of the rat ventral prostate nuclear matrix are highly sensitive to proteolytic degradation, an observation that has been reported as well for the nuclear

TABLE XI

Effect of a Protease Inhibitor on Nuclear Androgen Binding Capacity[a]

Inhibitor	Specific binding of [³H]DHT (fmol/100 μg starting DNA equivalents)		
	Total nuclei	Salt extract	Nuclear matrix
+ PMSF[b]	286 ± 35	130 ± 25	128 ± 23
− PMSF	102 ± 4	119 ± 51	6 ± 4

[a] Specific [³H]DHT binding was quantitated as described in footnote b to Table X. In experiments noted "+ PMSF," all buffers used in the isolation of nuclei and nuclear matrix contained 1 mM PMSF, which was added from a stock solution (0.1 M PMSF in anhydrous n-propanol) immediately before use. In experiments noted "− PMSF," the inhibitor of proteolysis, PMSF, was omitted from all buffers.

[b] PMSF, phenylmethylsulfonyl fluoride.

matrix of the rat liver (Shaper *et al.*, 1979). It is important to note, however, that the level of specific binding of estradiol to the nuclear matrix of chicken liver is not found to be affected significantly by the presence or absence of PMSF. The greater lability of androgen binding sites on the nuclear matrix of the ventral prostate is probably a reflection of the high concentrations of hydrolytic and proteolytic enzymes that are normally present in the prostatic secretions within the acinar lumina and in the intracellular lysosomes (Paris and Brandes, 1974). In addition, many investigators have noted the greater thermal lability of androgen receptors than estrogen receptors; this may be due to the presence of proteolytic enzymes in the fraction being studied. Phenylmethylsulfonyl fluoride is used, therefore, in all experiments on the rat prostate.

2. Correlation with Hormonal Status

We have been able to demonstrate a physiological basis for the binding of DHT to the ventral prostate nuclear matrix. The androgen-dependent ventral prostate, as well as the other male sex accessory tissues, involutes following castration of the animal. The cells decrease in size from tall columnar to cuboidal, secretory functions diminish, and by 7 days after castration there is a loss of about 80% of the cells. Cell number and secretory activities can be restored to normal following the administration of androgens to the animal (Coffey *et al.*, 1968; Brandes, 1974; DeKlerk *et al.*, 1976).

Figure 11 compares the number of specific binding sites for DHT on the ventral prostate nuclear matrix of intact and castrated rats. By 20–24 hours

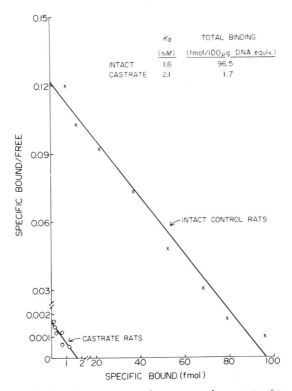

FIG. 11. Specific binding of DHT to ventral prostate nuclear matrix of intact and castrate rats. Specific binding of DHT to the nuclear matrix of intact adult rat ventral prostates ($\times$——$\times$) was obtained from data of Fig. 10B. Specific binding of DHT to the ventral prostate nuclear matrix of adult rats 20 hours after castration (O——O) was determined by saturation and Scatchard analysis. Specific binding data have been normalized to fmol/100 μg starting nuclear DNA equivalents. From Barrack and Coffey (1980).

after castration there is minimal cell loss; however, the amount of specific DHT binding activity on the nuclear matrix has decreased to 2% of intact control levels. The time course of the disappearance of DHT binding activity associated with the nuclear matrix following castration is shown in Fig. 12. When DHT injections are initiated 40 hours after castration, the level of matrix-associated DHT binding is restored to normal values within 1 hour (Fig. 12). In contrast, treatment of castrates with 5 mg of estradiol or cyproterone acetate does not increase the level of matrix-associated androgen binding sites above the castrate control value. Therefore, the presence of specific binding sites for DHT on the ventral prostate nuclear matrix is related to the response of the tissue to androgen.

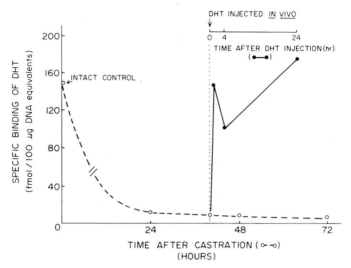

FIG. 12. Ventral prostate nuclear matrix DHT binding sites: time course of disappearance following castration and of reappearance following androgen treatment *in vivo*. Rats were castrated and sacrificed at various times thereafter (O---O). Another group of animals was castrated and 40 hours later received a single subcutaneous injection of 5 mg DHT (●——●). These rats were sacrificed at various times after DHT treatment. Ventral prostate nuclei and nuclear matrix fractions were isolated and the binding of DHT to nuclear matrix was assayed in the presence of 20 nM [^{3}H]DHT with and without 2 μM unlabeled DHT. Specific binding data are expressed as fmol/100 μg starting nuclear DNA equivalents. From Barrack and Coffey (1980).

3. Steroid Specificity

The androgen-specific nature of the binding sites on the ventral prostate nuclear matrix is demonstrated in Fig. 13. In competitive binding assays, the concentration of unlabeled DHT required to inhibit specific binding of [^{3}H]DHT by 50%, relative to the concentration of other unlabeled steroids required to produce the same inhibition, provides an indication of the relative binding affinity of these steroids for binding sites on the nuclear matrix. Unlabeled methyltrienolone (R 1881), a potent synthetic androgen, is as effective as dihydrotestosterone (relative binding affinity, 100%) in inhibiting specific binding of [^{3}H]DHT. Testosterone has a relative binding affinity of 20%. The relative binding affinities of progesterone, estradiol, cyproterone acetate (an antiandrogen), and cortisol are 1.0, 0.9, 0.6, and <0.1%, respectively. Steroid specificity patterns similar to those shown in Fig. 13 have been observed for other androgen receptor proteins (Wilson and French, 1976), and are in contrast to the more stringent steroid specificity of estrogen receptors for estrogens (Fig. 6).

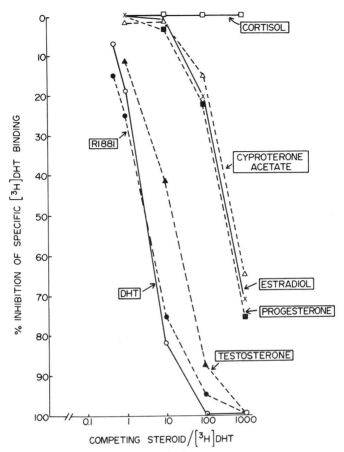

Fig. 13. Steroid-specific inhibition of DHT binding to rat ventral prostate nuclear matrix. Ventral prostate nuclear matrix from intact adult rats was incubated *in vitro* in the presence of [^{3}H]DHT (20 nM) with or without increasing concentrations of unlabeled steroids (10 nM to 20 μM). Specific binding of [^{3}H]DHT measured in the presence and absence of a 100-fold excess of unlabeled DHT (2 μM) was set equal to 100%. R 1881, Methyltrienolone. From Barrack and Coffey (1980).

VII. FRACTIONATION OF THE NUCLEAR MATRIX AND LOCALIZATION OF MATRIX-ASSOCIATED STEROID HORMONE BINDING SITES

A. COMPONENTS OF THE NUCLEAR MATRIX

The nuclear matrix preparations used in the studies described in the preceding sections consist of a peripheral lamina, residual nucleoli, and an

internal ribonucleoprotein network (e.g., Figs. 1 and 14). We and others
have noted that the presence of an internal network-like structure within
the isolated nuclear matrix appears to be dependent on the methods used
to extract the nuclei (Shaper *et al.*, 1979; Kaufmann *et al.*, 1981; see Section
II,C). For example, conditions that promote endogenous protease activity
(Shaper *et al.*, 1979), the use of high concentrations of MgCl₂ (Aaronson

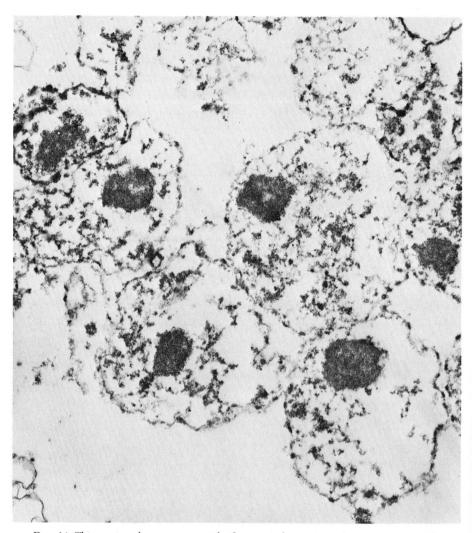

FIG. 14. Thin-section electron micrograph of intact nuclear matrix spheres. Nuclear matrix
spheres were isolated from hen liver nuclei as described in the legend to Fig. 1. Structures
similar to those shown here are obtained from rat ventral prostate nuclei using the procedure
outlined in the legend to Fig. 1. × 19,662.

and Blobel, 1975; Dwyer and Blobel, 1976), the use of alkaline (pH 8.5) conditions (Aaronson and Blobel, 1975; Dwyer and Blobel, 1976; Cobbs and Shelton, 1978), or the use of RNase (Herman *et al.*, 1978; Giese and Wunderlich, 1979; Adolph, 1980; Kaufmann *et al.*, 1981) have been noted to contribute to the isolation of nuclear matrix fractions that lack nucleoli and the majority of the internal fibrogranular network. Whether or not the internal network structure withstands the rigors of the extraction procedures, a reasonable body of evidence indicates that it is derived from ribonucleoprotein-containing structures of the nucleus (Berezney and Coffey, 1974; Berezney, 1979; Herman *et al.*, 1978; Miller *et al.*, 1978a; Faiferman and Pogo, 1975; Pogo, 1981; Shankar Narayan *et al.*, 1967; Monneron and Bernhard, 1969; Bouteille *et al.*, 1974; Ghosh *et al.*, 1978). Under certain conditions, the RNA components can be extracted, leaving a residual internal protein network (Berezney and Coffey, 1974, 1976, 1977; Comings and Okada, 1976; Wunderlich and Herlan, 1977; Miller *et al.*, 1978a; Mitchelson *et al.*,1979; van Eekelen and van Venrooij, 1981). Within the nuclear matrix the RNA and protein-containing network appears to be intimately associated with the peripheral pore complex-lamina (Berezney and Coffey, 1976, 1977; Comings and Okada, 1976; Hodge *et al.*, 1977; Herman *et al.*, 1978; Miller *et al.*, 1978a; Berezney *et al.*, 1979; Wunderlich and Herlan, 1977). The important observations that newly replicated DNA (Berezney and Coffey, 1975, 1976; Dijkwel *et al.*, 1979; Pardoll *et al.*, 1980; McCready *et al.*, 1980; Berezney and Buchholtz, 1981a,b) and rapidly labeled heterogeneous nuclear RNA (Herman *et al.*, 1978; Miller *et al.*, 1978a; van Eekelen and van Venrooij, 1981; Jackson *et al.*, 1981) are tightly associated with the nuclear matrix indicate the significance of this structure. Appropriate controls carried out by these investigators indicate that these associations are probably not the result of adventitious adsorption of RNA or DNA to these structures (Faiferman and Pogo, 1975; Herman *et al.*, 1978; Miller *et al.*, 1978a; Pardoll *et al.*, 1980; Jackson *et al.*, 1981; van Eekelen and van Venrooij, 1981; Berezney and Buchholtz, 1981a,b). Moreover, electron autoradiographic studies have demonstrated that the DNA replication sites (Pardoll *et al.*, 1980) and the newly labeled heterogeneous nuclear RNA (Fakan *et al.*, 1976; Herman *et al.*, 1978) are associated with the internal network structure, and indicate the potential biological importance of this internal component of the nuclear matrix.

B. RATIONALE FOR LOCALIZATION OF HORMONE
BINDING SITES

It was of considerable interest, therefore, to determine whether the hormone binding sites are distributed uniformly throughout the matrix structure, or are enriched in a specific morphological component of the matrix. To investigate this further, we have taken advantage of the observation that under certain conditions the internal RNA–protein network of the matrix is sensitive to RNase. For example, treatment of some types of nuclei with both DNase I and RNase A, followed by extraction of these nuclei with low- and high-ionic-strength salt solutions, leads to the isolation of a nuclear matrix fraction that lacks nucleoli and the majority of the internal fibrogranular network (Herman *et al.*, 1978; Giese and Wunderlich, 1979; Adolph, 1980; Kaufmann *et al.*, 1981). If the hormone binding sites were localized exclusively to the peripheral lamina, these empty nuclear matrix structures would contain as many binding sites as intact nuclear matrix spheres that contain internal network material. Moreover, as a result of extracting protein that had been a component of the internal network, these "lamina-associated" steroid binding sites would exhibit a higher specific activity per unit amount of protein than that in the intact nuclear matrix. In contrast, if the hormone binding sites were extensively enriched on the internal RNA–protein network of the nuclear matrix, then the number and specific activity of binding sites associated with the empty peripheral lamina fraction would be greatly diminished. In this latter situation, the hormone binding sites would be rendered salt extractable, and the specific activity of this soluble fraction would be increased. A third possibility would be that the hormone binding sites are distributed uniformly throughout all components of the nuclear matrix; in this case, the specific activity of binding for both intact nuclear matrix and empty spheres would be similar.

C. ENRICHMENT OF HORMONE BINDING SITES ON INTERNAL RNA–PROTEIN NETWORK OF THE PROSTATE NUCLEAR MATRIX

By comparing the distribution and specific activity of the hormone binding sites associated with intact versus empty matrix spheres, we have been able to show that the matrix-associated steroid binding sites appear to be enriched on internal matrix structures (Barrack and Coffey, 1980). Binding sites are not localized exclusively to the lamina and are not distributed uniformly on all matrix components.

Table XII shows the results of these experiments using the ventral prostate of intact adult rats as a model system. When nuclei are treated with DNase and RNase in the presence of 1 mM dithiothreitol (DTT), and then extracted with 2 M NaCl (Table XII, experiment D), matrix spheres are obtained that are devoid of internal structure (e.g., Fig. 15) and that contain only 60% as much protein as control matrix preparations (Table

TABLE XII

EFFECT OF VARIOUS TREATMENTS ON THE SUBNUCLEAR DISTRIBUTION OF DHT BINDING SITES IN THE RAT VENTRAL PROSTATE[a]

Pretreatment of nuclei[c]	N[d]	Protein distribution (μg protein/100 μg starting DNA equivalents)			Specific binding of DHT[b]				
					Distribution (fmol DHT/100 μg starting DNA equivalents)			Specific activity (fmol DHT/100 μg protein)	
		Nuclear matrix[e]	Salt extract[f]	Total[g]	Nuclear matrix	Salt extract	Total	Nuclear matrix	Salt extract
A. DNase (control)	6	55 ± 14 (100%)	254 ± 16	304 ± 21	101 ± 8 (100%)	49 ± 14	150 ± 17 (100%)	194 ± 48 (100%)	19 ± 6 (100%)
B. DNase + RNase	8	44 ± 9 (80%)	259 ± 11	300 ± 15	48 ± 10 (48%)	57 ± 13	106 ± 11 (71%)	121 ± 19 (62%)	21 ± 6 (111%)
C. DNase + DTT	2	41 ± 2 (75%)	285 ± 8	325 ± 6	29 ± 6 (29%)	129 ± 8	157 ± 1 (105%)	71 ± 19 (37%)	45 ± 4 (237%)
D. DNase + RNase + DTT	2	33 ± 4 (60%)	310 ± 32	343 ± 28	17 ± 4 (17%)	136 ± 3	153 ± 2 (102%)	52 ± 20 (27%)	44 ± 6 (232%)

[a] From Barrack and Coffey (1980).

[b] Binding assays were carried out in triplicate in the presence of 20 nM [^{3}H]L₄T with and without 2 μM unlabeled DHT. Specific DHT binding was calculated by subtracting nonspecific from total binding. Binding of DHT to nuclear matrix fractions was terminated by washing on Whatman GF/B glass fiber filters. Binding activity in soluble salt extracts was assayed following dilution to 1.2 M NaCl, and terminated by further dilution to 0.4 M NaCl prior to the addition of a slurry of hydroxyapatite to 12.5% (v/v). After 15 minutes at 4°C, the hydroxyapatite was pelleted, washed three times, and then extracted with ethanol.

[c] Pretreatments with nucleases alone extract no binding activity. Highly purified ventral prostate nuclei were obtained from intact, untreated rats. The protein/DNA ratio of these Triton-washed nuclei was 3.55 ± 0.33 (mean ± SD for six experiments) and the RNA/DNA ratio was 0.18 ± 0.06. Nuclei were incubated in 10 mM Tris, pH 7.4, 5 mM MgCl₂ with nucleases (4°C, 30 minutes) and pelleted prior to extraction with 2 M NaCl. Phenylmethylsulfonyl fluoride (1 mM) was added at all steps. In all experiments, nuclei were pretreated with DNase I at a final concentration of 20 μg/ml. RNase A, where indicated, was added at 40 μg/ml; the RNase had been pretreated by heating at 100°C, 15 minutes. Dithiothreitol, where indicated, was at 1 mM; the DTT was present only during the nuclease incubation.

[d] N, Number of individual experiments. Results are expressed as mean ± SD.

[e] The nuclear matrix fraction represents the insoluble pellet following 2 M NaCl extraction of the nuclease-treated nuclei, and washing in 10 mM Tris, pH 7.4, 1.5 mM EDTA.

[f] Supernatant obtained from extraction of nuclease-treated nuclei with 2 M NaCl.

[g] Total represents the sum of values for the nuclear matrix pellet and salt extract of each individual experiment.

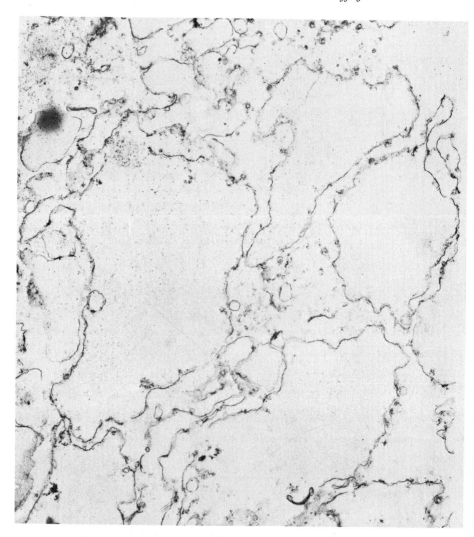

FIG. 15. Thin-section electron micrograph of empty nuclear matrix spheres. Nuclear matrix spheres lacking internal network material and residual nucleoli were obtained from hen liver nuclei. When Triton X-100-washed nuclei are digested with low concentrations of DNase I, RNase A, and 1 m*M* dithiothreitol, and then sequentially extracted with low magnesium and 2 *M* NaCl buffers, as described in more detail in Table XII, empty spheres like those shown here can be prepared from liver nuclei and prostate nuclei (also see text for discussion of considerations). × 19,662.

XII, experiment A). The recovery of specific DHT binding sites with these empty matrix spheres (consisting only of a peripheral pore complex-lamina) represents only 17% of the total matrix DHT binding activity associated with intact nuclear matrix structures that contain internal network material (17 versus 101 fmol/100 μg starting nuclear DNA equivalents). If this loss of binding activity and protein had simply been due to a loss of spheres, the specific activity of binding in the residual fraction would have been unchanged. We find, however, that the specific activity of the DHT binding sites that remain associated with these empty matrix spheres (52 fmol/100 μg protein) is only 27% of that of intact nuclear matrix structures (194 fmol/100 μg protein). The DHT binding sites that are extracted from the nuclear matrix as a result of this treatment are recovered in the salt extract. The specific activity of the DHT binding sites in the total salt extract is thereby increased 2.3-fold (19 versus 44 fmol/100 μg salt-extractable protein). The specific activity of the binding sites that become salt extractable as a result of the additional treatment with RNase and DTT (i.e., the difference between the amount of salt-resistant matrix binding and protein in Table XII, experiment A versus D) can be calculated to be approximately 400 fmol/100 μg of protein extracted from the matrix; if these DHT binding sites had been associated with the internal ribonucleoprotein network of the nuclear matrix, then the specific activity of these internal sites is about sevenfold greater than that of the sites remaining with the peripheral lamina fraction (52 fmol/100 μg protein). This distribution is not altered if the nuclei have not been extracted with Triton X-100.

Salt extraction of nuclei that had been digested with DNase plus RNase or with DNase plus DTT is less effective in removing intranuclear contents and matrix-associated hormone binding sites than if the nuclei had been digested with DNase, RNase, and DTT.

Treatment of nuclei with DNase and DTT (Table XII, experiment C) is almost as effective as DNase, RNase, and DTT (Table XII, experiment D) in allowing the subsequent solubilization by 2 M NaCl of specific DHT binding sites (71 and 83%, respectively) from the nuclear matrix. However, in contrast to experiment D, DNase and DTT pretreatment allows the subsequent removal by 2 M NaCl of some but not all of the internal RNA–protein network material of the matrix, as determined by protein and RNA analyses and microscopy. The specific activity of the salt-resistant DHT binding sites is reduced to 37% of control (Table XII, experiment A) values, and that of the total salt extract increases 2.4-fold. The difference between the amount of matrix DHT binding in experiments A and C is calculated to have a specific activity of about 620 fmol/100 μg of protein extracted from the matrix, or about sevenfold that of the sites remaining insoluble (71 fmol/100 μg protein).

Table XII (experiment B) also shows the subnuclear distribution of androgen binding sites when nuclei are digested with only DNase and RNase, and then extracted with 2 *M* NaCl. This experiment cannot be evaluated properly since the inclusion of RNase and omission of DTT result in the loss of 29% of the total nuclear DHT binding activity (150 versus 106 fmol/ 100 μg DNA equivalents). This loss of binding cannot be prevented by boiling the RNase to inactivate possible protease contaminants, and cannot be accounted for in any fraction. RNase effects were similar at three concentrations tested (20, 40, or 200 μg/ml). When the RNase was inhibited by pretreatment with diethylpyrocarbonate, the distribution, recovery and specific activity of DHT binding were similar to control (Table XII, A) values (data not shown).

D. Effects of Dithiothreitol

Therefore, comparing the experiments shown in Table XII, it appears that DTT not only prevents the destructive effect of RNase but also works in concert with RNase to destabilize intranuclear structures and promote a more complete solubilization by 2 *M* NaCl of internal matrix material and DHT binding sites. It is important to note that nuclease treatments alone, under the gentle conditions described, solubilize no binding activity.

With regard to the observed effects of dithiothreitol, it is also important to note that DTT treatment alone does not extract steroid binding sites; it only renders them capable of being solubilized by subsequent or simultaneous treatment with salt. Thus, even if DTT is added only to the tissue homogenization buffer, extraction of the isolated nuclei with NaCl will result in the solubilization of most of the nuclear receptors (E. R. Barrack and D. S. Coffey, unpublished data). Indeed, this effect of dithiothreitol may explain why some investigators do not find significant amounts of salt-resistant binding (e.g., Traish *et al.*, 1977; Müller *et al.*, 1977; Chamness *et al.*, 1978).

E. Estradiol Binding Sites in Avian Liver Nuclear Matrix

When detergent-washed hen liver nuclei are digested with DNase I plus RNase A in the presence of 1 m*M* DTT, and then extracted with 2 *M* NaCl, only 18% of the total nuclear specific estradiol binding sites remain in the residual nuclear matrix fraction (Table XIII, C; 10/54). From nuclei that are digested with only DNase I and then extracted with salt, 55% of total nuclear binding is recovered with the nuclear matrix (Fig. 14; Table XIII, A; 28/51). In addition, the nuclear matrix fraction obtained following salt

TABLE XIII

EFFECT OF VARIOUS TREATMENTS ON THE SUBNUCLEAR DISTRIBUTION OF ESTRADIOL BINDING SITES IN HEN LIVER[a]

Pretreatment of nuclei	Protein distribution (μg protein/100 μg starting DNA equivalents)			Specific binding of estradiol				
				Distribution (fmol E_2/100 μg starting DNA equivalents)[b]			Specific activity (fmol E_2/100 μg protein)	
	Nuclear matrix	Salt extract	Total	Nuclear matrix	Salt extract	Total	Nuclear matrix	Salt extract
A. DNase (control)	28 (100%)	188	216	28 (100%)	23	51 (100%)	99 (100%)	12 (100%)
B. DNase + RNase	25 (89%)	197	222	25 (89%)	26	51 (100%)	97 (98%)	13 (108%)
C. DNase + RNase + DTT	21 (75%)	194	215	10 (36%)	44	54 (106%)	45 (45%)	23 (192%)

[a] See footnotes to Table XII for explanation of pretreatment protocols and nuclear fractions.
[b] E_2, estradiol.

extraction of DNase-, RNase-, and DTT-treated nuclei (Fig. 15) contains only 36% as many specific estradiol binding sites as nuclear matrix obtained following salt extraction of DNase-pretreated nuclei, and only 75% as much protein (Table XIII, A versus C). As calculated for the ventral prostate, the hen liver matrix binding sites for estradiol that are released by the additional RNase and DTT pretreatment are calculated to have a specific activity of 300 fmol/100 μg of protein extracted from the matrix.

In contrast to the effects of DNase and RNase on androgen binding sites in rat ventral prostate nuclei (Table XII), estrogen binding sites in hen liver nuclei appear to be inert (Table XIII, B). Thus, not only does treatment of liver nuclei with DNase plus RNase not destroy any of the total nuclear binding activity, it also does not render any of the nuclear matrix protein *or* matrix-associated estradiol binding sites susceptible to salt extraction (Table XIII, B versus A). These observations are consistent with the findings of others that conditions that lead to the extraction of internal network components of the nuclear matrix from nuclei of some tissues (e.g., Shaper *et al.*, 1979; Kaufmann *et al.*, 1981) may not be applicable to all cell types (e.g., Wunderlich and Herlan, 1977; Miller *et al.*, 1978a; Wolfe, 1980) (also see Section II,C).

F. Summary

The distribution and specific activity of DHT binding sites associated with various subfractions of the nucleus and nuclear matrix of the ventral prostate are summarized in Table XIV. The solubilization of internal ribonucleoprotein network material from the nuclear matrix is associated with the extraction of up to 83% of the total matrix specific DHT binding sites. Matrix spheres can be isolated that are totally devoid of internal structure, and consist only of a peripheral lamina. These empty spheres still contain a limited number of DHT binding sites (11% of total nuclear). Dyhydrotestosterone binding sites do not appear to be localized exclusively to the peripheral lamina of the matrix or distributed uniformly on all matrix components. Rather, our data suggest that there is an enrichment of binding sites with internal matrix structures. Similarly, Agutter and Birchall (1979) find that whereas the intact nuclear matrix of rat uterine nuclei contains estradiol binding sites, the pore complex-lamina fraction, isolated by a different method, contains virtually none of these sites.

In this regard, it is interesting to note that Liao *et al.* (1973) have reported the ability of prostate cytosol DHT–receptor complexes to bind to isolated nuclear RNP particles that were resistant to solubilization from nuclei by 1 *M* KCl and DNase I but could be released by deoxycholate treatment.

TABLE XIV

DISTRIBUTION AND SPECIFIC ACTIVITY OF DHT BINDING SITES IN SUBFRACTIONS OF THE
NUCLEUS AND NUCLEAR MATRIX OF THE RAT VENTRAL PROSTATE[a]

	Specific binding of DHT			
	Distribution		Specific activity	
Isolate	fmol/100 μg starting DNA equivalents	Percentage of total binding	fmol/100 μg protein	Relative
Total[b]	152 ± 13	100	49 ± 6	1.0
Salt extract[c]	49 ± 14	33	19 ± 6	0.4
Total nuclear matrix[d]	101 ± 8	67	194 ± 48	4.0
Peripheral lamina[e]	17 ± 4	11	52 ± 20	1.1
Internal RNP network[f]	76 ± 9	50	395 ± 101	8.1

[a] From Barrack and Coffey (1980).

[b] Represents the sum of binding activities in the salt extract and total nuclear matrix fractions.

[c] Supernatant obtained from 2 M NaCl extraction of nuclei that had been pretreated with only DNase I (Table XII, control, experiment A).

[d] Control nuclear matrix preparations that contain an internal RNA–protein network; obtained following 2 M NaCl extraction of nuclei that had been pretreated with only DNase I (Table XII, control, experiment A).

[e] Residual nuclear matrix preparations that consist only of a peripheral lamina (empty spheres); obtained following 2 M NaCl extraction of nuclei that had been pretreated with DNase I, RNase A, and 1 mM DTT (Table XII, experiment D).

[f] This fraction is calculated from the difference between insoluble nuclear matrix preparations that contain an internal network (total nuclear matrix) and empty spheres that consist only of a peripheral lamina. The DHT binding activity in this fraction represents an average of 75% of the binding associated with total nuclear matrix (76/101).

That these RNP-associated binding sites (Liao *et al.*, 1973) may have been a component of the internal RNA–protein network that is observed in the isolated nuclear matrix (Herman *et al.*, 1978; Miller *et al.*, 1978a; Faiferman and Pogo, 1975) is supported by the observation of Miller *et al.* (1978a) that the RNP complexes of this RNP network are highly susceptible to disruption by deoxycholate treatment.

We have observed that a small percentage (10–15%) of the total matrix-associated DHT binding sites is associated with the lamina of empty matrix spheres. It is not known whether these binding sites are truly lamina associated, or whether they result from incomplete extraction of internal RNP network components. Since the majority of the matrix-associated hormone binding sites as well as the internal RNP network of the nuclear matrix are solubilized concomitantly, it is tempting to conclude that most of the binding sites are associated with this internal network. However, it is also possible that the conditions that lead to solubilization of the internal network also extract minor components of the lamina and pore complexes and that these components contain the hormone binding sites.

It is of interest to note that nuclear envelopes isolated from rat ventral prostate contain approximately 10% as many DHT binding sites as intact nuclei, and this binding is relatively resistant to Triton X-100 treatment (Lefebvre and Novosad, 1980) (cf. data in Table XIV). In addition, Jackson and Chalkley (1974) found specific, high-affinity binding sites for estradiol in a nuclear membrane fraction isolated from bovine endometrial tissue. These binding sites were also resistant to solubilization by 0.4 M KCl and appeared to have properties distinct from those of cytoplasmic receptors (Jackson and Chalkley, 1974). High-affinity binding of purified glucocorticoid–receptor complexes to isolated rat liver nuclear envelopes has also been observed; this binding, which represents 20% of total nuclear receptor binding capacity, is dissociated by 0.3 M KCl (Smith and von Holt, 1981). These authors further suggest that chromatin-associated receptors reflect binding to nuclear envelope fragments that are contaminants of chromatin preparations (Smith and von Holt, 1981).

In evaluating the aforementioned studies it is important to realize that the pore complex-lamina fraction of the nuclear matrix itself represents residual components of the nuclear envelope. When isolated nuclear membrane fractions are extracted by procedures similar to those used to prepare the matrix, a residual pore complex-lamina is obtained that contains many of the same polypeptides as those of the entire nuclear matrix fraction (Aaronson and Blobel, 1975; Dwyer and Blobel, 1976; Jackson, 1976a; Cobbs and Shelton, 1978; Peters and Comings, 1980).

VIII. SOME COMMENTS ON THE NATURE OF NUCLEAR MATRIX-ASSOCIATED STEROID BINDING SITES

A. Criteria for Steroid Hormone Receptors

The specific binding of estradiol and dihydrotestosterone to the nuclear matrix of rat uterus and chicken liver, and rat ventral prostate, respectively, satisfies the criteria that are commonly used to characterize steroid hormone receptors. The binding of these steroids is saturable, high affinity, and heat and Pronase sensitive. In addition, the steroid specificity of estradiol binding to the nuclear matrix of estrogen-responsive tissues (rat uterus and chicken liver) and of dihydrotestosterone binding to the nuclear matrix of an androgen-dependent tissue (rat ventral prostate) is characteristic of target tissue hormone–receptor systems. In these tissues, the appearance of specific steroid binding sites with the nuclear matrix occurs in response to an appropriate hormonal stimulus. Thus, the nuclear matrix of the liver of untreated roosters contains very few estradiol binding sites; following administration of a dose of estrogen to the rooster that stimulates synthesis of vitellogenin in the liver (Deeley *et al.*, 1977), there is a 12-fold increase in the number of specific estradiol binding sites associated with the nuclear matrix. The liver of the egg-laying hen, which is actively producing large quantities of vitellogenin, contains similarly high levels of nuclear matrix-associated specific estradiol binding sites. Likewise, in the rat ventral prostate the presence of specific dihydrotestosterone binding sites on the nuclear matrix is associated with androgen stimulation of this gland. These binding sites are present in the ventral prostate nuclear matrix of intact adult male rats. Following withdrawal of androgen (castration), there is a rapid loss (within 24 hours) of these nuclear matrix binding sites that precedes the involution of the gland. Androgen administration restores these sites to normal levels within 1 hour. Thus, the appearance of nuclear matrix-associated steroid binding sites correlates with the stimulation of biological response.

B. STEROID–RECEPTOR–ACCEPTOR INTERACTIONS

An important aspect of the nature of these specific steroid hormone binding sites associated with the nuclear matrix concerns the question of whether these sites represent a native steroid–receptor–acceptor interaction.

1. Occupancy of Matrix-Associated Hormone Binding Sites

The first point relates to whether these sites are occupied by steroid *in vivo*. The measurement of steroid binding sites on the nuclear matrix involves *in vitro* incubation of the isolated nuclear matrix fraction with labeled steroid. The underlying assumption of this approach is that the addition of labeled steroid will, under equilibrium conditions, exchange with unlabeled steroid that had become bound to these sites as a result of the *in vivo* processes of steroid hormone–receptor complex translocation following administration of the hormone (Anderson *et al.*, 1972a). However, the state of occupancy of these binding sites in the isolated nuclear matrix is not known. Thus, indirect binding studies such as those we have used do not distinguish between the binding of the labeled steroid to receptors previously occupied by endogenous unlabeled steroid (i.e., exchange) and direct binding to unoccupied sites. Unoccupied binding sites might represent receptor from which steroid has dissociated during the time it takes to isolate the nuclear matrix, or a form of unoccupied receptor that is bound to the nuclear matrix *in vivo* without steroid attached.

2. Receptor Interactions with the Nuclear Matrix

As to whether labeled steroid binds to the nuclear matrix via receptor proteins that had been translocated to the nucleus remains to be established directly. Although we find that the equilibrium dissociation constant for the interaction of steroids with the nuclear matrix is similar to that of the cytoplasmic and nuclear salt-extractable steroid receptors, this is consistent with but does not prove that the binding site on the matrix is the same receptor moiety. In this regard, however, soluble macromolecule-associated estradiol binding, which on sucrose density gradient analysis had a sedimentation coefficient of 7 S, somewhat larger than that of the nuclear salt-extractable estradiol receptor (Snow *et al.*, 1978), has been obtained by extracting the chicken liver nuclear matrix with 2 *M* LiCl and 4 *M* urea (Hardin and Clark, 1979). In addition, when the nuclear matrix-associated androgen binding sites of the rat ventral prostate are rendered salt soluble following NaCl extraction of nuclei that had been digested with DNase I plus RNase A and dithiothreitol (see Table XII), sucrose density gradient analysis reveals that the bound steroid is macromolecule associated (E. R. Barrack, unpublished observations).

Additional evidence that (steroid)–receptor complexes are associated with the nuclear matrix is the observation that in the hormone-withdrawn state (roosters or castrate rats) there are virtually no high-affinity, specific steroid binding sites in the nucleus, whereas shortly after appropriate hormonal treatment (within less than an hour in the androgen-treated castrate rat) significant levels of specific steroid binding activity are found associated with the nuclear matrix (Fig. 12). These data are consistent with the types of observations which form the basis for the well-established model of steroid hormone-mediated translocation of cytoplasmic receptors into the nucleus (Gorski and Gannon, 1976; Jensen, 1979; Liao *et al.*, 1979).

Of course, the possibility that these matrix-associated steroid binding sites do not reflect the native state, but rather merely result from adventitious adsorption of receptors, must always be considered. The adsorption of uncharged cytosol receptors to the nuclear matrix, however, can be ruled out, since in the prostate of the castrate there are large amounts of androgen receptor in the cytosol (Bruchovsky and Wilson, 1968; Fang *et al.*, 1969; E. R. Barrack, unpublished observations), but under these conditions only very few binding sites are found associated with the matrix (Fig. 11). Nevertheless, although high salt conditions are often used to eliminate nonspecific adsorption, one must still consider the possibility that during the isolation of nuclei and nuclear matrix some activated cytoplasmic steroid–receptor complexes or salt-extractable nuclear receptors might become associated with the nuclear matrix in a nonphysiological interaction that remains resistant to disruption and solubilization by high ionic strength.

On the other hand, however, since the precise mechanism by which steroid hormone–receptor complexes act in the nucleus to modulate gene expression by affecting the synthesis of premessenger heterogeneous nuclear RNA is still unresolved, the possibility that salt-resistant interactions of receptors with the nuclear matrix in fact reflect a meaningful association should not be discounted (see also Clark and Peck, 1976; Honma *et al.*, 1977; Ruh and Baudendistel, 1977, 1978; Sato *et al.*, 1979).

3. *Considerations of Salt-Extractable and Salt-Resistant Nuclear Receptors*

The apparent existence of two forms of steroid–receptor–acceptor complexes in the nucleus, one which is easily disrupted by high salt conditions and the other which is resistant, raises some interesting questions. For example, one possibility is that the acceptors are the same, but that the cytoplasm-derived nuclear receptors themselves are heterogeneous. Though there may be little evidence to support this notion, the methods that are currently used for characterizing receptors may not be sufficiently sensitive to detect such heterogeneity. A second possibility is that the receptors are homogeneous, but the acceptor sites for salt-extractable and salt-resistant receptors are different. It is not known whether the interactions of receptors with these acceptor sites (electrostatic versus hydrophobic) have different biological consequences. For example, Clark *et al.* (1976) have suggested that the salt-resistant form may represent a transformation of the salt-extractable receptor, whereas Ruh and Baudendistel (1978) have proposed that nuclear salt-extractable receptor–acceptor interactions are involved in the induction of both DNA and RNA synthesis, and that the salt-resistant receptor–acceptor interactions are involved in receptor processing. Both groups of investigators, nevertheless, attribute special biological significance to the salt-resistant receptor–acceptor interaction.

Additionally, one must keep in mind that salt-extractable and salt-resistant receptors are operationally defined, and may not reflect in a precise manner the *in vivo* interaction of receptors with the nucleus. For example, alterations in the conditions for extracting nuclear receptors, such as the inclusion of reducing agents (see Tables XII and XIII, and Sections VII, C, D, and E), can alter the relative proportions of nuclear receptor that are salt extractable and salt resistant. Therefore, the extent to which, for example, oxidation of protein sulfhydryl groups may be involved in the *in vivo* interaction of receptors with the nucleus remains to be elucidated.

Another example of operational considerations is that the inclusion of inhibitors of proteolysis can affect the amount of nuclear receptor found to be salt resistant (see Table XI). Proteolysis can also increase the proportion of nuclear steroid receptors that are solubilized by buffer and/or 0.4 M KCl (Katzenellenbogen *et al.*, 1980). This raises the intriguing question of whether under standard conditions the appearance of salt-extractable nuclear receptors might arise from endogenous proteolytic activity.

Problems associated with the characterization of subnuclear hormone receptors may also arise from the use of sodium molybdate which has been shown to stabilize steroid hormone receptors (Leach *et al.*, 1979; Toft and Nishigori, 1979; Noma *et al.*, 1980; Miller *et al.*, 1981). Several investigators have adopted this methodology but have included sodium molybdate in the homogenization buffer (Anderson *et al.*, 1980; Gaubert *et al.*, 1980; Hawkins *et al.*, 1981). It is important to point out that when sodium molybdate is added directly to the homogenization buffer, prostate nuclear androgen receptor levels are dramatically reduced while cytosol receptor levels increase, suggesting that there is a redistribution of a large proportion of the nuclear receptors to the cytosol fraction (Trachtenberg *et al.*, 1981; Barrack *et al.*, 1982). Other experiments have shown that sodium molybdate extracts glucocorticoid receptors from isolated liver nuclei (Murakami and Moudgil, 1981).

C. Relationship to Chromatin-Associated Receptors

The role of hormone binding components of chromatin, and subfractions thereof, in the mechanism of steroid hormone action has been investigated extensively (see review by Thrall *et al.*, 1978). Unfortunately, however, chromatin is operationally defined and a variety of different methods are used to prepare and subfractionate chromatin. Hence, individual preparations may represent different structural and functional components of the nucleus. In addition, chromatin preparations often contain fragments of the nuclear envelope (Jackson, 1976b; Smith and von Holt, 1981) and of the nuclear matrix (Berezney, 1979). Thus, the concept of "chromatin" is undergoing a redefinition in terms of modern concepts of the nucleus (Busch, 1978).

Since all DNA in the nucleus is organized into supercoiled loop domains which are tightly attached to the nuclear matrix (see Table II), it should not be surprising to find that isolated chromatin would contain components of the nuclear matrix, particularly if chromatin is prepared by simply washing nuclei with a low-ionic-strength buffer to extract the soluble nuclear proteins (Spelsberg *et al.*, 1971; Thrall and Spelsberg, 1980) or by sonicating nuclei to disrupt nuclear (and nuclear matrix) structure (e.g., Pederson, 1974; de Boer *et al.*, 1978; Rennie, 1979; Berezney, 1980; van Eekelen and van Venrooij, 1981). In this regard, it is important to note that nuclear acceptor sites for steroid hormone–receptor complexes have been found in chromatin fractions that resist solubilization by both low and high ionic strength (Klyzsejko-Stefanowicz *et al.*, 1976; Wang, 1978; Thrall *et al.*, 1978; Tsai *et al.*, 1980), and in chromatin subfractions obtained by sonicating nuclei (de Boer *et al.*, 1978).

Localization of hormone receptor binding sites has also been probed by DNase I or micrococcal nuclease digestion of nuclei or chromatin. Many of the receptors that are solubilized by nuclease digestion are associated with nucleosomes (Senior and Frankel, 1978; Scott and Frankel, 1980) or internucleosomal DNA (Rennie, 1979). On the other hand, Schoenberg and Clark (1981) find no such association. Only 5–70% of nuclear steroid receptors are released by nuclease digestion (Senior and Frankel, 1978; Alberga *et al.*, 1979; Scott and Frankel, 1980; Schoenberg and Clark, 1981), and some investigators find that these receptors can be dissociated from nuclease-sensitive sites by 0.4 *M* KCl or 0.6 *M* NaCl (Senior and Frankel, 1978; Rennie, 1979). These nuclease-sensitive hormone binding sites, therefore, appear to be distinct from the DNase I-resistant sites associated with the nuclear matrix. On the other hand, however, it is important to recognize that micrococcal nuclease will attack not only DNA, but also RNA, releasing both nucleosomes and RNP particles from nuclei or chromatin (Walker *et al.*, 1980). Therefore, the possibility exists that some of these nuclease-sensitive receptors might be derived from the internal RNA–protein network of the nuclear matrix (see also Section VII,F).

Template-active regions of chromatin are known to be preferentially sensitive to nuclease digestion (Garel and Axel, 1976; Weintraub and Groudine, 1976; Bloom and Anderson, 1978), yet hormone receptors have been found in association with both template-active and -inactive fractions (Alberga *et al.*, 1979; Scott and Frankel, 1980; Davies *et al.*, 1980). In MCF-7 cells, estradiol–receptor complexes were enriched in the transcriptionally active fraction of chromatin (Scott and Frankel, 1980). In contrast, the template-inactive fraction of the ventral prostate appears to contain about three times as many acceptor sites as the transcriptionally active chromatin (Davies *et al.*, 1980). These apparent discrepancies remain to be resolved.

It is important to comment on the observations that, on the one hand, transcriptionally active genes in nuclei and chromatin are preferentially sensitive to nuclease digestion, while on the other hand, certain actively transcribed genes are enriched in the regions of DNA that are tightly attached to the nuclease-resistant nuclear matrix (Pardoll and Vogelstein, 1980; Nelkin *et al.*, 1980; Robinson *et al.*, 1982). Although these two sets of data *appear* contradictory, they are not. It is precisely because of the former observations that experiments to investigate the spatial organization of genes along the loops of DNA must be carried out by first extracting all histones from the nuclei with 2 *M* NaCl (Nelkin *et al.*, 1980; Robinson *et al.*, 1982). With the histones removed, DNase I makes random cuts in the DNA, with no preference for active or inactive genes (Nelkin *et al.*, 1980; Robinson *et al.*, 1982). Following progressive cleavage of the DNA loops by controlled DNase I digestion, the DNA that remains associated with the nuclear matrix is believed to represent sequences at or near the base of the loops that are anchored to the matrix (Nelkin *et al.*, 1980; Robinson *et al.*, 1982).

Therefore, the ability of nuclease digestion to release transcriptionally active regions from chromatin belies the fact that their native localization may be in association with a discrete, nuclease-resistant structure, the nuclear matrix. Whether a similar situation applies to the preferential release of nuclear steroid hormone–receptor complexes by nucleases or salt remains to be determined (see also Section VIII,B,3).

IX. POTENTIAL ROLE OF CELLULAR STRUCTURAL COMPONENTS IN HORMONE ACTION

Cells contain extensive and elaborate three-dimensional skeletal networks which form integral structural components of the plasma membrane, the cytoplasm, and the nucleus. If these matrix systems were interconnected and could undergo dynamic shifts in structure and conformation, such as by polymerization, depolymerization, cross-linking, biochemical modifications, or contractile movements, then one might visualize how a change in one matrix component could transmit these changes to the rest of the system. Perhaps by such a mechanism externally applied signals might be transmitted along this communications network from one part of the cell to another. Alternatively, these interconnecting networks might act as "conveyor belts" or "railroad tracks" for the transport of informational molecules to their effector sites. A third function of these matrix systems might be to act as "solid-state catalysts" or organizational support structures that could facilitate the interactions of molecules. Since cellular skeleton networks are composed of a number of different types of macromolecules, one could imagine a system in which all three types of interactions might be feasible. The intrinsic appeal of such an organization is the capacity for vectorial chemomechanical coupling as a means of signal transduction. [For additional discussion of these concepts, see review by Isaacs *et al.* (1981).]

One of the basic questions to be resolved in endocrinology is how hormonal signals are transmitted to the nucleus to alter the structure and function of DNA. To date, the working hypothesis of steroid hormone action has been that steroids freely diffuse into the cell, where they become bound to specific intracellular soluble cytoplasmic proteins which then, by mechanisms not fully understood, enter the nucleus and bind with high affinity to specific acceptor sites on the chromatin. Given the recent discoveries about the cytoskeleton and the organization of DNA relative to the nuclear matrix and the organization and synthesis of hnRNA relative to the matrix, a conceptually attractive candidate for the site in the nucleus where steroid hormones might act to regulate specific gene transcription may be the nuclear matrix.

Hormones affect not only gene regulation but also structure. Such changes in cellular structure include nuclear swelling (Cavazos and Melampy, 1954; Ritter, 1969; Chung and Coffey, 1971) and rapid and extensive changes in the organization of large areas of chromatin (Tew *et al.*, 1980; Vic *et al.*, 1980). Given the possibility of interacting matrix systems throughout the cell, it is tempting to speculate that these structural changes may involve dynamic changes in the nuclear matrix following the interaction of steroid hormone–receptor complexes with the nuclear matrix.

Whether hormones might also affect other cellular structural components as part of their mechanism of action is not known, but a number of recent noteworthy observations deserve consideration in this regard. For example, there is evidence for specific estradiol receptors on the plasma membrane of target cells (Szego and Pietras, 1981; Nenci *et al.*, 1981), and that these membrane receptors undergo a temperature- and hormone-dependent capping process (Nenci *et al.*, 1981). In addition, Puca and Sica (1981) have reported the presence of specific, high-affinity binding sites for estradiol–receptor complexes on the plasma membrane cytoskeleton of erythrocytes. Moreover, given the possibility that few macromolecules may diffuse freely and randomly through the cell (see Section I,B and Table I), we note with interest the report by Szego and Pietras (1981) that membrane-associated estradiol receptors can be rendered soluble depending on the method of cell disruption. It is, therefore, conceivable that the soluble steroid receptors that have been studied previously have been solubilized by cell disruption and fractionation techniques, and might have been bound *in situ* to structural components (see also Sections I,B, VII,D, and VIII,B,3). These matrix systems may represent such structural components for the binding of hormone–receptor complexes. Further progress in resolving what the steroid receptor does in the nucleus to regulate DNA function must await a clearer understanding of the organization of the nucleus.

ACKNOWLEDGMENTS

We would like to thank Ms. Ruth Middleton for help in preparing the manuscript. This work was supported by Grant AM 22000, USPHS, National Institute of Arthritis, Metabolism, and Digestive Diseases.

REFERENCES

Aaronson, R. P., and Blobel, G. (1975). *Proc. Natl. Acad. Sci. U.S.A.* **72,** 1007–1011.
Adolph, K. W. (1980). *J. Cell Sci.* **42,** 291–304.
Agutter, P. S., and Birchall, K. (1979). *Exp. Cell Res.* **124,** 453–460.
Agutter, P. S., and Richardson, J. C. W. (1980). *J. Cell Sci.* **44,** 395–435.
Alberga, A., Tran, A., and Baulieu, E. E. (1979). *Nucleic Acids Res.* **7,** 2031–2044.
Allen, S. L., Berezney, R., and Coffey, D. S. (1977). *Biochem. Biophys. Res. Commun.* **75,** 111–116.
Anderson, J., Clark, J. H., and Peck, E. J., Jr. (1972a). *Biochem. J.* **126,** 561–567.
Anderson, J. N., Clark, J. H., and Peck, E. J., Jr. (1972b). *Biochem. Biophys. Res. Commun.* **48,** 1460–1468.
Anderson, J. N., Clark, J. H., and Peck, E. J., Jr. (1975). *Endocrinology (Baltimore)* **96,** 160–167.
Anderson, K. M., Phelan, J., Marogil, M., Hendrickson, C., and Economou, S. (1980). *Steroids* **35,** 273–280.
Aten, R. F., Weinberger, M. J., and Eisenfeld, A. J. (1978). *Endocrinology (Baltimore)* **102,** 433–442.
Barrack, E. R., and Coffey, D. S. (1980). *J. Biol. Chem.* **255,** 7265–7275.
Barrack, E. R., Hawkins, E. F., Allen, S. L., Hicks, L. L., and Coffey, D. S. (1977). *Biochem. Biophys. Res. Commun.* **79,** 829–836.
Barrack, E. R., Hawkins, E. F., and Coffey, D. S. (1979). In "Steroid Hormone Receptor Systems" (W. W. Leavitt and J. H. Clark, eds.), pp. 47–70. Plenum, New York.
Barrack, E. R., Bujnovszky, P., and Walsh, P. C. (1983). *Cancer Res.* (in press).
Basler, J., Berezney, R., and Sandberg, A. A. (1981). *J. Cell Biol.* **91,** 60a.
Bekhor, I., and Mirell, C. J. (1979). *Biochemistry* **18,** 609–616.
Berezney, R. (1979). In "The Cell Nucleus" (H. Busch, ed.), Vol. 7, pp. 413–456. Academic Press, New York.
Berezney, R. (1890). *J. Cell Biol.* **85,** 641–650.
Berezney, R., and Buchholtz, L. A. (1981a). *Exp. Cell Res.* **132,** 1–13.
Berezney, R., and Buchholtz, L. A. (1981b). *Biochemistry* **20,** 4995–5002.
Berezney, R., and Coffey, D. S. (1974). *Biochem. Biophys. Res. Commun.* **60,** 1410–1417.
Berezney, R., and Coffey, D. S. (1975). *Science* **189,** 291–293.
Berezney, R., and Coffey, D. S. (1976). *Adv. Enzyme Regul.* **14,** 63–100.
Berezney, R., and Coffey, D. S. (1977). *J. Cell Biol.* **73,** 616–637.
Berezney, R., Basler, J., Hughes, B. B., and Kaplan, S. C. (1979). *Cancer Res.* **39,** 3031–3039.

Blazsek, I., Vaukhonen, M., and Hemminki, K. (1979). *Res. Commun. Chem. Pathol. Pharmacol.* **23**, 611–626.

Bloom, K. S., and Anderson, J. N. (1978). *Cell* **15**, 141–150.

Boesel, R. W., Klipper, R. W., and Shain, S. A. (1977). *Endocr. Res. Commun.* **4**, 71–84.

Bouteille, M., Laval, M., and Dupuy-Coin, A. M. (1974). *In* "The Cell Nucleus" (H. Busch, ed.), Vol. 1, pp. 3–71. Academic Press, New York.

Bouvier, D., Hubert, J., and Bouteille, M. (1980). *J. Ultrastruct. Res.* **73**, 288–298.

Bowen, B., Steinberg, J., Laemmli, U. K., and Weintraub, H. (1980). *Nucleic Acids Res.* **8**, 1–20.

Brandes, D. (1974). *In* "Male Accessory Sex Organs: Structure and Function in Mammals" (D. Brandes, ed.), pp. 183–222. Academic Press, New York.

Brown, T. R., Rothwell, S. W., and Migeon, C. J. (1981). *J. Steroid Biochem.* **14**, 1013–1022.

Bruchovsky, N., and Wilson, J. D. (1968). *J. Biol. Chem.* **243**, 2012–2021.

Buckler-White, A. J., Humphrey, G. W., and Pigiet, V. (1980). *Cell* **22**, 37–46.

Busch, H. (1978). *In* "The Cell Nucleus" (H. Busch, ed.), Vol. 6, pp. xxiii–xxvii. Academic Press, New York.

Busch, H., and Smetana, K. (1970). "The Nucleolus," pp. 361–381. Academic Press, New York.

Cavazos, L. F., and Melampy, R. M. (1954). *Endocrinology (Baltimore)* **54**, 644–648.

Chamness, G. C., Zava, D. T., and McGuire, W. L. (1978). *Methods Cell Biol.* **17**, 325–333.

Chung, L. W. K., and Coffey, D. S. (1971). *Biochim. Biophys. Acta* **247**, 570–583.

Cidlowski, J. A., and Munck, A. (1980). *J. Steroid Biochem.* **13**, 105–112.

Ciejek, E. M., Nordstrom, J. L., Tsai, M.-J., and O'Malley, B. W. (1981). *J. Cell Biol.* **91**, 132a.

Clark, J. H., and Peck, E. J., Jr. (1976). *Nature (London)* **260**, 635–637.

Clark, J. H., Eriksson, H. A., and Hardin, J. W. (1976). *J. Steroid Biochem.* **7**, 1039–1043.

Clark, J. H., Markaverich, B., Upchurch, S., Eriksson, H., Hardin, J. W., and Peck, E. J., Jr. (1980). *Recent Prog. Horm. Res.* **36**, 89–134.

Cobbs, C. S., Jr., and Shelton, K. R. (1978). *Arch. Biochem. Biophys.* **189**, 323–335.

Cochran, D. L., Yeoman, L. C., Egle, P. M., and Shelton, K. R. (1979). *J. Supramol. Struct.* **10**, 405–418.

Coffey, D. S., Shimazaki, J., and Williams-Ashman, H. G. (1968). *Arch. Biochem. Biophys.* **124**, 184–198.

Comings, D. E., and Okada, T. A. (1976). *Exp. Cell Res.* **103**, 341–360.

Comings, D. E., and Peters, K. E. (1981). *In* "The Cell Nucleus" (H. Busch, ed.), Vol. 9, pp. 89–118. Academic Press, New York.

Comings, D. E., and Wallack, A. S. (1978). *J. Cell Sci.* **34**, 233–246.

Cook, P. R., Brazell, I. A., and Jost, E. (1976). *J. Cell Sci.* **22**, 303–324.

Danzo, B. J., and Eller, B. C. (1978). *J. Steroid Biochem.* **9**, 477–483.

Davies, P., Thomas, P., and Griffiths, K. (1977). *J. Endocrinol.* **74**, 393–404.

Davies, P., Thomas, P., Borthwick, N. M., and Giles, M. G. (1980). *J. Endocrinol.* **87**, 225–240.

de Boer, W., deVries, J., Mulder, E., and van der Molen, H. J. (1978). *Nucleic Acids Res.* **5**, 87–103.

Deeley, R. G., Gordon, J. I., Burns, A. T. H., Mullinix, K. P., BinaStein, M., and Goldberger, R. F. (1977). *J. Biol. Chem.* **252**, 8310–8319.

DeHertogh, R., Ekka, E., Vanderheyden, I., and Hoet, J. J. (1973). *J. Steroid Biochem.* **4**, 313–320.

DeKlerk, D. P., Heston, W. D. W., and Coffey, D. S. (1976). *In* "Benign Prostatic Hyperplasia" (J. T. Grayhack, J. D. Wilson, and M. J. Scherbenske, eds.), pp. 43–54. U.S. Govt. Printing Office, Washington, D.C.

Deppert, W. (1978). *J. Virol.* **26**, 165–178.

Dickson, R. B., and Eisenfeld, A. J. (1981). *Endocrinology (Baltimore)* **108**, 1511–1518.

Dickson, R. B., Aten, R. F., and Eisenfeld, A. J. (1980). *Mol. Pharmacol.* **18**, 215–233.

Dijkwel, P. A., Mullenders, L. H. F., and Wanka, F. (1979). *Nucleic Acids Res.* **6**, 219–230.

Dvorkin, V. M., and Vanyushin, B. F. (1978). *Biochemistry (USSR)* **43**, 1297–1301.

Dwyer, N., and Blobel, G. (1976). *J. Cell Biol.* **70**, 581–591.

Eastment, C. E., Scott, R. B., Shelton, K. R., and Haar, J. L. (1981). *Blood* **57**, 747–757.

Eriksson, H., Upchurch, S., Hardin, J. W., Peck, E. J., Jr., and Clark, J. H. (1978). *Biochem. Biophys. Res. Commun.* **81**, 1–7.

Faiferman, I., and Pogo, A. O. (1975). *Biochemistry* **14**, 3808–3816.

Fakan, S., Puvion, E., and Spohr, G. (1976). *Exp. Cell Res.* **99**, 155–164.

Fang, S., Anderson, K. M., and Liao, S. (1969). *J. Biol. Chem.* **244**, 6584–6595.

Feinberg, A. P., and Coffey, D. S. (1982). *In* "Nuclear Envelope and the Nuclear Matrix" (G. G. Maul, ed.), pp. 293–306. Liss, New York.

Franceschi, R. T., and Kim, K. H. (1979). *J. Biol. Chem.* **254**, 3637–3646.

Franke, W. W., Kleinschmidt, J. A., Spring, H., Krohne, G., Grund, C., Trendelenburg, M. F., Stoehr, M., and Scheer, U. (1981). *J. Cell Biol.* **90**, 289–299.

Gambino, J., Eckhardt, R. A., and Risley, M. S. (1981). *J. Cell Biol.* **91**, 63a.

Garel, A., and Axel, R. (1976). *Proc. Natl. Acad. Sci. U.S.A.* **73**, 3966–3970.

Gates, D. M., and Bekhor, I. (1980). *Science* **207**, 661–662.

Gaubert, C. M., Tremblay, R. R., and Dubé, J. Y. (1980). *J. Steroid Biochem.* **13**, 931–937.

Georgiev, G. P., and Chentsov, J. S. (1962). *Exp. Cell Res.* **27**, 570–572.

Georgiev, G. P., Nedospasov, S. A., and Bakayev, V. V. (1978). *In* "The Cell Nucleus" (H. Busch, ed.), Vol. 6, pp. 3–34. Academic Press, New York.

Gerace, L., and Blobel, G. (1980). *Cell* **19**, 277–287.

Gerace, L., Blum, A., and Blobel, G. (1978). *J. Cell Biol.* **79**, 546–566.

Ghosh, S., Paweletz, N., and Ghosh, I. (1978). *Exp. Cell Res.* **111**, 363–371.

Giese, G., and Wunderlich, F. (1979). *Anal. Biochem.* **100**, 282–288.

Giese, G., and Wunderlich, F. (1980). *J. Biol. Chem.* **255**, 1716–1721.

Goldman, R. D., and Knipe, D. M. (1972). *Cold Spring Harbor Symp. Quant. Biol.* **37**, 523–534.

Gorski, J., and Gannon, F. (1976). *Annu. Rev. Physiol.* **38**, 425–450.

Gschwendt, M., and Schneider, W. (1978). *Eur. J. Biochem.* **91**, 139–149.

Hampel, M. R., Peng, L.-H., Pearlman, M. R. J., and Pearlman, W. H. (1978). *J. Biol. Chem.* **253**, 8545–8553.

Hardin, J. W., and Clark, J. H. (1979). *J. Cell Biol.* **83**, 252a.

Hawkins, E. F., Lieskovsky, G., and Markland, F. S., Jr. (1981). *J. Clin. Endocrinol. Metab.* **53**, 456–458.

Hemminki, K., and Vainio, H. (1979). *Cancer Lett. (Shannon, Irel.)* **6**, 167–173.

Henderson, D., and Weber, K. (1979). *Exp. Cell Res.* **124**, 301–316.

Herlan, G., Eckert, W. A., Kaffenberger, W., and Wunderlich, F. (1979). *Biochemistry* **18**, 1782–1788.

Herman, R., Weymouth, L., and Penman, S. (1978). *J. Cell Biol.* **78**, 663–674.

Hodge, L. D., Mancini, P., Davis, F. M., and Heywood, P. (1977). *J. Cell Biol.* **72**, 194–208.

Honma, Y., Kasukabe, T., Okabe, J., and Hozumi, M. (1977). *J. Cell. Physiol.* **93**, 227–236.

Hozier, J., and Furcht, L. T. (1980). *Cell Biol. Int. Rep.* **4**, 1091–1099.

Hughes, M. R., Compton, J. G., Schrader, W. T., and O'Malley, B. W. (1981). *Biochemistry* **20**, 2481–2491.

Hunt, B. F., and Vogelstein, B. (1981). *Nucleic Acids Res*. **9**, 349–363.

Ierardi, L. A., Moss, S. B., and Bellvé, A. R. (1981). *J. Cell Biol*. **91**, 65a.

Isaacs, J. T., Barrack, E. R., Isaacs, W. B., and Coffey, D. S. (1981). *In* "The Prostatic Cell: Structure and Function" (G. P. Murphy, A. A. Sandberg, and J. P. Karr, eds.), Part A, pp. 1–24. Liss, New York.

Jackson, R. C. (1976a). *Biochemistry* **15**, 5641–5651.

Jackson, R. C. (1976b). *Biochemistry* **15**, 5652–5656.

Jackson, V., and Chalkley, R. (1974). *J. Biol. Chem*. **249**, 1615–1626.

Jackson, D. A., McCready, S. J., and Cook, P. R. (1981). *Nature* (*London*) **292**, 552–555.

Jensen, E. V. (1979). *Pharmacol. Rev*. **30**, 477–491.

Jensen, E. V., Suzuki, T., Kawashima, T., Stumpf, W. E., Jungblut, P. W., and DeSombre, E. R. (1968). *Proc. Natl. Acad. Sci. U.S.A*. **59**, 632–638.

Johnson, L. K., Vlodavsky, I., Baxter, J. D., and Gospodarowicz, D. (1980). *Nature* (*London*) **287**, 340–343.

Jost, E., and Johnson, R. T. (1981). *J. Cell Sci*. **47**, 25–53.

Juliano, J. V., and Stancel, G. M. (1976). *Biochemistry* **15**, 916–920.

Katzenellenbogen, B. S., Lan, N. C., and Rutledge, S. K. (1980). *J. Steroid Biochem*. **13**, 113–122.

Kaufman, M., Pinsky, K., Kubski, A., Straisfeld, C., Dobrenis, K., Shiroky, J., Chan, T., and MacGibbon, B. (1978). *J. Clin. Endocrinol. Metab*. **47**, 738–745.

Kaufmann, S. H., Coffey, D. S., and Shaper, J. H. (1981). *Exp. Cell Res*. **132**, 105–123.

Klyzsejko-Stefanowicz, L., Chiu, J.-F., Tsai, Y.-H., and Hnilica, L. S. (1976). *Proc. Natl. Acad. Sci. U.S.A*. **73**, 1954–1958.

Krohne, G., Franke, W. W., Ely, S., D'Arcy, A., and Jost, E. (1978). *Cytobiologie* **18**, 22–38.

Krohne, G., Dabauvalle, M.-C., and Franke, W. W. (1981). *J. Mol. Biol*. **151**, 121–141.

Kuzmina, S. N., Buldyaeva, T. V., and Zbarskii, I. B. (1980). *Biochemistry* (*USSR*) **45**, 1071–1077.

Kuzmina, S., Buldyaeva, T., Troitskaya, L., and Zbarsky, I. (1981). *Eur. J. Cell Biol*. **25**, 225–232.

Lam, K. S., and Kasper, C. B. (1979a). *Biochemistry* **18**, 307–311.

Lam, K. S., and Kasper, C. B. (1979b). *J. Biol. Chem*. **254**, 11713–11720.

Lazarides, E. (1981). *Cell* **23**, 649–650.

Lazarides, E., and Weber, K. (1974). *Proc. Natl. Acad. Sci. U.S.A*. **71**, 2268–2272.

Lazier, C. (1975). *Steroids* **26**, 281–298.

Leach, K. L., Dahmer, M. K., Hammond, N. D., Sando, J. J., and Pratt, W. B. (1979). *J. Biol. Chem*. **254**, 11884–11890.

Lebeau, M. C., Massol, N., and Baulieu, E. E. (1973). *Eur. J. Biochem*. **36**, 294–300.

Lefebvre, Y. A., and Novosad, Z. (1980). *Biochem. J*. **186**, 641–647.

Lenk, R., Ransom, L., Kaufmann, Y., and Penman, S. (1977). *Cell* **10**, 67–78.

Levinger, L., and Varshavsky, A. (1981). *J. Cell Biol*. **90**, 793–796.

Liao, S., Liang, T., and Tymoczko, J. K. (1973). *Nature* (*London*) *New Biol*. **241**, 211–213.

Liao, S., Mezzetti, G., and Chen, C. (1979). *In* "The Cell Nucleus" (H. Busch, ed.), Vol. 7, pp. 201–227. Academic Press, New York.

Long, B. H., Huang, C.-Y., and Pogo, A. O. (1979). *Cell* **18**, 1079–1090.

McCready, S. J., Godwin, J., Mason, D. W., Brazell, I. A., and Cook, P. R. (1980). *J. Cell Sci*. **46**, 365–386.

McDonald, J. R., and Agutter, P. S. (1980). *FEBS Lett*. **116**, 145–148.

Mainwaring, W. I. P., Rennie, P. S., and Keen, J. (1976). *Biochem. J*. **156**, 253–264.

Markaverich, B. M., Upchurch, S., and Clark, J. H. (1980). *J. Receptor Res*. **1**, 415–438.

Matsumoto, L. H. (1981). *Nature* (*London*) **294**, 481–482.

Matsuura, T., Ueyama, H., Nakayasu, H., and Ueda, K. (1981). *Cell Struct. Funct.* **6**, 79–82.
Maul, G. G., and Avdalović, N. (1980). *Exp. Cell Res.* **130**, 229–240.
Mayer, D. T., and Gulick, A. (1942). *J. Biol. Chem.* **146**, 433–440.
Mester, J., and Baulieu, E. E. (1975). *Biochem. J.* **146**, 617–623.
Miller, T. E., Huang, C.-Y., and Pogo, A. O. (1978a). *J. Cell Biol.* **76**, 675–691.
Miller, T. E., Huang, C.-Y., and Pogo, A. O. (1978b). *J. Cell Biol.* **76**, 692–704.
Miller, L. K., Tuazon, F. B., Niu, E.-M., and Sherman, M. R. (1981). *Endocrinology (Baltimore)* **108**, 1369–1378.
Mirsky, A. E., and Ris, H. (1951). *J. Gen. Physiol.* **34**, 475–492.
Mitchelson, K. R., Bekers, A. G. M., and Wanka, F. (1979). *J. Cell Sci.* **39**, 247–256.
Monneron, A., and Bernhard, W. (1969). *J. Ultrastruct. Res.* **27**, 266–288.
Müller, R. E., Traish, A. M., and Wotiz, H. H. (1977). *J. Biol. Chem.* **252**, 8206–8211.
Murakami, N., and Moudgil, V. K. (1981). *Biochem. J.* **198**, 447–455.
Nakayasu, H., and Ueda, K. (1981). *Cell Struct. Funct.* **6**, 181–190.
Nelkin, B. D., Pardoll, D. M., and Vogelstein, B. (1980). *Nucleic Acids Res.* **8**, 5623–5634.
Nenci, I., Marchetti, E., Marzola, A., and Fabris, G. (1981). *J. Steroid Biochem.* **14**, 1139–1146.
Noma, K., Nakao, K., Sato, B., Nishizawa, Y., Matsumoto, K., and Yamamura, Y. (1980). *Endocrinology (Baltimore)* **107**, 1205–1211.
Nomi, S., Matsuura, T., Ueyama, H., and Ueda, K. (1981). *J. Nutr. Sci. Vitaminol.* **27**, 33–41.
Norman, G. L., and Bekhor, I. (1981). *Biochemistry* **20**, 3568–3578.
Nyberg, L. M., and Wang, T. Y. (1976). *J. Steroid Biochem.* **7**, 267–273.
Osborn, M., and Weber, K. (1977). *Exp. Cell Res.* **106**, 339–349.
Pardoll, D. M., and Vogelstein, B. (1980). *Exp. Cell Res.* **128**, 466–470.
Pardoll, D. M., Vogelstein, B., and Coffey, D. S. (1980). *Cell* **19**, 527–536.
Parikh, I., Anderson, W. L., and Neame, P. (1980). *J. Biol. Chem.* **255**, 10266–10270.
Paris, J. E., and Brandes, D. (1974). *In* "Male Accessory Sex Organs: Structure and Function in Mammals" (D. Brandes, ed.), pp. 223–233. Academic Press, New York.
Pederson, T. (1974). *J. Mol. Biol.* **83**, 163–183.
Peters, K. E., and Comings, D. E. (1980). *J. Cell Biol.* **86**, 135–155.
Pogo, A. O. (1981). *In* "The Cell Nucleus" (H. Busch, ed.), Vol. 8, pp. 331–367. Academic Press, New York.
Pollard, T. D., and Weihing, R. R. (1973). *Crit. Rev. Biochem.* **2**, 1–65.
Porter, K. R., and Tucker, J. B. (1981). *Sci. Am.* **244**, 56–67.
Poznanović, G., and Sevaljević, L. (1980). *Cell Biol. Int. Rep.* **4**, 701–709.
Puca, G. A., and Bresciani, F. (1968). *Nature (London)* **218**, 967–969.
Puca, G. A., and Sica, V. (1981). *Biochem. Biophys. Res. Commun.* **103**, 682–689.
Puca, G. A., Nola, E., Hibner, U., Cicala, G., and Sica, V. (1975). *J. Biol. Chem.* **250**, 6452–6459.
Razin, S. V., Mantieva, V. L., and Georgiev, G. P. (1979). *Nucleic Acids Res.* **7**, 1713–1735.
Razin, S. V., Chernokhvostov, V. V., Roodyn, A. V., Zbarsky, I. B., and Georgiev, G. P. (1981). *Cell* **27**, 65–73.
Rennie, P. S. (1979). *J. Biol. Chem.* **254**, 3947–3952.
Rennie, P. S., Symes, E. K., and Mainwaring, W. I. P. (1975). *Biochem. J.* **152**, 1–16.
Riley, D. E., and Keller, J. M. (1976). *Biochim. Biophys. Acta* **444**, 899–911.
Riley, D. E., Keller, J. M., and Byers, B. (1975). *Biochemistry* **14**, 3005–3013.
Ritter, C. (1969). *Endocrinology (Baltimore)* **84**, 844–854.
Robinson, S. I., Nelkin, B. D., and Vogelstein, B. (1982). *Cell* **28**, 99–106.
Ross, D. A. (1980). *Fed. Proc., Fed. Am. Soc. Exp. Biol.* **39**, 2196.

Ruh, T. S., and Baudendistel, L. J. (1977). *Endocrinology (Baltimore)* **100**, 420–426.
Ruh, T. S., and Baudendistel, L. J. (1978). *Endocrinology (Baltimore)* **102**, 1838–1846.
Sanborn, B. M., Steinberger, A., and Tcholakian, R. K. (1979). *Steroids* **34**, 401–412.
Sato, B., Spomer, W., Huseby, R. A., and Samuels, L. T. (1979). *Endocrinology (Baltimore)* **104**, 822–831.
Scatchard, G. (1949). *Ann. N. Y. Acad. Sci.* **51**, 660–672.
Schliwa, M., and Van Blerkom, J. (1981). *J. Cell Biol.* **90**, 222–235.
Schoenberg, D. R., and Clark, J. H. (1981). *Biochem. J.* **196**, 423–432.
Scott, R. W., and Frankel, F. R. (1980). *Proc. Natl. Acad. Sci. U.S.A.* **77**, 1291–1295.
Senior, M. B., and Frankel, F. R. (1978). *Cell* **14**, 857–863.
Sevaljević, L., Poznanović, G., Petrović, M., Konstantinović, M., and Ratković, M. (1980). *Period. Biol.* **82**, 325–330.
Sevaljević, L., Poznanović, G., Petrović, M., and Krtolica, K. (1981). *Biochem. Int.* **2**, 77–84.
Shankar Narayan, K., Steele, W. J., Smetana, K., and Busch, H. (1967). *Exp. Cell Res.* **46**, 65–77.
Shaper, J. H., Pardoll, D. M., Kaufmann, S. H., Barrack, E. R., Vogelstein, B., and Coffey, D. S. (1979). *Adv. Enzyme Regul.* **17**, 213–248.
Shelton, K. R., and Cochran, D. L. (1978). *Biochemistry* **17**, 1212–1216.
Shelton, K. R., Higgins, L. L., Cochran, D. L., Ruffolo, P. J., Jr., and Egle, P. M. (1980). *J. Biol. Chem.* **255**, 10978–10983.
Sinibaldi, R. M., and Morris, P. W. (1981). *J. Biol. Chem.* **256**, 10735–10738.
Smetana, K., Steele, W. J., and Busch, H. (1963). *Exp. Cell Res.* **31**, 198–201.
Smith, H. C., and Berezney, R. (1980). *Biochem. Biophys. Res. Commun.* **97**, 1541–1547.
Smith, P., and von Holt, C. (1981). *Biochemistry* **20**, 2900–2908.
Snead, H. W., McDonald, T. F., Baker, M. D., and Lanclos, K. D. (1979). *J. Supramol. Struct.* **12**, 471–479.
Snow, L. D., Eriksson, H., Hardin, J. W., Chan, L., Jackson, R. L., Clark, J. H., and Means, A. R. (1978). *J. Steroid Biochem.* **9**, 1017–1026.
Spelsberg, T. C., Steggles, A. W., and O'Malley, B. W. (1971). *J. Biol. Chem.* **246**, 4188–4197.
Steele, W. J., and Busch, H. (1966). *Biochim. Biophys. Acta* **129**, 54–67.
Steer, R. C., Goueli, S. A., Wilson, M. J., and Ahmed, K. (1980). *Biochem. Biophys. Res. Commun.* **92**, 919–925.
Stick, R., and Hausen, P. (1980). *Chromosoma* **80**, 219–236.
Szego, C. M., and Pietras, R. J. (1981). *In* "Biochemical Actions of Hormones" (G. Litwack, ed.), Vol. 8, pp. 307–463. Academic Press, New York.
Tata, J. R. (1978). *In* "Biochemical Actions of Hormones" (G. Litwack, ed.), Vol. 5, pp. 397–431. Academic Press, New York.
Tew, K. D., Schein, P. S., Lindner, D. J., Wang, A. L., and Smulson, M. E. (1980). *Cancer Res.* **40**, 3697–3703.
Thrall, C. L., and Spelsberg, T. C. (1980). *Biochemistry* **19**, 4130–4138.
Thrall, C. L., Webster, R. A., and Spelsberg, T. C. (1978). *In* "The Cell Nucleus" (H. Busch, ed.), Vol. 6, pp. 461–529. Academic Press, New York.
Todorov, I. T., and Hadjiolov, A. A. (1979). *Cell Biol. Int. Rep.* **3**, 753–757.
Toft, D., and Nishigori, H. (1979). *J. Steroid Biochem.* **11**, 413–416.
Trachtenberg, J., Hicks, L. L., and Walsh, P. C. (1981). *Invest. Urol.* **18**, 349–354.
Traish, A., Müller, R. E., and Wotiz, H. H. (1977). *J. Biol. Chem.* **252**, 6823–6830.
Tsai, Y.-H., Sanborn, B. M., Steinberger, A., and Steinberger, E. (1980). *J. Steroid Biochem.* **13**, 711–718.
Ueyama, H., Matsuura, T., Nomi, S., Nakayasu, H., and Ueda, K. (1981). *Life Sci.* **29**, 655–661.

Van Doorn, E., Craven, S., and Bruchovsky, N. (1976). *Biochem. J.* **160**, 11–21.
van Eekelen, C. A. G., and van Venrooij, W. J. (1981). *J. Cell Biol.* **88**, 554–563.
Vic, P., Garcia, M., Humeau, C., and Rochefort, H. (1980). *Mol. Cell. Endocrinol.* **19**, 79–92.
Vogelstein, B., Pardoll, D. M., and Coffey, D. S. (1980). *Cell* **22**, 79–85.
Walker, B. W., Lothstein, L., Baker, C. L., and LeStourgeon, W. M. (1980). *Nucleic Acids Res.* **8**, 3639–3657.
Wang, T. Y. (1978). *Biochim. Biophys. Acta* **518**, 81–88.
Weintraub, H., and Groudine, M. (1976). *Science* **193**, 848–856.
Wilson, E. M., and French, F. S. (1976). *J. Biol. Chem.* **251**, 5620–5629.
Wolfe, J. (1980). *J. Cell Biol.* **84**, 160–171.
Wunderlich, F., and Herlan, G. (1977). *J. Cell Biol.* **73**, 271–278.
Wunderlich, F., Giese, G., and Bucherer, C. (1978). *J. Cell Biol.* **79**, 479–490.
Yamamoto, K. R., and Alberts, B. M. (1976). *Annu. Rev. Biochem.* **45**, 721–746.
Zbarsky, I. B. (1981). *Mol. Biol. Rep.* **7**, 139–148.
Zbarsky, I. B., and Georgiev, G. P. (1959). *Biochim. Biophys. Acta* **32**, 301–302.
Zbarsky, I. B., Dmitrieva, N. P., and Yermolayeva, L. P. (1962). *Exp. Cell Res.* **27**, 573–576.

CHAPTER 3

Nerve Growth Factor and Related Hormones

Ralph A. Bradshaw

I. INTRODUCTION

At all levels of sophistication, endocrine systems are composed of three basic elements: cells that synthesize chemical messengers, cells that respond to these messengers, and the messengers themselves. Since the elucidation of this fundamental concept in intercellular information transfer (see Wright, 1978), these entities have been referred to as hormones and it has been appreciated for some time that they are derived from three classes of chemical compounds, i.e., polypeptides, steroids, and amino acid derivatives. The substances originally held to be hormones are transported systemically from their sites of synthesis to their target cells. However, it was realized very early in the study of endocrine systems that there are hormone-like molecules, in terms of their action on target cells, that varied in their manner of delivery. Such interactions have been variously referred to as

BIOCHEMICAL ACTIONS OF HORMONES, VOL. X

autocrine, paracrine, or neurocrine interactions, depending on the nature of the system.

One group of hormone-like agents that have become of increased interest, particularly in the last decade, are the polypeptide growth factors. While most of these have been identified recently, primarily from work with cultured cells (Gospodarowicz and Moran, 1976), a few have been appreciated for a much longer period of time. One of these is the polypeptide nerve growth factor (NGF), which was discovered just over three decades ago (Levi-Montalcini and Hamburger, 1951). Its acceptance as a physiologically relevant agent for the regulation of developing and mature peripheral neurons was cemented by the observations that antibodies directed against it were effective, when injected into neonatal animals, in causing the destruction of responsibe target cells (Levi-Montalcini and Booker, 1960). Curiously, this identification of a physiological role for NGF still distinguishes it today from most of the other known growth factors, whose actions *in vivo* have been poorly defined at best. It is, therefore, not surprising that NGF remains one of the best-studied members of the growth factor family and has consistently provided important new insights into the biology, chemistry, and mechanism of action of other such substances. In this review the relationship of NGF to hormones in general and other growth factors in particular will be considered and the principal properties of NGF, as viewed as a hormone-like messenger in vertebrate organisms, will be considered.

II. THE RELATIONSHIP OF HORMONES AND GROWTH FACTORS

A. CLASSIFICATION SCHEME

Although any classification of hormones is at best a tenuous proposition because of the wide variety of substances and activities encompassed, a situation further compounded by the fact that new hormonal substances are being continuously discovered with regularity, it is often instructive to consider both the unifying as well as the distinguishing properties of hormones, as they are presently appreciated, in order to gain new perspectives. One such scheme, which emphasizes the properties of hormones and hormone-like substances and underscores their relationship to polypeptide growth factors, is shown in Fig. 1 (Bradshaw and Niall, 1978; Bradshaw and Rubin, 1980). In this presentation, hormonal substances are divided into two main categories, designated primary and secondary, with the latter group further subdivided into two types. Primary hormones are most readily distinguished

PROPERTIES	PRIMARY	SECONDARY	
		TYPE 1	TYPE 2
CHEMISTRY	POLYPEPTIDES, AA DERIVATIVES	POLYPEPTIDES	AA DERIVATIVES, STEROIDS
SITE OF INITIATION	EXTERNAL	EXTERNAL	INTERNAL
RESPONSE	RAPID	RAPID; SLOW	RAPID; SLOW
RECEPTOR OCCUPANCY	DIRECT	DIRECT; INDIRECT	DIRECT
DURATION OF EFFECT	SHORT	LONG	LONG
INTERNALIZATION	NO	YES	YES
TURNOVER	RAPID	SLOW	SLOW
PRIMARY EFFECT	$\uparrow$cAMP, $\uparrow$Ca^{2+} FLUX	$\uparrow$ANABOLISM; $\uparrow$METABOLITE UPTAKE	----
SECONDARY EFFECT	REGULATION OF METABOLISM	REGULATION OF GENE EXPRESSION	REGULATION OF GENE EXPRESSION

FIG. 1. Classification scheme for hormones and hormone-like substances.

from those in the secondary category by the nature of the response of the target cells following the interaction of the hormone with the cell surface membrane. This interaction is thought to occur exclusively on the cell surface and the effects produced to be directly proportional to the extent and duration of receptor occupancy. Under physiological conditions, the length of time that the hormone is in contact with the target cell would be expected to be short and is perhaps most analogous to the behavior of neurotransmitters. As a direct corollary, the turnover of these hormones is relatively rapid and in many cases results from the degradative action of enzymes found on the cell surface itself. Two primary effects are associated with hormones of this class: the increase in intracellular cyclic AMP and the mobilization of calcium ions. These changes result in the regulation of metabolism largely through modification of enzyme and protein molecules found in the cellular interior. In a majority of the cases, these modifications are the result of phosphorylation or dephosphorylation reactions.

The hormones in the secondary class are also characterized by rapid responses but are distinguished by the long-term effects that also result from the initial interaction. These "indirect" responses result from the fact that receptor occupancy is *not* required for their complete development, although the initiation of the effects is. Furthermore, in contradistinction to the primary hormones, both types of secondary hormones are internalized as a result of their initial interaction with the cell surface, albeit by apparently different mechanisms, and both are degraded as a result of the internalization process leading to the slower turnover.

The two types of secondary hormones are separated not only by their chemistry but also by their mechanism of uptake. Type 1 secondary hormones are polypeptides that include, at the present level of knowledge, all of the protein growth factors identified to date. These molecules have cell surface receptors, which are themselves largely proteinoid in nature and are intrinsically bound in the cell surface membrane. The mechanism of entry is apparently exclusively by receptor-mediated endocytosis (Neville and Chang, 1978; Goldstein *et al.*, 1979). In contrast, the type 2 secondary hormones are either amino acid derivatives or steroids which apparently can pass through the cell surface membrane without the agency of a specific receptor interaction. However, it should be noted that this latter conclusion has been difficult to prove rigorously and the details of how molecules of this class actually pass through the cell membrane still remain obscure. The type 2 secondary hormones are subsequently bound by intracellular receptors. In the case of steroids, these receptors are first encountered in the cytoplasm and are translocated to the nucleus after complexation (O'Malley *et al.*, 1976). The amino acid derivative hormones, exemplified by the thyroid hormones T_3 and T_4, apparently go directly to the nucleus where their initial interaction occurs. The polypeptide secondary hormones (type 1) do exert rapid effects as a result of their complexation with their cell surface receptors, and these "rapid" effects are clearly important in many physiological systems. Their slow, or indirect, responses are related, on the other hand, to alterations in gene expression either at the transcriptional or translational level. The type 2 hormones also modulate gene expression.

The type 1 secondary hormones include, in addition to the polypeptide growth factors, several agents normally listed as "classical" hormones. For example, insulin, growth hormone, and prolactin are found in this category. This is of particular interest because of the structural relatedness of some of these molecules to other growth factors. An excellent example of this is the subset of hormones and growth factors related to insulin, described in detail in the next section.

B. SUBSET OF INSULIN-RELATED HORMONES

1. Structural Relationships

Since the elucidation of the amino acid sequence of the active subunit (β) of mouse NGF by Angeletti and Bradshaw (1971), it has been appreciated that this molecule resembles the classical pancreatic hormone insulin (proinsulin) in a fashion associated with proteins that have evolved from a common ancestral gene (Frazier *et al.*, 1972). The structural relatedness, as manifested in amino acid identities in the sequence alignment, is confined to regions of NGF that align with the B and A chain segments of the proinsulin molecule. In NGF, these are separated by a polypeptide segment analogous to the C bridge of proinsulin, although it is not removed by limited proteolysis as occurs in the proinsulin-to-insulin conversion. The retention of a single conserved disulfide bond in the two molecules adds further support for the evolutionary relatedness. Without question, either the divergence of the NGF and insulin genes occurred long ago or they have evolved rapidly, since the molecules, in their present form, can best be described as distantly related. This has, in fact, led some investigators to question the common origin of these two molecules (Argos, 1976; Humbel and Rinderknecht, 1977). However, in a recent discussion of the problems of comparing distantly related sequences, Doolittle (1981) examined a large number of protein molecules that bear the same kind of distant relationship, some with similar functional properties and others with totally distinct actions, and established reasonable, if not rigorous, criteria for ascertaining "confidence" in a proposed relationship. Both the comparison of nerve growth factor and relaxin (see below) with insulin (proinsulin) were placed in the acceptable category. Although further evidence, such as may be provided by the determination of the three-dimensional structure of NGF (or relaxin) (Gunning and Blundell, 1981) or the genomic sequences of these molecules, may extend or detract from the hypothesis of a common ancestry, the value of the original proposal (Frazier *et al.*, 1972), i.e., establishing the hormonal character of NGF through its relationship to an established hormone, has already proved its worth many times over.

One additional line of support for the proposed relationship of NGF to insulin has been provided by the identification of three other substances with the same apparent ancestry. Two of these, insulin-like growth factors I and II (IGF I and II), were first recognized as substances in human blood that were insulin-like in their activity but unreactive with antibodies against the pancreatic hormone. This gave rise to the designation "nonsuppressible insulin-like activity" (NSILA). Subsequently, it was shown to occur in two principal forms, one associated with a high-molecular-weight entity (NSILAp) and one, a small soluble entity, referred to as NSILAs (Jakob *et al.*, 1968). Rinderknecht and Humbel (1976a) established that the NSILAs component could be subdivided into two activities, referred to originally as NSILA I and II, and, following complete sequence analysis (Rinderknecht and Humbel, 1978b,c), later renamed with their present designation. The basis for the new names was the pronounced insulin-like character of the primary structure which revealed that the two IGF molecules also contained the easily recognizable B and A domains of insulin, separated by a C-bridge region, with a small C-terminal extension. The IGF's differed from proinsulin in the same manner as NGF, i.e., the C-bridge region is not removed by limited proteolysis. However, the extent of amino acid sequence homology in the B and A chain regions was considerably greater than that found in NGF (approximately 50%) and the disulfide bonding pattern of insulin was totally conserved in both these molecules.

The other insulin-like growth factor recently identified is the porcine hormone, relaxin. Its discovery actually antedates that of the other insulin-like growth factors (NGF and IGF I and II), being first observed by Hisaw (1926) only a few years after the discovery of insulin itself. However, its characterization developed somewhat more slowly than other members of the subset and the sequence was only determined in 1977, following the preparation of pure material by Sherwood and O'Byrne (1974) (James *et al.*, 1977; Schwabe and McDonald, 1977). In one way, relaxin is more similar to insulin than the other factors in that it contains two polypeptide chains quite analogous in size to those found in vertebrate insulins and suggesting a precursor product relationship of the type characterizing proinsulin and insulin. This has been recently confirmed from the DNA sequencing studies of Hudson *et al.* (1981), who have established that the C bridge of rat relaxin contains some 130 amino acid residues in contrast to the 30–35 residues characterizing higher vertebrate insulins. As with the IGFs, relaxin also contains the identical disulfide pairing pattern found in insulin, which is the single strongest indicator of the homology since the overall number of identities in the remainder of the two constituent polypeptides is quite low (albeit statistically significant).

There are a number of other insulin-like polypeptides that have been suggested to exist on the basis of functional or immunological criteria. Among the most notable of these are various somatomedin preparations, isolated from either human or rat sources, that interact with receptors for known insulin-like peptides. However, these may, in fact, also represent only species variations or preparations of already identified molecules. For example, the rat basic somatomedin, first described by Chochinov *et al.* (1977), has been recently shown to correspond closely to the sequence of human IGF I (Rubin *et al.*, 1982). In a similar fashion, multiplication stimulating activity, another rat preparation, has been recently shown to be nearly identical to human IGF II (five residues different) by Marquardt *et al.* (1981). Similarly, human somatomedin C appears very similar to IGF I (Svoboda *et al.*, 1980) although some structural discrepancies still require further examination. These remarks should not be construed, however, as suggesting that the insulin-related subset will be confined to the five identified members. It seems more than likely that other factors related ancestrally to the common precursor of this family will ultimately be discovered as studies continue.

2. Functional Relationships

Although the structural relatedness of the five members of the insulin-related subset seems well established, the functional distinctions, as have been noted previously, are much greater (Bradshaw and Niall, 1978; Bradshaw and Rubin, 1980). In fact, when considered at the physiological level, any similarities in function seem superficial at best. The action of insulin in regulating blood sugar and carbohydrate metabolism by interacting with muscle, liver, and adipocytes is well established. However, it should also be noted that insulin acts, in many cultured cell lines, as a growth factor. Whether this is a bona fide activity of insulin or simply results from interaction with the receptors for other insulin-like growth factors remains the subject of some speculation.

The other members of the insulin-related subset are clearly more involved in such processes. Insulin-like growth factors I and II have been designated somatomedins, i.e., the agents that are produced in response to the action of pituitary growth hormone on one or another cell types (most likely liver) and that directly interact with skeletal tissue (Daughaday *et al.*, 1972). Such activity is manifested in their principal bioassay, the incorporation of radioactive sulfate into proteoglycan following stimulation of cartilage cells. They also show a spectrum of insulin-like responses with the normal target cells of insulin but their role in regulating blood sugar has been largely discounted, apparently because their circulating forms, as complexes with higher molecular weight carrier proteins, prevent their interaction with the normal target cells of insulin.

The activity of relaxin, which has been described in detail (Schwabe *et al.*, 1978), is, at our present level of understanding, related to the preparation of the birth canal prior to the delivery of the fetus in selected vertebrates. In those animals producing the hormone, its synthesis appears to be restricted to the granulosa cells of the corpora lutea. A bolus release of the hormone just prior to parturition causes loosening of the pubic symphysis and dilation of the cervix, and perhaps regulates uterine contraction. However, it is possible that the synthesis of relaxin is not limited to the corpora lutea and its apparent presence in placenta and testes may be indicative of other roles for the hormone as well. These activities are not strictly those that might be associated with a growth factor and its inclusion in this category is more a result of its relationship to insulin and the other insulin-related substances than by the description of its biological function. However, this may be more a semantic distinction than a real one since the remodeling processes that it directs can certainly be viewed as growth (or regrowth).

Nerve growth factor, the last member of the subset, has quite a different role as well as spectrum of target tissues (Levi-Montalchini and Angeletti, 1968). Responsive cells appear to be derived from the neural crest with particular emphasis on the neuronal elements. Sympathetic neurons are sensitive to and have a requirement for NGF from early in development through to the mature state while sensory neurons of the dorsal root ganglia arc somewhat more proscribed in their response. Evidence has also accrued from recent studies that embryonic adrenal chromaffin cells may also be responsive to NGF as judged by effects on this tissue caused by intrauterine injections of anti-NGF (see Harper and Thoenen, 1981). Several established cell lines from neoplastic origins, such as pheochromocytoma, melanoma, or neuroblastoma cells, have varying degrees of response to NGF reflecting their relationship to their neural crest origins as well (Gospodarowicz, 1981). The spectrum of responses of these cells to NGF, which have been reviewed in detail by Levi-Montalcini and Angeletti (1968), Greene and Shooter (1980), Gospodarowicz (1981), and Harper and Thoenen (1981), include a variety of trophic responses reflected in increased anabolic metabolism of the cell and, in many cases, proliferation of neurites and the maintenance of cell viability.

Despite the broad range of responses encompassed by the actions of the individual members of the insulin-related subset, it is still reasonable to ask to what extent, at the molecular or cellular level, there is some commonality in their mechanism of action. To some degree, all these molecules show the spectrum of rapid and slow responses described for type 1 secondary hormones (see above) and, with the possible exception of relaxin, for which a *defined* target cell population has yet to be established, all have been shown to initiate their responses by interaction with cell surface receptors. Although, as described below, the molecular features of these receptors appear to be somewhat different, the types of activities triggered show a "relatedness" that could imply common mechanistic features. Perhaps the aspect that links these molecules most closely together is the singular lack of detailed understanding of the molecular events following the formation of the hormone receptor complex at the cell surface. It is clear that none of these substances elevates intracellular cyclic AMP in the way associated with primary hormones. At best, only a transient rise has been observed. In the case of insulin, there is some suggestion that a small polypeptide may be released from a membrane protein following insulin complexation that can act as a second messenger to induce at least some of the characteristic insulin responses (Larner *et al.*, 1979; Seals and Jarett, 1980; Seals and Czech, 1980, 1981). A similar potential second messenger for the other insulin-related growth factors has not, as yet, been described, although the formation of some such entity is certainly a likely possibility. Thoenen and his colleagues (Thoenen and Barde, 1980; Thoenen *et al.*, 1979) have, in fact, argued strongly for such a messenger for NGF, although evidence for its existence is singularly lacking. Indeed, resolution of this issue will be of interest in terms of understanding the evolutionary development of this family of substances and it will probably be of greater importance in elucidating the exact mechanism of action of not only the insulin-related subset, but also many other polypeptide growth factors.

III. NERVE GROWTH FACTOR AS A HORMONE

A. BIOSYNTHESIS

1. Origins

The physiologically relevant sites of synthesis of NGF have been an enigma since the earliest observations of its activity in the two sarcoma cell lines (S37 and 180) used in the initial studies of Levi-Montalcini and Hamburger (1951). The fact that one of these cell lines (S180) originated as an axillary carcinoma of the male mouse (Bradshaw and Young, 1976) curiously presaged the ultimate discovery of one of the richest sources of nerve growth factor, the adult male mouse submaxillary gland (Cohen, 1960). This observation resulted from the prior discovery that the venom of several land poisonous snakes was a far richer source of NGF (Cohen, 1959) through their serendipitous use as reagents by Cohen during the purification of the tumor NGF. With the discovery of the adult male mouse submaxillary gland source, it became the principal source of the agent for chemical and biological studies and, for the most part, has remained so. Much more recently, Harper and Thoenen (1980) noted high concentrations of nerve growth factor in the prostate of several, but not all, higher vertebrates and, as with the submaxillary gland, observed that it was also present in the exocrine fluid of that gland. Thus, saliva and seminal plasma, in analogy with the snake venoms, are also excellent sources of the hormone. However, several lines of evidence suggest that all these sources represent exocrine functions, as yet undefined, for NGF. As recounted by Harper and Thoenen (1981), the NGF in these cells is neither released into the circulation as would be expected for an endocrine role nor does it find its way to any innervating neurons of the parent organ. It is presently quite unclear what the exocrine function of NGF may be in any of these tissues although it almost certainly has no relationship to any function in the nervous system.

The sites of synthesis of nerve growth factor which result in its delivery to responsive target neurons of the sympathetic and sensory nervous systems have remained considerably more elusive to identify. A wide variety of primary or established cells in culture manufacture small but detectable amounts of NGF and may well reflect *in vivo* sites of synthesis (Bradshaw and Young, 1976). However, rigorous evidence that this is the case is, unfortunately, lacking even though there are very sensitive assays for NGF.

Despite this limitation, there are several lines of indirect evidence that persuasively argue for such a model of NGF biosynthesis. Various immunological experiments have demonstrated that interruption of the flow of

NGF to responsive neurons results ultimately in degeneration and death. At the same time, artificial depots of NGF cause neurons to grow to and be maintained by this exogenous source and interruption of the flow of NGF by axotomy results ultimately in neuronal death, a condition that can be reversed by the addition of exogenous NGF at the point of interruption (see Harper and Thoenen, 1981). Direct evidence for the production of nerve growth factor by innervated organs may well have to await the construction of appropriate nucleic acid probes to determine the presence of messenger RNA for the hormone.

2. Chemistry

As a result of the fact that sufficient material from any of the postulated endocrine sources of nerve growth factor has not been obtained, knowledge of the chemistry of NGF is totally dependent on studies of material derived from the exocrine sources. Nerve growth factor from male mouse submaxillary gland has been the principal object of such studies. However, because the hormonally active subunit of this complex has provided the antigen for eliciting most antibodies used in immunological deprivation experiments, it is likely that at least this portion of the mouse submaxillary NGF complex is similar or identical to that produced by the endocrine (or endogenous) sources.

Mouse NGF, as isolated either from tissue or saliva, is composed of three types of polypeptide chains. The complete polypeptide sequence of two of these, i.e., β (Angeletti and Bradshaw, 1971) and γ (Thomas *et al.*, 1981b), have been determined. Studies on the elucidation of both the amino acid and nucleic acid (cDNA) sequences of the third subunit, α, are in progress (P. J. Isackson, R. James, D. Hopson, and R. A. Bradshaw, unpublished observations). Two copies of each of these polypeptides are assembled by noncovalent interactions to form the 7 S complex (indicating the sedimentation coefficient), the mature form of the hormone (Varon *et al.*, 1967). Zinc ions (probably two) are also found in the complex and apparently serve a stabilizing role (Pattison and Dunn, 1975). Ethylenediaminetetraacetic acid (EDTA) has the effect of destabilizing the complex at higher concentrations and the subunits can be readily dissociated above pH 8.0 or below pH 5.0. Silverman (1976) established that it was the α–β interactions that were primarily unstable at alkaline pH and the β–γ interactions that were unstable at lower pH. This study also showed that the α and γ subunits did not interact in a significant fashion in the absence of β polypeptides.

The chemistry of the α subunit is the least well understood of the three constituent polypeptides. Its native molecular weight is approximately

26,000, which may include some carbohydrate moieties (D. Hopson and R. A. Bradshaw, unpublished observations). It appears to occur mainly, if not exclusively, as a two-chain polypeptide unit, associated by disulfide bridges, with the fragments possessing molecular weights of 16,000 and 9000. At least three electrophoretic subforms have been detected which may be due to carbohydrate, deamidation, or further proteolysis (such as found with the γ subunit) that are not detected by molecular-weight measurements (Server and Shooter, 1977).

The amino acid sequence of the γ subunit has been determined by Thomas *et al.* (1981b). These studies revealed that the native protein consists of either two or three polypeptide chains associated by disulfide bonds. Although not firmly established, it is highly likely that the protein is synthesized as a single polypeptide chain, probably in a precursor form, that is processed to the mature protein which subsequently undergoes the further limited proteolysis, either *in situ* or during isolation, to produce the species isolated. Assuming that this is correct, the native protein consists of 233 amino acids with five intrachain disulfides. The first fragment consists of residues 1–83. A single glycosylated residue occurs at position 78 with a side chain composed largely of mannose and N-acetylglucosamine. The structure of the carbohydrate is presently under investigation (J. U. Baenziger, K. A. Thomas, and R. A. Bradshaw, unpublished experiments). In approximately 50% of the molecules, the remainder of the sequence is found in a single fragment, and in the other half this fragment is further subdivided into two smaller fragments comprising residues 84–136 and 137–233.

It has been appreciated for some time that the γ subunit is composed of multiple electrophoretic species, which can only partially be explained by the two internal cleavage sites (Server and Shooter, 1977). As a part of the sequence investigation, it was demonstrated (Thomas *et al.*, 1981a) that further electrophoretic heterogeneity results from an exopeptidase-like action on the carboxyl-terminal lysine and arginine residues of the first two fragments (1–83 and 84–136). This gives rise to six potential subspecies, two of which would be expected to have the same mobility, thus accounting for the five bands seen. Preliminary evidence suggests that the carbohydrate portion does not contribute to the electrophoretic heterogeneity.

From the early studies of Greene *et al.* (1969), it has been appreciated that the γ subunit is an enzyme with arginine esteropeptidase activity. As suggested by these workers and confirmed by Silverman (1976), this enzyme is a member of the well-established serine protease family and several features of the sequence confirm its relationship to molecules of that class. The amino-terminal Ile-Val-Gly-Gly sequence, the histidine at position 41 adjacent to the cystine loop and the serine residue (184), and the surrounding

sequence are all highly characteristic of such enzymes. The arginine specificity has also been associated with the proposed role of γ subunit as a
processing enzyme for precursors of the β subunit. Moore *et al.* (1974)
have established that removal of the C-terminal arginine residue of the β
subunit (see below) disrupts the interaction of the β and γ polypeptides,
an observation confirmed by Silverman (1976).

The β subunit of the 7 S complex has occupied the majority of the
attention in studies on the chemistry of this molecule. It contains the
insulin-like polypeptide sequences described in an earlier section and is
solely responsible for the activities observed with responsive peripheral
neurons. In fact, if the 7 S complex is covalently cross-linked to prevent
dissociation, no activity is observed (Stach and Shooter, 1980). The amino
acid sequence of the β subunit was first determined by Angeletti and
Bradshaw (1971) on preparations designated 2.5 S (Bocchini and Angeletti,
1969). These differ from preparations of β subunit isolated from the homogeneous complex in that they are more proteolyzed, presumably as a
result of exposing the subunit to contaminating proteases. Two principal
modifications can affect the 2.5 S preparation. One is the removal of the
C-terminal octapeptide by an enzyme identified as a kallikrein-like molecule,
and the other is the removal of the C-terminal arginine, presumably by a
carboxypeptidase B-like enzyme; both are endogenous to the glands (Bothwell
et al., 1979; Moore *et al.*, 1974). Neither modification has any affect on
the biological or immunological activity. The complete amino acid sequence
of the β subunit contains, in its longest form, 118 amino acids, and as a
result of the proteolysis, in its shortest form, 109 amino acids (Thomas and
Bradshaw, 1980). Several attempts to prepare shortened versions of nerve
growth factor with retention of activity have been made (Bradshaw *et al.*,
1977), but only one was reported to be successful (Mercanti *et al.*, 1977).
In that report it was suggested that a tryptic fragment surrounding the one
conserved disulfide bond in the NGF sequence contained biological activity
10^2 more potent on a molar basis than the native molecule. This curious
observation has not been confirmed.

Chemical modification studies on the β subunit have not been particularly
productive in predicting receptor binding sites on the NGF molecule.
Modification of two of the three tryptophan residues (positions 21 and 99)
were reported to lead to an inactivation of the molecule by Frazier *et al.*
(1973a). Cohen *et al.* (1980) reported that modification of the first tryptophan
residue (position 21) actually resulted in greater inactivation than was detected by Frazier *et al.* (1973a). Both lysine and arginine residues seem
particularly unsusceptible in terms of inactivation (Silverman, 1976) and
Levi *et al.* (1980) have reported a heavily modified derivative of NGF,

involving carboxyl groups, which is also fully active. The single methionine residue occurring at position 9 can be cleaved by cyanogen bromide to produce a fully active NGF molecule (Angeletti *et al.*, 1973) and modification of the two tyrosine residues either by iodination (Herrup and Shooter, 1973) or by nitration (Frazier *et al.*, 1973a) does not result in inactivation. At present, little is known about the topography of the NGF molecule in terms of the location of receptor binding residues. Hopefully, when the crystal structure of the β subunit of nerve growth factor is complete (J. Gunning and T. Blundell, unpublished experiments), it will provide some further insight into this interesting area of NGF chemistry.

3. Regulation of Synthesis

Considerable uncertainty remains concerning the biosynthesis of NGF. In the submaxillary gland, it appears that all three subunits are synthesized as the products of separate genes. Although not yet established, it is presumed that the γ subunit, in analogy to other serine proteases, will be synthesized minimally as a slightly larger precursor with at least one peptide removed from the amino terminus for activation. Since serine proteases (of the trypsin family) exhibit the common feature that the newly formed α-amino group forms a salt link with the aspartic acid residue adjacent to the active site serine, as a fundamental requirement for activity, it seems unlikely that the γ subunit will be materially different in this regard. Also, in analogy with other serine proteases made for export, it seems probable that a leader sequence will also precede the zymogen activation peptide. A similar situation for the α subunit seems likely, but evidence in support of this contention is, at present, lacking. Preliminary results suggesting that α is made as a larger precursor molecule have been obtained (I. Jeng and R. A. Bradshaw, unpublished observations) but remain to be confirmed.

Berger and Shooter (1978), in studies using tissue slices, have identified a precursor for the β subunit (proβ) of MW 22,000–23,000. They demonstrated that this entity contained the amino acid sequence of the mature β subunit by examining ^{35}S-labeled tryptic peptides of the precursor molecule. Proβ could be processed not only by the γ subunit but also by trypsin and the arginine esteropeptidase subunit of high-molecular-weight EGF. Although this conversion lacks specificity as performed *in vitro*, it appears, nonetheless, to at least be consistent with the supposition that the γ subunit is a processing enzyme for proβ. However, it should be emphasized that the proβ molecule identified may not represent the largest gene product since these studies were not performed using a cell-free protein synthesis system. In fact, it is possible that NGF is synthesized as part of a much larger species which may be processed by one or more of the many proteolytic enzymes known to be present in the mouse submaxillary gland into several different biological activities.

Little is also known concerning the agents that regulate the synthesis either in the submaxillary glands or in the endogeneous sites. It has been known for some time that testosterone markedly affects the production of NGF in the submaxillary gland (and presumably the prostate) since the large increases in the male of the species occur relative to puberty and can be mimicked in castrated males or females by exogenous testosterone injection (Caramia *et al.*, 1962; Levi-Montalcini and Angeletti, 1964; Ishii and Shooter, 1975). However, it is also possible that the synthesis is affected by a complex series of endocrine interactions. In any event, it is unlikely that testosterone plays any significant role in the production of nerve growth factor in other sites since there are no distinguishable sex differences with respect to neuronal dependence on NGF in the peripheral nervous system. There is also no evidence, as yet, to suggest that the control of NGF synthesis is related in any way to a potential releasing factor that would presumably be made by peripheral neurons, as has characterized many other endocrine systems. However, it is well known that these neurons can stimulate their target cells with trophic substances and that this interaction is fundamental for the development of these tissues. One or more of these molecules may well play a role in directing the synthesis and release of NGF.

B. Delivery to Target Cells

Unlike classical hormone systems, the available evidence mitigates against the fact that NGF is transported from its endogenous sites of synthesis to responsive neurons by systemic transport. Although there are many reports extant that the circulating levels of nerve growth factor are significant and are, in fact, in the case of the mouse, affected by removal of the salivary glands, it now appears that these measurements were largely in error (Thoenen and Barde, 1980). Suda *et al.* (1978) have established by two-site radioimmunoassay that the levels of NGF in rat and mouse serum are less than 5 ng/ml and Ishii and Shooter (1975) have shown that iodinated NGF, when injected intravenously, is rapidly cleared from the bloodstream. These results are inconsistent with systemic transport being the main vehicle for delivery of NGF to target neurons. The alternative hypothesis, that NGF is delivered from synthesis sites to target cells by diffusion (Dodson *et al.*, 1980), seems considerably more likely to be correct.

C. Interaction with Target Cells

1. Cell Surface Receptors

The initial demonstration that nerve growth factor was a substance which initiated its biological responses by interaction with a cell surface receptor grew directly from the observation concerning the relationship of insulin with NGF (Frazier *et al.*, 1972). It should be noted, however, that the putative hormonal status of NGF and the possibilities of cell surface receptors had been suggested earlier. One of the first observations pointing to the existence of specific, high-affinity cell surface receptors for NGF was the demonstration by Frazier *et al.* (1973b) that nerve growth factor covalently attached to Sepharose particles was capable of inducing neurite formation. In these studies, it was observed that responsive neurons clustered around and closely interacted with the modified beads, indicating that cells had the capacity to recognize the immobilized hormone.

The initial studies to characterize NGF receptors on responsive neurons utilized hormone specifically labeled with ^{125}I. Three independent studies (Herrup and Shooter, 1973; Banerjee *et al.*, 1973; Frazier *et al.*, 1974), using equilibrium and kinetic measurements, demonstrated the presence of high-affinity binding sites characterized by parameters consistent with the concentration dependence of biological activity. The study of Frazier *et al.* (1974) differed from the other two in that these workers reported that binding was not saturable at the concentrations of ligand employed and that Scatchard analyses of these data revealed two classes of binding sites with apparent high ($\sim 10^{10}$) and low ($\sim 10^6$) binding constants. Using the enhancement of dissociation paradigm developed by DeMeyts (1976) for insulin, they suggested that the curvilinear Scatchard plots resulted from negatively cooperative interactions that were dependent on the degree of receptor occupancy. Sutter *et al.* (1979) reexamined this phenomenon using a higher specific activity NGF tracer and concluded the data were more consistent with two classes of binding sites without negative cooperativity. It should be noted that the two classes of sites defined in these studies were of higher affinity (10^{11} and 10^9) than the apparent low-affinity binding sites reported by Frazier *et al.* (1974). In a more recent study, Tait *et al.* (1981) also reexamined the question of two sites versus negative cooperativity and in agreement with Sutter *et al.* (1979) concluded that the binding data could not be interpreted in terms of a strictly negatively cooperative model. However, they presented evidence that argued against a simple two-site model as well and concluded that the interaction of NGF, as measured by binding experiments, could not be described by either model probably because of the dynamic state of the receptor for NGF. In particular, the tendency of the receptors to form higher aggregates prior to and during interaction with the ligand may well be responsible for the deviations that invalidate the underlying assumptions on which the experiments are based.

Banerjee *et al.* (1976) first reported that the NGF receptor could be solubilized through the use of nonionic detergents such as Triton X-100. Solubilization was demonstrated using a soluble receptor assay where unbound ligand was separated from complexed ligand by use of the specific precipitant polyethylene glycol 6000. Costrini and Bradshaw (1979), using a similar assay, demonstrated that the receptor from this tissue possessed a Stokes radius of approximately 70 Å by means of calibrated gel filtration columns. In further studies (Costrini *et al.*, 1979), this value was found to correspond to a molecular weight of 135,000 ± 15,000. These experiments involved the determination of the sedimentation coefficient by sucrose density gradient centrifugation and the partial specific volume of the complex in H_2O and D_2O. The determined molecular weight was, in fact, considerably lower than expected from the Stokes radius, which, if the molecule had been spherical, should have been in excess of 300,000. In fact, the insulin receptor from a number of tissues possesses a molecular weight in excess of 350,000 but with a similar Stokes radius to that of the NGF receptor (Jacobs and Cuatrecasas, 1981). These findings are consistent with the measured f/f_0 of 1.8, indicating that the binding entity solubilized in these experiments is a largely asymmetrical molecule.

The molecular weight determined by hydrodynamic measurements (Costrini *et al.*, 1979) was confirmed with experiments using SDS gel electrophoresis and autoradiography of [^{125}I]NGF covalently cross-linked to the receptor (Massague *et al.*, 1981b). The photoaffinity cross-linking reagent, N-hydroxysuccinimidyl-*p*-azidobenzoate (HSAB), was utilized in a protocol in which [^{125}I]NGF was first complexed to its receptor and then the HSAB reagent added. The short dark reaction followed by light activation of the azido group to form the photoreactive nitrene allowed random modification of lysines in either the ligand or the receptor with insertion of the nitrene into the opposite half of the complex. Since protocols in which HSAB was reacted with [^{125}I]NGF prior to complex formation were ineffective in producing cross-links, it is likely that the productive reactions involved modification of lysine residues in the receptor rather than in NGF itself.

The results of these experiments demonstrated the presence of two receptor species with apparent molecular weights of 143,000 and 112,000, respectively. The amounts of these two forms varied with experimental conditions and Cleveland gel analysis (Cleveland *et al.*, 1977) using either *Staphylococcus aureus* V8 protease or α-chymotrypsin showed a fragmentation pattern consistent with the hypothesis that the lower molecular weight form was derived from the higher one by limited proteolysis. A similar modification of one of the insulin receptor subunits has also been observed (Massague *et al.*, 1981c). The formation of the covalent complex was specific for the NGF ligand and occurred only in tissues responsive to the hormone. Small reductions in molecular weight were observed on the SDS gels when reducing agents were omitted from the electrophoresis sample, suggesting the presence of intra- but not interchain disulfide bonds.

Both the size and the oligomeric structure (absence of subunits) of the NGF receptor, as identified in these experiments, distinguishes it from those reported for the insulin receptor. It is now widely held that this latter recognitive entity as isolated from a variety of insulin-sensitive tissues is an oligomeric structure composed of two different types of polypeptide chains, designated α and β (Jacobs and Cuatrecasas, 1981). Two editions occur in each receptor molecule which are linked covalently by disulfide bonds. The larger subunit, α, has a molecular weight of around 125,000, while the smaller, β, ~90,000. A β chain of only half the size (MW 49,000) is formed by limited proteolysis (Massague *et al.*, 1981c). The insulin-like growth factors appear to have two receptor types. The IGF I receptor closely resembles the structure described for the insulin receptor whereas the IGF II receptor, as judged by experiments using multiplication stimulating activity, the rat version of human IGF II (Marquadt *et al.*, 1981), represents a single polypeptide chain of molecular weight 255,000 (Massague *et al.*, 1981a). There is no molecular characterization of the receptor for the last member of the insulin-related subset, relaxin. A comparison of the properties of the receptors for insulin and the insulin-like growth factors with that of NGF suggests that there is no clear correlation. It may be that structural analyses of the receptor molecules will reveal homologies that are masked by the disparate molecular weights but it may also turn out that the receptors for the various insulin-related growth factors have, in fact, evolved in an independent fashion. As such it would represent a special case of convergent evolution. Should this latter concept prove to be correct, it will have a marked effect on the commonly held views on parallel evolution of ligand and receptor systems.

2. Internalization

In the last several years, it has become a widely recognized feature of many hormone systems that both the ligand and the receptor are internalized through receptor-mediated endocytosis. This phenomenon, which is not limited to hormones and growth factors (Neville and Chang, 1978), appears to be a common feature of macromolecular ligands that bind tightly to the cell surface through a specific receptor-like interaction and retain that position for sufficient time to allow the formation of receptor clusters that lead to endocytotic vesicles. This process is closely associated with "coated pits," which are indentations on the cell surface caused by polymerization of the intracellular protein, clathrin (Goldstein *et al.*, 1979). It follows that the process occurs with any receptor that is able to interact with the clathrin molecule.

Although the involvement of coated pits in the internalization of nerve growth factor has not been directly established (Levi *et al.*, 1980), NGF was among the first hormones observed to exhibit this behavior. This was due in part to the nature of its target cells, i.e., responsive neurons, because the characteristic axonal projections afforded the opportunity for the introduction of labeled ligand at a position distant from the cell body. Nerve growth factor so introduced was bound by receptors in the presynaptic membranes and internalization could be demonstrated by excision of the cell bodies at an appropriate later time without the complications of non-specifically bound tracer, because the internalized NGF was transferred to the cell bodies by retrograde axonal transport (Hendry *et al.*, 1974). The characteristics of retrograde axonal transport of NGF have been studied in great detail by Hendry, Thoenen, and their colleagues (see Thoenen and Barde, 1980; Hendry, 1980) who have shown it to be a process highly specific for responsive neurons that depends upon the presence of NGF receptors. It appears to be specific for neurons responsive to NGF with one possible exception, i.e., a class of neurons present in ciliary ganglia which are cholinergic in character (Max *et al.*, 1978). The significance of the transport by these neurons is unknown although they may, in fact, represent a heretofore unrecognized class of NGF-responsive cells.

The physiological significance of retrogradely transported NGF still remains a controversial issue. Thoenen and his colleagues (see Thoenen and Barde, 1980) have provided considerable indirect evidence in support of the action of internalized NGF in terms of induction of specific enzymes and general trophic stimulation. However, despite a temporal correlation between the arrival of NGF in the cell body and the induction processes, this model cannot really be distinguished from one in which a second messenger, generated at the presynaptic membrane, also arrives at the cell body at the same time and is responsible for the stimulation. Dissecting these two possible mechanisms is hampered by the fact that the amount of NGF transported is certainly in excess of what is required for the biological responses and that the appearance of large amounts of this material in the lysosomes, which would suggest internalization is solely for degradation, may simply reflect the saturation of the information transferring system. That is to say, the large excess of material directed to the lysosomes may mask the pathway associated with gene modulation.

Arguing in favor of internalization being part of the mechanism is the presence of intracellular receptors (binding sites) reported to be associated with the nucleus in both sensory neurons (Andres *et al.*, 1977) and pheochromocytoma cells (PC12) (Yankner and Shooter, 1979). In both cases, these receptors are distinguished from those present in the plasma membrane by their intractability to solubilization by nonionic detergents. Both represent specific, high-affinity binding molecules. In the PC12 cells, Yankner and Shooter (1979) established that the appearance of nuclear receptors, as a result of exposure of the cells to exogenous NGF, was in direct proportion to the decrease in cell surface receptors. This decrease, referred to in many endocrine systems as "down regulation," would appear to imply a transfer of the cell membrane receptors to the nucleus as a result of the receptor-mediated endocytosis process. It was established in both studies that the nuclear binding elements were not a result of the contamination of plasma membranes which could be distinguished easily on the basis of solubility in nonionic detergents. However, to date, it has not been established that the nuclear receptors are derived from receptors originally found on the cell surface or that they are in any way involved in the expression of the hormones.

3. Possible Mechanisms of Action

Although the mechanism of action of NGF clearly remains to be determined, the available information, as described above, suggests that the action of NGF on responsive cells may be a biphasic process. Clearly the initial interaction of NGF with its target cells results in the formation of a specific complex with a receptor molecule intrinsically bound in the surface membrane. This receptor, which can be readily solubilized in nonionic detergents and has an apparent molecular weight of $\sim$130,000, signals the onset of the trophic responses of NGF which are manifested in increases in anabolic metabolism, changes in ion fluxes, and perhaps the initiation of neurite outgrowth. Whether this results from the production of a second messenger, as yet unidentified, or can simply be explained by changes in membrane structure that allow specific alterations in permeability of the plasma membrane is not yet known. It is clear that the formation of this complex is sufficient to signal the onset of receptor-mediated endocytosis. This energy-dependent process apparently proceeds by the formation of clusters that lead to larger aggregates, ultimately resulting in the formation of endocytotic vesicles. Whether this vesicle is formed at the cell membrane of embryonic neurons or at the presynaptic membrane of mature cells, it eventually finds its way to the interior of the cells, presumably through the aid of cytoskeletal elements, in a similar fashion. Its fate when it reaches this location is not completely appreciated. Clearly large amounts of these vesicles ultimately fuse with lysosomes, resulting in the degradation of both the ligand and the receptor molecule. This process may be a prerequisite for the further propagation of the NGF response, perhaps by the release of a fragment from either of the two molecules which would then act as a second messenger. Alternatively, a select portion of the internalized vesicles may enjoy a separate fate, i.e., fusion with other intracellular organelles, in particular the nucleus, to direct the long-term effects in a different manner. This possibility would explain the presence of nuclear receptors in both sensory neurons and PC12 cells. However, it should be noted that either of the two molecules could be important for the subsequent gene regulation. The ligand itself might be introduced into the nucleus to interact specifically with portions of the chromatin material to effect the modulations, a view supported by the observation that some 30% of the retrogradely transported NGF can be detected in the nuclear fraction in subcellular fractionation experiments (Andres *et al.*, 1977). However, Thoenen and his colleagues (Schwab, 1977; Schwab and Thoenen, 1977) have been unable to detect, by sensitive methods, the presence of the ligand in the nuclear fraction and they correctly point out that subcellular fractionation might well induce an artifactual redistribution of $[^{125}I]$NGF during the process of tissue disruption. The other, and perhaps more likely, possibility is that the receptor molecule itself possesses the capacity to induce the changes in gene expression, perhaps acting as a generator of a second messenger once located in juxtaposition to the nuclear compartment. As with the receptor for epidermal growth factor (Carpenter *et al.*, 1979), it might act as a kinase to phosphorylate specific proteins in the nuclear compartment. Observations by Yu *et al.* (1978) and Halegoua and Patrick (1980) that several proteins are phosphorylated as a result of NGF activity on PC12 cells would be entirely consistent with such a model. It should be pointed out, however, that the requisite (kinase) activity for the NGF receptor has not yet been identified.

The internalization of NGF and its receptor may also simply be a degradation mechanism and perhaps a means for desensitizing the neurons by decreasing the number of cell surface receptors. A mechanism in which a second messenger is produced at the plasma membrane which must in turn induce the formation of a new protein molecule before the long-term effects are seen could explain the need for the long-term association of the ligand with the plasma membrane. Since molecules that are associated with the plasma membrane in this fashion ultimately are cleared by receptor-mediated endocytosis, as opposed to an extracellular mode of degradation, such a model would explain the occurrence of the internalization.

IV. CONCLUDING REMARKS

Nerve growth factor is a member of a larger set of polypeptide factors whose hormone-like activity is mainly directed toward maintenance of viability as well as growth and development of tissues in a wide variety of cell types. It is entirely possible that all cells will require one or more such growth factors for their proper development and maintenance. These entities interact with responsive cells in a fashion entirely analogous to many "classical" hormones, with the processes subsequently triggered being analogous as well. Therefore, an understanding of the mechanism of action of substances like NGF will be of pronounced importance in the elucidation of the mechanism of action of other hormones such as insulin, growth hormone, and prolactin. While each individual system will undoubtedly show unique aspects, it seems unlikely, based on our developing appreciation of common underlying themes in natural systems, that there will not be many common features as well. Although this increases the complexity of endocrine systems and their various interactions, it also serves to increase the spectrum of findings that can be applied to their overall understanding.

ACKNOWLEDGMENTS

Studies from the author's laboratory were supported by USPHS research grant NS 10229. The author is indebted to Ms. Solveig Storvick-Pollei and Mrs. Sophie Silverman for their assistance in the preparation of this manuscript.

REFERENCES

Andres, R. Y., Jeng, I., and Bradshaw, R. A. (1977). *Proc. Natl. Acad. Sci. U.S.A.* **74**, 2785–2789.
Angeletti, R. H., and Bradshaw, R. A. (1971). *Proc. Natl. Acad. Sci. U.S.A.* **68**, 2417–2420.
Angeletti, R. H., Hermodsen, M. A., and Bradshaw, R. A. (1973). *Biochemistry* **12**, 100–115.
Argos, P. (1976). *Biochem. Biophys. Res. Commun.* **70**, 805–811.
Banerjee, S. P., Synder, S. H., Cuatrecasas, P., and Greene, L. (1973). *Proc. Natl. Acad. Sci. U.S.A.* **70**, 2519–2523.
Banerjee, S. P., Cuatrecasas, P., and Synder, S. H. (1976). *J. Biol. Chem.* **251**, 5680–5685.
Berger, E. A., and Shooter, E. M. (1978). *J. Biol. Chem.* **253**, 804–810.
Bocchini, V., and Angeletti, P. U. (1969). *Proc. Natl. Acad. Sci. U.S.A.* **64**, 787–794.
Bothwell, M. A., Wilson, W. H., and Shooter, E. M. (1979). *J. Biol. Chem.* **254**, 7287–7294.
Bradshaw, R. A., and Niall, H. D. (1978). *Trends Biochem. Sci. (Pers. Ed.)* **3**, 274–278.
Bradshaw, R. A., and Rubin, J. S. (1980). *J. Supramol. Struct.* **14**, 183–199.
Bradshaw, R. A., and Young, M. (1976). *Biochem. Pharmacol.* **25**, 1445–1449.

Bradshaw, R. A., Jeng, I., Andres, R. Y., Pulliam, M. W., Silverman, R. E., Rubin, J., and Jacobs, J. W. (1977). *Endocrinology (Amsterdam)* **2**, 206–212.

Caramia, F., Angeletti, P. U., and Levi-Montalcini, R. (1962). *Endocrinology (Baltimore)* **70**, 915–922.

Carpenter, G., King, L., and Cohen, S. (1979). *J. Biol. Chem.* **254**, 4884–4891.

Chochinov, R. H., Mariz, I. K., and Daughaday, W. H. (1977). *Endocrinology (Baltimore)* **100**, 549–556.

Cleveland, D. W., Fisher, S. G., Kirshner, M. E., and Laemmli, U. K. (1977). *J. Biol. Chem.* **252**, 1102–1106.

Cohen, P., Sutter, A., Landreth, G., Zimmerman, A., and Shooter, E. M. (1980). *J. Biol. Chem.* **225**, 2949–2954.

Cohen, S. (1959). *J. Biol. Chem.* **234**, 1129–1137.

Cohen, S. (1960). *Proc. Natl. Acad. Sci. U.S.A.* **46**, 302–311.

Costrini, N. V., and Bradshaw, R. A. (1979). *Proc. Natl. Acad. Sci. U.S.A.* **76**, 3243–3245.

Costrini, N. V., Kogan, M., Kukreja, K., and Bradshaw, R. A. (1979). *J. Biol. Chem.* **254**, 11242–11246.

Daughaday, W. H., Hall, K., Raben, M. S., Salmon, W. D., Jr., Van Den Brande, J. L., and Van Wyk, J. J. (1972). *Nature (London)* **235**, 107.

DeMeyts, P. (1976). *J. Supramol. Struct.* **4**, 241–258.

Dodson, G. G., Isaacs, N., Bradshaw, R. A., and Niall, H. D. (1980). *In* "Insulin: Chemistry, Structure and Function of Insulin and Related Hormones" (D. Brandenburg and A. Wollmer, eds.), pp. 695–701. Walter de Gruyter, Berlin.

Doolittle, R. F. (1981). *Science* **214**, 149–159.

Frazier, W. A., Angeletti, R. H., and Bradshaw, R. A. (1972). *Science* **176**, 482–488.

Frazier, W. A., Angeletti, R. A. H., Sherman, R., and Bradshaw, R. A. (1973a). *Biochemistry* **12**, 3281–3293.

Frazier, W. A., Boyd, L. F., and Bradshaw, R. A. (1973b). *Proc. Natl. Acad. Sci. U.S.A.* **70**, 2931–2935.

Frazier, W. A., Boyd, L. F., and Bradshaw, R. A. (1974). *J. Biol. Chem.* **249**, 5513–5519.

Goldstein, J. L., Anderson, R. G. W., and Brown, M. S. (1979). *Nature (London)* **279**, 679–685.

Gospodarowicz, D. (1981). *Annu. Rev. Physiol.* **43**, 251–263.

Gospodarowicz, D., and Moran, J. S. (1976). *Annu. Rev. Biochem.* **45**, 531–558.

Greene, L. A., and Shooter, E. M. (1980). *Annu. Rev. Neurosci.* **3**, 353–402.

Greene, L. A., Shooter, E. M., and Varon, S. (1969). *Biochemistry* **8**, 3735–3741.

Gunning, J., and Blundell, T. (1981). *In* "The Peptides" (E. Gross and J. Meienhofer, eds.), Vol. 4, pp. 54–84. Academic Press, New York.

Halengoua, S., and Patrick, J. (1980). *Cell* **22**, 571–581.

Harper, G. P., and Thoenen, H. (1980). *J. Neurochem.* **77**, 391–402.

Harper, G. P., and Thoenen, H. (1981). *Annu. Rev. Pharmacol. Toxicol.* **21**, 205–229.

Hendry, I. A. (1980). *In* "Proteins of the Nervous System" (R. A. Bradshaw and D. M. Schneider, eds.), pp. 183–211. Raven, New York.

Hendry, I. A., Stockel, K., Thoenen, H., and Iverson, L. L. (1974). *Brain Res.* **68**, 103–121.

Herrup, K., and Shooter, E. M. (1973). *Proc. Natl. Acad. Sci. U.S.A.* **70**, 3884–3888.

Hisaw, F. L. (1926). *Proc. Soc. Exp. Biol. Med.* **23**, 661–663.

Hudson, P., Haley, J., Cronk, M., Shine, J., and Niall, H. (1981). *Nature (London)* **291**, 127–131.

Humbel, R. E., and Rinderknecht, E. (1977). *Growth Factors* **48**, 55–58.

Ishii, D. N., and Shooter, E. M. (1975). *J. Neurochem.* **25**, 843–851.

Jacobs, S., and Cuatrecasas, P. (1981). *Endocr. Rev.* **2**, 251–263.
Jakobs, A., Hauri, Ch., and Froesch, E. R. (1968) *J. Clin. Invest* **47**, 2678–2688.
James, R., Niall, H., Kwok, S., Bryant-Greenwood, G. (1977). *Nature* (London) **267**, 544–546.
Larner, J., Galasko, G., Cheng, K., DePaoli-Roach, A. A., Huang, L., Daggy, P., and Kellog, J. (1979). *Science* **206**, 1408–1410.
Levi, A., Schechter, Y., Neufield, E. J., and Schlessinger, J. (1980). *Proc. Natl. Acad. Sci. U.S.A.* **77**, 3469–3473.
Levi-Montalcini, R., and Angeletti, P. U. (1964). *In* "Salivary Glands and Their Secretion" (M. Sreebney and J. Meyer, eds.), pp. 129–141. Pergamon, Oxford.
Levi-Montalcini, R., and Angeletti, P. U. (1968). *Physiol. Rev.* **48**, 534–569.
Levi-Montalcini, R., and Booker, B. (1960). *Proc. Natl. Acad. Sci. U.S.A.* **46**, 384–391.
Levi-Montalcini, R., and Hamburger, V. (1951). *J. Exp. Zool.* **116**, 321–363.
Marquardt, H., Todaro, G. J., Henderson, L. E., and Oroszlan, S. (1981). *J. Biol. Chem.* **256**, 6859–6863.
Massague, J., Guillette, B. J., and Czech, M. P. (1981a). *J. Biol. Chem.* **256**, 2122–2125.
Massague, J., Guillette, B. J., Czech, M. P., Morgan, C. J., and Bradshaw, R. A. (1981b). *J. Biol. Chem.* **256**, 9419–9424.
Massague, J., Pilch, P. F., and Czech, M. P. (1981c). *J. Biol. Chem.* **256**, 3182–3190.
Max, J. R., Schwab, M., Dumas, M., and Thoenen, H. (1978). *Brain Res.* **159**, 411–415.
Mercanti, D., Butler, R., and Revoltella, R. (1977). *Biochim. Biophys. Acta* **496**, 412–419.
Moore, J. B., Mobley, W. C., and Shooter, E. M. (1974). *Biochemistry* **13**, 833–840.
Neville, D. M., and Chang, T.-M. (1978). *Curr. Top. Memb. Transp.* **10**, 65–150.
O'Malley, B. W., Schwartz, R. J., and Schrader, W. T. (1976). *J. Steroid Biochem.* **7**, 1151–1159.
Pattison, S. E., and Dunn, M. F. (1975). *Biochemistry* **14**, 2733–2739.
Rinderknecht, E., and Humbel, R. E. (1976a). *Proc. Natl. Acad. Sci. U.S.A.* **73**, 2365–2369.
Rinderknecht, E., and Humbel, R. E. (1978b). *J. Biol. Chem.* **253**, 2769–2776.
Rinderknecht, E., and Humbel, R. E. (1978c). *FEBS Lett.* **89**, 283–286.
Rubin, J. S., Mariz, I., Jacobs, J. W., Daughaday, W. H., and Bradshaw, R. A. (1982). *Endocrinology (Baltimore)* **110**, 734–740.
Schwab, M. E. (1977). *Brain Res.* **130**, 190–196.
Schwab, M. E., and Thoenen, H. (1977). *Brain Res.* **122**, 459–474.
Schwabe, C., and McDonald, J. K. (1977). *Science* **197**, 914–915.
Schwabe, C., Steinetz, B., Weiss, G., Segaloff, A., McDonald, J. K., O'Bryne, E., Hochman, J., Carriere, B., and Goldsmith, L. (1978). *Recent Progr. Horm. Res.* **34**, 123–211.
Seals, J. R., and Czech, M. P. (1980). *J. Biol. Chem.* **255**, 6529–6531.
Seals, J. R., and Czech, M. P. (1981). *J. Biol. Chem.* **256**, 2894–2899.
Seals, J. R., and Jarett, L. (1980). *Proc. Natl. Acad. Sci. U.S.A.* **77**, 77–81.
Server, A. C., and Shooter, E. M. (1977). *Adv. Protein Chem.* **31**, 339–409.
Sherwood, C. D., and O'Byrne, E. M. (1974). *Arch. Biochem. Biophys.* **160**, 185–196.
Silverman, R. E. (1976). Ph.D. Thesis, Washington Univ., St. Louis, Missouri.
Stach, R. W., and Shooter, E. M. (1980). *J. Neurochem.* **34**, 1499–1505.
Suda, K., Barde, Y.-A., and Thoenen, H. (1978). *Proc. Natl. Acad. Sci. U.S.A.* **75**, 4042–4046.
Sutter, A., Riopelle, R. J., Harris-Warrick, R. M., and Shooter, E. M. (1979). *J. Biol. Chem.* **254**, 5972–5982.
Svoboda, M. E., Van Wyk, J. J., Klapper, D. G., Fellows, R. E., Grissom, F. E., and Schlueter, R. J. (1980). *Biochemistry* **19**, 790–797.
Tait, J. F., Weinman, S. A., and Bradshaw, R. A. (1981). *J. Biol. Chem.* **256**, 11086–11092.

Thoenen, H., and Barde, Y.-A. (1980). *Physiol. Rev.* **60**, 1284–1335.

Thoenen, H., Barde, Y.-A., Edgar, D., Hatanaka, H., Otten, U., and Schwab, M. (1979). *Prog. Brain Res.* **51**, 95–107.

Thomas, K. A., and Bradshaw, R. A. (1980). *In* "Proteins of the Nervous System" (R. A. Bradshaw and D. M. Schneider, eds.), pp. 213–230. Raven, New York.

Thomas, K. A., Silverman, R. E., Jeng, I., Baglan, N. C., and Bradshaw, R. A. (1981a). *J. Biol. Chem.* **256**, 9147–9155.

Thomas, K. A., Baglan, N. C., and Bradshaw, R. A. (1981b). *J. Biol. Chem.* **256**, 9156–9166.

Varon, S., Nomura, H., and Shooter, E. M. (1967). *Biochemistry* **6**, 2202–2209.

Wright, R. D. (1978). *Trends Biochem. Sci. (Pers. Ed.)* **3**, 275.

Yankner, A. B., and Shooter, E. M. (1979). *Proc. Natl. Acad. Sci. U.S.A.* **76**, 1269–1273.

Yu, M. W., Hori, S., Tolson, N., Huff, K., and Guroff, G. (1978). *Biochem. Biophys. Res. Commun.* **81**, 941–946.

CHAPTER 4

Hormonal Regulation of Growth Hormone Synthesis in Cell Cultures: Role of Thyroid and Glucocorticoid Hormone Receptors

Herbert H. Samuels, Juan Casanova,
Zebulun D. Horowitz, Bruce M. Raaka,
Lawrence E. Shapiro, Frederick Stanley,
Jir S. Tsai, and Barry M. Yaffe

BIOCHEMICAL ACTIONS OF HORMONES, VOL. X

I. INTRODUCTION

Growth hormone (somatotropin) is a polypeptide with a molecular weight of approximately 22,000 which is important for linear growth in man and a wide variety of vertebrates. Growth hormone is secreted from the somatotroph cells of the pituitary gland in episotic fashion, which appears to be modulated by a variety of stimuli. Control of secretion appears to involve a putative hypothalamic growth hormone-releasing factor, which has not yet been identified, and somatostatin, which can inhibit growth hormone release. Growth hormone secretion is also modified by stress, as well as protein and glucose intake. Although thyroid hormone does not appear to modify growth hormone secretion it plays an important role in controlling growth hormone production rates in the somatotroph *in vivo*. The growth hormone content of the thyroidectomized rat pituitary is markedly reduced compared to the rat with normal thyroid function (Solomon and Greep, 1959; Lewis *et al.*, 1965; Hervas *et al.*, 1975). Furthermore, similar alterations in growth hormone production rates have been identified in patients with thyroid disease (Finkelstein *et al.*, 1974). Steroid hormones also play a role in influencing growth hormone production *in vivo*. Glucocorticoid hormones administered at the time of thyroidectomy tend to prevent the decrease in growth hormone abundance in the anterior pituitary (Lewis *et al.*, 1965). However, if the animals are first rendered chronically thyroid hormone deficient, glucocorticoid hormones do not increase the abundance of growth hormone in the pituitary gland (Lewis *et al.*, 1965; Peake *et al.*, 1973).

Therefore, based on *in vivo* studies, thyroid and/or glucocorticoid hormones appear to play an important role in modulating the pituitary abundance of growth hormone, presumably by influencing either growth hormone synthetic rates and/or degradation.

Several growth hormone-producing rat pituitary cell lines (GH cells) originally isolated by Yasumura *et al.* (1966) have proved to be highly useful models to study the hormonal regulation of growth hormone production. Using GH_1 cells cultured in serum-containing medium, Kohler *et al.* (1969) showed that glucocorticoid hormones stimulate the rate of growth hormone production. Similar observations were also made using cultured GH_3 cells, a related cell line by Bancroft *et al.* (1969). Using medium supplemented with serum depleted of the thyroid hormones [L-triiodothyronine (L-T_3), L-thyroxine (L-T_4)] Samuels *et al.* (1973) demonstrated that GH_1 cells respond to physiological concentrations of L-T_3 and L-T_4. In GH_1 cells thyroid hormone stimulates the rate of growth hormone production (Tsai and Samuels, 1974) which occurs as a result of an increase in steady-state growth hormone mRNA levels (Shapiro *et al.*, 1978).

An examination of the multihormonal control of growth hormone by thyroid and glucocorticoid hormones using cultured GH_1 cells and related cell lines indicates a synergistic interaction between both hormones (Samuels *et al.*, 1977a; Martial *et al.*, 1977a). The induction of growth hormone response by glucocorticoid appears to be highly dependent on thyroid hormone action (Samuels *et al.*, 1977a, 1979a; Martial *et al.*, 1977a; Shapiro *et al.*, 1978). In the absence of glucocorticoid, thyroid hormone induces growth hormone synthesis approximately five- to tenfold and glucocorticoids increase this response sixfold further. In the absence of thyroid hormone glucocorticoids induce a small growth hormone response which is only observed after 48 hours of incubation. Quantitation of growth hormone mRNA levels demonstrates that the regulation of growth hormone synthesis by thyroid and glucocorticoid hormones is explained by a synergistic pre-translational control mechanism, presumably at the level of the growth hormone gene (Martial *et al.*, 1977a; Shapiro *et al.*, 1978; Samuels *et al.*, 1979a). This chapter reviews the regulation of growth hormone synthesis by thyroid and glucocorticoid hormones in cultured cells in relation to the interaction of thyroid and glucocorticoid hormones with intercellular receptors that regulate this response.

II. CELL CULTURE CONSIDERATIONS

In order to assess the effects of hormones on the regulation of specific cellular processes in cells cultured with medium supplemented with serum it is essential to utilize serum in which the respective hormone under study has been depleted. GH_1 cells were the first cell culture system shown to be responsive to physiological concentrations of L-T_3 and L-T_4 (Samuels *et al.*, 1973). An essential aspect of the experimental design was the use of hypothyroid calf serum as a component of the medium which promotes the development of a thyroid hormone-depleted state under cell culture conditions. This proved necessary since commercially obtained fetal calf or calf serum contains physiological concentrations of L-T_3 and L-T_4 which would not permit a precise analysis of thyroid hormone action in cultured cells. Thyroid hormone-depleted serum for cell culture studies using GH_1 cells were initially obtained from a thyroidectomized calf. As previously discussed (Samuels, 1978), it is essential to monitor all serum samples obtained after thyroidectomy for L-T_3 and L-T_4 levels. Even if only small amounts of residual thyroid tissue remain after thyroidectomy, L-T_3 and L-T_4 levels may increase with time resulting in serum hormone levels that are not sufficiently low for use in cell culture studies.

Alternatively, serum can be depleted of both L-T_3 and L-T_4 using an anion exchange resin [AG 1-X-8 or AG 1-X-10 (Bio-Rad)] (Samuels *et al.*, 1979b). This resin effectively depletes L-T_3 and L-T_4 from calf serum without significantly altering the amino acid or total protein content, or the electrophoretic pattern of serum proteins. Although this resin reduces estradiol concentrations, it does not markedly change serum glucocorticoid levels. In GH_1 cells, calf serum depleted of thyroid hormone using the anion exchange resin procedure yields serum that, when used as a medium supplement, results in a biological response identical to those obtained with media supplemented with thyroidectomized calf serum. Furthermore, resin treatment of euthyroid calf serum does not alter the replication of different growth hormone-producing cell lines if the thyroid hormone concentrations are restored (Samuels *et al.*, 1979b). However, the resin may remove certain growth-promoting factors required for other cell types. Glucocorticoid concentration in calf serum or fetal calf serum can be effectively depleted by incubating serum with activated charcoal (20 mg/ml) for 5 hours, followed by a second overnight incubation with activated charcoal. In studying the effects of thyroid and/or glucocorticoid hormones on growth hormone synthesis in culture it is essential to first preincubate the cells for at least 24–48 hours with hormone-depleted medium. This removes endogenous hormone from cells and allows for the establishment of a new "basal" steady-state condition prior to subsequent incubation with hormone.

III. CONTROL OF GROWTH HORMONE SYNTHESIS BY THYROID HORMONE IN CULTURED CELLS

GH_1 cells synthesize growth hormone and rapidly release the peptide into the medium (Tsai and Samuels, 1974; Samuels and Shapiro, 1976).

Growth hormone is not degraded within these cells or after release, and the intracellular half-life (70 minutes) appears to solely reflect rates of hormone release (Samuels and Shapiro, 1976). Therefore, quantitation of the level of the medium growth hormone as a function of time gives an estimation of the synthetic rate of the polypeptide hormone. Evidence to support this comes from studies in which growth hormone synthetic rates were assessed by incubating cells with L-[^{35}S]methionine or L-[^{3}H]leucine for 5–12 minutes followed by selective immunoprecipitation of the intracellular radiolabeled growth hormone using highly specific antigrowth hormone antibody raised in baboons (Samuels and Shapiro, 1976; Shapiro *et al.*, 1978; Samuels *et al.*, 1979a). Figure 1 illustrates the time course of stimulation of growth hormone synthesis by L-T$_3$ in GH$_1$ cells. No increase in total cell protein synthesis or L-[^{3}H]leucine uptake was observed during the course of the study (Samuels and Shapiro, 1976). L-T$_3$ increased the rate of growth hormone synthesis by 50% in 1.25 hours, twofold in 2.5 hours, and to a maximum of threefold in this experiment by 21 hours of incubation. The time course of induction of growth hormone synthesis (Fig. 1) is in good agreement with the kinetics of induction of growth hormone production as estimated by radioimmunoassay of the growth hormone that accumulates in the medium (Samuels, 1978).

Quantitation of growth hormone mRNA levels in GH$_1$ cells using an *in vitro* translation system has documented that stimulation of growth hormone synthetic rates by L-T$_3$ results from an increase in the abundance of growth hormone mRNA (Shapiro *et al.*, 1978; Samuels *et al.*, 1979a). Similar observations have been made using cultured GH$_3$ cells (Seo *et al.*, 1977) and cultured GC cells (Martial *et al.*, 1977b), two closely related pituitary cell culture lines. The physiological relevance of the induction of growth hormone synthesis using GH$_1$ cells and related cell lines in culture is underscored by the observation that thyroid hormone plays an important role in controlling

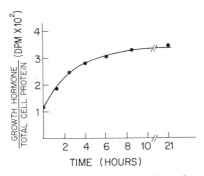

Fig. 1. Kinetics of induction of growth hormone synthesis by L-T$_3$. [^{3}H]Leucine incorporation into total cell protein was 2.6 × 10^6 dpm ± 5%/25 cm^2 flask. From Samuels and Shapiro (1976).

the production of growth hormone in the rat pituitary *in vivo* (Solomon and Greep, 1959; Hervas *et al.*, 1975). Furthermore, thyroid hormone stimulates an increase in the pituitary content of growth hormone in the thyroidectomized rat (Hervas *et al.*, 1975) with the same onset and time course as in cultured GH_1 cells (Samuels and Shapiro, 1976; Samuels, 1978).

A. STIMULATION OF GROWTH HORMONE SYNTHESIS IS MEDIATED BY A CHROMATIN-ASSOCIATED THYROID HORMONE RECEPTOR

Cellular receptors that mediate the action of thyroid hormone can be expected to have specific properties that might be predicted by the characteristics of the induced biological response and the relative affinity of such a receptor for $L-T_3$, $L-T_4$, and synthetic hormone analogues. If the association of thyroid hormone with such a receptor regulates a rate-limiting step in thyroid hormone action, the characteristics of hormone binding might be expected to demonstrate a good correlation with the observed biological properties of the system. In 1972, Schadlow, Oppenheimer, and co-workers reported that increasing concentrations of $L-T_3$ administration to rats resulted in a progessive decrease in the pituitary-to-plasma concentration ratio of $L-T_3$, indicating that the pituitary demonstrated limited capacity to bind thyroid hormone. Cell fractionation studies demonstrated that the limited-capacity binding components for $L-T_3$ were restricted to the cell nucleus. Using cultured GH_1 cells, Samuels and Tsai (1973) demonstrated that these cells contained high-affinity, limited-capacity binding sites for $L-T_3$ and $L-T_4$ that were localized to the cell nucleus and not to the extranuclear fraction.

Figure 2 illustrates the kinetics of binding of 30 pM $L-[^{125}I]T_3$ to nuclei, mitochondria, and cytosol, which were isolated after $L-T_3$ incubation with intact cells. The magnitude of limited-capacity or saturable binding was quantitated by carrying out a simultaneous incubation of $L-[^{125}I]T_3$ in the presence of a 200-fold molar excess of nonradioactive $L-T_3$. Binding of $L-[^{125}I]T_3$ to mitochondria and cytosol of intact cells occurred very rapidly and attained an apparent equilibrium with the hormone concentration in the medium within 10–15 minutes. At this concentration of $L-[^{125}I]T_3$, binding to nuclei occurred more slowly and attained a maximal value after 1 hour of incubation. As shown in Fig. 2, nonradioactive $L-T_3$ inhibited the binding of $L-[^{125}I]T_3$ to nuclei by greater than 95% but did not alter binding to the mitochondrial or cytosol fractions. Figure 3 illustrates an analysis of the binding of $L-T_3$ and $L-T_4$ to nuclei by the method of Scatchard (1949) using intact cells under completely serum-free conditions (Samuels and Tsai,

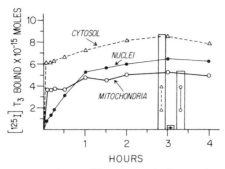

FIG. 2. Time course of binding of L-[^{125}I]T$_3$ (30 pM) after incubation of intact GH$_1$ cells with serum-free media. The bar graphs illustrate the magnitude of L-[^{125}I]T$_3$ binding in the presence of a 200-fold molar excess of nonradioactive L-T$_3$. From Samuels and Tsai (1973).

1973). Both ligands yield linear Scatchard plots indicating a simple non-cooperative interaction between hormone and the nuclear binding component. The estimated equilibrium dissociation constant (K_d) was 0.029 nM for L-T$_3$ and 0.26 nM for L-T$_4$. Therefore, a 10-fold higher concentration of L-T$_4$ resulted in half-maximal binding indicating that the affinity for L-T$_4$ was one-tenth that of L-T$_3$. Analysis of the ^{125}I radioactivity bound to nuclei indicated that the L-[^{125}I]T$_4$ remained intact and did not represent L-[^{125}I]T$_3$ formed as a result of possible L-T$_4$-to-L-T$_3$ conversion by the cells (Samuels and Tsai, 1973). In addition the Scatchard plot for each hormone extrapolated to the same point indicating that an identical number of binding sites for L-T$_3$ and L-T$_4$ existed in GH$_1$ cell nuclei. In GH$_1$ cells the abundance of receptor varies from 8000 to 20,000 binding sites per cell nucleus. As

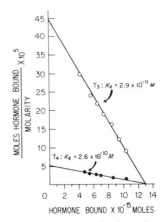

FIG. 3. Scatchard plot of L-T$_3$ and L-T$_4$ nuclear binding after incubation with intact cells and serum-free media. Redrawn from Samuels and Tsai (1973).

discussed below, the level of the nuclear binding component in GH_1 cells is regulated by the ambiant thyroid hormone concentration (Samuels *et al.*, 1976, 1977b, 1979c; Raaka and Samuels, 1981a).

1. Dose–Response Induction of Growth Hormone Synthesis by Thyroid Hormone Analogues; Relation to the Relative Affinity for the Thyroid Hormone Nuclear Binding Component

Figure 4 illustrates the dose–response stimulation of growth hormone synthesis induced by different concentrations of L-T_3, triiodothyroacetic acid (TRIAC), D-T_3, and L-T_4 using medium supplemented with 10% thyroid hormone-depleted calf serum (Samuels *et al.*, 1979c). L-T_3 and TRIAC showed virtually identical dose–response relationships with half-maximal responses occurring at 0.17 nM for L-T_3 and 0.19 nM for TRIAC. D-T_3 induced a half-maximal growth hormone response at 4 nM and L-T_4 at 9 nM. Therefore, under conditions in which medium is supplemented with 10% thyroid hormone-depleted calf serum, L-T_3 and TRIAC show identical dose–response curves while D-T_3 had 1/20 and L-T_4 showed 1/50 of the activity of the L-T_3. An estimate of the relative affinity of L-T_3, TRIAC, D-T_3, and L-T_4 for the thyroid hormone nuclear receptor was performed at intact cells in medium that contained thyroid hormone-depleted calf serum to allow for a relative comparison to the growth hormone dose–response curves (Samuels *et al.*, 1979c). Figure 5 illustrates these results in which cells were incubated with 2 nM L-$[^{125}I]T_3$ plus different concentrations of

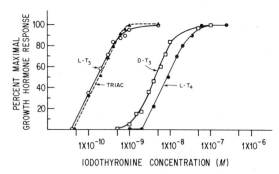

FIG. 4. Dose–response induction of growth hormone synthesis by iodothyronines. GH_1 cells were incubated with different concentrations of L-triiodothyronine (L-T_3), triiodothyroacetic acid (TRIAC), D-triiodothyronine (D-T_3), or L-thyroxine (L-T_4). The growth hormone that accumulated in the serum-containing medium between 24 to 48 hours of incubation was determined by radioimmunoassay and is a direct measurement of growth hormone synthetic rates (Samuels and Shapiro, 1976). From Samuels *et al.* (1979c).

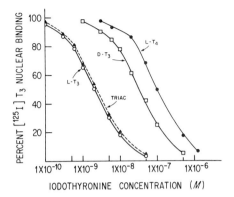

FIG. 5. Relative affinity of iodothyronines for the nuclear receptor in intact cells in serum-containing medium. GH_1 cells were incubated with 2 nM L-[^{125}I]T_3 and the indicated concentrations of nonradioactive L-T_3, TRIAC, D-T_3, and L-T_4 for 3 hours in medium containing 10% thyroid hormone-depleted calf serum. From Samuels *et al.* (1979c).

nonradioactive L-T_3, TRIAC, D-T_3, and L-T_4 for 3 hours. Inhibition of binding of L-[^{125}I]T_3 to the nuclear binding component in serum-containing medium is identical to the relative growth hormone responses induced by each iodothyronine (Fig. 4).

This observation supports the concept that the thyroid hormone nuclear binding component functions as a biologically relevant receptor which regulates the growth hormone response in these cells. To make a direct comparison between the relative affinity for the receptor and the induction of growth hormone synthesis, the cellular responses were studied using medium supplemented to 10% with thyroid hormone-depleted calf serum. Although this allows a valid relative comparison between iodothyronine analogue binding characteristics and growth hormone induction, it does not allow a direct measurement of the intrinsic differences in biological activity as a result of differences in serum binding of the hormone analogues. For example, based on the 10-fold difference in the relative affinity of L-T_3 and L-T_4 for the nuclear binding component using serum-free medium (Fig. 3), L-T_3 would be expected to have a 10-fold greater intrinsic biological activity in stimulating growth hormone synthesis than L-T_4. This value contrasts with the approximate 50-fold difference in the L-T_4 and L-T_3 effect (Figs. 4 and 5) observed using serum-containing media. This difference was documented to be due to the relative difference in the serum binding of L-T_3 and L-T_4. Free hormone concentrations were estimated by equilibrium dialysis using medium which contained 10% thyroid hormone-depleted calf serum (Samuels *et al.*, 1979c). For concentrations of between 0.01 and 5 nM L-T_3, and between 0.1 and 50 nM L-T_4, the percentage of total media hormone concentration which was in the free fraction and available for interaction of cells was estimated to be 5% for L-T_3 and 1% for L-T_4 (Samuels *et al.*, 1979c). After correction for the fivefold difference in serum binding, L-T_4 appears to have 1/10 of the intrinsic biological activity of L-T_3 and 1/10 of the relative affinity for the thyroid hormone nuclear binding component.

2. Properties of Thyroid Hormone Nuclear Receptors

Based on the excellent agreement between the relative affinity for the nuclear binding component and the relative biological activity of the hormonal analogues in GH$_1$ cells (Figs. 4 and 5), the nuclear binding component appears to function as a biologically relevant receptor which controls the induction of growth hormone synthesis by thyroid hormone in these cells. Thyroid hormone nuclear receptors have been identified in a wide variety of cells and tissues (Oppenheimer and Surks, 1975; Oppenheimer and Dillmann, 1978). The nuclear receptor protein can be solubilized from nuclei using 0.4 M KCl and this procedure can extract between 60 and 80% of thyroid hormone receptors from GH$_1$ cells or rat liver nuclei (Samuels *et al.*, 1974). The affinity of L-T_3, L-T_4, and hormonal analogues for nuclear receptors *in vitro* (Koerner *et al.*, 1975; Samuels, 1978) showed good agreement with that observed from intact animal (Goslings *et al.*, 1976) and cell culture studies (Samuels *et al.*, 1974, 1979c). The salt-extracted receptor from rat liver has been reported to have an estimated sedimentation coefficient of 3.5 S and a Stokes radius of 3.5 nm (Latham *et al.*, 1976). From GH$_1$ cells the KCl-extracted receptor has an estimated Stokes radius of 3.3 nm, a sedimentation coefficient of 3.8 S, and an estimated particle density of 1.36 gm/cm^3 (Samuels *et al.*, 1980; Perlman *et al.*, 1982). The difference in the physical parameters of the salt-extracted receptor from rat liver and GH$_1$ cells likely reflects differences in exerimental measurements rather than intrinsic differences in the receptor-binding component. Using the above physical parameters for the salt-extracted receptor, the binding component has an estimated molecular weight of 54,000.

In contrast with the salt-extracted receptor form, studies using micrococcal nuclease digestion have demonstrated that the thyroid hormone receptor is excised from GH$_1$ cell nuclei as a predominant 6.5 S form and as a less abundant 12.5 S species (Samuels *et al.*, 1980; Perlman *et al.*, 1982). Studies in rat liver (Jump and Oppenheimer, 1980; Groul, 1980) also indicate that the predominant excised form of the receptor sediments at about 6.5 S. The 12.5 S form of the receptor likely represents association of receptor with a subset of mononucleosome particles, which appear to be excised more rapidly than the bulk of the mononucleosomes generated by micrococcal nuclease (Samuels *et al.*, 1982). The 6.5 S receptor form appears to represent the 3.8 S receptor in association with other chromatin protein components which are excised as a complex bound to a DNA fragment of approximately 35–40 base pairs (Perlman *et al.*, 1982). Unlike steroid hormone receptors (O'Malley and Means, 1974), a cytoplasmic form of the thyroid hormone receptor has not been identified (Samuels *et al.*, 1974; Oppenheimer and Surks, 1975). Furthermore, thyroid hormone does not appear to elicit an increase in the concentration of nuclear-associated receptors as a result of a cytosolic-to-nuclear translocation as has been reported for steroid hormone receptors. Dense amino acid labeling of thyroid hormone receptors in GH_1 cells (Raaka and Samuels, 1981a) indicates that the level of nuclear bound receptor reflects a steady state that is solely determined by the rates of receptor synthesis and degradation and that a significant pool of cytoplasmic binding protein which functions as a precursor to nuclear receptor does not exist. Therefore, unlike steroid hormone receptors, the nuclear abundance of receptor is not increased by ligand and the level of receptor appears to be solely reflected by the intrinsic rates of receptor synthesis and receptor degradation.

B. Modulation of Thyroid Hormone Nuclear Receptor Levels

1. L-T₃ Reduces Thyroid Hormone Receptors in GH₁ Cells

Although Figs. 4 and 5 demonstrate an excellent relationship between the relative biological response induced by different iodothyronines and their relative affinity for the thyroid hormone nuclear receptor, these studies do not resolve whether the biological response is a complete linear function of the occupancy of the total receptor population by hormone. GH_1 cells appear to be uniquely suited for a receptor occupancy–biological response analysis, since unlike intact animals hormone concentrations can be maintained at a constant level. Therefore, the magnitude of L-T_3–receptor binding can be directly related to the output of the biological response of the system. Figure 6 illustrates a comparison of the dose–response relationship of growth hormone synthesis (Fig. 6A) and L-$[^{125}I]T_3$ nuclear binding (Fig. 6B) in cells cultured in medium containing 10% thyroid hormone-depleted calf serum. Growth hormone synthetic rates were estimated after a 24-hour incubation with L-T_3 followed by a 12-minute incubation with L-$[^3H]$leucine to estimate synthetic rates (Samuels and Shapiro, 1976). L-T_3 up to 5 nM had no effect on total protein synthetic rates while growth hormone synthetic rates increased fourfold to approximately 2% of total cell protein synthesis with a half-maximal response at 0.22 nM L-T_3. The L-T_3 nuclear binding curve was

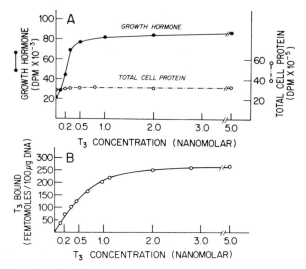

FIG. 6. Relationship of L-T$_3$ concentrations to growth hormone synthesis (A) and L-T$_3$ nuclear binding (B). Both studies were carried out with medium supplemented with 10% (v/v) thyroid hormone-depleted calf serum. L-T$_3$ nuclear binding was determined after a 3-hour incubation with L-[^{125}I]T$_3$. Growth hormone and total cell protein synthetic rates were determined with L-[^{3}H]leucine after 24 hours of L-T$_3$ incubation. From Samuels *et al.* (1976).

determined by incubating various L-[^{125}I]T$_3$ concentrations with cells for 3 hours using identical media conditions. With serum-containing medium the L-T$_3$ concentration that resulted in half-maximal nuclear binding was 0.5 nM and therefore the biological response curve is shifted leftward of the L-T$_3$ nuclear occupancy curve. In addition to this deviation of the biological and binding curves, the shapes of the curves are dissimilar over the range of L-T$_3$ concentrations and imply that the stoichiometry of the biological response differs from that of the L-T$_3$–receptor interaction.

Since the growth hormone dose–response curve was determined after a 24-hour L-T$_3$ incubation while the receptor binding curve was determined after a 3-hour incubation, the possibility was considered that L-T$_3$ altered the nuclear receptor population during the 24-hour incubation prior to the time that growth hormone synthesis was determined. Therefore, L-[^{125}I]T$_3$ binding at different concentrations was determined with intact cells for short (4-hour) and long (24-hour) incubation times (Samuels *et al.*, 1976). Figure 7 illustrates that although the binding of L-T$_3$ after a 24-hour incubation is similar at low L-T$_3$ concentrations, the maximal amount of L-T$_3$ bound in the 24-hour incubation was 60% of the 4-hour incubation. Expressed as a function of maximal L-T$_3$ binding, the concentration of L-T$_3$ that results in half of the maximal level of L-T$_3$ receptor complexes was 0.5 nM for the

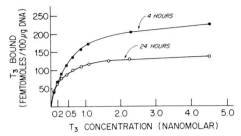

FIG. 7. Binding of L-[^{125}I]T$_3$ to nuclear receptors after a 4-hour and 24-hour incubation with intact GH$_1$ cells. From Samuels *et al.* (1976).

4-hour incubation and 0.3 nM for the 24-hour incubation. The value determined for the 24-hour incubation demonstrated a closer agreement with the L-T$_3$ concentration (0.22 nM) that induced a half-maximal growth hormone response during the same period of incubation. These results are consistent with a time- and dose-dependent depletion of L-T$_3$ nuclear receptor levels by hormone.

Figure 8 illustrates the kinetics of receptor reduction in GH$_1$ cells mediated by L-[^{125}I]T$_3$. Receptor depletion was examined by incubating one group of flasks with 5 nM L-[^{125}I]T$_3$ from the beginning of the study; control flasks initially received no L-[^{125}I]T$_3$. Both groups of flasks were incubated at 37°C, and 1 hour before the cells were harvested 5 nM L-[^{125}I]T$_3$ was added to the control cells to quantitate receptor levels. This concentration of L-T$_3$ binds to greater than 95% of the nuclear receptor population and permits an indirect estimate of total receptor levels (Samuels *et al.*, 1976). Thyroid hormone receptor levels remained constant in the control cells but rapidly decreased in a time-dependent fashion in the cells that received L-[^{125}I]T$_3$

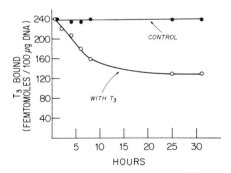

FIG. 8. Kinetics of nuclear receptor depletion by 5 nM L-[^{125}I]T$_3$. To study receptor depletion one group of cells received 5 nM L-[^{125}I]T$_3$ (O) at the beginning of the study, while control cells (●) received 5 nM L-[^{125}I]T$_3$ 1 hour prior to nuclear isolation. From Samuels *et al.* (1976).

from the beginning of the study to 55% of the control cell levels. Scatchard analysis indicated that the reduction of L-T$_3$ receptor binding reflects a decrease in total receptor and does not reflect an alteration in affinity of receptor for hormone (Samuels *et al.*, 1976). Furthermore, the total reduction of receptor levels was virtually identical whether examined with nuclei or whole cells and, therefore, L-T$_3$ does not reduce receptor levels by eliciting a shift of receptor from the nuclear to the cytoplasmic compartment.

2. *Relationship of Nuclear Receptor Occupancy to Reduction of Receptor by Iodothyronines*

Figure 9 illustrates the influence of L-T$_3$ concentrations on total nuclear receptor levels after a 24-hour incubation in GH$_1$ cells. In curve 1, the cells were first incubated with the L-[^{125}I]T$_3$ concentrations indicated for 24 hours. The L-[^{125}I]T$_3$ concentration was then adjusted to 5 nM and the cells were incubated for an additional 3 hours to estimate total receptor levels. As shown by curve 1, nuclear receptor levels decreased approximately 50% with increasing L-T$_3$ concentrations and half-maximal depletion occurred at 0.17 nM L-T$_3$. To exclude the possibility that the effect of L-[^{125}I]T$_3$ on receptor depletion reflected a dose-related toxic effect of the ^{125}I radioactivity, cells were first incubated with various concentrations of nonradioactive L-T$_3$ for 24 hours followed by a 3-hour incubation with 5 nM L-[^{125}I]T$_3$. The femtomoles of total L-T$_3$ bound was calculated from the resultant L-[^{125}I]

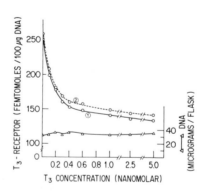

FIG. 9. Dose-dependent depletion of nuclear receptors by L-T$_3$ in GH$_1$ cells. Curve 1 received only different concentrations of L-[^{125}I]T$_3$ while curve 2 received only nonradioactive L-T$_3$. In each case after 24 hours L-[^{125}I]T$_3$ was added to adjust the final L-[^{125}I]T$_3$ concentration to 5 nM and the cells were incubated for an additional 3 hours. Total receptor binding was determined in curve 2 after correction of specific activity differences and assumes full equilibration of the system. From Samuels *et al.* (1976).

T_3 specific activity at each L-T_3 concentration. The results are illustrated by curve 2 of Fig. 9 and are identical to the study that utilized only L-[^{125}I]T_3 in curve 1. This excludes the possibility that receptor depletion occurred secondary to ^{125}I radiation damage to the cells during the 24-hour incubation. Furthermore, the concentration of L-T_3 that results in half of the maximal level of receptor depletion was 0.17 nM, which is not identical but in good agreement with the L-T_3 concentration that results in half-maximal occupancy of the receptor (0.5 nM). This suggests that L-T_3-mediated receptor depletion occurs secondary to a process that is dependent on the association of L-T_3 with the receptor binding site.

This conclusion is supported by (1) studies of iodothyronine analogue concentrations on reducing total nuclear receptor (Samuels *et al.*, 1979c) and (2) the relationship between the initial rates of disappearance of receptor and the fractional occupancy of the receptor population by L-T_3. Figure 10 compares the dose-dependent reduction of total thyroid hormone nuclear receptor levels by different concentrations of L-T_3, TRIAC, D-T_3, and L-T_4 (Samuels *et al.*, 1979c). Each compound elicited a 40% decrease in total nuclear receptor levels and the dose-dependent reduction of receptor parallels the affinity of each analogue for the receptor binding site (see Fig. 5). Figure 11 illustrates the kinetics of receptor depletion examined at five L-T_3 concentrations that are known to occupy a specific percentage of total receptor (0.2 nM, 25%; 0.35 nM, 40%; 0.5 nM, 50%; 0.8 nM, 69%; and 5 nM, 95%) (Samuels *et al.*, 1977b). At each L-T_3 concentration the initial rates of receptor depletion demonstrate first-order kinetics. A comparison of the disappearance rate constant calculated from the initial rates of receptor disappearance indicates that the kinetics of receptor loss is a linear function of the percentage of total receptor binding sites occupied by L-T_3 (Samuels *et al.*, 1977b).

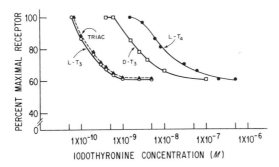

FIG. 10. Relative effect of iodothyronine analogues on receptor depletion in GH$_1$ cells. From Samuels *et al.* (1979c) (for experimental details see this reference).

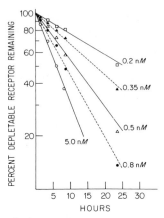

FIG. 11. Kinetics of receptor depletion at five L-T₃ concentrations. GH₁ cells were incubated with L-[¹²⁵I]T₃ concentrations of 5, 0.8, 0.5, 0.35, and 0.2 nM. One hour prior to the times indicated, the L-[¹²⁵I]T₃ concentrations were each adjusted to 5 nM which gives an estimate of total receptor levels. From Samuels *et al.* (1977b).

C. Assessment of Receptor Half-Life and the Nuclear Accumulation of Newly Synthesized Receptor Using Dense Amino Acid Labeling

It is possible to directly quantitate the half-life of the receptor and estimate the rate of receptor synthesis by density labeling cell proteins with amino acids uniformly labeled with the nonradioactive dense isotopes ^{15}N, ^{13}C, and ^{2}H. Newly synthesized proteins will be of higher density than the preexisting proteins and can be separated using gradient centrifugation techniques (Hunttermann and Wendelberger, 1976). The densities of most proteins are approximately 1.3–1.4 gm/cm^{3}. The total substitution of amino acids containing all three heavy isotopes results in a maximal density shift of 0.123 gm/cm^{3} which increases the density of proteins approximately 8%. The velocity of sedimentation of a particle is directly related to the difference between the particle density (ρ) and the density of the gradient (ρ_0). Since the density of most proteins is approximately 1.36 gm/cm^{3}, an 8% increase will yield protein with a density of 1.47 gm/cm^{3}. If a gradient can be constructed such that the average density is 1.2 gm/ml, the value of ρ minus ρ_0 for the dense protein is 0.27 while the value for the protein of normal density is 0.16.

Thus, under the correct gradient conditions an 8% increase in the density of the protein can result in a 1.7-fold (0.27/0.16) increase in the velocity of sedimentation. To achieve a gradient density of approximately 1.2 gm/ml, sucrose gradients can be constructed using D$_2$O instead of H$_2$O.

The newly synthesized protein of higher density can be separated from the preexisting protein of normal density by velocity sedimentation, and the respective populations of dense and normal receptor are identified using radiolabeled ligand. This approach was initially used to quantitate the half-life and the synthetic rate of the acetylcholine receptor (Devreotes *et al.*, 1977) and the position of receptor of different densities was identified using $[^{125}I]\alpha$-bungarotoxin. Dense amino acid labeling was utilized in GH_1 cells to quantitate receptor half-life and synthetic rates, and to examine the mechanism by which thyroid hormone modulates receptor levels in these cells. With this technique receptor half-life is measured without the use of protein synthetic inhibitors such as cycloheximide, which may itself alter the rate of protein turnover (Hersko and Tomkins, 1971). Since purification of the protein of interest is not required, density labeling is particularly useful in studies of receptor proteins of low abundance.

GH_1 cells were cultured in medium containing dense amino acids for 1.5, 5, or 20 hours (Raaka and Samuels, 1981a). One hour prior to harvesting the cells, 5 nM L-$[^{125}I]T_3$ was added to the culture medium to identify and quantitate the receptor. This concentration of L-T_3 occupies greater than 95% of the receptor population and gives an estimate of total receptor levels (Samuels *et al.*, 1976). Normal and dense receptors were then extracted from isolated GH_1 cell nuclei with 0.4 M KCl and separated by velocity sedimentation in 17–32% sucrose gradients constructed in D_2O (Fig. 12). After 1.5 hours in dense amino acid medium approximately 90% of the receptor is of normal density and only a small, faster sedimentation peak corresponding to newly synthesized dense receptor is detected. After 5 hours in dense medium, the receptor of normal density is reduced and an almost equal amount of dense receptor is present. Finally, after 20 hours about 95% of the receptor is of high density. By quantitating the amount of receptor of normal density after different times of incubation with dense amino acids the receptor half-life can be determined. Furthermore, by following the kinetics of appearance of receptor of high density, the rate of receptor synthesis can be calculated.

Using this approach it has been shown that in the absence of hormone, the steady-state level of receptor is determined by a 5-hour half-life and a synthetic rate of 29 fmol of receptor/hour/100 μg of cell DNA, which is equivalent to the synthesis of 1700 molecules of receptor/hour/cell (Raaka and Samuels, 1981a). Within the first 10 hours of incubation with 5 nM L-T_3, dense amino acid labeling studies have shown that the reduction of receptor elicited by thyroid hormone in cells is primarily due to an inhibition in the accumulation of newly synthesized dense receptor. At longer incubation times (greater than 24 hours) thyroid hormone also resulted in a shortening of receptor half-life. This decrease in receptor half-life does not appear to

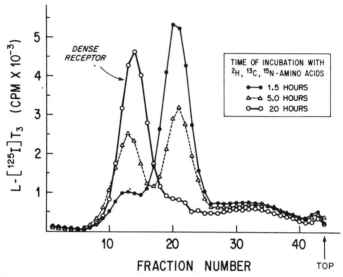

FIG. 12. Separation of normal and dense thyroid hormone receptors in sucrose–D$_2$O gradients. GH$_1$ cells were cultured in medium without thyroid hormones for a total of 43 hours. Normal medium was replaced with dense medium 1.5, 5, or 20 hours prior to harvesting the cells. The dense medium was supplemented with 5 nM L-[^{125}I]T$_3$ 1 hour before harvesting the cells to identify the receptor. Extraction of hormone–receptor complexes from isolated nuclei and conditions for sucrose gradient centrifugation are described in the text. The direction of sedimentation is from right to left. From Raaka and Samuels (1981a).

be a direct consequence of hormone binding to the receptor but appears to reflect late changes in cell metabolism and/or chromatin structure (Raaka and Samuels, 1981a). Figure 13 is a dose–response study that demonstrates that, during a 5-hour incubation, thyroid hormone reduces the accumulation of newly synthesized receptor without changing the half-life of preexisting receptor. Cells were incubated for 6 hours in dense amino acid medium. During the first 5 hours of this incubation the medium contained the indicated concentrations of L-[^{125}I]T$_3$. The hormone concentrations were adusted to 3.8 nM in each cell culture for the final hour of incubation, which gives a good estimate of total receptor levels.

Half-maximal depletion of total receptor occurred at about 0.3 nM L-T$_3$, which is in good agreement with the L-T$_3$ concentration which results in half-maximal occupancy of receptor binding sites (Fig. 6), further indicating that receptor occupancy is necessary for receptor depletion. From the amounts of total receptor and receptor of normal density in the cells cultured without L-T$_3$, the receptor half-life was estimated to be 4.8 hours, which is in the expected range determined in cells cultured without hormone (Raaka and Samuels, 1981a). Since the amount of receptor of normal

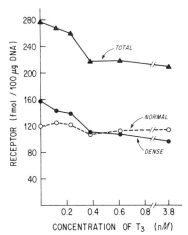

Fɪɢ. 13. Effect of L-[¹²⁵I]T₃ concentration on accumulation of newly synthesized dense receptor. GH₁ cells were grown in normal amino acid medium without thyroid hormone for 24 hours. Exactly 6 hours before harvesting the cells, the normal medium was replaced with dense medium containing the indicated concentrations of L-[¹²⁵I]T₃. The concentration of L-[¹²⁵I]T₃ was adjusted to 3.8 nM in each culture 1 hour before harvesting the cells to identify and quantitate receptor. Normal and dense receptors were separated and quantitated as described in Fig. 12. The contribution of normal and dense receptors to the total amount of nuclear receptor at each concentration of L-T₃ is shown on the figure. From Raaka and Samuels (1981a).

density remains constant as the hormone concentration is increased, receptor half-life was not influenced by L-T₃ during the 6-hour incubation. A hormone-dependent decrease in the accumulation of newly synthesized dense receptor completely accounted for the decrease in total receptor levels. To explain the rapid thyroid hormone-mediated decrease in accumulation of newly synthesized receptor, which is dependent on occupancy of the nuclear bound receptor, we have proposed that the nuclear thyroid hormone–receptor complex can inhibit the production of the receptor mRNA (Raaka and Samuels, 1981a). Clearly, documentation of this model will require direct quantitation of the mRNA for the receptor.

D. Bɪoʟoɢɪcaʟ Iᴍᴘʟɪᴄaᴛɪoɴs oꜰ Rᴇᴄᴇᴘᴛoʀ Rᴇᴅᴜᴄᴛɪoɴ ʙʏ Tʜʏʀoɪᴅ Hoʀᴍoɴᴇ

Hormone-mediated receptor depletion may play a role influencing the characteristics of the induced biological response in GH₁ cells (Samuels *et al.*, 1976). Figure 14 compares the growth hormone synthetic dose–response curve with the receptor binding and depletion curves. The synthetic curve

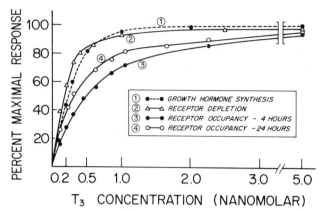

FIG. 14. Relationship of receptor depletion and receptor occupancy to growth hormone synthesis. For comparison the results are expressed as a percentage of maximal response or binding. From Samuels *et al.* (1976).

is from Fig. 6 and the binding and receptor depletion curves are from Figs. 7 and 9. For purpose of comparison the results are expressed as a percentage of maximal growth hormone synthesis (curve 1), receptor depletion (curve 2), or nuclear binding determined after a 4-hour (curve 3) or a 24-hour (curve 4) incubation. Compared to the 4-hour occupancy curve, the 24-hour receptor occupancy curve shows a very good agreement (half-maximal binding, 0.3 nM) with the growth hormone synthetic curve (half-maximal response, 0.22 nM). Of interest is that the response curve for receptor depletion (curve 2) is virtually identical over the entire range of L-T$_3$ concentrations to the dose–response curve for the induction of growth hormone synthesis. Therefore, thyroid hormone action could result from the binding of L-T$_3$ to the remaining nondepleted receptor population which regulates a rate-limiting nuclear event proportional to the number of L-T$_3$–receptor complexes. Alternatively, hormone-mediated receptor depletion may be the rate-limiting event in thyroid hormone action. By this mechanism the receptor could function as a regulatory repressor, and the action of thyroid hormone would be secondary to hormone-mediated receptor reduction and result in derepression of a specific nuclear response.

These alternative mechanisms predict a difference in cell responses to L-T$_3$ as the receptor is progressively reduced. In the first case, the biological response would be expected to decrease in association with a reduction in receptor levels, while in the second case the biological response would increase as a function of time as the receptor is depleted. Quantitation of the instantaneous rates of growth hormone mRNA synthesis should distinguish between these two possibilities. If hormone-mediated receptor loss initiated the action of thyroid hormone, the instantaneous rate of mRNA synthesis would be expected to increase with time and be inversely related to the level of receptor. Alternatively, if the binding of L-T_3 with the nondepleted remaining receptor population is rate limiting for initiating the action of thyroid hormone, the instantaneous rate of growth hormone mRNA synthesis would be expected to decrease with time as the receptor is progressively reduced. Although this analysis has not yet been carried out, indirect evidence suggests that as the receptor population is reduced the cellular response to L-T_3 decreases in a parallel fashion. In GH$_1$ cells in the absence of thyroid hormone, nuclear receptor levels decrease with increasing cell density even though the total rate of protein synthesis per cell remains constant (Samuels *et al.*, 1977b). In association with this reduction in nuclear receptor levels is a parallel decrease in the magnitude of induction of growth hormone synthesis by thyroid hormone (Samuels *et al.*, 1977b). This suggests that the induction of the growth hormone response by L-T_3 is proportional to the number of L-T_3–receptor complexes and that the thyroid hormone induced response is not initiated as a result of reduction of receptor levels mediated by thyroid hormone.

It should be pointed out that hormone-modulated receptor depletion has not been reported to occur *in vivo*. Using labeling studies in intact animals, Oppenheimer *et al.* (1975) reported that the concentration of receptor binding sites in rat liver was identical in euthyroid rats and animals rendered hypothyroid by thyroidectomy. In addition, in an examination of the binding of L-[^{125}I]T_3 to isolated nuclei *in vitro*, Spindler *et al.* (1975) quantitated an identical number of binding sites in nuclei obtained from the livers of hypothyroid and euthyroid rats. A similar assessment of receptor in nuclei of pituitary cells has not been carried out *in vivo*. However, L-T_3 incubation elicits a reduction in nuclear receptor levels in dispersed cells obtained from rat pituitary (Samuels *et al.*, 1979c). Therefore, it remains possible that depletion of receptor by thyroid hormone may be restricted to the somatotroph cell or to only several tissues *in vivo*.

If thyroid hormone controlled the level of nuclear receptors in somatotrophs *in vivo*, the observations on hormone-mediated reduction of receptor in GH$_1$ cells may allow for prediction of the growth hormone response in different thyroidal states *in vivo*. In the hypothyroid rat, receptor levels would be high and the somatotroph would be expected to show a marked stimulation of the growth hormone response to a single injection of thyroid hormone. This has been reported by Hervas *et al.* (1975). In addition, with chronic thyroid hormone administration sufficient to induce thyrotoxicosis, reduction of the receptor might be expected to lower the magnitude of growth hormone response relative to that of the euthyroid state. Only a limited number of studies, however, have examined the effects of chronic thyroid hormone administration on the growth hormone response in the rat (Solomon and Greep, 1959; Coulombe *et al.*, 1978). In studies relating thyroid function to the pituitary content of growth hormone, Solomon and Greep (1959) estimated the growth hormone content of the rat pituitary to be 26 μg/mg pituitary $\pm$ 36.1% in the hypothyroid rat and 170 μg/mg pituitary $\pm$ 36% in the euthyroid rat. After chronic thyroid hormone administration sufficient to induce thyrotoxicosis, the growth hormone content of the pituitary decreased to 75.2 μg/mg pituitary $\pm$ 35.5%. Coulombe *et al.* (1978) reported that daily injection of thyroid hormone in euthyroid rats sufficient to develop thyrotoxicosis decreased the pituitary growth hormone content compared to euthyroid controls. Therefore, the growth hormone response parameters in the rat as a function of the thyroidal state approximates a bell-shaped curve with a reduction in pituitary growth hormone content both in the hypothyroid and thyrotoxic state.

Modulation of the thyroid hormone nuclear receptor level in the somatotroph provides a plausible explanation for the influence of the thyroidal state on the growth hormone response *in vivo*. Whether receptor regulation by thyroid hormone occurs in different tissues *in vivo* remains open to question and warrants additional investigation. Since modulation of receptor levels by thyroid hormone would tend to sensitize cells in hypothyroid animals to thyroid hormone and partially desensitize the cell in the thyrotoxic state to hormone, this putative autoregulatory mechanism in the cell would result in an additional mechanism that influences tissue response to thyroid hormone over and above the regulation of thyroid hormone levels in serum controlled by the pituitary–thyroid axis.

IV. CONTROL OF GROWTH HORMONE SYNTHESIS BY GLUCOCORTICOID HORMONES IN CULTURED CELLS

A. GLUCOCORTICOID INDUCTION OF GROWTH HORMONE SYNTHESIS AND mRNA IS INFLUENCED BY THYROID HORMONE

As discussed in Section I, *in vivo* studies showed that glucocorticoid hormones administered at the time of thyroidectomy tend to prevent the decrease in the growth hormone content of the pituitary during hypothyroidism (Lewis *et al.*, 1965). However, if the animals are first rendered chronically thyroid hormone deficient, glucocorticoid hormones do not increase the abundance of growth hormone in the pituitary gland (Lewis *et al.*, 1965; Peake *et al.*, 1973). Therefore, *in vivo* studies suggest a multihormonal relationship of thyroid and glucocorticoid hormones on regulating the abundance of growth hormone in the anterior pituitary gland. Using several different cultured GH cell lines (GH₁, GH₃, and GC) a number of laboratories have documented that glucocorticoids stimulate the production of growth hormone in culture (Kohler *et al.*, 1969; Bancroft *et al.*, 1969; Yu *et al.*, 1977; Martial *et al.*, 1977b). These studies on glucocorticoid effects, however, utilized medium supplemented with commercial serum containing endogenous thyroid hormone.

To examine the intrinsic response of these cell lines to glucocorticoids it is necessary to use medium supplemented with serum containing very low thyroid hormone levels. Using culture media supplemented with hypothyroid calf serum, Samuels *et al.* (1977a) showed that in the absence of thyroid hormone, glucocorticoid hormones do not appear to stimulate growth hormone production rates within a 24- to 48-hour incubation time. L-T₃ stimulates a rapid increase in growth hormone production rates which is increased two- to fivefold further when cells are incubated with L-T₃ plus glucocorticoid. This interrelationship can be observed using either serum-supplemented media (Samuels *et al.*, 1977a; Shapiro *et al.*, 1978) or completely serum-free conditions (Samuels *et al.*, 1979a).

Figure 15 illustrates the effects of 5 n*M* L-T₃, 100 n*M* cortisol, and L-T₃ plus cortisol on the time course of growth hormone synthesis using medium supplemented with thyroidectomized calf serum (Samuels *et al.*, 1979b). Cells that received no added hormone served as controls. Five n*M* L-T₃ induced a five- to tenfold increase in growth hormone synthesis compared to control cells, while cortisol alone induced a minimal response which is observed only after 24 hours of incubation. In contrast, growth hormone synthesis in cells incubated with L-T₃ plus cortisol was fourfold greater than

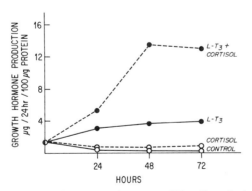

FIG. 15. Kinetics of growth hormone induction in GH₁ cells with thyroidectomized calf serum-supplemented media. (O——O) Control cells which received no additions; (O--O) cortisol (100 n*M*); (●——●) L-T₃ (5 n*M*); (●--●) L-T₃ (5 n*M*) plus cortisol (100 n*M*). The results reflect a mean of triplicate cell cultures with less than ± 8% variation. From Samuels *et al.* (1979b).

138   *Herbert H. Samuels* et al.

those incubated with L-T$_3$ alone. Figure 16 illustrates that the change in growth hormone production rates observed with thyroid and/or glucocorticoid hormones is paralleled by changes in growth hormone mRNA levels (Shapiro *et al.*, 1978). GH$_1$ cells were cultured with either cortisol (100 nM), L-T$_3$ (5 nM), or L-T$_3$ plus cortisol. The medium was replaced every 24 hours with the same concentration of hormones for 72 hours. The medium obtained from the last 24-hour incubation was used to quantitate growth hormone production by radioimmunoassay and the RNA derived from the cells was translated in a wheat germ system to estimate growth hormone mRNA levels. Figure 16 indicates that the rate of growth hormone synthesis is directly related to growth hormone mRNA levels, and that L-T$_3$ and cortisol appear to function synergistically to stimulate growth hormone mRNA accumulation in GH$_1$ cells. In an initial study Martial *et al.* (1977b) showed that glucocorticoid hormones markedly induce growth hormone mRNA when GC cells are cultured in thyroidectomized calf serum. In this study, however, the serum was not sufficiently depleted of thyroid hormone and a subsequent analysis (Martial *et al.*, 1977a) demonstrated the synergistic effects of thyroid and glucocorticoid hormones on growth hormone mRNA levels as shown in Fig. 16. Therefore, in performing these studies it is essential that thyroid hormone levels in the serum-supplemented media

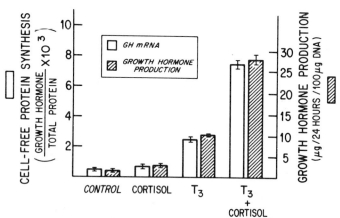

Fig. 16. Influence of L-T$_3$ and cortisol on growth hormone mRNA levels and growth hormone production. GH$_1$ cells were incubated in triplicate with cortisol (100 nM), T$_3$ (5 nM), and both, for 72 hours. The growth hormone production rate was determined from the accumulation of growth hormone in the media between 48 and 72 hours of incubation. Growth hormone mRNA was determined by cell-free synthesis and is expressed relative to the total stimulated protein synthesis. Immunoprecipitation was performed with 0.25 ml of the 120,000 g wheat germ supernatant. The total stimulated incorporation of L-[^{35}S]methionine into protein by RNA was 3 × 10^6 cpm ± 15%. The results are expressed as the mean ± range of triplicate determinations. From Shapiro *et al.* (1978).

are markedly reduced and that the cells are depleted of endogenous thyroid hormone prior to addition of glucocorticoid hormones.

This is further emphasized in Fig. 17 which illustrates a parallel study using the same cells as in Fig. 15 but with medium supplemented with euthyroid calf serum before (Fig. 17A) and after treatment with AG-1X-10 resin to remove endogenous thyroid hormone levels (Fig. 17B). The characteristics of the growth hormone response to hormone with commercially obtained euthyroid calf serum were markedly different than with thyroidectomized calf serum (Fig. 15). The growth hormone production rate of the control cells which received no added hormone was five- to eightfold greater than that of cells with thyroidectomized calf serum. Incubation with 5 nM L-T$_3$, which induces maximal growth hormone synthetic rates (Fig. 6), increased the response by only 25%. Therefore, the basal rate of growth hormone synthesis in cells cultured with euthyroid calf serum was 79% of the maximal L-T$_3$-stimulated response and is likely a reflection of the en-

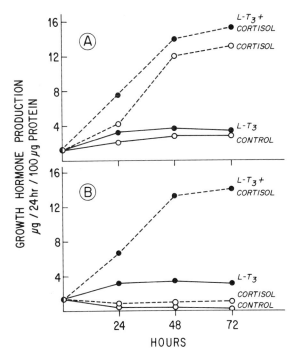

FIG. 17. Kinetics of growth hormone induction with medium supplemented with euthyroid calf serum before (A) and after (B) resin treatment. (O——O) Control cells with no additions; (O--O) cortisol (100 nM); (●——●) L-T$_3$ (5 nM); (●--●) L-T$_3$ (5 nM) plus cortisol (100 nM). The results reflect the mean of triplicate cell cultures which showed less than ± 10% variation. From Samuels et al. (1979b).

dogenous L-T_3 and L-T_4 in the serum. In euthyroid calf serum, the L-T_3 is 2 nM and L-T_4 is 90 nM (Samuels *et al.*, 1979b). Since the medium was composed of 10% serum (v/v) the final hormone concentrations were 0.2 nM L-T_3 and 9 nM L-T_4. Based on the affinity of the thyroid hormone nuclear receptor for L-T_3 and L-T_4 (Samuels *et al.*, 1979c), these concentrations of endogenous hormone would result in 50% occupancy of the nuclear receptor and would be expected to elicit growth hormone synthetic rates which are 80% of maximal (Samuels *et al.*, 1976).

The second major difference in the behavior of GH$_1$ cells cultured with euthyroid calf serum (Fig. 17A) and with thyroidectomized calf serum is the magnitude of the response stimulated by addition of only glucocorticoid which is 85% of the maximal response observed with the addition of both L-T_3 and cortisol. Therefore, the induction of growth hormone synthesis by glucocorticoid appears to be influenced by the endogenous thyroid hormone levels in the euthyroid calf serum. This conclusion is supported by the results of Fig. 17 with medium supplemented with resin-treated euthyroid calf serum. With depletion of endogenous thyroid hormone levels the characteristics of the growth hormone response were identical to that observed with thyroidectomized calf serum (Fig. 15). Furthermore, the maximal rate of growth hormone synthesis induced by L-T_3 plus cortisol was identical in the cells cultured with medium supplemented with euthyroid calf serum or with medium in which the endogenous thyroid hormone levels were depleted using AG-1X-10 resin (Fig. 17). These studies indicate that the influence of thyroid hormone on glucocorticoid action does not reflect factors accumulating in calf serum in the hypothyroid state after thyroidectomy which prevent glucocorticoid action and can be reversed by thyroid hormone. Furthermore, the identical results in the cells cultured with thyroidectomized calf serum and resin-treated euthyroid calf serum (Figs. 15 and 17) indicate that, except for thyroid hormone, the resin does not appear to remove other factors regulating growth hormone synthesis. Moreover, the level of growth hormone synthesis induced by cortisol as well as the basal rate of synthesis without added hormones in cells cultured with medium supplemented with euthyroid calf serum are predicted by the endogenous concentrations of L-T_3 and L-T_4 in the euthyroid calf serum. As described in Section IV,C identical multihormonal regulation of the growth hormone response occurs in serum-free defined media.

B. Evidence for Thyroid Hormone-Dependent and -Independent Glucocorticoid Actions in GH Cells

Since glucocorticoid hormones do not significantly stimulate growth hormone synthesis in the absence of thyroid hormone, an important question relates to whether the effect of thyroid hormone on the glucocorticoid stimulation of the growth hormone response reflects a general influence on glucocorticoid action in GH cell lines or whether thyroid hormone only influences certain glucocorticoid-inducible functions. In GH_1 cells the induction of glutamine synthetase by dexamethasone occurs independent of thyroid hormone action, while in the same study the glucocorticoid induction of growth hormone is highly dependent on thyroid hormone action (Samuels *et al.*, 1978). Figure 18 illustrates the induction of glutamine synthetase (A) and growth hormone (B) by different concentrations of dexamethasone with or without 1 nM L-T_3. The dose–response induction of glutamine synthetase by dexamethasone is independent of thyroid hormone action while the induction of the growth hormone response is dependent on thyroid hormone. With L-T_3, half-maximal induction of growth hormone synthesis occurred at 4 nM dexamethasone and this is similar to that determined for glutamine synthetase induction (3 nM) with or without L-T_3. Using two-dimensional gel analysis, Ivarie *et al.* (1981) have provided additional evidence for thyroid hormone-dependent and -independent glucocorticoid action in GH cells. Of 1000 gene products detected in GH_3 cells, 8–15

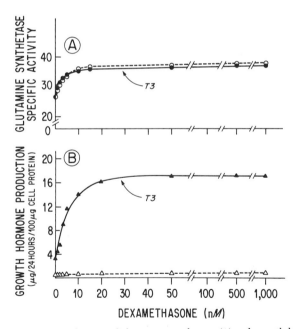

FIG. 18. Dose–response induction of glutamine synthetase (A) and growth hormone (B) by dexamethasone. The L-T_3 concentration was 1.0 nM. Glutamine synthetase response: with L-T_3 (●); without L-T_3 (○). Growth hormone response: with L-T_0 (▲); without L-T_3 (△). Cell protein per culture well was 30–35 μg. From Samuels *et al.* (1978).

proteins were shown to be independently regulated by L-T₃ and dexamethasone. The glucocorticoid induction of growth hormone and a protein designated as p16 required thyroid hormone for expression.

The similar dose–response characteristics for dexamethasone induction of growth hormone and glutamine synthetase suggested that both responses are controlled by the same glucocorticoid receptor mechanism. Regulation of total cell glucocorticoid receptor levels by L-T₃ could result in thyroid hormone-dependent and -independent glucocorticoid responses. This might occur if the nuclear "regulatory sites" that controlled the growth hormone response have a low affinity, and the glutamine synthetase "regulatory sites" have a very high affinity for activated glucocorticoid–receptor complexes. Therefore, the discordant results of the glutamine synthetase and growth hormone responses (Fig. 18) may be consistent with a mechanism in which the level of cell glucocorticoid receptor and, therefore, the total concentration of nuclear-associated glucocorticoid–receptor complexes is regulated by thyroid hormone. Figure 19 illustrates a study in which the nuclear-associated [³H]dexamethasone–receptor level was determined as a function of dexamethasone concentrations using intact cells which were incubated without

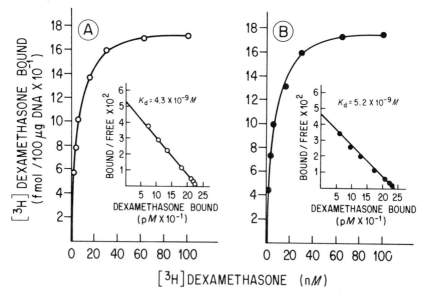

Fig. 19. Influence of dexamethasone on nuclear-associated glucocorticoid receptor. (A) Control cells; (B) cells incubated with L-T₃. The inset Scatchard-type plots were constructed from the concentration of [³H]dexamethasone bound to nuclear-associated receptor and from the concentration in the medium. The binding curves are expressed as femtomoles of [³H]dexamethasone bound/100 μg of DNA and were calculated from the DNA content per assay tube (125–130 μg of DNA). From Samuels *et al.* (1978).

(A) and with (B) 1 nM L-T_3. The inset Scatchard-type (1949) plots were used to estimate the maximal number of glucocorticoid receptors bound to nuclei and the medium concentration of [^{3}H]dexamethasone which resulted in a half-maximal level of nuclear-associated receptor.

In GH$_1$ cells approximately 70–75% of receptor is translocated to the cell nucleus and the maximal number of dexamethasone–receptor complexes associated with nuclei (12,000) were virtually identical in control cells and cells incubated with thyroid hormone. The dexamethasone concentrations that resulted in a half-maximal level of nuclear bound glucocorticoid receptors were 4.3 nM in the control and 5.2 nM in the L-T_3-incubated cells. These values show good agreement with the steroid concentrations which stimulate a 50% increase in glutamine synthetase activity (3 nM) with or without L-T_3, and a 50% increase in the growth hormone response (4 nM) with thyroid hormone (Fig. 18). Therefore, thyroid hormone does not appear to modulate translocation of nuclear glucocorticoid receptors in GH$_1$ cells. Furthermore, other studies have shown that glucocorticoid hormones do not modify the level of thyroid hormone nuclear receptors or prevent the depletion of thyroid hormone receptors by L-T_3 or other iodothyronine derivatives (Samuels *et al.*, 1977a).

C. Influence of Glucocorticoid Agonists and Antagonists on the Regulation of Growth Hormone Synthesis and mRNA Using Serum-Free Defined Conditions

Based on the induction of tyrosine aminotransferase in hepatoma tissue culture (HTC) cells, Samuels and Tomkins (1970) classified steroid compounds into four groups: (1) full agonists (optimal inducers), e.g., cortisol and dexamethasone, which can induce a maximal response; (2) partial agonists–antagonists (suboptimal inducers), e.g., 17α-hydroxyprogesterone, 11-deoxycortisol, and progesterone, which even at high concentrations only induce a submaximal response, but also can inhibit induction by full agonists to the submaximal level at appropriate concentrations; (3) antagonists (antiinducers), e.g., 17α-methyltestosterone, which do not induce a response but at appropriate concentrations can competitively inhibit induction by full agonists and partial agonists–antagonists; and (4) inactive steroids which neither induce nor inhibit a response. Depending on the cell system, progesterone appears to act either as a weak partial glucocorticoid agonist and a strong antagonist (Samuels and Tomkins 1970; Foster and Perkins, 1977) or as a pure glucocorticoid antagonist (Young *et al.*, 1975; Ringold *et al.*, 1975; Feldman and Loose, 1977).

To explore the interactions of glucocorticoid agonists and antagonists on biological responses and to relate these observations to receptor interactions, studies were performed under serum-free defined conditions (Samuels *et al.*, 1979a). This eliminates effects that may result from steroid–protein interactions with binding proteins in serum-containing medium. In GH_1 cells dexamethasone and cortisol show typical full agonist activities under serum-free conditions (Fig. 20). With L-T_3, half-maximal growth hormone synthesis occurred at 12 nM cortisol and 3.5 nM dexamethasone. In GH_1 cells progesterone alone does not increase growth hormone production rates but acts as a partial glucocorticoid agonist–antagonist in the presence of L-T_3. 17α-methyltestosterone acts as a glucocorticoid antagonist of the growth hormone response induced by glucocorticoid plus L-T_3 and inhibits the glucocorticoid component of the response to that observed with L-T_3 alone.

Figure 21 illustrates the effect of progesterone and 17α-methyltestosterone on the growth hormone response induced by L-T_3 (5 nM) and L-T_3 plus cortisol (50 nM) (Samuels *et al.*, 1979a). L-T_3 stimulated a fivefold increase in growth hormone production and 17α-methyltestosterone at concentrations up to 10 μM did not alter the L-T_3-induced response. The growth hormone response observed with L-T_3 plus cortisol is 2.5-fold greater than with L-T_3 alone, and 17α-methyltestosterone inhibited the multihormonal response to that of L-T_3 alone. Half-maximal inhibition of the glucocorticoid component of the growth hormone response occurred at 1.8 μM 17α-methyltestosterone. Progesterone increased the growth hormone response 1.5-fold in the presence of L-T_3 with half-maximal stimulation at 1 μM progesterone. In cells incubated with L-T_3 plus cortisol, progesterone progressively inhibited the growth

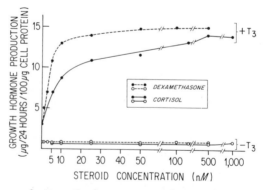

FIG. 20. Influence of L-T_3 on the dose–response induction of growth hormone by cortisol and dexamethasone. The cells were incubated with serum-free Ham's F-10 medium with or without 5 nM L-T_3. The results reflect the growth hormone produced between 24 and 48 hours of incubation. With L-T_3: cortisol (●——●); dexamethasone (●--●). Without L-T_3: cortisol (○——○); dexamethasone (○--○). From Samuels *et al.* (1979a).

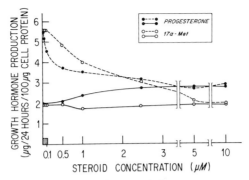

FIG. 21. Influence of progesterone and 17α-methyltestosterone concentrations on growth hormone production in serum-free media. The results reflect the growth hormone produced between 24 and 48 hours of incubation. The steroid concentration refers to the level of progesterone or 17α-methyltestosterone (17α-Met) in the study. L-T₃ (5 nM) plus 17α-meth-yltestosterone (O——O); L-T₃ (5 nM) plus progesterone (●——●); L-T₃ (5 nM) plus cortisol (50 nM) plus 17α-methyltestosterone (O--O); L-T₃ (5 nM) plus cortisol (50 nM) plus proges-terone (●--●). The shaded bar in the lower left represents the growth hormone produced in control cells which received no hormone. From Samuels *et al.* (1979a).

hormone response to the final level observed for L-T₃ plus progesterone, and half-maximal inhibition occurred at 250 nM progesterone.

The 17α-methyltestosterone inhibition of the glucocorticoid component of the growth hormone response in cells incubated with L-T₃ plus cortisol results from a decrease in the abundance of growth hormone mRNA. Figure 22 compares the influence of 17α-methyltestosterone on the rate of growth hormone production in intact GH₁ cells to the level of cytoplasmic growth hormone mRNA estimated by translation using a wheat germ system. 17α-Methyltestosterone did not alter growth hormone mRNA levels or growth hormone synthetic rates in control cells or cells incubated with L-T₃. 17α-Methyltestosterone decreased growth hormone production rates and mRNA levels in cells incubated with L-T₃ and cortisol to the values determined in cells incubated with L-T₃ or L-T₃ plus 17α-methyltestosterone.

Figures 20 and 21 indicate that thyroid hormone is capable of inducing the growth hormone response independent of glucocorticoid action since the L-T₃-induced response is not significantly modified by 17α-methyltes-tosterone which acts as a pure glucocorticoid antagonist (Samuels and Tomkins, 1970). Furthermore, other studies which utilize serum treated with charcoal to remove endogenous glucocorticoid (Samuels *et al.*, 1979a,b), as well as studies in serum-free conditions (Figs. 20–22), further support the notion that L-T₃ can act independently of glucocorticoid in this system. In contrast, the stimulation of growth hormone synthesis and mRNA ac-cumulation by glucocorticoid hormones appear to be highly dependent on

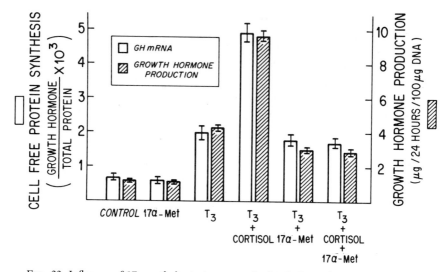

FIG. 22. Influence of 17α-methyltestosterone on the level of cytoplasmic growth hormone mRNA. GH₁ cells (150 × 10⁶) were incubated in roller bottles using serum-free Ham's F-10 medium with hormone as indicated in the text. The growth hormone production rate was determined from the accumulation of growth hormone in the medium between 48 and 72 hours of incubation (hatched bars). Each roller bottle of cells yielded approximately 2 mg of DNA and 40 μg of poly(A⁺) mRNA based on 41 μg of RNA/A unit at 260 nm, and the mRNA was translated in the wheat germ system at a concentration of 20 μg/ml. Growth hormone mRNA, determined by cell-free synthesis, is expressed relative to the total stimulated protein synthesis (open bars). Immunoprecipitation was performed with 0.25-ml fractions of the 120,000 g wheat germ supernatant. The total stimulated incorporation of L-[³⁵S]methionine into the released peptide fraction was 2 × 10⁶ cpm ± 15%. The results are expressed as the mean ± range of triplicate assays. Hormone concentrations were 17α-methyltestosterone (17α-Met), 10 μM; L-triiodothyronine (T₃) 5 nM; cortisol, 50 nM. From Samuels *et al.* (1979a).

an action of thyroid hormone in these cells, and the combination of L-T₃ and glucocorticoid hormones synergistically increases the rate of growth hormone production and mRNA accumulation.

V. GLUCOCORTICOID RECEPTORS IN GH₁ CELLS: PHYSICAL CHARACTERISTICS AND NATURE OF THE ACTIVATION (TRANSFORMATION) PROCESS

Multiple lines of evidence indicate that the control of the growth hormone response involves the nuclear-associated receptors for both thyroid (see Section III) and glucocorticoid hormones. First, this is implied by the observation that the multihormonal stimulation of growth hormone synthesis parallels growth hormone mRNA levels (Figs. 16 and 22) (Martial *et al.*,

1977a; Shapiro *et al.*, 1978). Second, the concentration of dexamethasone (4–5 nM) that results in half-maximal translocation of glucocorticoid receptors to GH$_1$ cell nuclei (Fig. 19) (Samuels *et al.*, 1978) is in excellent agreement with the dexamethasone concentration (3–4 nM) that results in half-maximal induction of growth hormone synthesis in the presence of L-T$_3$ (Figs. 18 and 20). Furthermore, glucocorticoid antagonists, which have been reported to bind to glucocorticoid receptors but not to elicit nuclear translocation (Rousseau *et al.*, 1973; Shyamala, 1975), decreased the glucocorticoid component of the growth hormone response by decreasing growth hormone mRNA levels (Fig. 22).

The interaction of glucocorticoid agonists and antagonists with cytosol glucocorticoid receptors from GH$_1$ cells is illustrated in Fig. 23 and shows the inhibition of binding of 50 nM [^{3}H]cortisol by nonradioactive dexamethasone, cortisol, progesterone, and 17α-methyltestosterone. Half-maximal inhibition of [^{3}H]cortisol binding to receptor occurred at 35 nM dexamethasone, 120 nM cortisol, 300 nM progesterone, and 1500 nM 17α-methyltestosterone. The relative affinity of the steroids for the cytosol glucocorticoid receptor parallels their relative effects on the stimulation or inhibition of the growth hormone response. Dexamethasone is 3.5-fold more active than cortisol in stimulating the growth hormone response (Fig. 20) (Samuels *et al.*, 1979a), and this value is in agreement with the relative difference in the affinity of these agonists for the receptor. In addition, the relative affinity of the receptor for progesterone and 17α-methyltestosterone parallels the relative effect of these compounds on inhibiting the growth hormone response observed with 50 nM cortisol and 5 nM L-T$_3$ (Fig. 21).

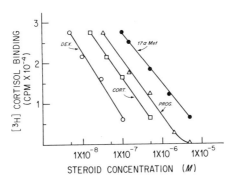

FIG. 23. Association of glucocorticoid agonists and antagonists with cytosol glucocorticoid receptor. Cytosol from GH$_1$ cells equivalent to 800 μg of protein was incubated with 50 nM [^{3}H]cortisol and different concentrations of dexamethasone (○), cortisol (□), progesterone (△), and 17α-methyltestosterone (●) for 15 hours at 0°–4°C. The [^{3}H]cortisol bound to cytosol glucocorticoid receptor was determined with dextran–charcoal. Without nonradioactive steroid, cytosol bound 3.5 × 10^4 ± 800 cpm of [^{3}H]cortisol. From Samuels *et al.* (1979a).

Therefore, GH_1 cells contain glucocorticoid receptors whose affinity for ligand parallels that of glucocorticoid receptor in other systems (Rousseau *et al.*, 1973) and suggests that these cells may represent a useful model system to study the mechanism involved in the ligand-mediated translocation of cytosolic glucocorticoid receptors to the cell nucleus.

A. Properties of Cytosolic Glucocorticoid Receptors *in Vitro*

The cytosolic glucocorticoid receptor undergoes a ligand-mediated modification in the intact cell which transforms the receptor to its nuclear binding form. The process whereby steroid agonists elicit this change has been referred to as receptor transformation or activation. In isolated cytosol *in vitro*, transformation of the receptor can result from warming the steroid–receptor complex, by raising the ionic strength, or by dilution or gel filtration (Higgins *et al.*, 1973; Goidl *et al.*, 1977). Receptor transformation by high-ionic-strength buffer or dilution of cytosol is consistent with a mechanism that involves dissociation of a multimeric receptor form yielding subunits with exposed regions that bind to DNA or other nuclear components (Goidl *et al.*, 1977). Receptor transformation with isolated cytosol *in vitro* has yielded inconsistent results regarding the nature of the receptor species which form as a result of the activation process. Kalimi *et al.* (1975) reported that both the untransformed and transformed glucocorticoid receptor of rat liver sediment at 7–8 S at low ionic strength and at 3–4 S at high ionic strength, suggesting no change in the sedimentation profile of receptor as a result of activation. Others have shown that incubation of glucocorticoid receptors in cytosol with 0.3–0.4 M KCl results in the formation of a 4–5 S-sedimenting species having a lower molecular weight than receptor studied under low-ionic-strength conditions (Middlebrook and Aronow, 1977; McBlain *et al.*, 1981). The transformation process appears to involve a change that results in the exposure of positively charged regions allowing it to interact with DNA and other negatively charged components. This is suggested by studies that showed that pyridoxal 5′-phosphate inhibits the binding of the activated receptor to DNA by forming a Schiff base with an ε-NH_2 of lysine which is localized to the receptor domain that is essential for nuclear binding (Cake *et al.*, 1978). Cidlowski and Thanassi (1979) showed that pyridoxal phosphate shifts the sedimentation profile of the cytosolic glucocorticoid receptor from a 7–8 S form to a 4–5 S form and extracts glucocorticoid receptors from rat thymocyte nuclei as a single 3.5 S peak.

A potential problem in the evaluation of the molecular forms and size of untransformed and transformed states of steroid receptors is the generation of multiple receptor species by cellular proteases in isolated cell systems. Sherman *et al.* (1978) demonstrated that progesterone, glucocorticoid, and mineralocorticoid receptors can be converted from large asymmetric forms to a relatively small species (meroreceptors) (20,000–40,000 daltons) that contain the steroid binding sites but lack the DNA binding site. This conversion appears to be secondary to a proteolytic process and was prevented by 20 to 50 mM concentrations of the protease inhibitor leupeptin. Extraction of nuclear-associated glucocorticoid receptors in the presence of leupeptin using 0.6 M KCl yields a 3.7 S nuclear form of the receptor with an estimated molecular weight of approximately 90,000 (Stevens *et al.*, 1979). This value is in good agreement with the molecular weight of the hormone-activated glucocorticoid receptor purified from rat liver cytosol (Wrange *et al.*, 1979). This species has a molecular weight of 89,000 and a sedimentation coefficient of 3.4 S.

Recent studies have shown that sodium molybdate can inhibit the transformation of steroid hormone receptors to a nuclear binding form in isolated cytosol *in vitro*. Although molybdate is a phosphatase inhibitor, its effect on inhibition of receptor transformation appears to occur by different mechanisms (Nishigori and Toft, 1980). Cytosolic glucocorticoid receptors in the presence of molybdate show sedimentation coefficients of 9–10 S and estimated molecular weights of 308,000–323,000 (Niu *et al.*, 1981). This value is approximately fourfold greater than the molecular weight estimated for the nuclear form of the receptor extracted by 0.6 M KCl (Stevens *et al.*, 1979) and for the cytosolic activated form of the glucocorticoid receptor from rat liver (Wrange *et al.*, 1979). This suggests that the untransformed molybdate-stabilized receptor may represent a tetramer of steroid binding subunits which dissociate upon activation to yield a 3.5–4.5 S-sedimenting species with a molecular weight of approximately 90,000 which represents the activated nuclear binding form of the receptor.

In addition to inhibiting receptor transformation, molybdate may also act to protect the receptor from proteolytic digestion. Sherman *et al.* (1980) demonstrated that 20 mM molybdate inhibited the conversion of steroid hormone receptors to smaller forms and was as effective as leupeptin in preventing the degradation of receptor to smaller components by proteolytic enzymes. In the absence of molybdate or leupeptin, rat kidney cytosolic glucocorticoid receptors were converted to smaller sedimenting species and concentrations of molybdate which inhibit a cytosolic protease prevented these modifications of receptor (Moran *et al.*, 1980). With molybdate or leupeptin, the unactivated glucocorticoid receptor from rat kidney cytosol sediments as a 9.9 S species in low-ionic-strength gradients. Therefore, although molybdate prevents receptor transformation, possibly by directly interacting with the receptor, some reported effects of molybdate on stabilizing the receptor may reflect inhibition of cytosol proteolytic activity. Although the large molecular size of the untransformed receptor with molybdate or leupeptin under low-salt conditions (Sherman *et al.*, 1980; Niu *et al.*, 1981) may represent a nonspecific aggregate, this may reflect the native state of the untransformed receptor in the intact cell. Whether the 9–10 S untransformed receptor represents artifactual aggregates, a multimer of hormone binding subunits, or the interaction of receptor with a nonligand binding component which dissociates on transformation has not yet been clarified with isolated cytosolic preparations.

B. Conversion of Receptor from a 10 S to a 4 S Form Occurs with Hormone-Mediated Activation in Intact GH$_1$ Cells

We have recently explored the properties of receptor activation in intact GH$_1$ cells in conjunction with dense amino acid labeling of glucocorticoid receptors (Raaka and Samuels, 1981b, 1983). These studies suggest an equilibrium model for hormone-mediated receptor activation and nuclear translocation in which the unactivated receptor is a multimeric protein (tetramer?) with a sedimentation coefficient of about 10 S and is composed of hormone-binding, 3.5–4 S subunits. Binding of hormone to the 10 S unactivated receptor appears to shift the equilibrium between the oligomeric 10 S receptor and its 4 S subunit toward the 4 S form. The 4 S species represents activated receptor, is a DNA binding protein, and is in equilibrium with receptor bound to chromatin in the cell nucleus. Evidence to support this model comes from (1) dense amino acid labeling studies; (2) agonist dose–response conversion of the 10 S to the 4 S form; (3) inhibition of the kinetics of translocation and the conversion of the 10 S to the 4 S species in intact cells incubated with molybdate; (4) the recycling of nuclear translocated receptor to cytosol after removal of hormone regenerates the 10 S form without requirement for new receptor synthesis; and (5) the inhibition of the 10 S-to-4 S conversion and nuclear translocation of the receptor by antiglucocorticoid compounds.

Figure 24 illustrates the sedimentation profile of cytosolic glucocorticoid receptors from GH$_1$ cells incubated with 10 n*M* [^{3}H]triamcinolone acetonide at 37°C for 1 hour. This concentration occupies greater than 90% of the receptor population and elicits translocation of 70% of cytosolic receptors. The control cells received no hormone at 37°C but were incubated at 0°C with 10 n*M* [^{3}H]triamcinolone acetonide to occupy untransformed cytosolic receptors in intact cells. Cells incubated with [^{3}H]triamcinolone acetonide at 0°C showed no nuclear translocation of receptor and a single cytosolic

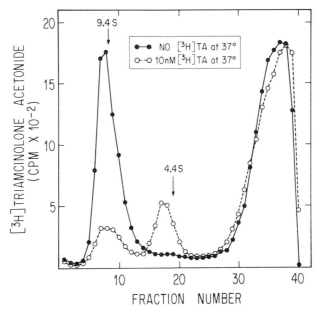

FIG. 24. Sedimentation of cytosolic receptor from GH₁ cells incubated with [³H]triamcinolone acetonide. GH₁ cells were incubated for 1 hour at 37°C with 10 nM [³H]triamcinolone acetonide ([³H]TA). The cells were then incubated for 4 additional hours in an ice-water bath (○). Parallel cell cultures were incubated with 10 nM [³H]triamcinolone acetonide only at 0°C for the entire 5-hour period (●). Cytosol was then prepared in low-ionic-strength buffer and was sedimented in low-ionic-strength sucrose gradients. Sedimentation was from right to left. Parallel gradients contained protein standards β-amylase (9.4 S) and bovine serum albumin (4.4 S). From Raaka and Samuels (1983).

form which sedimented at 10 S. In contrast, cells incubated with 10 n*M* [³H]triamcinolone acetonide at 37°C showed a decrease in the amount of the 10 S form as well as increase in receptor which sedimented at about 4 S. Dose–response studies at 37°C with [³H]triamcinolone acetonide from 1 to 10 n*M* showed a dose-dependent decrease in the 10 S cytosolic form and a dose-dependent increase in the 4 S form which increased in parallel with the amount of nuclear-associated receptor. This suggests that the 10 S receptor represents unactivated receptor and the 4 S cytosolic form represents the activated nuclear binding form of the receptor (Raaka and Samuels, 1983). This conclusion was further supported by experiments which showed that the 4 S form binds to highly polymerized duplex DNA while the 10 S form is not a DNA binding species. In addition, incubation of GH₁ cells with 30 m*M* sodium molybdate decreased the ligand-mediated kinetics of nuclear translocation as well as the kinetics of conversion of the 10 S to the 4 S cytosolic form of the receptor.

C. 17α-METHYLTESTOSTERONE INHIBITS 10 S-TO-4 S RECEPTOR CONVERSION BY GLUCOCORTICOID AGONISTS

Figure 25 shows that conversion of receptor from the 10 S to the 4 S form is important for receptor translocation and hormone action. This study illustrates the distribution of glucocorticoid receptors in cells incubated for 1 hour at 37°C with 2 n*M* [³H]triamcinolone acetonide and various concentrations of nonradioactive 17α-methyltestosterone. After incubation, cytosol was isolated and incubated for 3 hours at 4°C with 100 n*M* [³H]triamcinolone acetonide to exchange for receptor-bound 17α-methyltestosterone. Binding of [³H]triamcinolone acetonide to nuclei was assessed from the first incubation without a second exchange incubation. In the absence of 17α-methyltestosterone, 2 n*M* [³H]triamcinolone acetonide elicits nuclear translocation of 40% total cell receptor, which is expected since this is a subsaturating concentration of hormone (Raaka and Samuels, 1983).

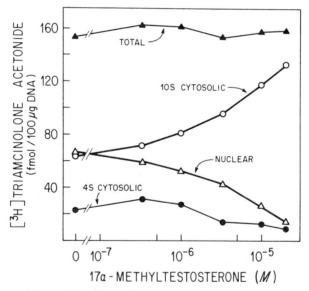

FIG. 25. Distribution of glucocorticoid receptor forms in cells incubated with 17α-methyltestosterone. GH₁ cells were incubated for 1 hour at 37°C with 2 n*M* [³H]triamcinolone acetonide and the indicated concentrations of nonradioactive 17α-methyltestosterone. Cytosol was prepared and then incubated for 3 hours at 4°C with 100 n*M* [³H]triamcinolone acetonide to exchange for bound unlabeled 17α-methyltestosterone. Unbound steroid was removed by chromotography on Sephadex LH-20 columns and the eluted receptor was sedimented in low-ionic-strength sucrose gradients to quantitate the amount of 10 S and 4 S receptor forms. Specific hormone binding in nuclei was assessed without exchange. From Raaka and Samuels (1981b).

With increasing concentrations of 17α-methyltestosterone, the amounts of nuclear and 4 S receptors decrease and the amount of 10 S cytosolic receptor increases while the total amount of receptor remains constant. This indicates that exchange of bound unlabeled 17α-methyltestosterone for [³H] triamcinolone acetonide in the cytosol was complete and that no receptor occupied with 17α-methyltestosterone was translocated to the nucleus. Therefore, 17α-methyltestosterone appears to function as an antiglucocorticoid by inhibiting nuclear translocation as a result of binding to the 10 S cytosolic receptor but without converting the 10 S form to the DNA-binding 4 S form.

D. DENSE AMINO ACID LABELING OF RECEPTOR INDICATES THAT THE 10 S RECEPTOR IS A MULTIMER THAT CONTAINS HORMONE BINDING SUBUNITS

The above studies support the notion that ligand-mediated receptor activation in intact GH_1 cells involves the conversion of a 10 S to a 4 S receptor form. The 10 S receptor form may represent a large polypeptide which is converted to the 4 S form by specific proteases in the cell. Alternatively, it may represent a multimer that contains hormone binding subunits that dissociate upon ligand activation. Such a multimeric species could consist of steroid receptor binding subunits as well as components that do not bind hormone and would therefore go undetected. Dense amino acid labeling studies in intact GH_1 cells indicate that the 10 S cytosolic glucocorticoid receptor represents a multimeric structure composed of hormone binding subunits (Raaka and Samuels, 1983).

Figure 26 illustrates density labeling of the glucocorticoid receptor in cells not incubated with glucocorticoid. In this study cells were incubated with dense amino acids for 11.5 hours and 46 hours while control cells were incubated with amino acids of normal density. Cytosol was isolated, incubated with [³H]triamcinolone acetonide, and treated with 0.4 M KCl *in vitro* prior to sedimentation in 15–30% sucrose–D_2O gradients containing 0.4 M KCl. Under these conditions, the KCl-treated, normal-density receptor sediments as a sharp peak at about 4 S. After 11.5 hours with dense amino acids, approximately equal amounts of normal-density receptor and faster sedimenting dense receptor are present. Finally, after 46 hours, almost all the KCl-treated receptor is dense. The density labeling results for the KCl-treated glucocorticoid receptor showing discrete dense and normal receptor peaks on sucrose gradients are similar to those shown for the thyroid hormone nuclear receptor (Fig. 12).

The study shown in Figure 27 is from the same experiment shown in

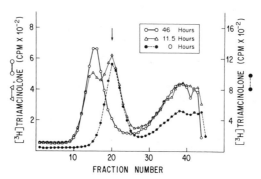

FIG. 26. Separation of normal and dense glucocorticoid receptors in sucrose–D$_2$O gradients containing 0.4 M KCl. GH$_1$ cells were cultured in normal or dense medium without glucocorticoids for a total of 48 hours. Normal medium was replaced with dense medium 11.5 or 46 hours before harvesting the cells. Cytosol was prepared in low-salt buffer and incubated for 3 hours at 4°C with 50 nM [^{3}H]triamcinolone acetonide. After unbound steroid was removed on a column of Sephadex LH-20, the cytosol was adjusted to contain 0.4 M KCl by addition of 4 M KCl. The KCl-treated cytosol was incubated for 1 hour at 4°C and then applied to 15–30% sucrose gradients prepared in D$_2$O containing 0.4 M KCl. The arrow marks the sedimentation position in a parallel gradient of ovalbumin, which sediments at 3.5 S. Sedimentation is from right to left. From Raaka and Samuels (1983).

Fig. 26 except that the cytosol was not treated with KCl and was sedimented in 30–45% sucrose–D$_2$O gradients without KCl. Under these conditions, the normal-density receptor sediments as a sharp peak at about 10 S. After 46 hours with dense amino acids, the receptor sediments considerably faster and produces a broader peak than the normal-density receptor. The receptor peak after 11.5 hours with dense amino acids is extremely broad and positioned midway between the normal and 46-hour dense receptor peaks. Other experiments confirmed that the 10 S receptor form undergoes a gradual increase in density as the time of incubation of cells with dense amino acids is increased. This result is in contrast to that observed for the 4 S receptor form, where discrete normal and dense receptor peaks were seen after density labeling for 11.5 hours (Fig. 26). This suggests that the species of intermediate density observed after the 11.5-hour incubation with dense amino acids (Fig. 27) represents an oligomeric structure of newly synthesized dense and preexisting 4 S receptor subunits. Mixing experiments at 4°C with [^{3}H]triamcinolone acetonide-labeled 10 S receptor of normal density and receptor obtained from a 46-hour incubation with dense amino acids and occupied with nonradioactive triamcinolone acetonide showed a single radiolabeled peak of 10 S receptor of normal density. This indicates that randomization of 4 S receptor subunits does not occur in buffer or during centrifugation in the gradient. Therefore, the receptor of intermediate density (Fig. 27) indicates that randomization of newly synthesized dense and preexisting normal subunits occurs in the intact cell.

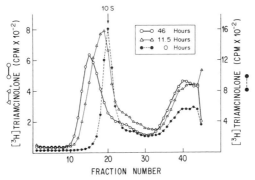

Fig. 27. Sedimentation of normal and dense forms of the glucocorticoid receptor in sucrose–D_2O gradients without KCl. GH_1 cells were cultured in medium without glucocorticoids. Normal medium was replaced with dense medium at the times indicated before harvesting the cells. Cytosol was prepared in low-salt buffer and incubated for 3 hours at 4°C with 50 nM [^3H]triamcinolone acetonide. Unbound steroid was then removed on a column of Sephadex LH-20 and the cytosol was applied to 30–45% sucrose gradients prepared in D_2O without KCl. Sedimentation is from right to left. From Raaka and Samuels (1983).

This explains both the gradual density shift as well as the broadening of the dense amino acid labeled 10 S receptor form. Incubation of GH_1 cells with dense amino acids for varying times, followed by KCl treatment *in vitro* and resolution of the individual dense and normal receptor forms, indicates that the 4 S receptor form has a half-life of approximately 10 hours (Raaka and Samuels, 1983). This is in keeping with the results of Fig. 26 which shows that 11.5 hours of dense amino acid labeling results in almost equal amounts of 4 S receptor of high and normal density. Dense amino acid labeling for one half-life will convert about 50% of the 4 S subunit pool to the dense form. If the 10 S receptor is a homologous tetramer in rapidly exchanging equilibrium with its 4 S subunit, when 50% of the 4 S component is dense, the 10 S receptor will show a density shift intermediate between 10 S receptor of normal and high density. Broadening is consistent with random distribution of 4 S forms into the 10 S tetramer, which results in a proportion of the 10 S receptor being more and less dense than 10 S receptor composed of equal numbers of dense and normal 4 S forms.

E. An Equilibrium Model for Receptor Activation, Translocation, and Recycling

These studies are consistent with an equilibrium model for glucocorticoid receptor activation and translocation as shown in Fig. 28 (Raaka and Samuels, 1983). In the absence of hormone, the receptor is a 10 S cytosolic protein, compatible with a tetrameric structure of identical 4 S subunits,

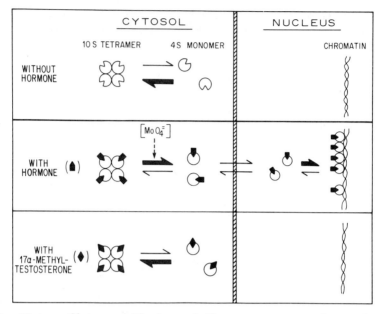

FIG. 28. An equilibrium model for glucocorticoid receptor activation, nuclear translocation, and recycling.

which is in rapid equilibrium with the 4 S monomer. Without hormone, the equilibrium between the 10 S and 4 S form strongly favors the 10 S form. The binding of glucocorticoid agonists shifts the 10 S–4 S equilibrium in the direction of the 4 S form which appears to represent activated receptor and is a DNA binding species. Competition studies indicate that the glucocorticoid antagonist 17α-methyltestosterone binds to the 10 S receptor but does not shift the equilibrium toward the 4 S activated form and consequently does not elicit translocation of the receptor to the cell nucleus.

This equilibrium model predicts that if hormone is removed from cells after receptor has been translocated to the nucleus, the nuclear-bound receptor and the 4 S cytosolic form should recycle and regenerate the 10 S species. This was verified in a study that examined the sedimentation profile of cytosol receptor 2 hours after removal of hormone from cells in which 70% of the receptor had been translocated to the nucleus (Raaka and Samuels, 1983). Hormone removal was achieved by incubating cells for 2 hours with hormone-free dense amino acid medium. All nuclear-associated receptor and 4 S cytosolic receptor were recovered as a 10 S receptor form. Virtually no density shift of the 10 S receptor was observed, indicating that all the reformed 10 S receptor was composed of nuclear receptor and 4 S cytosolic receptor of normal density that recombined in the cytosol in the absence of hormone to generate the 10 S unactivated receptor form.

VI. CONCLUDING REMARKS

Cultured GH_1 cells and related cell lines (GH_3 and GC) provide useful models to study the control of growth hormone synthesis in cell culture. In addition these cell lines have also shown to be useful in characterizing the biological properties in thyroid and glucocorticoid hormone receptors. Studies in these cells have shown that the thyroid hormone receptor is a chromatin-associated regulatory protein which can be extracted from nuclei using high-ionic-strength conditions. The hormone binding component is not identified in the cytosolic fraction and the steady-state level of nuclear-bound receptor appears to be solely defined in the absence of chronic hormone incubation by a half-life of approximately 5 hours and a synthetic rate of 1700 molecules/hour/cell. Thyroid hormone can elicit a reduction in receptor and the earliest change is due to an effect in which thyroid hormone decreases the accumulation of newly synthesized receptor while late effects also result in shortening of receptor half-life. The change in receptor levels may influence the characteristics of the growth hormone response to thyroid hormone in cell culture and in the somatotroph cell *in vivo*.

In the absence of thyroid hormone, glucocorticoid agonists do not significantly stimulate growth hormone synthesis or mRNA accumulation in GH_1 cells. Cells incubated with both thyroid and glucocorticoid hormones show a synergistic response which is two- to fivefold greater than that observed with thyroid hormone alone. The stimulation of growth hormone synthesis and mRNA by glucocorticoid in the presence of thyroid hormone appears to be mediated by the classical glucocorticoid receptor. Antiglucocorticoid compounds inhibit the glucocorticoid component of the growth hormone response by decreasing growth hormone mRNA levels to the value observed for thyroid hormone alone. This suggests that thyroid hormone may act as a primary regulator of the response and glucocorticoids act to further amplify the response initiated by thyroid hormone. In GH_1 cells, the mechanism of glucocorticoid receptor activation and nuclear translocation is consistent with an equilibrium model in which the unactivated receptor is a 10 S tetramer that is in rapid equilibrium with a 4 S monomer. Glucocorticoid agonists shift the 10 S–4 S equilibrium in the direction of the 4 S form, which appears to be activated receptor and shows high affinity for DNA. Antiglucocorticoids (17α-methyltestosterone) bind to the 10 S receptor but do not shift the equilibrium to the 4 S DNA binding form and consequently can inhibit the action of glucocorticoid agonists.

Thyroid hormone does not influence total nuclear glucocorticoid receptor levels (Fig. 19) (Samuels *et al.*, 1978), and glucocorticoids do not influence the abundance of thyroid hormone nuclear receptors (Samuels *et al.*, 1977a). This suggests that the nuclear-associated receptors for both hormones interact to regulate the growth hormone response. Whether this interaction occurs at the level of the growth hormone gene or distant regulatory loci has not yet been defined. The rat growth hormone gene has recently been cloned and has been shown to contain five structural gene segments (exons) and four intervening sequences with a total length estimated to be 2.1 kb (Chien and Thompson 1980). Maurer *et al.* (1980) showed that nuclear RNA from GC cells contained a 2.3-kb species that can hybridize to a $[^{32}P]$cDNA rat growth hormone probe and presumably represents the primary transcript of the growth hormone gene. Using GH_3 cells cultured in medium supplemented with a serum substitute, Dobner *et al.* (1981) reported that L-T_3 stimulated an increase of growth hormone mRNA fourfold, while glucocorticoids alone stimulated growth hormone mRNA sequences 22-fold. In contrast, the combination of L-T_3 plus glucocorticoid increased the response 13-fold, which was intermediate between that observed with L-T_3 or glucocorticoid alone. In each case a parallelism was noted between the abundance of the 1-kb growth hormone mRNA species in the cytoplasm and a 2.7-kb nuclear species which presumably represents the primary gene transcript. These results are discordant with those previously reported in GH_1 cells (Shapiro *et al.*, 1978; Samuels *et al.*, 1979b) and GC cells (Martial *et al.*, 1977a) in that the response observed for L-T_3 plus glucocorticoid was less than that of those observed for glucocorticoid alone. Whether this is a characteristic of GH_3 cells or reflects the properties of culturing cells with a serum substitute is not clear. However, in each case the abundance of the putative primary nuclear transcript of the growth hormone gene and cyptoplasmic growth hormone mRNA levels were parallel, suggesting that thyroid and glucocorticoid hormone receptors can act to accelerate the transcription of the growth hormone gene. Whether multihormonal regulation of the growth hormone gene involves a direct interaction of thyroid and glucocorticoid receptors with the gene or from the indirect stimulation of other factors which can regulate the gene may be resolved in the near future using recombinant DNA studies.

ACKNOWLEDGMENTS

Research carried out in the author's (H. H. S.) laboratory was supported by Research Grants BC123 from the American Cancer Society and AM 16636 and AM 21566 from the National Institutes of Health. We would like to thank Mary McCarthy for her patience and expert assistance in typing this manuscript.

REFERENCES

Bancroft, F. C., Levine, L., and Tashjian, A. H., Jr. (1969). *J. Cell Biol.* **43**, 432–441.

Cake, M. H., DiSorbo, D. M., and Litwack, G. (1978). *J. Biol. Chem.* **253**, 4886–4891.

Chien, Y.-H., and Thompson, E. B. (1980). *Proc. Natl. Acad. Sci. U.S.A.* **77**, 4583–4587.

Cidlowski, J. A., and Thanassi, J. W. (1979). *Biochemistry* **18**, 2378–2384.

Coulombe, P., Schwartz, H. L., and Oppenheimer, J. H. (1978) *J. Clin. Invest.* **62**, 1020–1028.

Devreotes, P. N., Gardner, J. M., and Fambrough, D. M. (1977). *Cell* **10**, 365–373.

Dobner, P. R., Kawasaki, E. W., Yu, L.-Y., and Bancroft, F. C. (1981). *Proc. Natl. Acad. Sci. U.S.A.* **78**, 2230–2234.

Feldman, D., and Loose, D. (1977). *Endocrinology (Baltimore)* **100**, 398–405.

Finkelstein, J. W., Boyer, R. M., and Hellman, L. (1974). *J. Clin. Endocrinol. Metab.* **38**, 634–637.

Foster, S. J., and Perkins, J. P. (1977). *Proc. Natl. Acad. Sci. U.S.A.* **74**, 4816–4820.

Goidl, J. A., Cake, M. H., Dolan, K. P., Parchman, G., and Litwack, G. (1977). *Biochemistry* **16**, 2125–2130.

Goslings, B., Schwartz, H. L., Dillmann, W., Surks, M. I., and Oppenheimer, J. H. (1976). *Endocrinology (Baltimore)* **98**, 666–675.

Gruol, D. J. (1980). *Endocrinology (Baltimore)* **107**, 994–999.

Hershko, A., and Tomkins, G. M. (1971). *J. Biol. Chem.* **256**, 710–714.

Hervas, F., Morreale de Escobar, G., and Escobar Del Ray, F. (1975). *Endocrinology (Baltimore)* **97**, 91–101.

Higgins, S. J., Rousseau, G. G., Baxter, J. D., and Tomkins, G. M. (1973). *J. Biol. Chem.* **248**, 5866–5872.

Huntlermann, A., and Wendelberger, G. (1976). *Methods Cell Biol.* **13**, 153–170.

Ivarie, R. D., Baxter, J. D., and Morris, J. D. (1981). *J. Biol. Chem.* **256**, 4520–4528.

Jump, D. B., and Oppenheimer, J. H. (1980). *Science* **209**, 811–813.

Kalimi, M., Colman, P., and Feigelson, P. (1975). *J. Biol. Chem.* **250**, 1080–1086.

Koerner, D., Schwartz, H. L., Surks, M. I., Oppenheimer, J. H., and Jorgensen, E. C. (1975). *J. Biol. Chem.* **250**, 6417–6423.

Kohler, P. O., Frohman, L. A., Bridson, W. E., Vanha-Perttula, T., and Hammond, J. M. (1969). *Science* **166**, 633–634.

Latham, K. R., Ring, J. C., and Baxter, J. D. (1976). *J. Biol. Chem.* **251**, 7388–7397.

Lewis, U. J., Cheever, E. V., and Vanderlaan, W. P. (1965). *Endocrinology (Baltimore)* **76**, 362–368.

McBlain, W. A., Toft, D. O., and Shyamala, G. (1981). *Biochemistry* **20**, 6790–6798.

Martial, J. A., Seeburg, P. H., Guenzi, D., Goodman, H. M., and Baxter, J. D. (1977a). *Proc. Natl. Acad. Sci. U.S.A.* **74**, 4293–4295.

Martial, J. A., Baxter, J. D., Goodman, H. M., and Seeburg, P. H. (1977b). *Proc. Natl. Acad. Sci. U.S.A.* **74**, 1816–1820.

Maurer, R. A., Gubbins, E. J., Erwin, C. R., and Donelson, J. E. (1980). *J. Biol. Chem.* **255**, 2243–2246.

Middlebrook, J. L., and Aronow, L. (1977). *Endocrinology (Baltimore)* **100**, 271–282.

Moran, M. C., Tuazon, F. B., and Sherman, M. R. (1980). *62nd Annu. Meet. Endocr. Soc.* Abstract No. 170, p. 117.

Nishigori, H., and Toft, D. (1980). *Biochemistry* **19**, 77–83.

Niu, E. M., Neal, R. M., Pierce, V. K., and Sherman, M. R. (1981). *J. Steroid Biochem.* **15**, 1–10.

O'Malley, B. W., and Means, A. R. (1974). *Science* **183**, 610–620.

Oppenheimer, J. H., and Dillmann, W. H. (1978). In "Receptors and Hormone Action" (B. W. O'Malley and L. Birnbaumer, eds.), Vol. 3, pp. 1–33. Academic Press, New York.

Oppenheimer, J. H., and Surks, M. I. (1975). In "Biochemical Actions of Hormones" (G. Litwack, ed.), Vol. 3, pp. 119–157. Academic Press, New York.

Oppenheimer, J. H., Schwartz, H. L., Koerner, D., and Surks, M. I. (1975). *Endocr. Res. Commun.* **2**, 309–325.

Peake, G. T., Birge, C. A., and Daughaday, W. H. (1973). *Endocrinology (Baltimore)* **92**, 487–493.

Perlman, A. J., Stanley, F., and Samuels, H. H. (1982). *J. Biol. Chem.* **257**, 930–938.

Raaka, B. M., and Samuels, H. H. (1981a). *J. Biol. Chem.* **256**, 6883–6889.

Raaka, B. M., and Samuels, H. H. (1981b). *Clin. Res.* **29**, 507a.

Raaka, B. M., and Samuels, H. H. (1983). *J. Biol. Chem.* **258**, 417–425.

Ringold, G. M., Yamamoto, K. R., Tomkins, G. M., Bishop, J. M., and Varmus, H. E. (1975). *Cell* **6**, 299–305.

Rousseau, G. G., Baxter, J. D., Higgins, S. J., and Tomkins, G. M. (1973). *J. Mol. Biol.* **79**, 539–554.

Samuels, H. H. (1978). In "Receptors and Hormone Action" (B. W. O'Malley and L. Birnbaumer, eds.), Vol. 3, pp. 35–74. Academic Press, New York.

Samuels, H. H., and Shapiro, L. E. (1976). *Proc. Natl. Acad. Sci. U.S.A.* **73**, 3369–3373.

Samuels, H. H., and Tomkins, G. M. (1970). *J. Mol. Biol.* **52**, 57–74.

Samuels, H. H., and Tsai, J. S. (1973). *Proc. Natl. Acad. Sci. U.S.A.* **70**, 3488–3482.

Samuels, H. H., Tsai, J. S., and Cintron, R. (1973). *Science* **181**, 1253–1256.

Samuels, H. H., Tsai, J. S., Casanova, J., and Stanley, F. (1974). *J. Clin. Invest.* **54**, 853–865.

Samuels, H. H., Stanley, F., and Shapiro, L. E. (1976). *Proc. Natl. Acad. Sci. U.S.A.* **73**, 3877–3881.

Samuels, H. H., Horowitz, Z. D., Stanley, F., Casanova, J., and Shapiro, L. E. (1977a). *Nature (London)* **268**, 254–257.

Samuels, H. H., Stanley, F., and Shapiro, L. E. (1977b). *J. Biol. Chem.* **252**, 6052–6060.

Samuels, H. H., Klein, D., Stanely, F., and Casanova, J. (1978). *J. Biol. Chem.* **253**, 5895–5898.

Samuels, H. H., Stanley, F., and Shapiro, L. E. (1979a). *Biochemistry* **18**, 715–721.

Samuels, H. H., Stanley, F., and Casanova, J. (1979b). *Endocrinology (Baltimore)* **105**, 80–85.

Samuels, H. H., Stanley, F., and Casanova, J. (1979c). *J. Clin. Invest.* **63**, 1229–1240.

Samuels, H. H., Stanley, F., and Shao, T. C. (1980). *J. Biol. Chem.* **255**, 2499–2508.

Samuels, H. H., Perlman, A. J., Raaka, B. M., and Stanley, F. (1982). *Recent Prog. Horm. Res.* **38**, 557–599.

Scatchard, G. (1949). *Ann. N. Y. Acad. Sci.* **51**, 660–672.

Schadlow, A. R., Surks, M. I., Schwartz, H. L., and Oppenheimer, J. H. (1972). *Science* **176**, 1253.

Seo, H., Vassart, G., Brocas, H., and Refetoff, S. (1977). *Proc. Natl. Acad. Sci. U.S.A.* **74**, 2054–2058.

Shapiro, L. E., Samuels, H. H., and Yaffe, B. M. (1978). *Proc. Natl. Acad. Sci. U.S.A.* **75**, 45–49.

Sherman, M. R., Pickering, L. A., Rollwagen, F. M., and Miller, L. K. (1978). *Fed Proc., Fed. Am. Soc. Exp. Biol.* **37**, 167–173.

Sherman, M. R., Tuazon, F. B., and Miller, L. K. (1980). *Endocrinology (Baltimore)* **106**, 1715–1727.

Shyamala, G. (1975). *Biochemistry* **14**, 437–444.

Solomon, J., and Greep, R. O. (1959). *Endocrinology (Baltimore)* **65**, 158–164.

Spindler, B. J., MacLeod, K. M., Ring, J., and Baxter, J. D. (1975). *J. Biol. Chem.* **250**, 4113–4119.

Stevens, J., Stevens, Y.-W., and Rosenthal, R. L. (1979). *Cancer Res.* **39**, 4939–4948.

Tsai, J. S., and Samuels, H. H. (1974). *Biochem. Biophys. Res. Commun.* **59**, 420–428.

Wrange, O., Carlstedt-Duke, J., and Gustafsson, J.-A. (1979). *J. Biol. Chem.* **254**, 9284–9290.

Yasumura, Y., Tashjian, A. H., Jr., and Sato, G. H. (1966). *Science* **154**, 1186–1189.

Young, H. A., Scolnick, E. M., and Parks, W. P. (1975). *J. Biol. Chem.* **250**, 3337–3343.

Yu, L.-Y., Tushinski, R. J., and Bancroft, F. C. (1977). *J. Biol. Chem.* **252**, 3870–3875.

CHAPTER 5

Factors Affecting Mammary Cells in Culture

Tamiko Kano-Sueoka

I. INTRODUCTION

Extensive studies in the past three decades have clearly demonstrated the role of ovarian and adrenal corticosteroid hormones and pituitary peptide hormones in growth and development of mammary gland *in vivo*. These hormones have primarily been identified by ablating various endocrine organs in experimental animals and replacing possible missing hor-

BIOCHEMICAL ACTIONS OF HORMONES, VOL. X

mones. Estrogen, progesterone, prolactin or placental lactogen, and growth hormone were thus identified as being mammogenic hormones in rodents. (Lyons *et al.*, 1958; Topper and Freemen, 1980). Puzzling but interesting facts about the action of these hormones are that obvious proliferative responses of mammary cells to these mammogenic hormones have rarely been observed in various *in vitro* culture systems where direct effects of hormones can be examined. Several reasons can be delineated to explain this paradox.

1. These mammogenic hormones act directly on mammary epithelial (ME) cells. However, the culture methods so far used by various investigators do not allow ME cells to express their *in vivo* hormone responsiveness because the ME cells require a particular spatial organization for them to be hormone responsive.

2. These mammogenic hormones act directly, but the culture systems generally used lack some essential growth factor(s) for these hormones to exert the mitogenic effect.

3. Action of these hormones on ME cells is not direct, but involves some indirect actions mediated by adjacent cells of different cell types or by remote organs. In this case, the primary target of the hormones could be ME cells or other types of cells, and the mediating cells should produce a mammary growth factor or factors in response to the hormones.

4. Any combination of the above three.

It is at present largely unknown which case is correct. The hormone-primed immature gland, if whole mammary glands are used, can develop to the lobuloalveolar structure of pregnant animals only in the presence of prolactin and ovarian or corticosteroid hormones (Ichinose and Nandi, 1966; Mehta and Banerjee, 1975). These results indicate that the mammogenic hormones suffice at least for the requirement of growth of the whole gland culture. In principle, we should then be able to analyze the mechanism of action of these hormones by dissecting various elements of the whole gland culture. There are also strong indications that estrogen and prolactin can stimulate growth of some neoplastic ME cells in culture (Lippman *et al.*, 1979; Kano-Sueoka and Errick, 1982). These can also be used as a handle to understand the mammogenic hormone action.

Regarding indirect action of the mammogenic hormones, there is some evidence suggesting that estrogen may be acting indirectly, mediated by the agents produced in tissues other than mammary cells, as reviewed extensively in the previous volume of this treatise (Sirbasku and Leland, 1982).

In this chapter we will summarize known facts about direct and indirect mitogenic actions *in vitro* of mammogenic hormones and growth factors which may or may not be regarded as candidates for mediators of these hormones. Some other nutritional elements, which may be unique to growth of ME cells, will also be discussed. An attempt will also be made, wherever possible, to resolve the paradox of *in vivo* and *in vitro* observations. Although meaningful *in vitro* results are not yet abundant, a brief account of the present knowledge presented in this chapter is enough to indicate the complex nature of the mitogenic action of mammogenic hormones.

II. METHODS TO CULTURE MAMMARY CELLS

The mammary gland consists of two kinds of epithelial cells, mammary epithelial cells and myoepithelial cells, which are organized into ducts and terminal units, and mesenchymal cells which form mammary fat pads. In this chapter we are mainly concerned with proliferation of ME cells that produce milk.

In order to examine the mechanism of action of hormones and growth factors, it is important that a given *in vitro* culture system retain and express the *in vivo* behavior of the original tissue. There have been several different ways to culture the mammary cells. There are advantages and disadvantages to each method depending on the purpose of the study. A brief summary of various culture methods which have been used to study ME cells will be summarized below.

Whole gland culture. Hormone-responsive whole gland culture was developed using estrogen- and progesterone-primed mouse mammary glands (Ichinose and Nandi, 1966). The whole gland culture has a definite advantage in that the spatial relationships of ME cells among themselves and with other cell types are undisturbed. However, it is difficult to analyze the direct effect of a given agent on ME cells. Using this system, important information has been obtained showing that only mammogenic hormones satisfy the need of immature mammary gland to develop to pregnancy-like lobuloalveolar structure when ovarian steroid-primed glands are used.

Organ culture. Integral organization of the gland is largely preserved when pieces of the gland are cultured. When animals larger than the mouse are used, this may be the closest to the *in vivo* situation. Historically, this method has been used frequently for culturing both normal and neoplastic tissues.

Organoid culture. Collagenase digestion of minced mammary gland and removal of stromal cells by differential centrifugation yield an epithelial structure consisting of ME cells and myoepithelial cells, which mimics the *in vivo* intercellular relationship among epithelial cells but lacks stromal cells. The organoid preparations have been used successfully to obtain sustained growth of ME cells.

Cell culture. Both primary culture and permanently established cell lines have been used. Monodispersed normal ME cells do not survive very well in culture. However, long-term culture of neoplastic mammary cells is relatively easy to accomplish, and many established cell lines of mammary carcinoma have been used to investigate the growth-promoting effects of hormones and growth factors.

Serum-free defined medium. Traditionally, culture media have been supplemented with serum to supply hormones, growth factors, and undefined nutrients required for cell growth. Therefore, the effect of hormones and growth factors to be tested can be obscured by the presence of serum. Recent progress in establishing hormone-supplemented serum-free media for various types of cells facilitates greatly the study of hormone action using cultured cells, and mammary cells are no exception (Allegra and Lippman, 1978; Barnes and Sato, 1979). As described in the following sections, use of the serum-free medium has contributed considerably to an understanding of mammogenic hormone action in mammary cells.

III. MAMMOGENIC HORMONES AS MITOGENS

As stated in the Introduction, there exists a paradox that mammogenic hormones defined by *in vivo* studies do not exert mitogenic activities on ME cells in the majority of *in vitro* studies. In this section the studies where positive mitogenic effects have been indicated will be presented.

A. ESTROGEN AND PROGESTERONE

Taylor-Papadimitriou and Fentiman (1981) have shown that estrogen (1 ng/ml) and progesterone (1 μg/ml) stimulate the growth of human milk epithelial cells if the cells are cultured in the absence of serum and in the presence of fibroblast feeder layers. The results were variable, but most of the time these hormones gave 1.5- to 3.5-fold stimulation of [^{3}H]thymidine incorporation when added singly.

Lippman and his colleagues (1979) have shown that growth of human breast carcinoma cell lines ZR-75-1 and MCF-7 is significantly stimulated by 17β-estradiol at 10^{-9} M in a serum-free hormone-supplemented medium.

The antiestrogen tamoxifen is inhibitory to the growth-promoting effect of estrogen, and its inhibitory effect can be overcome by one-thousandth the amount of estradiol. These cells contain estrogen receptors and the action of antiestrogen has been shown to act via estrogen receptors. Nawata *et al.* (1981a,b) have isolated a variant of MCF-7 cells which is resistant to the inhibition of growth by antiestrogen and is not stimulated to grow by estrogen. Properties of estrogen receptors of this variant were shown to be different from those of the parent line, indicating again that estrogen–antiestrogen effects on proliferation of MCF-7 cells are mediated by estrogen receptors. These results indicate rather convincingly that estrogen can be a mitogen to ME cells. The fact that Shionogi mouse mammary carcinoma, which is dependent on androgen for growth *in vivo*, is clearly growth responsive to androgen *in vitro* (Desmond *et al.*, 1976) supports further the notion that a steroid hormone can be a mitogen.

Whole gland culture of estrogen- and progesterone-primed mouse mammary gland can undergo extensive lobuloalveolar develdpment in the presence of estrogen, progesterone, insulin, and prolactin (Mehta and Banerjee, 1975). This also shows that the mammary gland as a whole is capable of a growth response to the ovarian steroid.

Reasons why ME cells respond poorly to estrogen in many *in vitro* studies could be the following. (1) Estrogen is a direct mitogen, but somehow the culture conditions usually employed do not allow the cells to express the responsiveness, and only a few cases of highly responsive cells, such as human breast carcinoma cell lines MCF-7 or ZR-75-1, can demonstrate the mitogenic response to estrogen. (2) Estrogen is a weak mitogen itself and its major function is to stimulate other types of cells to produce mammary growth factors. The cells responding to estrogen could be included in the mammary gland, since the whole gland in culture can respond to estrogen. The second idea has been proposed by Sirbasku (1978) and will be discussed in Section IV,F.

B. CORTICOSTEROIDS

Corticosteroids enhance growth of mammary tissue *in vivo*. To support lobuloalveolar growth in whole gland culture, estrogen and progesterone or aldosterone and hydrocortisone are necessary (Mehta and Banerjee, 1975; Tonelli and Sorof, 1980). However, corticosteroids are not always required for growth of mammary carcinoma cells in culture. For example, a serum-free medium devised to culture human breast carcinoma cell line MCF-7 does not contain any glucocorticoid (Barnes and Sato, 1979).

C. PROLACTIN

Prolactin (placental lactogen or human growth hormones may be used interchangeably in most experiments) is regarded as a key hormone that affects the development of normal mammary gland as well as growth of neoplastic mammary tissue. However, there is only limited evidence indicating the mitogenic effect of prolactin in *in vitro* studies. In the following discussion, the cases where the proliferative effect of prolactin has been indicated will first be presented, and then we will consider the reasons for the scarcity of such data.

For the whole gland of mouse to develop extensive lobuloalveolar structure *in vitro*, prolactin is necessary along with insulin and steroid hormones (Ichinose and Nandi, 1966; Mehta and Banerjee, 1975). If prolactin is omitted in the hormone mix, the gland does not develop. The amount of prolactin added in these experiments was 5 μg/ml, which is much higher than normal physiological levels. It is possible that the prolactin preparation was contaminated with macromolecular components. According to our estimate, the most recent preparation of ovine prolactin provided by NIH (NIAMDD-O-PRL-14) contains about 0.5% protein contaminant, having a molecular weight different from that of prolactin. It is possible that some contaminant included in the prolactin preparation is growth stimulatory. There is also a possibility that prolactin is acting through some kind of interaction between ME cells, which contain prolactin receptors, and other cell types which surround ME cells in the gland.

Our laboratory has been interested in solving the paradox of *in vitro* mammogenic hormone action and has made extensive analyses of the effect of prolactin on normal as well as neoplastic rat ME cells *in vitro*. First, we could demonstrate a small but significant mitogenic response of ME cells to ovine prolactin by using primary culture of rat mammary organoid free of stromal cells (J. E. Errick and T. Kano-Sueoka, unpublished observations). The organoids were plated on plastic culture dishes in the presence of 5% fetal calf serum. A day later the medium was changed to 1% fetal calf serum with or without prolactin. [^{3}H]Thymidine incorporation was stimulated about 50% in the presence of prolactin compared to 1% fetal calf serum alone. This increase, though modest, is statistically significant. From the results of over a dozen separate experiments (each experimental point had duplicate or triplicate plates) the extent of stimulation by prolactin versus 1% fetal calf serum alone was 1.47 $\pm$ 0.05 (SE). Moreover, the number of labeled nuclei among ME cells but not myoepithelial cells definitely increased ~50% in the presence of prolactin when examined by radioautography. Dose–response experiments indicated that at 100 ng/ml the proliferative effect of prolactin is obvious, although 1.0 μg/ml gives better stimulation. When prolactin was added together with insulin, a synergistic effect was observed. The degree of stimulation by insulin alone was 2.26 ± 0.12 (SE) while the stimulation by insulin plus prolactin was 3.36 ± 0.38 (SE). It is important to note that the responsiveness of ME cells to prolactin decreases as the culture period increases. Accordingly, by the third day in culture prolactin no longer exerts its proliferative effect in our system. These results suggest rather strongly that prolactin can act as a mitogen to ME cells. However, under the above culture conditions, a possibility exists that myoepithelial cells, which are included in an organoid culture, are somehow indirectly involved in prolactin action.

Many dimethylbenzanthracene (DMBA)-induced rat mammary carcinomas are found to be prolactin responsive *in vivo*. Rudland *et al*. (1977) have shown that secondary cultures of DMBA-induced tumors of the rat are stimulated by bovine prolactin (500 ng/ml) to synthesize DNA at three- to fourfold the rate of controls. This stimulation occurs in the presence of a combination of insulin, hydrocortisone, and prolactin, whereas insulin and hydrocortisone when used without prolactin have no effect. Our laboratory has recently made a detailed study of the growth-promoting effect of prolactin on a clonal rat mammary carcinoma cell line, 64-24, which was isolated from a prolactin-dependent mammary carcinoma (Kano-Sueoka and Hsieh, 1973). Using a serum-free hormone-supplemented medium, a distinct growth-promoting effect of ovine prolactin on these cells was shown, the first such result with carcinoma cells in a long-term culture. In our study the growth stimulation was estimated by the rate of increase in cell numbers. The 64-24 cells could grow in a hormone-supplemented serum-free medium without prolactin. However, in the presence of 0.1 μg/ml ovine prolactin the generation time was 60% shorter than that without prolactin (Kano-Sueoka and Errick, 1982). Dose–response experiments indicate that even at 30–60 ng/ml the stimulatory effect of prolactin can be observed. These are physiological levels. A puzzling phenomenon regarding the prolactin effect in our study was the variability in the degree of stimulation obtained from experiment to experiment: some experiments showed hardly any prolactin response, while others indicated a distinct response. Unfortunately the cause of the variability is not known at present. At any rate, the mitogenic effect of prolactin is highly significant and the value 1.54 ± 0.19 (SE) has been obtained for the ratio of the number of cells in experimental versus control plates after 5 days of growth. Considering the fact that the parent tumor of 64-24 cells is prolactin dependent *in vivo*, the extent of stimulation observed *in vitro* is rather modest. Prolactin can be growth stimulatory under a variety of hormone backgrounds (e.g., with insulin only, or with transferrin and hydrocortisone), indicating that a very specific set of hormones and growth factors is not required for prolactin to be mitogenic under our experimental conditions. It is possible that the mitogenic activity of prolactin may be due to contaminants in ovine prolactin preparations, as stated above. Sodium dodecyl sulfate–acrylamide gel electrophoresis of the ovine prolactin showed about 1/200 to 1/100 contamination by other protein(s). This means that about 1–10 ng protein contaminant is present in the culture medium when 0.1–1 μg/ml prolactin is added. Extensive dialysis of the prolactin solution did not reduce the activity of the prolactin, excluding the possibility that some growth-stimulating material having a small molecular weight was included in the prolactin preparation. These results suggest that the mitogenic effect observed with 64-24 cells is most likely due to prolactin per se.

As summarized above, the mitogenic effect of prolactin on ME cells observed by several investigators is rather modest. Together with many examples of the ineffectiveness of prolactin in ME cell cultures of neoplastic and normal origin, it presents an interesting problem in the field of hormone action.

The following possibilities may be suggested for the behavior of the ME cells in culture.

1. The properties of the cells change in some unknown ways when they are placed in culture such that prolactin cannot act effectively as a mitogen, even if prolactin is really a direct mitogen to ME cells.

2. The environment of the cells in culture is not proper for ME cells to respond to prolactin: the spatial relationship among ME cells, and growth factors or some agents that may be necessary for prolactin to exert a mitogenic effect are among the possible necessary environmental elements.

3. Prolactin action is more complex than just having ME cells as the primary target. Prolactin may cause a cascade effect on more than one cell type which eventually influences the growth of ME cells.

In later sections these possibilities will be discussed as indeed a probable mechanism of prolactin action.

IV. GROWTH FACTORS AND NUTRIENTS

A. FATTY ACIDS

Mammary epithelial cells are located adjacent to a large mass of adipose tissue. This is perhaps because a plentiful supply of fat is necessary for ME cells to proliferate. Indeed, delipidized serum does not support the growth of normal ME cells in culture, while the addition of unsaturated free fatty acids such as linoleic, oleic, or linolenic acid to serum-containing medium stimulates growth of both normal and neoplastic ME cells. Saturated fatty acids, on the other hand, inhibit the growth. Along this line, perphenazine-treated, developing mammary gland contains twice as much linoleic acid as compared to the untreated virgin gland and, conversely, palmitic and stearic acid content is low (Hosick *et al.*, 1978; Wicha *et al.*, 1979). The membrane fraction of chick embryo extract is effective in stimulating growth of mouse mammary carcinoma cells in culture. Since delipidized embryo extract is ineffective, the lipid components of the membrane fraction (embryo is rich in stromal elements) may be growth promoting (Baumann and Hosick, 1978; H. L. Hosick, personal communication). The growth-promoting effect of unsaturated fatty acids is more enhanced if the culture medium contains a mixture of mammogenic hormones (insulin, hydrocortisone, progesterone, estrogen, and prolactin), suggesting a role of hormones in fat metabolism (Wicha *et al.*, 1979). Recently, Kidwell *et al.* (1982b) have suggested an important role of prolactin in fatty acid metabolism. According to their findings, prolactin stimulates the release of fatty acids from rat mammary gland explants; 300 ng/ml ovine prolactin brings about the release of about four times as much free fatty acids as those cultured without prolactin. In addition, ME cells free of fat cells were tested for the ability to incorporate fatty acids. These cells took up unsaturated fatty acids, particularly linoleic acid, very effectively if the medium contained prolactin. From these results Kidwell *et al.* postulate the following scheme.

1. Prolactin acts on ME cells (ME cells are the only cells having prolactin receptors in the mammary gland).
2. Prolactin-stimulated epithelial cells signal adjacent fat cells to release free fatty acids.
3. ME cells take up unsaturated fatty acids, a process that is stimulated by prolactin.
4. Stimulation of ME cell proliferation.

Prostaglandin F2 could be the signal molecule mediating prolactin action in adipose cells, since this agent can stimulate the release of free fatty acid from mammary gland (Kidwell *et al.*, 1982). In this regard, a few years ago we observed that the prolactin-dependent parent tumor of 64-24 cells possesses a high level of lipoprotein lipase when the tumor is growing in the presence of a high level of prolactin (Horn *et al.*, 1976).

B. Phosphoethanolamine and Ethanolamine

Originally when the growth properties of cell lines isolated from apparently prolactin-dependent and -independent rat mammary carcinomas were compared, we found that the prolactin-dependent lines grew well in a medium supplemented with fetal calf serum, but not in a medium supplemented with calf serum, while the prolactin-independent lines grew well with either serum. Addition of prolactin in calf serum-containing medium did not stimulate growth of the prolactin-dependent cell lines (Kano-Sueoka and Hsieh, 1973). We postulated that pituitaries may produce some factor other than prolactin that stimulated the mammary tumor cell growth. Indeed, bovine pituitary extract was found to be rich in growth-promoting activity of 64-24 cells derived from the prolactin-dependent tumor (Kano-Sueoka *et al.*, 1977). Subsequently, the active component was purified and identified as phosphoethanolamine (PEtn) (Kano-Sueoka *et al.*, 1979). When PEtn (10^{-7}–10^{-6} M) is added to calf serum-containing medium, 64-24 cells grow optimally with a generation time of about 9 hours, but without PEtn the cells do not grow at all or grow very slowly depending on the batch of calf serum used. Phosphoethanolamine is a substrate for the biosynthesis of one of the major membrane phospholipids, phosphatidylethanolamine, and the effective concentration, 10^{-7}–10^{-6} M, required for growth of 64-24 cells seemed rather low to us. The role of PEtn as a growth-promoting material was investigated further using 64-24 cells (Kano-Sueoka and Errick, 1982). Among the compounds related to PEtn, ethanolamine was found to be equally effective. Both PEtn and ethanolamine added to the medium were taken up by the cells efficiently, and the majority of these molecules taken up by the cells was incorporated into phosphatidylethanolamine. After 3–4 days in culture more than 50% of the cellular phosphatidylethanolamine appeared to be derived from exogenous PEtn or ethanolamine. Moreover, phospatidylethanolamine content in phospholipid became three times higher than that without ethanolamine in the medium. Among several neoplastic ME cell lines of human and rat, a human line, T-47D, showed a positive growth response to ethanolamine and PEtn. Several mammary carcinoma cell lines including ethanolamine-responsive and -nonresponsive ones were then grown in the presence or absence of ethanolamine, and the phospholipid compositions were compared. The results indicated that the relative content of phosphatidylethanolamine of all the ethanolamine-responsive cell lines increased two- to threefold when the cells were cultured with exogenous PEtn or ethanolamine, while that of nonresponsive cells did not change whether the medium contained these precursors or not. The phosphatidylethanolamine content of the responsive cells grown with PEtn is similar to that of the nonresponsive cells. These results suggest that the PEtn-responsive cells cannot synthesize phosphatidylethanolamine at the rate necessary to support growth without the exogenous supply. It may mean also that the membrane synthesized in the absence of PEtn (low in phosphatidylethanolamine content) does not have fluidity or ionic environment suitable to function properly. Whether fatty acid composition is altered in the membranes that have altered phospholipid composition (in terms of polar head groups) is not known. Another interesting aspect of the PEtn-responsive and -nonresponsive cells is that so far two mammary carcinoma cell lines found to be PEtn responsive, 64-24 cells of rat and T-47D of human, are also the only cell lines that were found to grow in response to prolactin. In this regard, primary cultures of normal rat ME cells are also growth responsive to both PEtn and prolactin (Kano-Sueoka and Errick, 1980). It is quite possible that membrane phospholipids may play a crucial role in prolactin action.

C. Epidermal Growth Factor

Epidermal growth factor (EGF) is a polypeptide known to stimulate growth of many epithelial cells. Therefore, it is quite possible that EGF also stimulates growth of ME cells. The first indication of the role of EGF on mammary cells in culture was shown by Stoker *et al.* (1976), where growth of human ME cells obtained from spillage of fibroadenoma was stimulated by EGF if the cells were plated with feeder cells in the presence of serum. The necessity of EGF for growth of normal ME cells has been well established. While the direct effect of mammogenic hormones on growth of ME cells in culture is not obvious, EGF exhibits an unquestionably clear mitogenic effect. In serum-free hormone-supplemented medium, normal mouse ME cells require EGF (10 ng/ml) to grow (Y. Tomooka and S. Nandi, personal communication). Using whole gland culture, Tonelli and Sorof (1980) have shown that the gland can undergo two cycles of development, separated in time by a period of regression in a serum-free medium. For the first cycle, insulin, hydrocortisone, prolactin, and aldosterone are the sufficient hormone additives to achieve full lobuloalveolar development and EGF has only a moderate effect. The developed gland *in vitro* undergoes regression (involution) in the presence of insulin only. For the second cycle of development to occur, now EGF, in addition to the hormone mix, is necessary. For the first cycle development residual EGF may be sufficient. As elaborated in a later section, EGF stimulates the synthesis of basement membrane components in myoepithelial cells (Salomon *et al.*, 1981). For the involuted gland to regrow, the reestablishment of basement membrane may be necessary and, therefore, EGF may be essential for the mammary gland development.

Neoplastic mammary epithelial cells are also stimulated to grow by EGF. Growth of secondary cultures of DMBA-induced rat mammary carcinoma is stimulated by EGF (Rudland *et al.*, 1977). Growth of 64-24 cells from a rat mammary carcinoma is also stimulated significantly by EGF (10 ng/ml) (T. Kano-Sueoka, unpublished observation). Serum-free culture of pre-neoplastic mouse ME cells requires EGF also (Medina and Oborn, 1980). Many transplantable mammary tumors do not have basement membranes (Kidwell *et al.*, 1981). 64-24 cells do not seem to contain basement membrane components either (W. R. Kidwell, personal communication). For these cells EGF must act in a different manner than to stimulate basement membrane synthesis.

D. CHOLERA TOXIN AND cAMP

Cholera toxin raises intracellular cAMP level (Green, 1978) and a high intracellular level of cAMP is favorable for growth of normal ME cells in culture. Human ME cells, isolated either from milk or reduction mammoplasty, were stimulated to synthesize DNA by 10 ng/ml cholera toxin or by 0.5 nM dibutyryl-cAMP when the cells were grown on feeder cells or in rat tail collagen matrix. Either serum or EGF is necessary for cholera toxin to exert the growth-promoting effect and a definite synergism exists between cholera toxin and EGF effect (Taylor-Papadimitriou *et al.*, 1980; Yang *et al.*, 1980b, 1981).

In contrast to normal ME cells, neoplastic cells (cell lines derived from human breast cancers and virally transformed human ME cells) do not respond to cholera toxin as a growth factor (J. Taylor-Papadimitriou, personal communication) and mouse tumor cells in culture also showed a variable response to cholera toxin (Yang *et al.*, 1980b).

At present, it is unknown whether raising cAMP is one of the mechanisms that promotes ME cell growth *in vivo*, and if so, which hormone or growth factor achieves this.

E. GROWTH FACTORS CONTAINED IN SERUM

Traditionally, serum has been used to supplement the culture medium to supply undefined hormones, growth factors, and nutrients to the cells. Serum, therefore, can be a good source to find a novel growth factor specific for a certain type of cell, and so far several growth factors have been identified. Many investigators have looked for mammary-specific growth factors in serum, but facts so far known indicate that it is premature to assume that they do exist.

Kano-Sueoka and Hsieh (1973) found that fetal calf serum contains a macromolecular factor (apparent molecular weight ≃ 70,000) which stimulates growth of 64-24 cells derived from a hormone-dependent tumor. This factor, on the other hand, does not have any growth-promoting effect on cell lines originated from variant tumors that were no longer hormone dependent. This activity can be precipitated at 50–65% saturation of ammonium sulfate, but is distinct from albumin. Further purification has been unsuccessful because of the unstable nature of the activity in a partially purified fraction.

Stockdale and his colleagues have been characterizing a mammary growth-stimulating activity in porcine serum. This activity may indeed be mammary specific (Hsueh and Stockdale, 1974; Ptashne *et al.*, 1979). The factor stimulates DNA synthesis in mouse ME when organ culture or monolayer culture is used. The active material precipitates with 50% ammonium sulfate, has a high molecular weight (~100,000) at neutral pH, and is relatively stable to heat. At acidic pH the molecular weight is about 10,000 with pI of 5.5. By four-step purification, 250-fold purification has been achieved. The factor cross-reacts at high concentrations with somatomedins or multiplication stimulating activity (MSA), yet it is distinct from insulin, EGF, nerve growth factor (NGF), fibroblast growth factor (FGF), MSA, and somatomedin A or C by various criteria (Porzic and Stockdale, 1982). This factor can stimulate DNA synthesis in other cell types such as mouse 3T3, but stimulates mammary cells most efficiently. Because of the preference for mammary cells, this factor has been named as MSF (mammary-specific factor). It can stimulate DNA synthesis of mouse ME cells of virgin or pregnant gland but not of lactating gland (S. M. Rybak, S. Conlon, and F. E. Stockdale, personal communication).

F. GROWTH FACTORS IN TISSUE EXTRACTS

1. Pituitary Gland

Functional pituitaries are required for the development of normal mammary gland and also for growth of many mammary tumors. Since *in vivo* mammogenic hormones secreted from pituitary glands, particularly prolactin, do not work as effectively *in vitro* as expected, a number of investigators thought that pituitary gland may produce, in addition to prolactin and growth hormone, some novel growth factor(s) that stimulate ME cell growth. Serum from hypophysectomized rats has low growth-promoting activity on rat mammary tumor cells in culture compared to normal serum, indicating that the pituitary produces mammary growth-promoting material(s) (Kano-Sueoka and Hsieh, 1973; Rudland *et al.*, 1980a). The activity is highest in pregnant females or estrogen-treated males and lowest in males, and ad-

dition of prolactin cannot make hypophysectomized serum fully active
(J. A. Smith and P. S. Rudland, personal communication). These results
suggest that pituitaries may indeed produce mammary growth factors.

Bovine and rat pituitary extracts contain high growth-promoting activity
for various rat mammary tumor cells (Kano-Sueoka *et al.*, 1977; Rudland
et al., 1977, 1980a; Sirbasku *et al.*, 1982). As mentioned above, one of
these activities was found to be phosphoethanolamine. A macromolecular
fraction containing ovarian growth factor has been partially purified using
a carboxymethylcellulose column. This fraction is 10 times as active on a
per weight basis as pure prolactin on normal secondary ME cell cultures
of rat (Rudland *et al.*, 1980b). A rat pituitary tumor GH_3, which produces
prolactin and growth hormone, seems also to produce growth-promoting
activity for rat mammary tumor cells (Sirbasku *et al.*, 1982). The nature of
these pituitary growth factor(s) is not yet known.

2. Uterus and Kidney

From the observation that cells originating from apparently estrogen-
responsive tissue show poor growth response or none at all to estrogen in
culture, Sirbasku (1978) proposed the idea that estrogen acts indirectly on
these estrogen-responsive cells. Thus, tissues other than the supposed target
tissue may produce a growth factor(s) in response to estrogen, which, in
turn, stimulates growth of estrogen-responsive cells. It is well known that
estrogen stimulates pituitaries to secrete prolactin. Therefore, there is no
reason why other tissues cannot similarly respond to estrogen. He termed
this putative growth factor(s) estromedin. In fact, Sirbasku *et al.* (1981) and
Sirbasku and Leland (1982) have shown that uterus and kidney are rich
sources of estrogen-induced activities for a cell line derived from a transplantable estrogen-dependent rat mammary tumor MTW9. After partial
purification, there appear to be two protein components in the uterus which
are abundant in estrogen-treated animals and act synergistically (Sirbasku
et al., 1981). This subject was reviewed extensively by Sirbasku and Leland
(1982) in the previous volume of this treatise.

G. Growth Factors Provided by Cocultured Cells

When primary cultures of epithelial cells grow poorly, a feeder layer
consisting of fibroblastic cells can be provided to aid the primary culture
cells to attach and to grow. Likewise, ME cells have been cultured successfully
in the presence of feeder cells. Taylor-Papadimitriou *et al.* (1977) have
found that human milk epithelial cells need a feeder layer to grow in culture

in the presence of serum. The feeder cells can be mouse fibroblasts, human mammary fibroblasts, or cells isolated from milk. They have also shown that direct contact between the feeder cells and ME cells is not necessary to promote growth of ME cells. Therefore, some diffusible factors must be produced by the feeder. For EGF to be effective on long-term growth of human ME cells, the factors provided by the feeders are required (Taylor-Papadimitriou *et al.*, 1977). The above results suggest that conditioned medium from certain cell types can support growth of ME cells. In fact, human ME cells isolated from reduction mammoplasty grow well in a medium supplemented with conditioned medium prepared with human intestinal or bladder epithelial cell lines and a mammary myoepithelial cell line, if a combination of hormones is added together (Stampfer *et al.*, 1980). The nature of the growth-promoting material provided by the feeder cells is not known at present. However, there are some suggestions as indicated below. The rat mammary stromal cell line, Rama 27, produces prostaglandins (probably E2) (G. Tsao and P. S. Rudland, personal communication), and a rat myoepithelial line, Rama 401, produces basement membrane components, laminin, fibronectin, and collagen type IV (Warburton *et al.*, 1981), as well as some additional growth-promoting activity to ME cells which is distinct from known growth factors (M. Ellison and P. S. Rudland, personal communication).

V. SPATIAL ORGANIZATION OF THE CELLS AND THE CELL–SUBSTRATUM INTERACTION

The facts that primary cultured mammary epithelial cells grow poorly on plastic and that little effect has been observed on ME cell proliferation by the mammogenic hormones led several investigators to think that spatial organization of the cells (shape and ultrastructure of individual cells, relationship with surrounding homologous or heterologous cells, etc.) is important for ME cells to respond to natural growth stimuli.

Organoid preparations of mammary glands, prepared by collagenase treatment of the diced glands and by differential centrifugations, consist of a group of alveolar or ductal epithelial cells surrounded by myoepithelial cells mostly free of stromal cells. For the most part they retain their *in vivo* relationship between and among ME cells and myoepithelial cells.

Rat tail collagen gels consist mostly of collagen type I, a large amount of which can be prepared easily. This gel provides an ideal substratum or matrix for ME cells to proliferate and differentiate. Since Emmerman and Pitelka (1977) found that mouse ME cells can remain healthy for a prolonged period and can express differentiated function by ultrastructural and biochemical criteria, rat tail collagen gels have been used frequently to grow ME cells. Particularly, when the organoids are embedded in the gel matrix, ME cells are able to retain the spatial relationships that exist *in vivo*, so that the importance of integral structure in mammary cell proliferation can be examined.

Mammary epithelium is bounded by basement membrane which contains type IV collagen, fibronectin, sulfated glycosaminoglycans, etc., and is further surrounded by type I collagen-producing stromal cells. The importance of basement membrane for growth of ME cells has been indicated by *in vivo* studies carried out by Wicha *et al.* (1980). According to these authors, virgin gland was stable against treatment with *cis*-hydroxyproline, which is an analogue of proline, but in glands induced to proliferate by perphenazine the administration of *cis*-hydroxyproline produced glands whose basement membrane seemed to be deteriorated. Moreover, degradation of epithelial cells was observed, mimicking the phenomenon of involution. Myoepithelial cells were seemingly intact. These results suggest the importance of basement membrane in maintenance and proliferation of ME cells and also suggest a possibility that basement membrane may play a role in the action of mammogenic hormones.

Using primary cultures of normal mouse and human organoid, systematic studies have been carried out to estimate the role of collagen as a substrate or a matrix for growth of ME cells (Hallowes *et al.*, 1980; Nandi *et al.*, 1982). First, a plastic surface provides the least efficient substrate for the organoid culture. When the plates are coated with rat tail collagen, the organoid attaches efficiently and grows well, and ME cells exhibit several morphological and immunological characteristics of *in vivo* mammary tissue. However, contaminating fibroblasts grow as well as the epithelial cells and the two types of cells compete for the substrate surface. Eventually, fibroblasts can take over the culture plate. On the collagen gel surface the attachment of organoid cells is slower than on the dried collagen film. However, once attached, ME cells undergo sustained growth. Growth within the gel matrix is more sustained and manyfold greater than that observed in the same cells cultured on the gel surface. The gels from crude rat tail collagen preparations support the growth better than purified type I collagen gels. Organoids cultured in the gel matrix form ductal structures with extensive branching resembling the glands *in vivo*.

There is an indication that neoplastic mammary cells also grow better in a collagen matrix. Primary culture of mouse mammary tumor cells cannot achieve sustained growth on plastic, while within a matrix of rat tail collagen with high serum concentration in the medium these cells can grow for several weeks (Yang *et al.*, 1979). Therefore, at least certain mammary carcinomas seem to favor the collagen gel matrix for growth.

It is interesting to know whether hormone responsiveness of ME cells growing in the gel matrix is different from those grown on a plastic surface. Yang *et al.* (1980b,c) investigated the growth requirement of mammary organoids in collagen matrix. Normal mouse ME cells grow well in the matrix if the medium is supplemented with 50% horse serum and 0.01 μg/ml cholera toxin; however, they do not grow in a medium supplemented with 15% serum. The 15% serum–cholera toxin-supplemented medium was used as a maintenance medium and the effect of various hormones was examined. Insulin, prolactin, estrogen, progesterone, cortisol, aldosterone, or testosterone showed little if any growth-promoting effect on virgin or midpregnant ME cells when they were added singly or in combinations at various dosages. Epidermal growth factor and cholera toxin, on the other hand, stimulated growth almost equivalent to the 50% horse serum medium. As has been stated in a previous section, EGF and cholera toxin also stimulate DNA synthesis of human ME cells grown on feeder cells. Crude extracts prepared from various organs such as kidney, brain, spleen, and uterus and urine extract were shown to contain active growth-promoting materials when tested in medium containing 15% serum and 0.01 μg/ml cholera toxin. In contrast to the results of Sirbasku, the hormonal status of the donor animals has no significance for the activity. Thus, kidneys from virgin or pregnant animals or ones with pituitary isografts had equal growth-promoting activities. Therefore, the active components in these studies may be different from estromedins. The nature of any of the growth-promoting activities is not yet known, however. Similarly, normal human ME cells in primary culture in gel matrix can be maintained, but do not grow in media containing 15% serum. When urine extract, insulin, aldosterone (or estrogen plus progesterone), hydrocortisone, and human placental lactogen were added to the above medium, the cells grew well. The hormone mixture or urine extract alone did not give growth stimulation. The extracts from brain or kidney or EGF could replace the activity in urine extract. Yang *et al.* (1980a, 1981) have shown further that the only essential hormone that has to be added together with EGF or urine extract is hydrocortisone.

Recently, growth requirement of ME cells cultured as organoids in the gel matrix has been investigated using serum-freee medium. Imagawa *et al.* (1982) have shown that ME cells of virgin and pregnant mice can grow well in the presence of insulin, cholera toxin, EGF, transferrin, and bovine serum albumin (BSA). Epidermal growth factor is absolutely essential for ME cells to grow in the serum-free medium. In this system, estradiol, progesterone, and prolactin give no significant growth-stimulatory effect. Human ME cells have similarly been cultured with insulin, cholera toxin, transferrin, cortisol, and BSA. Estradiol cannot replace the function of cortisol (W. Imagawa, Y. Tomooka, and S. Nandi, personal communication).

A serum-free culture medium devised by R. C. Hallowes, R. Steiner, and S. A. Cox (personal communication) for human mammary organoid culture in the gel matrix is very similar to the above, i.e., it contains insulin, EGF, transferrin, hydrocortisone and retinoic acid. According to these researchers, again, mammogenic hormones do not seem to be necessary for proliferation.

Rat tail collagen consists mainly of type I collagen. Mammary epithelial cells and myoepithelial cells rest on basement membrane containing type IV collagen produced by myoepithelial cells. Wicha *et al.* (1979) have observed that rat mammary cells attach well on collagen type IV, but poorly on collagen type I, II, or III. However, once they are attached on type I, II, or III collagens, they grow well if *de novo* synthesis of type IV collagen is allowed; namely, the cells are resistant to *cis*-hydroxyproline and grow well if they are attached to collagen type IV, but on collagen type I, *cis*-hydroxyproline inhibits the growth of ME cells.

When normal human mammary organoids are plated on rat tail collagen gel, these cells secrete collagen type IV, mucopolysaccharide, and fibronectin (basement membrane components) at basal side, although no ultrastructurally identifiable basal lamina is formed. Therefore, collagen gel composed mainly of type I allows the cells to deposit extracellular matrix having some features in common with basement membrane. On this basement membrane ME cells now grow (R. C. Hallowes and W. Jones, personal communication). The type of cells responsible for depositing basement membrane components are likely to be myoepithelial cells. A myoepithelial cell line, Rama 401, produces basement membrane components, type IV collagen, laminin, and fibronectin as determined by immunofluorescent staining and gel electrophoresis of radiolabled products (Warburton *et al.*, 1981).

As in the case of mouse and human mammary tissue, rat mammary organoids can proliferate in primary culture in a serum-free medium supplemented with insulin, transferrin, hydrocortisone, EGF, and fetuin and synthesize type IV collagen (Salomon *et al.*, 1981). When the cells are plated on type I collagen or plastic, ME cells are more sensitive to omission of EGF or glucocorticoid than when plated on type IV collagen. This finding suggested to Salomon *et al.* (1981) that EGF and glucocorticoid are involved in type IV collagen synthesis by the mammary cells. First, it was found that rat organoids plated on plastic, rat tail collagen (type I), or type IV collagen grow equally well if the medium contains the complete hormone supplement, including EGF and glucocorticoid. Second, it was found that EGF stimulates type IV collagen synthesis and glucocorticoid suppresses collagen IV collagenolytic activity. These results explain why the cells plated on collagen type I require EGF and glucocorticoid. As described above, human or mouse organoid cultures also require EGF and glucocorticoid to grow in a rat tail collagen matrix, and this must also be because these cells respond to EGF and glucocorticoid to synthesize and stabilize type IV collagen, which is necessary for growth of ME cells. These results clearly indicate the indirect action of EGF and glucocorticoid on ME cells via myoepithelial cells.

The growth characteristics of neoplastic cells have diverged from those of the normal counterpart to varying degrees. Kidwell and his colleagues have investigated the requirement for basement membrane components in the growth of mammary carcinomas (Kidwell *et al.*, 1982a). According to their results, the tumor cells bounded by basement membrane *in vivo* (mostly primary tumors) need the collagenous components for growth, while if the tumor does not contain basement membrane components, its growth is insensitive to *cis*-hydroxyproline treatment. It was also found that the tumor cell growth *in vitro* was relatively unresponsive to EGF whether collagen type IV was synthesized or not. The reason was that tumors that synthesize basement membrane produce EGF-like material having a potent stimulating activity for collagen type IV synthesis. Interestingly, transplantable methylnitrosourea (NMU)- or DMBA-induced tumors grown without basement membrane synthesize little or no type IV collagen, and they also exhibit little or no EGF-like activities. These transplantable tumors produce only stromal-type collagens.

Another component of basement membrane is sulfated glycosaminoglycans. These components are abundant in a young primary culture of normal rat organoid, but they fall rapidly within a few days of culture, and the fall in the amount of the sulfated glycosaminoglycans is correlated with the cessation of growth of ME cells (Kidwell *et al.*, 1982a). At present, it is not known what controls the synthesis or maintenance of these compounds or how important these compounds are for growth regulation. However, these results suggest a role of the glycans on growth of ME cells. So far no hormone mix that supports the synthesis of the glycans has been found. It is quite possible that a basement membrane whose composition is unique to mammary tissue is necessary to support the growth of normal ME cells.

VI. DISCUSSION AND SUMMARY

This chapter briefly summarizes various elements that might affect growth of normal and neoplastic ME cells in culture. A particular attempt was made to give possible solutions to the paradox of the mammogenic hormone action *in vivo* and *in vitro*.

First, there are indications that ovarian steroids and prolactin can stimulate growth of ME cells of both normal and neoplastic origin, although their effects are for the most part modest. Experiments carried out with normal ME cells included myoepithelial cells and, in some cases, adipose cells. Therefore, it is quite possible that these other cell types are necessary for estrogen or prolactin to exert their mitogenic effect. However, studies with tumor cells usually dealt with ME cells only, indicating that these hormones indeed can act directly on ME cells.

Organoid cultures in rat tail collagen gel matrix provide ME cells with the structural environment mimicking the *in vivo* situation. Organoids prepared from normal mammary glands or primary culture of mammary carcinoma cells grow well in the gel matrix, and it is often possible to obtain sustained growth of mammary cells for several weeks without contamination of fibroblasts. However, having the spatial relationship of ME cells among themselves similar to the *in vivo* state did not bring about a mitogenic effect of prolactin or estrogen on ME cells. Instead, EGF and hydrocortisone have the most profound effect. These hormones were found to be involved in stimulating synthesis and maintenance of a basement membrane component, collagen type IV. Maintenance and synthesis of type IV collagen and probably other basement membrane components seem to be essential for proliferation of ME cells. The basement membrane components are synthesized by myoepithelial cells, and the organoid cultures include myoepithelial cells. However, it is not known whether glucocorticoid or EGF acts on myoepithelial cells through ME cells or acts directly on myoepithelial cells. Having a three-dimensional spatial organization intact in organoid culture does not seem to be necessary to obtain sustained growth of ME cells. As long as intact organoids are plated and type IV collagen synthesis is allowed to occur, ME cells seem to grow even on plastic surfaces or type I collagen gel surfaces. Primary tumors still have a requirement for basement membrane, but transplantable tumors are seemingly free from the requirement of basement membrane components.

The role of prolactin on fat metabolism has been unraveled and seems to involve direct and indirect actions on ME cells. According to Kidwell and his colleagues (1982b), prolactin binds to ME cells; ME cells send out signal(s) to adjacent fat cells; the fat cells release free fatty acids; ME cells in response to prolactin take up fatty acids (particularly unsaturated); and proliferation of ME cells follows. The mitogenic effect of prolactin observed in tumor ME cell culture may indeed be related to the uptake of fatty acids from culture medium. Along this line, the importance of balanced membrane phospholipid biosynthesis has also been indicated, based on the discovery that some ME cells require ethanolamine or phosphoethanolamine for growth.

The complex nature of ME cell proliferation is also indicated by the fact that feeder cells or conditioned medium of certain cell types, including fibroblasts and myoepithelial cells, provide some growth-stimulating materials. There may be growth factors or nutrients such as fatty acids that affect ME cell growth. Not much is known regarding mammary growth factors produced outside of the mammary gland. There are certainly strong indications of the possible existence of such factors. Some of these factors may be tumor specific since, at least, whole gland culture in defined culture medium with the mammogenic hormone mixture is self-sufficient. The fact that only estrogen–progesterone-primed ME cells proliferate in whole gland cultures may indicate that factors produced in other organs function to program the growth of ME cells.

An integrated picture of normal and neoplastic mammary cell growth has yet to emerge. However, enough evidence has been accumulated to show the complex roles of hormones and growth factors in mammary cell growth. Dissection of the whole gland culture into various elements should provide valuable information, as already indicated by the contribution made by organoid cultures. Clonal cell lines of mammary carcinoma cells will also be useful in the detailed analysis of culture elements, and also in characterizing deviations of neoplastic cells from their normal counterparts.

REFERENCES

Allegra, J. C., and Lippman, M. E. (1978). *Cancer Res* **38**, 3823–3829.

Barnes, D., and Sato, G. (1979). *Nature (London)* **281**, 388–389.

Baumann, K. R., and Hosick, H. L. (1978). *Exp. Cell Biol.* **46**, 325–337.

Desmond, W. J., Jr., Wolbers, S. J., and Sato, G. (1976). *Cell* **8**, 79–86.

Emmerman, J. T., and Pitelka, D. R. (1977). *In Vitro* **13**, 316–328.

Green, H. (1978). *Cell* **15**, 801–811.

Hallowes, R. C., Bone, E. J., and Jones, W. (1980). "Tissue Culture in Medical Research" (R. J. Richards and K. T. Rajan, eds.), Vol. 2, pp. 213–220. Pergamon, Oxford.

Horn, T. M., Mendelson, C., and Kano-Sueoka, T. (1976). *J. Cell Biol.* **70**, 179a.

Hosick, H. L., Angello, J. C., and Anderson, M. E. (1978). *Proc. Am. Assoc. Cancer Res.* **19**, 178.

Hsueh, H. W., and Stockdale, F. E. (1974). *J. Cell. Physiol* **83**, 297–308.

Ichinose, R., and Nandi, S. (1966). *J. Endocrinol.* **35**, 331–340.

Imagawa, W., Tomooka, Y., and Nandi, S. (1982). *Proc. Natl. Acad. Sci. U.S.A.* **79**, 4074–4077.

Kano-Sueoka, T., and Errick, J. E. (1980). "Control Mechanisms in Animal Cells" (L. Jimenez de Asua, R. Levi-Montalcini, R. Shield, and S. Iacobelli, eds.), pp. 299–305. Raven, New York.

Kano-Sueoka, T., and Errick, J. E. (1982). *Cold Spring Harbor Conf. Cell Proliferation* **9**, 729–740.

Kano-Sueoka, T., and Hsieh, P. (1973). *Proc. Natl. Acad. Sci. U.S.A.* **70**, 1922–1926.

Kano-Sueoka, T., Campbell, G. R., and Gerber, M. (1977). *J. Cell. Physiol.* **93**, 417–424.

Kano-Sueoka, T., Cohen, D. M., Yamaizumi, Z., Nishimura, S., Mori, M., and Fujiki, H. (1979). *Proc. Natl. Acad. Sci. U.S.A.* **76**, 5741–5744.

184   *Tamiko Kano-Sueoka*

Kidwell, W. R., Salomon, D. S., Liotta, L. A., and Zweibel, J. A. (1982a). *Cold Spring Harbor Conf. Cell Proliferation* **9**, 807–829.
Kidwell, W. R., Knazek, R. A., Vonderhaar, B. K., and Losonczy, I. (1982b). "Molecular Interrelation in Nutrition in Cancer" (M. S. Arnott, J. Van Iys, and Y. M. Wang, eds.), pp. 219–236. Raven, New York.
Lippman, M. G., Allegra, J. C., and Strobb, J. S. (1979). *Cold Spring Harbor Conf. Cell Proliferation* **6**, 545–557.
Lyons, W. R., Li, C. H., and Johnson, R. E. (1958). *Recent Prog. Horm. Res.* **14**, 219–254.
Medina, D., and Oborn, C. J. (1980). *Cancer Lett. (Shannon, Irel.)* **13**, 333–344.
Mehta, R. G., and Banerjee, M. R. (1975). *Acta Endocrinol. (Copenhagen)* **80**, 501–516.
Nandi, S., Imagawa, W., Tomooka, Y., Shiurba, R., and Yang, J. (1982). *Cold Spring Harbor Conf. Cell Proliferation* **9**, 779–788.
Nawata, H., Bronzert, D., and Lippman, M. E. (1981a). *J. Biol. Chem.* **256**, 5016–5021.
Nawata, H., Chong, M. T., Bronzert, D., and Lippman, M. E. (1981b). *J. Biol. Chem.* **256**, 6895–6902.
Porzig, E. F., and Stockdale, F. E. (1982). *Exp. Cell Res* (in press).
Ptashne, K., Hsueh, H. W., and Stockdale, F. E. (1979). *Biochemistry* **18**, 3533–3539.
Rudland, P. S., Hallowes, R. C., Durbin, H., and Lewis, D. (1977). *J. Cell Biol.* **73**, 561–577.
Rudland, P. S., Bennett, D. C., and Warburton, M. J. (1980a). "Hormones and Cancer" (L. Jimenez de Asua, R. Levi-Montalcini, R. Shield, and S. Iacobelli, eds,), pp. 255–269. Raven, New York.
Rudland, P. S., Smith, J., and Warburton, M. J. (1980b). *Cell Biol. Int. Rep.* **4**, 765.
Salomon, D. S., Liotta, L. A., and Kidwell, W. R. (1981). *Proc. Natl. Acad. Sci. U.S.A.* **78**, 382–386.
Sirbasku, D. A. (1978). *Proc Natl. Acad. Sci. U.S.A.* **75**, 3786–3790.
Sirbasku, D. A., and Leland, F. E. (1982). *In* "Biochemical Actions of Hormones" (G. Litwack, ed.), Vol. 9, pp. 115–140. Academic Press, New York.
Sirbasku, D. A., Leland, F. E., and Benson, R. H. (1981). *J. Cell. Physiol.* **7**, 345–358.
Sirbasku, D. A., Officer, J. B., Leland, F. E., and Iio, M. (1982). *Cold Spring Harbor Conf. Cell Proliferation* **9** (in press).
Stampfer, M., Hallowes, R. C., and Hackett, A. J. (1980). *In Vitro* **16**, 415–425.
Stoker, M. W. P., Pigott, D., and Taylor-Papadimitriou, J. (1976). *Nature (London)* **264**, 764–767.
Taylor-Papadimitriou, J., Shearer, M., and Stoker, M. W. P. (1977). *Int. J. Cancer* **20**, 903–908.
Taylor-Papadimitriou, J., Purkis, P., and Fentiman, I. S. (1980). *J. Cell. Physiol.* **102**, 317–321.
Taylor-Papadimitriou, J., and Fentiman, I. S. (1981). *Commentar. Res. Breast Dis.* **2**, 87–102.
Tonelli, Q. J., and Sorof, S. (1980). *Nature (London)* **285**, 250–252.
Topper, Y. J., and Freeman, C. S. (1980). *Physiol. Rev.* **60**, 1049–1106.
Warburton, M. J., Ormerod, E. J., Monaghan, P., Ferns, S., and Rudland, P. S. (1981). *J. Cell Biol.* **91**, 827–836.
Wicha, M. S., Liotta, L. A., and Kidwell, W. R. (1979). *Cancer Res.* **39**, 426–435.
Wicha, M. S., Liotta, L.A., Vonderhaar, B. K., and Kidwell, W. R. (1980). *Dev. Biol.* **80**, 253–266.
Yang, J., Richard, J., Bowman, P., Guzman, R., Enami, J., McCormick, K., Hamamoto, S., Pitelka, D., and Nandi, S. (1979). *Proc. Natl. Acad. Sci. U.S.A.* **76**, 3401–3405.
Yang, J., Guzman, R., Richard, J., Jentoft, V., DeVault, M. R., Wellings, S. R., and Nandi, S. (1980a). *J. Natl. Cancer Inst.* **65**, 337–343.

Yang, J., Guzman, R., Richard, J., Imagawa, W., McCormick, K., and Nandi, S. (1980b). *Endocrinology (Baltimore)* **107**, 35–41.

Yang, J., Richard, J., Guzman, R., Imagawa, W., and Nandi, S. (1980c). *Proc. Natl. Acad. Sci. U.S.A.* **77**, 2088–2092.

Yang, J., Elias, J. J., Petrakis, N. L., Wellings, S. R., and Nandi, S. (1981). *Cancer Res.* **41**, 1021–1027.

CHAPTER 6

The Secretion and Actions of Melatonin

Franz Waldhauser and Richard J. Wurtman

I. INTRODUCTION

Scientific knowledge usually grows in alternating steps—now at the top, then at the bottom, then the top, and so on. Topside growth is conceptual, the framing of hypotheses or paradigms to explain existing data and predict the supporting data that will be obtained when prescribed experiments are performed. Growth at the bottom involves the acquisition of data by experimenters testing hypotheses or applying paradigms to some new situation (e.g., a different species or age or time of day). When a paradigm stops working, the experimenter may modify the experimental design, propose a new hypothesis, or lose interest and choose to work on a different topic.

BIOCHEMICAL ACTIONS OF HORMONES, VOL. X

An era in the history of a research topic is roughly coincident with the period during which most investigators share a common hypothesis about the nature of the topic being explored, and use common paradigms to elucidate that nature. The mammalian pineal organ has survived at least three eras during the twentieth century. We live in its *neuroendocrine* era, which probably can be dated from about 1965 (Wurtman and Axelrod, 1965). This era replaced two others: the *pineal-as-photoreceptor-turned-vestige* era (whose paradigms worked well for lower vertebrates with third eyes, but were unable to yield information about pineal function in mammals) and the *pineal-as-a-gland* era, initiated by clinicians a century ago (which overlooked the organ's control by and actions on neurons). The hypothesis underlying the present era is that the pineal is a neuroendocrine transducer (Wurtman and Axelrod, 1965) which secretes a hormone, melatonin, in response to norepinephrine release from its sympathetic nerves, especially nocturnally, when the nerves are firing most frequently, and whose hormone provides the brain and possibly other organs with a time signal that cues other time-dependent physiological processes such as gonadal maturation, gonadal cyclicity, and perhaps sensitivity to environmental stimuli.

This chapter focuses on this last component of the neuroendocrine–transducer hypothesis, i.e., evidence that melatonin administration, melatonin withdrawal (by pinealectomy or exposure to high-intensity continuous illumination), or cyclic variations in melatonin secretion can have important effects. Our ability to design experiments that display these consequences has been considerably enhanced during the past decade by the use of new assays to characterize melatonin levels in human and animal body fluids; the information thus generated tells us how best to look for melatonin effects, and suggests when experiments involving melatonin administration are most likely to mimic physiological events. A decade ago scientists (Wurtman and Anton-Tay, 1969) knew a great deal about the input side of pineal function, the factors controlling its synthesis and secretion, and a little about melatonin's pharmacological effects, but very little about what it and its source, the mammalian pineal, might be for. The imbalance is now being redressed, especially concerning melatonin's effects on reproductive systems and the brain.

Melatonin is not the only pineal substance thought to have a physiological role: the pineal also synthesizes and secretes other methoxyindoles (e.g., methoxytryptophol), which also can suppress gonadal functions when administered to experimental animals (McIsaac *et al.*, 1964; Fraschini *et al.*, 1968; Minneman and Wurtman, 1976). Moreover, the pineal may liberate one or more biologically active peptides (Benson and Ebels, 1981; Vaughan, 1981). This chapter omits discussion of pineal methoxyindoles on the grounds that their actions resemble, and their synthesis and secretion parallel, those of melatonin. It also makes no further mention of pineal peptides because the authors, like others (Fernstrom *et al.*, 1980; Pevet *et al.*, 1981), doubt that the most discussed of these, arginine vasotocin, is a characteristic pineal peptide, and conclude that the remainder of the peptide literature still fails to support generalizations about functions.

II. THE MAMMALIAN PINEAL ORGAN

The mammalian pineal is a new organ; it shows extraordinary morphological and physiological differences when compared with pineals of lower vertebrates (Kelly, 1962). Although it continues to originate embryologically as an evagination of the ependymal cells which line the roof of the third ventricle, the mammalian pineal has lost all photoreceptor cells and has instead acquired a new cell type, the pinealocyte or parenchymal cell, whose metabolic activity is controlled indirectly by environmental lighting (Wurtman *et al.*, 1964a). The organ has lost most or all of its neural connections, afferent or efferent, with the brain and has instead acquired a unique, direct, sympathetic innervation which originates, surprisingly, outside the cranial cavity, i.e., in the superior cervical ganglia (Ariens-Kappers, 1965). It has become the main locus in the body of the enzyme hydroxyindole-*O*-methyltransferase (HIOMT), which is needed to synthesize melatonin and other methoxyindoles (Axelrod *et al.*, 1961), and probably the only locus at which this enzyme (Axelrod *et al.*, 1965) and the serotonin-acetylating enzyme serotonin-*N*-acetyl transferase (SNAT) (Klein and Weller, 1970) display circadian rhythmicity. Melatonin, in turn, may not produce in mammals the physiological response in lower vertebrates which allowed its discovery (Lerner *et al.*, 1959), i.e., the blanching of frog skin, caused by aggregation of the pigment granules with melanophores. Instead, it influences brain neurons controlling various cyclic processes. In humans, the pineal accumulates characteristic calcified interstitial concretions with age; their significance remains unknown, save, perhaps, as landmarks for the neuroradiologist.

A. THE PINEAL AS A SECRETORY ORGAN

Before enunciation of the neuroendocrine transducer hypothesis two decades ago, two widely held and contradictory formulations existed concerning vertebrate pineal function. One group of investigators, basing its view on the appearance of frog and human pineals and on electrophysiological studies, proposed that while the pineals of certain lower vertebrates could function as a "third eye," transducing photons of particular wavelengths to nerve impulses and transmitting them to the brain, the pineal had, with evolution, lost this (and any other) function, becoming instead a calcified vestigial structure.

Other investigators, basing their view on data from experimental biology and, to a larger extent, from clinical studies on sequellae of pineal tumors, proposed that the mammalian pineal was in reality a gland, perhaps analogous to the thyroid or pituitary. The most consistent experimental data supporting the glandular hypothesis derived from studies on the effects of adding bovine pineal extracts to the media in which tadpoles were swimming (McCord and Allen, 1917); something in the extracts, later shown to be melatonin, caused the tadpole skin to blanch by facilitating the aggregation of melanin granules around the nuclei of melanophore cells. Although no similar pigmentary effects were noted when mammals received pineal extracts, the observations at least suggested that mammalian pineals might secrete a substance that acted as a hormone, at a distance, to affect cutaneous pigmentation. Experiments on rats (discussed below), which showed that pinealectomy could accelerate and pineal extracts suppress gonadal maturation, supported the view of the pineal as a gland. (The third criterion for "glandness," the ability of transplanted organs to reverse the effects of pinealectomy, was never satisfied, and indeed could not be, inasmuch as the pineal is not a gland, controlled by circulating compounds, but a neuroendocrine transducer, dependent on intact innervation.) However, clinical observations probably provided greatest credibility for this view: in 1898, Heubner, a pediatrician, described a 4-year-old boy with a pineal tumor and precocious puberty. Between then and 1954, when Kitay and Altschule reviewed the world's literature of some 1750 papers dealing with the pineal, numerous additional case reports appeared describing associations of pineal pathology and reproductive malfunction, and numerous experimental studies were generated by investigators seeking to determine how the pathology caused the endocrine derangements. The first clear articulation of the hypothesis that the pineal is a gland that functions to inhibit the genitals was made by Marburg (1909). In 1930, Marburg expanded his hypothesis to suggest that all "pineal affections prior to puberty which are accompanied by a decrease in pineal parenchymal tissue, can cause precocious sexual maturation, at least in boys." On the basis of this working hypothesis, numerous experiments were performed on the effects of giving pineal substances to humans, orally or parenterally. The desired therapeutic end point was usually suppression of sexual activity, a decrease in "hyperlibidism," or the cessation of uterine bleeding, dysmenorrhea, or menopausal symptoms (Hofstaetter, 1936). In 1938, at least 15 pineal preparations were commercially available in Europe, each based on its own proprietary extraction procedure (Hofstaetter, 1938). Unfortunately, little or no effect of these preparations could be demonstrated in children with precocious puberty or, for that matter, on any of the other end points examined.

Animal research on the pineal, largely based on use of pinealectomy or administration of pineal extracts, tended also to suggest an inhibitory role for the pineal in reproductive mechanisms. In 1912, Foa reported a dramatic acceleration of sexual maturation among young cockerels pinealectomized at age 20–30 days. These findings were confirmed by Zoia (1914) and Izawa (1923). Other investigators, studying the effects of pinealectomy in rats, mice, dogs, sheep, or tadpoles, variously observed an acceleration, a delay, or no effect on sexual maturation (Engel, 1936). (In retrospect, this variability probably indicates that the consequences of melatonin removal depend on the age of the experimental animal, the extent to which its gonads are normally affected by light, and various other factors completely unknown to the investigators.) Even more contradictory and discouraging, if also not surprising, were the results obtained after administration of pineal extracts to animals. None of the extracts was assayed for melatonin, but the aqueous extraction procedures used to make them probably lost most of the indole.

B. The Pineal as a Neuroendocrine Transducer Releasing Melatonin

In 1958, Lerner and his associates at Yale University identified the chemical structure of the constituent of bovine pineal extracts that lightened frog skin as 5-methoxy-*N*-acetyltryptamine, and named the compound melatonin (Lerner *et al.*, 1959). Soon thereafter Axelrod and Weissbach showed that the mammalian pineal organ was the apparently unique locus in the body of the enzyme, HIOMT, required for synthesizing melatonin from *N*-acetylserotonin (Axelrod *et al.*, 1965). [Later studies showed that small amounts of this enzyme also are present in the retina (Cardinali and Rosner, 1971a) and the Harderian gland (Vlahakes and Wurtman, 1972). That it may also produce melatonin in these tissues is suggested by the persistence of small amounts of melatonin in the urines of pinealectomized animals (Lynch *et al.*, 1975a).] Lerner attempted to demonstrate an effect of melatonin on human skin, but was unable to do so; its physiological role in mammals remained obscure.

Fiske *et al.* (1960), working at Wellesley College, reported that prolonged exposure of rats to continuous illumination decreased the weights of their pineals. Since this experimental condition was also known to accelerate pubescence and gonadal growth in rats, and since administration of pineal extracts suppressed gonadal development in these animals (Wurtman *et al.*, 1959), Wurtman and his associates, then at Harvard Medical School, examined

the possibility that light might stimulate the gonads by inhibiting the production or release of an inhibitory pineal hormone. They found that either
pinealectomy or light exposure caused similar increases in rat gonadal weight,
but that the effects of the two treatments were not additive (Wurtman *et
al.*, 1961). Moreover, bovine pineal extracts could block the effects of both
pinealectomy and light exposure.

In 1962, Wurtman and Axelrod initiated studies to determine the identity
of the gonad-inhibiting substance in pineal extracts. They used as their
bioassay the ability of the unknown compound to block the enhancement
in gonad weight caused by placing young rats under constant light. Melatonin,
the first pineal constituent to be tested, was found to inhibit the gonadal
enlargement in microgram doses; it also slowed the growth of the gonads
among animals kept under a standard diurnal lighting environment (Wurtman
et al., 1963a). On this basis it was first proposed that melatonin was *the*
pineal hormone, or at least *a* pineal hormone. [In retrospect, it is obvious
that these investigators had considerable good fortune: subsequent studies
have shown that the gonadal responses of rodents to melatonin can vary
from great to nonexistent, depending on, among other things, species and
strain, the time of day that the hormone is administered, the lighting
environment in which the animals are kept (Reiter, 1980), and their age
and nutritional status. None of these factors was controlled systematically
in the early studies.]

If melatonin were indeed the pineal hormone that mediated the effects
of environmental light on the gonads, was its synthesis or release then
suppressed when animals were exposed to continuous illumination? Since
rat pineal melatonin levels could not then be measured, this possibility was
examined indirectly by measuring HIOMT activity *in vitro* in pineals taken
from animals previously exposed to light or darkness. It was conjectured
that a rise or fall in the enzyme's activity might be associated with a parallel
change in melatonin's synthesis and release. An inhibitory effect of continuous
illumination on HIOMT activity was indeed observed (Wurtman *et al.*,
1963b), as well as a daily rhythm, in animals exposed to a normal diurnal
light cycle, with peak enzyme activities demonstrable a few hours after the
onset of darkness (Axelrod *et al.*, 1965). Subsequent studies by others (Klein
and Weller, 1970) demonstrated similar *in vivo* light effects on SNAT, the
pineal enzyme that converts serotonin to N-acetylserotonin. [The magnitude
of that enzyme's response and the amplitude of its daily rhythm make it
especially useful for experimental studies on the photic control of pineal
function. For example, SNAT assays have been used to show that the
intensity of light needed to cause a half-maximal suppression of melatonin-
forming activity is about 0.5 μwatt/cm^2, which is in the same range as the
intensity present on the earth's surface under full moonlight (Minneman

and Wurtman, 1974).] About a decade later, the development of sensitive bioassays (BIO) (Ralph and Lynch, 1970) and then radioimmunoassays (RIAs) (Arendt *et al.*, 1975) made it possible to test directly the relationship between environmental lighting and melatonin synthesis and secretion; fortunately, the changes in HIOMT or SNAT activity observed when animals had been exposed to particular lighting environments were found to parallel those in pineal, blood, or urinary melatonin levels.

If melatonin were a hormone, it seemed reasonable to propose that the pineal was a gland, in spite of the fact that at least one of the criteria for "glandness," the ability of transplanted organs to substitute for ablated pineals, had never been satisfied. However, this possibility was quickly excluded by experiments on the pathway by which the pineal is "informed" about the animal's lighting environment; it became apparent that the pineal was not a gland like the thyroid or pituitary, communicating with the rest of the body solely via the circulation, but a neuroendocrine transducer, homologous with the adrenal medulla. In 1960, Ariens-Kappers showed that mammalian pineals receive their major, and perhaps sole, innervation from postganglionic sympathetic neurons originating in the superior cervical ganglion. When these neurons were removed surgically, light and darkness no longer affected pineal HIOMT activity (Wurtman *et al.*, 1964a). Blinding the experimental animal (by bilateral orbital enunceation) similarly blocked pineal responses to light; however, removal of the pituitary or of other "classic" glands had no effect on these responses. Thus, the pineal is critically dependent on its nerves for the signals that control the synthesis and release of its hormone* in a manner analogous to the adrenal medulla, which requires acetylcholine release from its preganglionic cholinergic nerves in order to secrete its hormone, epinephrine.

That the pineal's sympathetic nerves control melatonin synthesis by releasing norepinephrine was shown using pineals maintained in organ culture: glands incubated for 24–48 hours with isotopically labeled tryptophan produced large amounts of $[^{14}C]$serotonin, and even larger quantities of $[^{14}C]$melatonin; however, melatonin synthesis was markedly enhanced when nonrepinephrine was added to the medium (Axelrod *et al.*, 1969; Wurtman *et al.*, 1969). Other transmitters or hormones were without effect. Norepinephrine acts by combining with pineal β-receptors (Wurtman *et al.*, 1971) and thereby accelerating cAMP synthesis (Shein and Wurtman, 1969). The precise step in melatonin's formation at which norepinephrine acts to accelerate its

---

* That rhythms in melatonin secretion from the human pineal similarly depend on neuronal inputs is suggested by their disappearance in patients with high cervical cord lesions (Kneisley *et al.*, 1978). Severe stress or hypoglycemia can cause sufficient epinephrine to be released from the rat's adrenal medulla, and delivered to the pineal via the circulation, to increase melatonin synthesis independent of the pineal's sympathetic nerves (Lynch *et al.*, 1973a).

synthesis is not yet clear: norepinephrine elevates SNAT activity to a greater extent than HIOMT activity; however, it also accelerates the production of methoxyindoles like 5-methoxytryptophol (Wilson *et al.*, 1978), whose production requires HIOMT but not SNAT. It currently seems most likely that melatonin synthesis is controlled not by *either* enzyme, but by variations in the amounts of intracellular serotonin made available for enzymatic transformation, i.e., by SNAT and by monoamine oxidase. Perhaps these variations depend on changes in serotonin's binding to an organelle or cytoplasmic protein in pinealocytes.

III. MELATONIN

A. ASSAYS

Only very recently have sufficiently sensitive and precise assay methods become available to permit the measurement of melatonin levels in body fluids, and the generation of reasonably secure hypotheses relating changes in these levels to possible physiological effects. Melatonin was discovered and isolated using bioassays (Lerner *et al.*, 1960); rhythmic changes in its pineal concentrations were first demonstrated using fluorometric assays (Quay, 1963b); its absolute identification in body fluids was accomplished by gas chromatography–mass spectrometry (GC–MS) (Smith *et al.*, 1976b); and melatonin levels in physiological states are now measured conveniently and reliably using RIAs (Wetterberg, 1977). A summary of melatonin levels in pineals and body fluids, as determined using various assay methods, is provided in Table I.*

1. Melatonin Estimates by Bioassay

Bioassay methods for measuring melatonin use its most striking physiological effect, the dermal melanophore response of amphibians, specifically, the melatonin-induced nucleocentric aggregation of melanin pigment granules within the living melanophore. The assay methods use either (1) photometric measurement of changes in the transmission or reflectance of incident light

---

* With regard to Tables I–IV, we apologize for any distortion of the facts that may have resulted from placing information in a Procrustean table. Some of the numerical values listed here were estimated from published graphs. We also realize that such terms as "day" and "night" might be misleadingly vague as descriptions of environmental conditions or as time points for describing the phenomenon under consideration. Before judging the merit of a particular datum, the reader is urged to consult the reference cited.

by isolated frog skin exposed to melatonin solution (Lerner *et al.*, 1960) or (2) microscopic assessment of the degree of melatonin aggregation within the melanophore in intact amphibian larvae, as judged by an arbitrary scale of melanophore stages, the Hogben index (Waring, 1963).

Both methods have documented merit. Lerner *et al.* (1960) used the first method to trace the isolation of melatonin from bovine pineal tissue. The second method, involving the microscopic evaluation of pigment dispersion in melanophores, exchanges the reflectometer's objectivity for the eye's capacity to discriminate. With this technique, attention is restricted to the unicellular effector organ that responds to melatonin stimulation, the melanophore. Most bioassay studies have used this latter method.

The first quantitative bioassay used to measure physiological changes in pineal melatonin content, that of Tomatis and Orias (1967), combined elements of both methods. Melanophores were scored relative to the Hogben index in pieces of isolated toad skin exposed to homogenates of pineal tissue. Following an experimental design suggested by earlier work with HIOMT measurements, Tomatis and Orias (1967) showed that pineal glands of rats exposed to constant darkness contained significantly more melatonin than those of rats exposed to constant light; moreover, blinding or superior cervical ganglionectomy increased pineal melatonin content.

Most studies using bioassays to measure melatonin levels in animal tissues have used an adaption of the quantitative bioassay developed by Ralph and Lynch (1970). This method is based on the dermal melanophore response of larval *Rana pipiens* to melatonin in their bathing medium. The assay is sensitive to as little as 100 pg/ml melatonin in the final test solution and is largely unaffected by the presence of naturally occurring melatonin analogues. Thus, melatonin in homogenates of pineal tissue can be measured by bioassay without further purification. Similarly, melatonin in extracts of body fluids can be assayed readily if the extracts are cleared of organic solvents which might modify melanophore responsiveness.

While the dermal melanophores of tadpoles respond discernibly to melatonin concentrations of 100 pg/ml, replicate sampling at various concentrations is needed for bioassaying melatonin in tissues or body fluids. When the total melatonin content of a given sample approximates the melanophores' limit of sensitivity, the accuracy of the quantitative estimate diminishes; hence, while pineal melatonin content can be bioassayed readily, its measurement in small samples of rat or hamster blood or human cerebrospinal fluid (CSF) has not been feasible. Nevertheless, Pelham *et al.* (1973), and then Vaughan *et al.* (1976), using 20-ml blood samples, successfully demonstrated diurnal variations (with nocturnal peaks) in the concentration of a "melatonin-like substance" in human plasma.

To measure urinary melatonin by bioassay, Lynch and his collaborators

TABLE I

REPRESENTATIVE MELATONIN CONCENTRATIONS (MEAN VALUES) IN PINEAL AND BODY FLUIDS FROM VARIOUS ANIMALS

Animal	Pineal (pg/gland) D[a]	N	Serum/plasma (pg/ml) D	N	CSF (pg/ml) D	N	Method	Reference
Monkey			7–18	8–23	2–6	9–32	RIA	Reppert et al. (1980)
Pig			22	76			RIA	Kennaway et al. (1977)
Calf, cattle	200[b]						BIO	Lerner et al. (1960)
Cow			19	121			RIA	Hedlund et al. (1977)
			20	320			RIA	Kennaway et al. (1977)
Monkey			24	128			RIA	Kennaway et al. (1977)
Camel			29	221			RIA	Kennaway et al. (1977)
Lizard			20	500			RIA	Kennaway et al. (1977)
Sheep			10–30	100–300			RIA	Rollag and Niswender (1976)
			80	100–160			RIA	Kennaway et al. (1977)
			140	297			RIA	Rollag et al. (1978a)
	40,000	180,000					GC–MS	Kennaway et al. (1977)
Hamster	95–232	760–1335					RIA	Panke et al. (1979)
	14	443					RIA	Tamarkin et al. (1979)
	40–91	847					RIA	Rollag et al. (1980)

					Urine (μg/12 hours)			
					D	N		
Rat	500			20–50			BIO	Lynch (1971)
		6800	ND[c]				BIO	Pang and Ralph (1975)
	118						RIA	Giarman and Day (1959)
			6.3		0.18	1.4	RIA	Ozaki et al. (1976)
				75			RIA	Kennaway et al. (1977)
					0.53	1.44	RIA	Lynch and Wurtman (1979)
	3,900						GC–MS	Cattabeni et al. (1972)
	500	3,000	20	80			GC–MS	Wilson et al. (1978)
			4	52			GC–MS	Lewy et al. (1980b)
Chicken	5,800	38,000	ND	190			BIO	Lynch (1971)
				200			BIO	Pelham (1975)
			50				RIA	Kennaway et al. (1977)
			ND	71			GC–MS	Pelham et al. (1972)
Quail	600	3200	ND				BIO	Lynch (1971)

[a] D, day; N, night.
[b] Ng/mg pineal tissue.
[c] ND, not detectable.

(1975b) developed a column chromatographic technique, concentrating on Amberlite XAD-2 the melatonin in 4- or 8-hour urine collections. Studies using this method first demonstrated the relationship between diurnal lighting and rhythmic melatonin excretion, showed that the nocturnal increase persisted through 28 hours of constant light (Jimerson *et al.*, 1977), and showed that 5–7 days were required to reentrain rhythmic melatonin excretion after a 12-hour shift in the phase of the lighting schedule (i.e., lights off at 11 AM instead of 11 PM) (Lynch *et al.*, 1978b). Studies of human urinary melatonin also showed that, in an environment lacking overt time cues, the rhythmic pattern of melatonin excretion can be dissociated from a "self-selected" wake–sleep schedule (Weitzman *et al.*, 1978), and that blind human subjects exhibit a circadian rhythm in melatonin excretion which is different in phase from their customary wake–sleep schedule (Lynch *et al.*, 1975a).

2. Melatonin Estimates by Spectrophotofluorometric Assay

All 5-hydroxy- and 5-methoxyindoles emit fluorescent light at 540–550 nm when dissolved in strong mineral acids and activated with ultraviolet light at 295 nm. This phenomenon, discovered by Udenfriend *et al.* (1955), provided the basis of a sensitive chemical method for measuring serotonin and for studying its tissue distribution (Giarman and Day, 1959). Attempts to use melatonin's native fluorescence (Quay, 1963a, 1964) or its enhanced fluorescence after condensation with *O*-phthaldehyde (OPT) (Maickel and Miller, 1968) as the basis of a melatonin assay have also been described; however, the problem of separating melatonin from other, closely related compounds before measuring its fluorescence was never resolved satisfactorily, and in the interim the other, more sensitive and specific methods described in this section were developed. Perhaps a procedure based on the separation of methoxyindoles by high-performance liquid chromatography (HPLC) followed by OPT condensation and fluorescence measurement would be competitive with existing melatonin assays.

3. Melatonin Estimates by Radioimmunoassay

Various methods have been used to produce antimelatonin antisera for melatonin RIA. As the melatonin molecule is not itself antigenic, it or one of its analogues must first be coupled to a carrier molecule that will impart antigenicity to the complex. This product is then used to stimulate antibody production in an animal, usually a rabbit or goat. The specificity and potency of the resulting antisera are functions of the biochemical nature of the antigens used, the program of treatment, and above all, the individual animal's immune response. Thus, a variety of relatively specific antisera have been produced for use in melatonin RIA. In a recent review, Arendt (1978a) summarized the brief history of melatonin RIAs, outlined some of the methods used to produce antimelatonin sera in rabbits, and proposed criteria for assessing the specificity of particular antisera.

Grota and Brown (1974) reported that antibodies to indoles could be raised after conjugation of serotonin or N-acetylserotonin to an antigenic protein by condensation with formaldehyde. The resulting antisera were proposed as the basis for an RIA and for immunohistochemical localization of the melatonin in brain structures. The first report of a practical melatonin RIA, validated by comparison with bioassay measurements and accompanied by data on human plasma melatonin levels, was that of Arendt *et al.* (1975). At least five additional RIA methods were developed (Levine and Riceberg, 1975; Pang *et al.*, 1976; Rollag and Niswender, 1976; Wurtzburger *et al.*, 1976; Kennaway *et al.*, 1977) within the next 2 years; their application has already yielded abundant information about melatonin levels in pineal tissue, blood, CSF, and urine of humans and other animal species. The development of melatonin RIAs also required tritiated melatonin of high specific activity; most current RIAs use material of 25–30 Ci/mmol. The RIA method developed by Rollag and Niswender (1976) uses a radioiodinated melatonin analogue as a tracer; the highly specific activity obtainable with radioiodine (1620 Ci/mmol) allows a 10-fold increase in sensitivity over that obtained using tritiated melatonin.

An international cross-validation study was conducted by Wetterberg (1977) using a reference serum containing 0.86 nmol/liter (200 pg/ml) melatonin. Results obtained in seven laboratories using six different antisera indicate that melatonin can be measured with reasonable accuracy by the various RIA methods. Estimates of the melatonin concentrations in the reference samples ranged from 128 ± 15 to 239 ± 35 pg/ml; the mean value obtained was 176 pg/ml.

All the RIA methods currently in use involve initial extraction of melatonin from its biological source into a nonpolar organic solvent. It is then purified further by aqueous washes or by column or thin-layer chromatography, according to the specificity of the anitserum used and the requirements of the specific tissue or fluid under study. In the method developed by Lynch *et al.* (1978b) at MIT, using an antiserum provided by Lawrence Levine of Brandeis University (Levine and Riceberg, 1975), melatonin is extracted into chloroform from pineal tissue homogenates, plasma, or CSF, and washed with aqueous solutions before assay. Urine extracts, in contrast, present a very serious challenge, and require isolation of melatonin by multiple (Thoma, 1963) or continuous (Brenner and Niederwieser, 1961) unidimensional development on thin-layer chromatography plates.

Representative contributions to our understanding of pineal function based on the use of RIA methods to estimate melatonin levels include the following: (1) documentation of the apparently universal relationship between environmental light and darkness and rhythmic changes in blood melatonin levels among various wild and domesticated animals, and also species, strain, and individual differences in the time course and amplitude of rhythmic changes in blood melatonin (Kennaway *et al.*, 1977); (2) evaluation of the temporal and quantitative relationships between serum and CSF melatonin levels in the partially restrained rhesus monkey; (3) noninvasive monitoring of melatonin secretion (i.e., urinary melatonin levels) in longitudinal studies on the photic entrainment of melatonin rhythms in individual human subjects (Jimerson *et al.*, 1977; Lynch *et al.*, 1978b; Wetterberg, 1978) and experimental animals (Adler *et al.*, 1979; Lynch and Wurtman, 1979); and (4) correlation of rhythmic variations in the melatonin content of hamster pineals with dramatic changes in the animal's reproductive status caused by seasonal or experimentally imposed changes in the daily photoperiod (Panke *et al.*, 1978, 1979; Tamarkin *et al.*, 1979; Rollag *et al.*, 1980).

4. Melatonin Estimates by Gas Chromatography

The specificity and sensitivity of gas-chromatographic procedures makes them a valuable analytical tool for affirming that a particular compound in a biological sample is indeed melatonin. Assays for melatonin have been described using detection by gas chromatography and electron-capture mass spectroscopy (GC–MS) and negative-chemical-ionization mass spectrometry.

For electron-capture detection, melatonin is extracted from its biological source and a volatile, halogenated derivative is formed. Degen and Barchas (1970), using the extraction procedure of Miller and Maickel (1970) followed by the derivatization procedure, reported that as little as 100 pg of melatonin could be measured in pineal tissue. Greiner and Chan (1978) used the method to measure melatonin contents of 22 human pineals collected at autopsy; melatonin values ranged from 0 to 71.1 ng/gland. A diurnal variation in pineal melatonin content was observed, correlated with time of death; melatonin concentration increased in the evening and throughout the night and started to fall in the morning.

In the GC–MS assay for melatonin, specificity is derived both from melatonin's properties (i.e., retention time) in the gas chromatograph and the characteristic ion densities of its specific fragments in the mass spectrometer. To form derivatives of indoles with appropriate vapor pressure for gas chromatography, a variety of reactions have been employed (Degen and Barchas, 1970; Pelham *et al.*, 1972; Smith *et al.*, 1976b; Kennaway *et al.*, 1977). Gas chromatography–mass spectroscopy methods have been used for quantification and absolute identification of melatonin in extracts of various tissues (Koslow and Green, 1973; Kennaway *et al.*, 1977) and body fluids (Kennaway *et al.*, 1977; Wilson *et al.*, 1977, 1978), and to validate various melatonin RIAs (Rollag and Niswender, 1976; Kennaway *et al.*, 1977; Wilson *et al.*, 1978). Gas chromatography–mass spectroscopy has also been used to identify and measure related compounds, e.g., to provide the initial evidence of a rhythmic variation in the concentration of 5-methoxytryptophol in rat serum (Wilson *et al.*, 1978) and to quantitate the 6-hydroxymelatonin (20 ng/ml) in human urine (Sisak *et al.*, 1979). The general utility of the GC–MS technique for measuring melatonin in body fluids is, unfortunately, limited by the expense of the instrumentation and the need for a highly skilled operator.

Negative chemical ionization increases GC–MS sensitivity for electron-capturing compounds by 150-fold. It permits routine measurement of melatonin in human plasma at concentrations as low as 1 pg/ml. In one study, its application revealed daytime values as low as 1.5 pg/ml and nighttime values as high as 42.6 pg/ml in plasmas from two male and two female subjects (Lewy and Markey, 1978). In another study, daytime plasma melatonin levels in rats were 4 pg/ml, nighttime levels were 52 pg/ml, and $2\frac{1}{2}$ hours after treatment with 3 mg/kg isoproterenol in the daytime, 30 pg/ml (Lewy *et al.*, 1980b).

B. PHYSIOLOGICAL DISPOSITION

The physiological disposition of melatonin has been studied by administering isotopically labeled hormone to animals systemically or by placing it in the CSF. Circulating melatonin is rapidly cleared ($t_{1/2} = 2$ minutes), and disappears from the blood by first-order decay (Kopin *et al.*, 1961); it is taken up within all tissues (Wurtman *et al.*, 1964b), including the brain [especially the brainstem and hypothalamus (Wurtman *et al.*, 1964b)], and metabolized chiefly within the liver (by 6-hydroxylation) followed by conjugation with glucuronic or sulfuric acid (Kveder and McIsaac, 1961). A number of melatonin analogues have been synthesized, chiefly those containing a halogen in the 6 position; these compounds tend to have a significantly longer circulating half-life than melatonin itself, and to exhibit greater potency in inhibiting reproductive function (Frohn *et al.*, 1980).

As discussed below, brain tissue can also metabolize melatonin by ring cleavage followed by removal of the carbon atom adjacent to the indole nitrogen (Hirata *et al.*, 1974). It remains to be determined whether melatonin is primarily secreted into the bloodstream or the CSF; most likely the locus of its secretion varies among species (Reppert *et al.*, 1979), e.g., its CSF levels were higher than those in blood among calves (Hedlund *et al.*, 1977) and children with leukemia (Smith *et al.*, 1976a), but lower in sheep (Rollag *et al.*, 1978b) and rhesus monkeys (Reppert *et al.*, 1979).

C. Receptors in Brain and Other Tissues

In the absence of highly sensitive assays for endogenous melatonin, investigators have attempted to characterize tissue distribution indirectly by studying the fate of isotopically labeled hormone injected systemically or into the CSF: if the actual locus at which the pineal secretes melatonin happens to be the bloodstream, then the former route is most likely to provide an accurate assessment of melatonin's true fate; if its secretion is, as some propose, into the CSF, then the latter type of experiment is more likely to be meaningful. When the radioactive melatonin is given systemically it becomes most concentrated within the pineal itself and in the gonads; however, relatively large quantities also enter the brain (Wurtman *et al.*, 1964b), probably reflecting melatonin's high degree of lipid solubility, and the fact that it binds only with relatively low affinity to albumin and other circulating proteins (Cardinali *et al.*, 1972).

When rats receive isotopically labeled melatonin systemically or by injection into the CSF, the hormone tends to become localized within particular brain regions, the brainstem, and the hypothalamus (Anton-Tay and Wurtman, 1969). Its uptake into these regions is saturable, as indicated by the fact that the concurrent administration of unlabeled melatonin diminishes accumulation of the isotopically labeled hormone (Cardinali *et al.*, 1973). At all times studied, only about half of the total radioactivity in brain regions was unchanged melatonin (Anton-Tay and Wurtman, 1969); the identity of the other labeled material was not determined, but it lacked a chemical characteristic of indolic compounds, failing to yield a positive reaction with Ehrlich's reagent. The subsequent discovery by Hayaishi and his associates of a brain enzyme (Hirata *et al.*, 1974), indole dioxygenase, that cleaves indole nuclei and generates biologically active compounds like N-acetyl-N'-formyl-5-methoxykynurenamine [which binds to benzodiazepine receptors with a very high affinity (Patel *et al.*, 1981)] suggests that the unidentified radioactive metabolites may have been members of this series of compounds. Endogenous melatonin has also been reported to exist in hypothalamus (Koslow and Green, 1973; Bubenik *et al.*, 1976); moreover, melatonin's neuroendocrine (Fraschini *et al.*, 1968; Heath and Lynch, 1981) and behavioral (Marczynski *et al.*, 1964; Barchas *et al.*, 1967; Minneman and Wurtman, 1976) effects most likely reflect actions on the brain. For these reasons, investigators have recently begun to explore the possibility that the retention of melatonin or its active metabolites in brain reflects its combination with soluble or membrane-bound neuronal receptors, akin to the receptors mediating effects of other hormones.

Initial attempts to identify such receptors (by incubating cerebral cortical slices or synaptosomes with isotopically labeled melatonin) were unsuccessful (Cardinali *et al.*, 1975), probably because the specific activity of the radioactive melatonin then available was too low. However, later attempts, using melatonin of very high specific activity, have yielded data interpreted in one laboratory (Niles *et al.*, 1979), but not another (Cohen *et al.*, 1978a), as demonstrating the existence of cytoplasmic neuronal receptors, and in a third (Cardinali *et al.*, 1979) as demonstrating membrane-bound neuronal receptors.

The membrane receptors reportedly have a high affinity ($K_d = 1.2 \times 10^{-8}$) for melatonin; moreover, their numbers in mediobasal hypothalamus change diurnally, in a pattern suggesting down-regulation by melatonin itself: receptor levels at 8 PM, after a period of daylight and *low* melatonin availability, are 34–56% greater than at 7 AM, at the end of the daily dark period (Vacas and Cardinali, 1979). Since this change is compatible with physiological evidence that when melatonin has been available continuously its antigonadal effects are blocked (Reiter, 1980), it suggests that the macromolecules measured may indeed function physiologically as receptors. Cytoplasmic melatonin receptors have also been identified in ovary, testis, skin, and eye (Cohen *et al.*, 1978a).

The evidence that melatonin can act centrally to produce behavioral and electroencephalographic changes is not appreciably greater at present than it was when last reviewed (Minneman and Wurtman, 1976; for example, see Datta and King, 1977; Golus *et al.*, 1979), probably reflecting the fact that melatonin's cost has inhibited investigators from doing large-scale studies of its effects on the species with the most complex and most measurable set of behaviors: the human. However, some new information is available concerning the biochemical mechanisms by which melatonin may affect the brain and other organs. It was shown some years ago that melatonin administration could modify brain serotonin levels in a regional pattern suggestive of enhanced release of the idolamine (Anton-Tay *et al.*, 1968; Vermes *et al.*, 1972). Little additional information has accumulated on the mechanism of these neurochemical changes, and there has been no direct evidence that they are associated with serotonergic neurotransmission. Low concentrations of melatonin ($10^{-8}–10^{-7}$ M, but not higher or lower) have been shown to release somatostatin from rat hypothalamus *in vitro* (Richardson *et al.*, 1981); similar concentrations have also been shown to enhance the release of prostaglandin E from this tissue (Cardinali *et al.*, 1980), to increase its levels of cGMP, and to reduce its levels of cAMP (Vacas *et al.*, 1981). Melatonin apparently also increases cGMP levels in rat testis (Kano and

Miyachi, 1976), CSF (Rudman, 1976), human monocytes (Sandler *et al.*, 1975), and various endocrine organs (Vesely, 1981).

Very recently, melatonin was reported by Hakanson and Bergstrom (1981) to reverse the hypocalcemia produced by exposing newborn rats to high-intensity lighting similar to that used clinically in the phototherapy of hyperbilirubinemia. The authors speculated that melatonin might act by inhibiting a peripheral action of corticosterone or estradiol. If, indeed, melatonin does influence calcium metabolism this could involve it in a very large number of physiological systems.

D. Effects on Reproductive Functions in Mammals, and Correlations with Secretory Patterns

A complete review of the literature describing melatonin's effects on reproductive function is beyond the scope of this chapter. Such effects have been reviewed by other authors (Minneman and Wurtman, 1975, 1976; Reiter *et al.*, 1978). Briefly, in 1963, melatonin administration (1–10 μg/day) to female rats was observed to diminish ovarian weight and suppress the vaginal estrous cycle (Wurtman *et al.*, 1963a); its probable site of action is the neuroendocrine structures in the brain (Anton-Tay *et al.*, 1968; Fraschini *et al.*, 1968; Glass and Lynch, 1981) even though some evidence exists that melatonin may also affect the gonads directly (Ellis, 1972).

The efficacy of a melatonin dose in modifying reproductive function varies markedly depending on the time of its administration (relative to the prevailing light–dark schedule) and on the species studied. The first evidence of this dependence was the demonstration that melatonin administration blocked the daily rhythm in pineal serotonin content when given in the eighth hour, but not during the fourteenth hour, of the daily 14-hour photoperiod (Fiske and Huppert, 1968). It was later shown that large doses of the methoxyindole (1.25–5 mg) completely inhibited ovulation if administered to rats during the critical period of proestrus (2–4 PM). [This inhibition could be overcome by administration of luteinizing hormone, which suggests that melatonin does not act directly on the ovaries (Ying and Greep, 1973).] In general, the reproductive effects of exogenous melatonin are quantitatively far greater in hamsters than in the albino rat. Recent studies have shown that if exogenous melatonin is administered late in the daily photoperiod to intact hamsters (kept under a lighting regimen that maintains their reproductive competence) (Tamarkin *et al.*, 1975, 1976; Tamarkin and Goldman, 1978), the gonads regress; moreover, if the melatonin is administered three times daily (25-μg injections at 3-hour intervals) to pinealectomized hamsters, gonadal regression is seen regardless of the lighting schedule (even constant light) (Tamarkin and Goldman, 1978; Goldman *et al.*, 1979). The recent development of a technique for programmed intermittent or cyclic subcutaneous infusion of melatonin (Lynch *et al.*, 1981) should facilitate further study of the relationship between the time and the physiological consequences of melatonin administration.

As described above, compelling evidence exists that the mammalian pineal organ synthesizes melatonin, and that this organ constitutes the source of most of the melatonin in the body. Thus, each of the enzymes needed to convert circulating tryptophan (melatonin's amino acid precursor) to melatonin has been found in pineal organs (Weissbach and Axelrod, 1960); the pineal has been shown to synthesize isotopically labeled melatonin from isotopically labeled tryptophan in organ culture (Wurtman *et al.*, 1968); and pineal melatonin levels are far higher than those present in any other tissue (Wurtman *et al.*, 1968). Just the same, the view that the pineal is the sole locus of melatonin secretion is challenged by evidence that HIOMT activity is found in the retina (Cardinali and Rosner, 1971b) and Harderian gland (Vlahakes and Wurtman, 1972), and that melatonin can also be synthesized from tryptophan in mammalian retina (Cardinali and Rosner, 1971a). The extent to which these organs contribute to circulating melatonin remains controversial; however, it is well established that some melatonin continues to circulate after pinealectomy, even if melatonin levels do not exhibit their normal circadian or diurnal rhythms. Melatonin has been detected in urines of pinealectomized rats both by bioassay and RIA (Ozaki and Lynch, 1976), in the blood of pinealectomized sheep by RIA (Kennaway *et al.*, 1977), and in hypothalamic tissues of pinealectomized rats by GC–MS (Koslow and Green, 1973). [Other investigators failed to detect melatonin by bioassay (Pang and Ralph, 1975) or GC–MS (Lewy *et al.*, 1980) in blood of pinealectomized rats; this may reflect differences in the sensitivity of assay methods used.] Does this residual material have physiological effects? Probably not, for there is abundant evidence (Wurtman *et al.*, 1968; Reiter *et al.*, 1975) that pinealectomy accelerates gonadal maturation and modifies subsequent reproductive functions, and that most or all of these reproductive effects can be reversed by exogenous melatonin.

A number of photoperiodic events are known to be influenced by the pineal gland. Winter regression of the gonads in response to shorter days (Reiter and Hester, 1966), the normal initiation and timing of estrus in seasonally breeding animals (Herbert, 1969), and change in pelage which occurs in some animals (Rust and Meyer, 1961), all seem to depend on a functioning pineal gland. Clearly, many of these regulatory functions are mediated by melatonin secretion. It has also become evident that the *temporal pattern* of circulating melatonin is critical, rather than melatonin's mere presence or absence, or its absolute levels.

The precise temporal pattern of melatonin secretion (and its blood levels) tends to vary among mammalian species. Most detailed investigations, involving high-frequency sampling, have been performed on blood and CSF melatonin levels in cattle, sheep, humans, and rhesus monkeys, and blood and urinary melatonin levels in humans. Studies involving less frequent sampling have also characterized these patterns in hamsters and rats, and rat rhythms have been assessed indirectly by measuring changes in the activities of pineal melatonin-forming enzymes (Axelrod *et al.*, 1965).

Unless otherwise indicated, all tissues and fluids examined in the following species exhibit characteristic and similar daily rhythms in melatonin concentrations, with melatonin levels peaking during the daily dark period. The rhythms themselves persist when animals are kept in constant darkness, but disappear in constant light.

1. Cattle

Melatonin levels in the blood (Hedlund *et al.*, 1977; Kennaway *et al.*, 1977) and CSF (Hedlund *et al.*, 1977) show a daily rhythm, with a marked rise at the onset of darkness which is sustained throughout the dark period. The average melatonin concentration in CSF was five times higher than that in plasma during the night, but only twice as high during the day (Hedlund *et al.*, 1977). Neither the effect of exposure to constant light or constant darkness nor the effect of imposing light during the normal dark period was tested.

2. Sheep

Plasma melatonin levels are abruptly elevated with the onset of darkness, remain high throughout the dark period, and promptly decrease with the onset of light (Rollag and Niswender, 1976; Kennaway *et al.*, 1977). Melatonin concentrations in blood collected at 1-minute intervals increased 5–10 minutes after the abrupt imposition of darkness and reached peak values over a 2- to 10-minute interval. When light was resumed, melatonin fell to base line levels after 5–10 minutes (Rollag and Niswender, 1976). When sheep were exposed to constant darkness, a circadian rhythm persisted in blood melatonin; however, no rhythm was detectable among sheep exposed to constant light. When light was turned on at a time of high melatonin concentrations, serum melatonin levels dropped precipitously; they returned to peak values when the lights were extinguished. In a study done over a year-long period with ewes exposed to seasonal alterations in length of the photoperiod, nocturnal melatonin elevations were longest during estrus (long nights) and shortest during anestrus (short nights). There were no significant differences in mean melatonin concentrations during the light or dark periods associated with these different photoperiods and reproductive states (Rollag *et al.*, 1978a). In another study, CSF melatonin levels paralleled blood levels during darkness, and the quantity of melatonin normally secreted into the blood was estimated to be more than 100 times greater than that secreted into the CSF. The increase in CSF melatonin after the onset of darkness lagged behind that in the blood (Rollag *et al.*, 1978b).

3. Monkeys

Parallel increases in plasma and CSF melatonin levels were observed in rhesus monkeys during darkness. More extensive studies with CSF samples showed that the increase in melatonin levels occurs shortly after the lights are turned off, that these levels remain high during darkness, and that they decrease soon after the lights are turned on. The magnitude of the rhythm remains relatively stable from day to day in each animal, but shows substantial variation among animals (Reppert *et al.*, 1979). Constant light suppresses the melatonin rhythms, although sporadic increases of melatonin can still be detected. During exposure to constant darkness, melatonin rhythms persist, but the number of hours per day during which melatonin levels are elevated increases from 12 to 16–18 hours (Perlow *et al.*, 1980).

4. Hamsters

The pineal itself is apparently the only hamster tissue in which melatonin has been measured. In Syrian prepubertal and adult hamsters, melatonin contents increase in the latter portion of the dark period, and return to daytime values before or with the onset of light (Panke *et al.*, 1979; Tamarkin *et al.*, 1979; Rollag *et al.*, 1980). The peak concentrations reached during darkness, and the duration of these high levels (approximately 4 hours) apparently are not altered by the photoperiod; instead, the phase difference between the onset of darkness and the peak in pineal melatonin increases as the dark period is lengthened. Melatonin concentrations remained at daytime values when the light period was extended into the night (Tamarkin *et al.*, 1979), while a pulse of light given during the dark period rapidly decreased dark-time levels (Tamarkin *et al.*, 1979; Rollag *et al.*, 1980). The half-life of plasma melatonin is approximately 9 minutes in hamsters, and the total quantity of melatonin synthesized throughout the 24-hour day is estimated to be approximately 18.6 ng (Rollag *et al.*, 1980).

5. Rats

Melatonin levels in the pineal, plasma, and urine change in parallel throughout the 24-hour period (Ozaki *et al.*, 1976; Adler *et al.*, 1979).

Frequent measurements of blood and pineal melatonin show significant elevations in melatonin levels 3 hours into the dark phase, and abrupt decreases about 3 hours before the onset of light (Wilkinson *et al.*, 1977). Experimental imposition of light during the normal dark period causes rapid declines in plasma and pineal melatonin levels, with half-life of approximately 5 minutes (Illnerova *et al.*, 1978). Urinary melatonin levels are suppressed in animals exposed to constant light of sufficient intensity, but persist in animals exposed to constant darkness (Ralph *et al.*, 1970; Lynch and Wurtman, 1979), in blinded animals (Reiter *et al.*, 1971; Adler *et al.*, 1979), and in animals exposed to constant light of sufficiently low intensity (Rivest *et al.*, 1980). The urinary melatonin rhythm shifts after a phase shift in the lighting regimen (Adler *et al.*, 1979); the rate of shifting appears to depend on the intensity of the light presented during the light portion of the light–dark cycle (Rivest *et al.*, 1980).

E. STUDIES ON HUMANS

1. Normal Values for Melatonin in Body Fluids

Melatonin levels in plasma and serum apparently do not differ significantly (Wetterberg, 1978), and values obtained using RIA are in good agreement with those based on bioassays or GC–MS, i.e., up to about 40 pg/ml during daytime and 40–150 pg/ml during nighttime (Table II). No sex difference was noted in plasma melatonin levels (Arendt *et al.*, 1975). Measurements of melatonin levels in human urine have been difficult to make because of the abundance of unknown cross-reacting substances. However, available data (Table III) do indicate a substantial daily rhythm, and a very good correlation between blood and urinary levels when these levels are changing (Lynch *et al.*, 1978b; Lang *et al.*, 1981). At present, CSF melatonin levels have been measured mainly in patients with particular diseases, and only in samples obtained during the daytime (Table IV). These levels are apparently similar to (Vaughan *et al.*, 1978b) or are slightly lower than (Arendt *et al.*, 1977a; Tan *et al.*, 1981) those in blood. In an early study (Smith *et al.*, 1976a) of children with leukemia, the opposite conclusion was drawn: serum melatonin levels averaged 14 pg/ml while melatonin concentrations in CSF samples drawn simultaneously averaged 98 pg/ml.

2. Secretion Pattern and Rhythms

a. Pulsatile Secretions. Three groups of investigators (Vaughan *et al.*, 1978a; Weitzman *et al.*, 1978; Mullen *et al.*, 1981) have sampled melatonin

TABLE II. BLOOD MELATONIN VALUES IN ADULTS

Method	Sample	Daytime (pg/ml)[a]	Nighttime (pg/ml)[a]	Subject Number	Subject Sex	Reference
Bioassay	Plasma	ND[b]–12	49.6 ± 10.5	5	M	Pelham et al. (1973)
	Plasma	162 ± 41	258 ± 44	3	M	Arendt et al. (1975)
				2	F	
RIA	Plasma	ND	20–150	16	M	Vaughan et al. (1976)
	Plasma	132 ± 10	188 ± 15	14	M	Arendt et al. (1975)
	Serum	47 –481	—	5	F	Wetterberg et al. (1976)
	Serum	63 ± 22[c]	—	8	M	Arendt et al. (1977a)
	Serum	100 ± 45[c]	—	7	F	
	Plasma	<20	50–100	2	M	Kennaway et al. (1977)
	Serum	20 ± 3	78 ± 13	5	M	Smith et al. (1977)
	Serum	~12–14 spring and autumn / ~20–24 winter and summer		5	M	Arendt et al. (1977b)
	Plasma	14.6 ± 0.9	49.1 ± 3.8	47	M	Arendt and Wilkinson (1978)
		13.9 ± 0.5	66.1 ± 5.3	50	F	
	Plasma	23 ± 7	97 ± 33	2	M	Lynch et al. (1978b)
	Plasma	32 ± 8	179 ± 26	5	M	Vaughan et al. (1978a)
	Serum	19 ± 7[c]	74 ± 26[c]	7 (Mult. sample)		Smith et al. (1979)
	Plasma	—	36 ± 14 (12 PM); 51 ± 11 (4 AM)	7	M	Sizonenko et al. (1979)
	Plasma	50 – 180[d]	150–450[d]	5	M	Weinberg et al. (1979)
	Serum	24 ± 1.6	79 ± 8.6	8	M	
GC–MS	Plasma	25 – 40	125–440	15	F	Waldhauser et al. (1981)
	Plasma	10 – 55	—	3		Wilson et al. (1977)
				5		
	Plasma	1.5 – 4.9	19.4–42.6	2	M	Lewy and Markey (1978)
				2	F	
	Serum	11 – 21	—	18		Silman et al. (1979)

[a] Mean ± SE.   [b] ND, not detectable.   [c] SD.   [d] Range of mean values from five individuals obtained by sampling every 15 minutes over 24 hours.

TABLE III
URINE MELATONIN VALUES IN ADULTS

Method	Daytime (ng/4 hours[a])	Nighttime (ng/4 hours[a])	Subject Number	Subject Sex	Reference
Bioassay	ND[b]–1.3	0.55–13.4	2	M	Lynch et al. (1975b)
			4	F	
RIA	1.3 ± 0.1	4.3 ± 0.4	4	M	Lynch et al. (1975a)
	—	38.2 ± 7.8[c]	3	M	Wetterberg (1979)
	—	31.7 ± 9.5[c]	3	F	
	10.1 ± 1.7	23.2 ± 2.4	4	M	Lang et al. (1981)
			10	F	
		67.75 ± 29[d]	12		Lemaitre et al. (1981a)

[a] Mean ± SE.
[b] ND, not detectable.
[c] On basis of first morning urine sample.
[d] On basis of a 24-hour urine collection.

levels in blood with sufficient frequency (i.e., at intervals of 30 minutes or less) to affirm that the hormone is secreted in pulses, like LH, prolactin, and ACTH. All observed evidence for such pulses, and concluded that this pattern is superimposed on the day–night melatonin secretory rhythm. The frequency of pulses appears to be about one per hour (Weinberg et al., 1979), and their amplitude sufficient to raise plasma levels by as much as

TABLE IV
MELATONIN CONTENT IN CSF OF HUMANS[a]

Method	Daytime (pg/ml[b])	Nighttime (pg/ml[b])	Subject Number	Subject Sex	Reference
GC–MS	55 – 80	—	2		Wilson et al. (1977)
RIA	59 ± 33[c]	—	8	M	Arendt et al. (1977a)
	57 ± 28[c]	—	7	F	
	<10–30	—	10	M	Vaughan et al. (1978b)
	<10–23	—	5	F	
	1.7–68.7	—	12	M	Brown et al. (1979)
	2.2–25.2	—	7	F	
	<2.5–41.8[d]	—	15	M	
	1.6–35.7[d]	—	11	F	
	39 ± 15[c]	—	3		Smith et al. (1979)

[a] All samples except those indicated otherwise were obtained by lumbar puncture.
[b] Mean ± SE.
[c] SD.
[d] Cerebrospinal fluid obtained by cisternal puncture.

200%. In addition to these hourly pulses, melatonin may also be secreted in even more frequent pulses: when Vaughan *et al.* (1979a,b) measured melatonin levels in bloods sampled at intervals of 2.5 minutes, they observed nighttime secretory bursts with frequencies of 8.25 and 12.14 minutes, and amplitudes of 35 and 33% (nadir to peak). These amplitudes are not much greater than melatonin's usual interassay variance; thus the bursts, if real, are not very robust. Arendt *et al.* (1982), measuring daytime serum levels every 60 minutes, did not find evidence of pulsatile secretion. This is in agreement with preliminary observations by the present authors who could not find evidence for melatonin pulses in seven male volunteers sampled every 30 minutes between 7 AM and 11 AM.

b. Day–Night Rhythms. Day–night rhythms in human blood (Table II) and urinary (Table III) melatonin levels have been demonstrated by all investigators who have looked for them. Highest blood levels have been noted in samples taken between midnight and 2 AM (Arendt *et al.*, 1977a; Smith *et al.*, 1977), and lowest between noon and 2 PM (Vaughan *et al.*, 1978a). Expressed in cosinor terminology, the acrophase of the melatonin rhythm in nine healthy subjects was − 357° from mid-sleep, and its amplitude was 65% from the mesor (Scheving *et al.*, 1981). Similar results were reported by Birkeland and Halberg (1980) and Fevre-Montange *et al.* (1981). The physiological basis of the day–night rhythm in melatonin secretion was originally thought to be an endogenous oscillator whose effects could be amplified or diminished by light and darkness but did not completely depend on the lighting environment. Consistent with this hypothesis, Vaughan *et al.* (1976) found that a plasma melatonin rhythm persisted among subjects kept under continuous illumination (12 footcandles) for 60 hours. Jimerson *et al.* (1977) and Akerstedt *et al.* (1979) also described persistent urinary melatonin rhythms among subjects exposed to continuous illumination. Furthermore, some investigators have found a clear dissociation between the time of onset of darkness and the time of melatonin secretion: Arendt *et al.* (1977a) and others (Vaughan *et al.*, 1978a) observed that melatonin secretion can precede dark onset, while Weinberg *et al.* (1979) observed a considerable delay in melatonin secretion after dark onset. If light or darkness per se did not trigger the day/night changes in melatonin secretion, what then did? Apparently not sleep stage (Vaughan *et al.*, 1978a), even though, in one very preliminary study (Sizonenko *et al.*, 1979), a correlation was noted between the nocturnal plasma melatonin peak and the number of preceding REM sleep periods.

More recent observations have again focused on light as the phase setter for the melatonin rhythm. Lynch *et al.* (1978b) found that an artificial phase shift of 180° in the light/dark regime did cause a corresponding shift in plasma and urinary melatonin after 5–7 days. A similar delay was observed after a natural phase shift, i.e., a transatlantic flight (Wetterberg, 1978; Fevre-Montange *et al.*, 1981). Blindness was also found to affect melatonin secretion from the human pineal: among two of four blind subjects studied by Lynch *et al.* (1975a), highest urinary melatonin levels were found in the morning or at noon. Serum melatonin contents in four blind subjects sampled at nighttime (11 PM) and during the day (2 PM) were higher at daytime (Smith and O'Hara, 1981). This may indicate a free-running diurnal melatonin cycle in blind humans.

Most compelling, Lewy *et al.* (1980a) found that light of sufficient intensity could cause a rapid fall of serum melatonin to daytime levels among normal volunteers awakened at 2 AM and then exposed to light for 2 hours. If they were then returned to darkness melatonin again rose within 30 minutes. A light intensity of 500 lux had no effect on melatonin levels, while light intensity of 2500 lux was extremely effective (2500 lux is about three times the intensity normally present in an artificially lit office, but only 3–5% of the intensity present out of doors on a sunny day).

Hence, the only difference between humans and experimental animals, in terms of pineal responses, is sensitivity to light. In retrospect it should not be surprising that humans, who normally work outside in daylight, are less sensitive to light than albino rats, which normally spend daylight hours sleeping in a completely dark burrow.

c. Menstrual Rhythms. Wetterberg *et al.* (1976) measured morning serum melatonin levels in five healthy women at 2- to 3-day intervals. Melatonin was lowest at the time of ovulation, increased during the following days, and, after a small decrease during the late follicular phase, exhibited a second peak at the time of menstruation. A 4.5-fold increase was found between ovulation and menstruation. Later, using a more specific antibody, Arendt (1978a) confirmed this relationship. However, Fellenberg *et al.* (1982) failed to detect changes in urinary levels of melatonin's main metabolite, 6-OH-melatonin, in association with the menstrual cycle.

d. Annual Rhythms. By monthly estimations of morning (8 AM) serum melatonin levels for 1 year, Arendt *et al.* (1977b) found a significant seasonal variation of melatonin in five men, with peak values in winter and summer and lower values in spring and autumn. In a later study (Arendt *et al.*, 1979) the same pattern was found among females, using either midday or midnight melatonin levels. The latter finding was taken as evidence that the annual rhythm is real, and not simply due to a shift in the day/night rhythm. Wetterberg *et al.* (1981b) confirmed this interpretation by showing no seasonal alteration in the acrophase of the 24-hour urinary melatonin excretion among 13 normal volunteers.

e. Changes with Age and Pubescence. That age, in general, and the stage of puberty, in particular, are factors that influence pineal activity has been suggested since the first publications concerning the pineal (Marburg, 1909; Kitay and Altschule, 1954).

Several studies have addressed the question of changes in melatonin levels with puberty. Arendt (1978a) estimated serum midday and midnight levels in six prepubertal and three pubertal children: In all nine, noontime levels were less than 14 pg; in the postpubertal children midnight levels averaged 128 pg/ml, and in the prepubertal subjects, 162 pg/ml. Thus, in this small sample no significant differences in melatonin levels were noted. Lenko *et al.* (1981) recorded daytime plasma and 24-hour urinary melatonin values among children aged 7 years and more. Plasma levels (n = 116) did not change with pubertal stage. Urine levels (n = 43) averaged 42.1 ng/24 hours/m^2 for prepubertal and 30.5 ng/24 hours/m^2 for pubertal children (Tanner Stage II–V). These did not differ significantly. Willig and Schroder (1979) also failed to detect significant differences between daytime and nighttime plasma melatonin levels of pre- and postpubertal children; nor did Ehrenkranz *et al.* (1982) detect differences between the plasma melatonin rhythms of normal adults and those of constitutionally short pre- and post-pubertal males or children with precocious puberty.

The opposite results were recorded by other groups. Silman *et al.* (1979) measured serum daytime melatonin levels by GC–MS in a school class of 51 healthy boys and girls aged 11.5–14 years. Melatonin concentrations in girls ranged from less than 5 to 280 pg/ml, and did not change with puberty. However, in boys they ranged from less than 10 to 2300 pg/ml, and were significantly higher during Tanner Stage I than during other stages. Wald-hauser *et al.* (1981) performed a cross-sectional study throughout childhood by measuring daytime and nighttime melatonin levels in 101 children and 25 adults. They found highest concentrations of immunologically active material in the group aged 1–3 years and a tendency to decreasing values in both daytime and nighttime samples during childhood. Apparent melatonin levels were lower in infancy than at ages 2–6. Since the patients were taking drugs that can cross-react with melatonin antibody (e.g., pyrazolidine derivatives) the findings are suspect. Hartmann *et al.* (1982), who estimated morning blood samples in 26 male infants, found undetectable or low values during the first 3 months of life and then values up to 1508 pg/ml.

Given these data, melatonin appears to show an inverse pattern to that of LH, which is high during the first months of life, then suppressed until the onset of puberty (Winter *et al.*, 1975).

The view that melatonin production is elevated in children is supported by observations on urinary melatonin and 6-OH-melatonin, its main me-tabolite. Among 58 male subjects, Lemaitre *et al.* (1981a) found a significantly higher melatonin excretion in children aged 4–15 years than in adults. Tetsuo *et al.* (1981), measuring 6-OH-melatonin by GC–MS in 101 children and 20 adults, observed that similar total quantities of 6-OH-melatonin were excreted per day by children and adults. Unfortunately, results were not analyzed with regard to the body weights of the children. But, if small children excrete the same amount of 6-OH-melatonin as adults do, it can be assumed that the relative excretions per body weight are enhanced in the children.

The available results are conflicting and additional data may help to clarify the relationship, if one exists, between melatonin levels and puberty. However, the important aspect of melatonin secretion for sexual maturation might not be its plasma levels per se, but the duration of its nocturnal elevation, as appears to be the case in rodents (see Section III,D).

The extent to which increasing pineal calcification during aging affects melatonin secretion is uncertain. Increasing age was not associated with changes in the activity of various pineal enzymes (Wurtman *et al.*, 1964c), but was associated with reduced melatonin concentration in the CSF (Brown *et al.*, 1979) and serum (Iguchi *et al.*, 1982).

3. Effects of Treatment on Melatonin Secretion

a. Stimulation.   It would be very useful to identify an innocuous treatment capable of stimulating melatonin secretion in humans. Such a treatment could serve as the basis of a pineal function test. Since the pineal is controlled by norepinephrine released from its sympathetic nerves and since administration of L-dopa, a norepinephrine precursor, increases melatonin synthesis in rats (Deguch and Axelrod, 1972; Lynch *et al.*, 1973b), L-dopa seemed a reasonable candidate as a pineal stimulator. Unfortunately, L-dopa was without effect on melatonin secretion in humans (Arendt, 1978a; Wetterberg, 1978; Moore *et al.*, 1979; Vaughan *et al.*, 1979c). Infusions of β-receptor agonists like isoproterenol (Vaughan *et al.*, 1976) or orciprenaline (Moore *et al.*, 1979) also failed to increase melatonin secretion. One possible explanation for this lack of action, i.e., an inhibitory effect of daylight or a diminished number of pineal β receptors during daytime, was excluded by the observation that L-dopa and orciprenaline given in the evening also failed to increase blood melatonin levels (Moore *et al.*, 1979).

Psychosocial stress (Akerstedt *et al.*, 1979) and stress due to insulin administration (Vaughan *et al.*, 1979c; Wetterberg, 1979), pneumoencephalography (Vaughan *et al.*, 1978b), electroconvulsive therapy (Wetterberg, 1978), and sprinting (Vaughan *et al.*, 1979c) also failed to elevate blood melatonin. However, Carr *et al.* (1981) did find a 100–200% increase in blood levels among seven healthy women after 1 hour of exercise on a bicycle ergometer during daytime. If this preliminary report can be confirmed, it could provide the basis for a pineal function test.

In very preliminary studies, such other neuroactive substances as sco-polamine (Vaughan et al., 1976), amphetamine, thyroid-releasing hormone (TRH), luteinizing hormone releasing hormone (LHRH), and desaminocys-D-arg-vasopressin (Wetterberg, 1978, 1979) also failed to affect melatonin secretion.

b. Suppression. As described above, bright light (2500 lux) can suppress nocturnal melatonin secretion (Lewy et al., 1980a).

The nocturnal release of melatonin can also be prevented by administration of propanolol, a β-receptor blocker (Vaughan et al., 1976; Wetterberg 1978; Moore et al., 1979; Lewy et al., 1981). This effect can be produced by as little as 40 mg propanolol, given po at 8 PM (Moore et al., 1979). It is not clear why β-receptor blockers prevent nocturnal melatonin secretion while β-receptor agonists fail to elicit its secretion in the daytime.

Preliminary reports suggest that clonidine (Lewy, 1981) and dexamethasone (Wetterberg, 1979) can inhibit melatonin secretion.

4. Melatonin Levels in Various Diseases

In the last few years much speculation has been offered suggesting re-lationships between melatonin secretion and various disease states. Unfor-tunately, very little supporting evidence has been discovered.

a. Neurological Diseases. To our knowledge, melatonin secretory patterns have been described in seven patients with pineal tumors, unfortunately most with inadequate clinical and histological data (Arendt, 1978b; Barber et al., 1978; Tapp, 1978; Kennaway et al., 1979; Vaughan et al., 1979c). Kennaway et al. (1979) described two males, one with a histologically un-identified pineal tumor, the other with a pineoblastoma. Both had undetectable serum melatonin levels on several occasions. Arendt (1978b) described two males, one with low and the other with unusually high melatonin levels. Interestingly, Barber et al. (1978) found elevated serum melatonin levels in one patient whose pinealoma showed much lower HIOMT activity than pineal tissue itself. A similar case with a germinoma of the pineal and high melatonin levels was reported by Tapp (1978). Thus, it seems possible that high or low serum melatonin levels can occur in association with pineal tumors, and perhaps circumstances are more complex than Marburg (1909) and Kitay and Altschule (1954) supposed in suggesting that parenchymatous pineal tumors produce an excess of an antigonadal hormone, while pineal-destroying tumors cause a lack of the hormone.

Kneisley et al. (1978) demonstrated abolition of the day/night urinary melatonin rhythm among six patients with clinical evidence of transected cervical spinal cords. This constitutes evidence that a similar neural pathway mediates the central control of pineal function among humans and rats.

b. Psychiatric Disease.   Since depression and possibly other psychiatric diseases can be associated with alterations in neuroendocrine rhythmicity (Bunney *et al.*, 1977) and since these disorders often have a seasonal pattern of exacerbations and remissions, it is not surprising that psychiatrists have become interested in examining disease-related rhythms in melatonin secretion.

Wetterberg *et al.* (1979) described a single depressed woman in whom nocturnal melatonin levels were lower and cortisol levels higher during depression than during remission. Later a similar pattern was found in 4 out of 12 depressive patients (Wetterberg *et al.*, 1981a) and in a number of schizophrenics (Ferrier *et al.*, 1982). Mendlewicz *et al.* (1979) described diminished circadian melatonin rhythms in 4 depressed patients, both during the depressive phase and after recovery.

Lewy *et al.* (1979) described significantly higher melatonin levels in 4 manic patients than in healthy controls. However, possible effects of medication were apparently not ruled out and may have been involved: chlorpromazine has been reported to elevate melatonin in rats (Ozaki *et al.*, 1976) and humans (Smith *et al.*, 1979) and certain antidepressive drugs have similar effects in rats (Wirz-Justice *et al.*, 1980).

Very recently, Lewy *et al.* (1981) reported that depressive patients are considerably more sensitive than normal controls to the photic inhibition of nocturnal melatonin secretion. Failure of other investigators to take light intensities into consideration may explain why, for example, Jimerson *et al.* (1977) found no difference in melatonin excretion between controls and depressive patients. At this point, perhaps the best lead relating depression to melatonin and pineal function seems to be the possibility of altered (i.e., enhanced) light sensitivity. It will be important to determine how general this alteration is, and whether its presence is correlated with such other neuroendocrine disturbances as abnormal dexamethasone-suppression tests.

c. Carcinoma.   In several animal models, melatonin administration reportedly diminished the growth of tumors and their metastases (Karmali *et al.*, 1978; Lapin, 1979). Cohen *et al.* (1978b) proposed that diminished melatonin production might be a factor in the etiology of breast cancer. This same group (Tamarkin *et al.*, 1982) subsequently reported lower nocturnal melatonin levels among 10 women with estrogen receptor-positive breast cancers than among control subjects or women whose cancers lacked estrogen receptors. Tapp *et al.* (1980) found no differences in serum melatonin levels among patients with benign or malignant tumors.

d. Other Disorders.   Birau and Schloot (1979) reported plasma melatonin levels to be elevated in spina bifida and sarcoidosis and diminished in psoriasis vulgaris, Turner's syndrome, and Klinefelter's syndrome. Elevated melatonin values were also found in hepatic cirrhosis, reflecting a reduction in its rate of metabolism (Iguchi *et al.*, 1982).

5. *Effects of Melatonin Administration on Humans*

Published reports describe approximately 100 subjects who have received melatonin (Lerner and Nordlund, 1978). Its only consistent effect in the doses given has been to cause mild sedation and analgesia, probably by acting on the CNS (Cramer *et al.*, 1979; Wetterberg, 1977; Vollrath *et al.*, 1981). No effect, or in some cases an exacerbation of clinical findings, has been observed after its administration to people with schizophrenia (Lerner and Nordlund, 1978), parkinsonism (Papavasiliou *et al.*, 1972), and depression (Carman *et al.*, 1976). Its influence on epilepsy is not clear, but justifies careful exploration (Anton-Tay *et al.*, 1971).

Very few studies have been performed on melatonin's gonadal effects in humans. Apparently melatonin does not suppress gonadotropin secretion caused by giving LHRH (Fideloff *et al.*, 1976; Weinberg *et al.*, 1980); gonadotropin values in people receiving only melatonin were reported to be unaffected (Fideloff *et al.*, 1976) or blunted (Nordlund and Lerner, 1977). Acute melatonin administration reportedly reduces the rise in plasma growth hormone after insulin (Smythe and Lazarus, 1979) or L-tryptophan (Kolu and Lammintausta, 1979) administration. Melatonin did not modify the increase in plasma growth hormone after apomorphine or L-dopa (Kolu and Lammintausta, 1979).

No side effects of melatonin have been described except for mild headache or abdominal cramps, even when as much as 6.6 gm were administered orally each day for 35 days (Lerner and Nordlund, 1978). Melatonin is thus probably a highly nontoxic substance, and deserves considerable further study in humans. In mice even 800 mg/kg failed to cause death; the LD_{50} could not be estimated because solubility limitations precluded testing higher doses (Barchas *et al.*, 1967).

IV. SUMMARY

The prevailing view among scientists is that the most effective way of approaching the mammalian pineal organ is as a neuroendocrine transducer, which responds to a neuronal input by releasing its hormone, melatonin, into the blood or CSF. The particular neuronal input that stimulates melatonin's synthesis and secretion is norepinephrine released from the pineal's sympathetic nerves; the catecholamine acts via β-receptors and cyclic AMP.

The increase that it causes in melatonin's synthesis is associated with increases in the activities of the two enzymes (serotonin-N-acetyltransferase and hydroxyindole-O-methyltransferase) that catalyze the conversion of serotonin to N-acetylserotonin, and thence to melatonin. However, the most likely locus at which serotonin's conversion to melatonin is accelerated is not either of these enzymes but the liberation of serotonin from an intracellular binding site, which then makes it available for biotransformation.

This chapter focuses on recent developments in the assay of melatonin, and on the probable significance of the data acquired using these assays. It describes the daily and other rhythms in melatonin secretion found in humans, rats, and other mammals, and summarizes the information now available on the biochemical and physiological consequences of melatonin's administration or secretion.

ACKNOWLEDGMENTS

These studies were supported in part by grants from the National Science Foundation (PCM 77-15700) and the National Institutes of Health (HD 11722). F. W. is supported by the Postdoctoral Research Exchange Program of the Max Kade Foundations Inc., New York.

REFERENCES

Adler, J., Lynch, H. J., and Wurtman, R. J. (1979). *Brain Res.* **163**, 111–120.

Akerstedt, T., Froberg, J. E., Friberg, Y., and Wetterberg, L. (1979). *Psychoneuroendocrinology (Oxford)* 4, 219–225.

Anton-Tay, F., and Wurtman, R. J. (1969). *Nature (London)* **221**, 474–475.

Anton-Tay, F., Chou, C., Anton, S., and Wurtman, R. J. (1968). *Science* **162**, 277–278.

Anton-Tay, F., Diaz, J. L., and Fernandex-Guardiola, A. (1971). *Life Sci.* **10**, 841–850.

Arendt, J. (1978a). *J. Neural Transm., Suppl.* **13**, 265–278.

Arendt, J. (1978b). *Br. Med. J.* **II**, 635–636.

Arendt, J., and Wilkinson, M. (1978). *In* "Methods of Hormone Radioimmunoassay" (B. M. Jaffe and M. R. Behrman, eds.), 2nd Ed., pp. 101–119. Academic Press, New York.

Arendt, J., Paunier, L., and Sizonenko, P. C. (1975). *J. Clin. Endocrinol. Metab.* **40**, 347–350.

Arendt, J., Wetterberg, L., Heyden, T., Sizonenko, P. C., and Paunier, L. (1977a). *Horm. Res.* **8**, 65–75.

Arendt, J., Wirz-Justice, A., and Bradtke, J. (1977b). *Neurosci. Lett.* **7**, 327–330.

Arendt, J., Wirz-Justice, A., Bradtke, J., and Kornemark, M. (1979). *Ann. Clin. Biochem.* **16**, 307–312.

Ariens-Kappers, J. (1960). *Anat. Record.* **136**, 220–221.

Ariens-Kappers, J. (1965). *Prog. Brain Res.* **10**, 87–153.

Axelrod, J., MacLean, P. D., Albers, R. W., and Weissbach, H. (1961). *In* "Regional Neurochemistry" (S. S. Kety and J. Elkes, eds.), pp. 307–311. Pergamon, Oxford.

Axelrod, J., Wurtman, R. J., and Snyder, S. H. (1965). *J. Biol. Chem.* **240**, 949–955.

Axelrod, J., Shein, H. M., and Wurtman, R. J. (1969). *Proc. Natl. Acad. Sci. U.S.A.* **62**, 544–549.

Barber, S. G., Smith, J. A., and Hughes, R. C. (1978). *Br. Med. J.* **I**, 328.

Barchas, J. D., Da Costa, F., and Spector, S. (1967). *Nature (London)* **214**, 919–920.

Benson, B., and Ebels, I. (1981). *In* "The Pineal Gland" (R. J. Reiter, ed.), Vol. II, pp. 165–188. CRC Press, Boca Raton, Florida.

Birau, N., and Schloot, W. (1979). *IRCS Med. Sci. Libr. Compend.* **7**, 400.

Birkelund, A. J., and Halberg, F. (1980). *Chronobiologia (Milan)* **7**, 277.

Brenner, M., and Niederwieser, A. (1961). *Experientia* **17**, 237–238.

Brown, G. M., Young, S. N., Gauthier, S., Tsui, H., and Grota, L. J. (1979). *Life Sci.* **25**, 929–936.

Bubenik, G. A., Brown, G. M., and Grota, L. G. (1976). *Brain Res.* **118**, 417–427.

Bunney, W. E., Wehr, T. R., Gillin, J. C., Post, R., Goodwin, F. K., and van Kammen, D. P. (1977). *Ann. Intern. Med.* **87**, 319–335.

Cardinali, D. P., and Rosner, J. M. (1971a). *Endocrinology (Baltimore)* **89**, 301–303.

Cardinali, D. P., and Rosner, J. M. (1971b). *J. Neurochem.* **18**, 1769–1770.

Cardinali, D. P., Lynch, H. J., and Wurtman, R. J. (1972). *Endocrinology (Baltimore)* **91**, 1213–1218.

Cardinali, D. P., Hyyppa, M. T., and Wurtman, R. J. (1973). *Neuroendocrinology* **12**, 30–40.

Cardinali, D. P., Nagle, C. A., Friere, F., and Rosner, J. M. (1975). *Neuroendocrinology* **18**, 72–85.

Cardinali, D. P., Vacas, M. I., and Boyer, E. E. (1979). *Endocrinology (Baltimore)* **105**, 437–441.

Cardinali, D. P., Ritta, M. N., Fuentes, A. M., Gimeno, M. F., and Gimeno, A. L. (1980). *Eur. J. Pharmacol.* **67**, 151–153.

Carman, J. S., Post, R. M., Buswell, R., and Goodwin, F. K. (1976). *Am. J. Psychiatry* **133**, 1181–1186.

Carr, D. B., Reppert, S. M., Bullen, B., Skrinar, G., Beitins, I., Arnold, M., Rosenblatt, M., Martin, J. B., and McArthur, J. W. (1981). *J. Clin. Endocrinol. Metab.* **53**, 224–225.

Cattabeni, F., Koslow, S. H., and Costa, E. (1972). *Science* **178**, 166–168.

Cohen, M., Roselle, D., Chabner, B., Schmidt, T. J., and Lippman, M. (1978a). *Nature (London)* **274**, 894–895.

Cohen, M., Lippman, M., and Chabner, B. (1978b). *Lancet* **II**, 814–816.

Cramer, M., Rudolph, J., Consbruch, U., and Kendel, K. (1979). *Adv. Biochem. Psychopharmacol.* **11**, 187–191.

Datta, P. C., and King, M. G. (1977). *Pharmacol. Biochem. Behav.* **6**, 449–452.

Degen, P. H., and Barchas, J. D. (1970). *Proc. West. Pharmacol. Soc.* **13**, 34–35.

Deguchi, T., and Axelrod, J. (1972). *Proc. Natl. Acad. Sci. U.S.A.* **69**, 2208–2211.

Ehrenkranz, J. R. L., Tamarkin, L., Comite, F., Johnsonbaugh, R. E., Bybee, D. E., Loriaux, D. L., and Cutler, G. B. (1982). *J. Clin. Endocrinol. Metab.* **55**, 307–310.

Ellis, L. C. (1972). *Endocrinology (Baltimore)* **90**, 17–28.

Engel, P. (1936). *Ergeb. Inn. Med. Kinderheilkd.* **50**, 116–171.

Fellenberg, A. J., Phillipou, G., and Seamark, R. F. (1982). *Clin. Endocrinol.* **17**, 71–75.

Fernstrom, J. D., Fisher, L. A., Cusack, B. M., and Gillis, M. A. (1980). *Endocrinology (Baltimore)* **106**, 243–251.

Ferrier, I. N., Johnstone, E. C., and Crow, T. J. (1982). *Lancet* **I**, 1070.

Fevre-Montange, M., van Cauter, E., Refetoff, S., Desir, D., Tourniaire, J., and Copinschi, G. (1981). *J. Clin. Endocrinol. Metab.* **52**, 642–649.

Fideloff, M., Aparico, N. J., Guitelman, A., Debeljuk, L., Mancini, A., and Cramer, C. (1976). *J. Clin. Endocrinol. Metab.* **42**, 1014–1017.

Fiske, V. M., and Huppert, L. C. (1968). *Science* **162**, 279–280.

Fiske, V. M., Bryant, K., and Putnam, J. (1960). *Endocrinology (Baltimore)* **66**, 489–491.

Foa, C. (1912). *Pathologica* **4**, 445–454.

Fraschini, F., Mess, B., Piva, F., and Martini, L. (1968). *Science* **159**, 1104–1105.

Frohn, M. A., Seaborn, C. J., Johnson, D. W., Phillipou, G., Seamark, R. F., and Mathews, C. D. (1980). *Life Sci.* **27**, 2043–2046.

Giarman, N. J., and Day, M. (1959). *Biochem. Pharmacol.* **1**, 235.

Glass, J. D., and Lynch, G. R. (1981). *Science* **214**, 821–823.

Goldman, B., Hall, V., and Hollister, C., Roychoudhury, P., Tamarkin, L., and Westrom, W. (1979). *Endocrinology (Baltimore)* **104**, 82–88.

Golus, P., McGee, R., and King, M. G. (1979). *Pharmacol. Biochem. Behav.* **11**, 367–369.

Greiner, A. C., and Chan, S. C. (1978). *Science* **199**, 83–84.

Grota, L. J., and Brown, G. M. (1974). *Can. J. Biochem.* **52**, 196–202.

Hakanson, D. O., and Bergstrom, W. H. (1981). *Science* **214**, 807–809.

Hartmann, L., Roger, M., Lemaitre, B. J., Massias, J. F., and Chaussain, J. L. (1981). *Clin. Chim. Acta* **121**, 37–42.

Heath, H. W., and Lynch, G. R. (1981). *J. Exp. Zool.* **216**, 193–195.

Hedlund, L., Lischko, M. M., Rollag, M. D., and Niswender, G. D. (1977). *Science* **195**, 686–687.

Herbert, J. (1969). *J. Endocrinol.* **43**, 625–636.

Heubner, O. (1898). *Dtsch. Med. Wochenschr.* **24**, 215.

Hirata, F., Hayaishi, O., Tokuyama, T., and Senoh, S. (1974). *J. Biol. Chem.* **249**, 1311–1313.

Hofstaetter, R. (1936). *Wien. Klin. Wochenschr.* **49**, 136–137.

Hofstaetter, R. (1938). *Zentralbl. Gynaekol.* **62**, 1192–1196.

Iguchi, H., Kato, K., and Ibayashi, H. (1982). *J. Clin. Endocrinol. Metab.* **54**, 1025–1027.

Iguchi, H., Kato, K., and Ibayashi, H. (1982). *J. Clin. Endocrinol. Metab.* **55**, 27–29.

Illnerova, H., Vanecek, J., Krecek, J., Wetterberg, L., and Saaf, J. (1978). *J. Neurochem.* **32**, 673–675.

Izawa, C. (1923). *Am. J. Med. Sci.* **166**, 185–196.

Jimerson, D. C., Lynch, H. J., Post, R. M., Wurtman, R. J., and Bunney, W. E. (1977). *Life Sci.* **23**, 1501–1508.

Kano, T., and Miyachi, Y. (1976). *Biochem. Biophys. Res. Commun.* **72**, 969–975.

Karmali, R. A., Morrobin, D. F., and Ghayur, T. (1978). *Lancet* **II**, 1002.

Kelly, D. E. (1962). *Am. Sci.* **50**, 597–625.

Kennaway, D. J., Frith, R. G., Phillipou, G., Matthews, C. D., and Seamark, R. F. (1977). *Endocrinology (Baltimore)* **101**, 119–127.

Kennaway, D. J., McCulloch, G., Matthews, C. D., and Seamark, R. F. (1979). *J. Clin. Endocrinol. Metab.* **49**, 144–145.

Kitay, J. I., and Altschule, M. D. (1954). "The Pineal Gland: A Review of the Physiologic Literature." Harvard Univ. Press, Cambridge, Massachausetts.

Klein, D., and Weller, J. (1970). *Science* **169**, 1093–1095.

Kneisley, L. W., Moskowitz, M. A., and Lynch, H. J. (1978). *J. Neural. Transm., Suppl.* **13**, 311–324.

Kolu, M., and Lammintausta, R. (1979). *J. Clin. Endocrinol. Metab.* **49**, 70–72.

Kopin, I. J., Pierce, C. M., Axelrod, J., and Weissbach, H. (1961). *J. Biol. Chem.* **236**, 3072–3075.

Koslow, S. H., and Green, A. R. (1973). *Adv. Biochem. Psychopharmacol.* **7**, 33–43.

Kveder, S., and McIsaac, W. M. (1961). *J. Biol. Chem.* **236**, 3214–3220.

Lang, U., Kornemark, M., Aubert, M. L., Paunier, L., and Sizonenko, P. C. (1981). *J. Clin. Endocrinol. Metab.* **53**, 645–650.

Lapin, V. (1979). *Prog. Brain Res.* **52**, 523–533.

Lemaitre, B. J., Bouillie, J., and Hartmann, L. (1981a). *Clin. Chim. Acta* **110**, 77–84.

Lemaitre, B. J., Roger, M., Gendrel, D., Chaussain, J. L., and Hartmann, L. (1981b). *Proc. 1st Jt. Meet. LWPS ESPE, Geneva*, p. 67.

Lenko, H. L., Lang, U., Aubert, M. L., Paunier, L., and Sizonenko, P. C. (1981). *Pediatr. Res.* **15**, 74.

Lerner, A. B., and Nordlund, J. J. (1978). *J. Neural. Transm., Suppl.* **13**, 339–347.

Lerner, A. B., Case, J. D., and Heinzelman, R. V. (1959). *J. Am. Chem. Soc.* **80**, 2587.

Lerner, A. B., Case, J. D., and Takahashi, Y. (1960). *J. Biol. Chem.* **235**, 1992–1997.

Levine, L., and Riceberg, L. J. (1975). *Res. Commun. Chem. Pathol. Pharmacol.* **10**, 693–702.

Lewy, A. J. (1981). *Proc. 11th Annu. Meet. Soc. Neurosci., Los Angeles, California, Oct. 1981*, p. 717.

Lewy, A. J., and Markey, S. P. (1978). *Science* **201**, 741–743.

Lewy, A. J., Wehr, T. A., Gold, P. W., and Goodwin, F. K. (1979). In "Catecholamines: Basic and Clinical Frontiers" (E. Usdin, I. J. Kopin, and J. D. Brachas, eds.), Vol. II, pp. 1173–1175. Pergamon, Oxford.

Lewy, A. J., Wehr, T. A., Goodwin, F. K., Newsome, D. A., and Markey, S. P. (1980a). *Science* **210**, 1267–1269.

Lewy, A. J., Tetsuo, M., Markey, S. P., Goodwin, F. K., and Kopin, I. J. (1980b). *J. Clin. Endocrinol. Metab.* **50**, 204–205.

Lewy, A. J., Wehr, T. A., Goodwin, F. K., Newsome, D. A., and Rosenthal, N. E. (1981). *Lancet* **I**, 383–384.

Lynch, H. J. (1971). *Life Sci.* **10**, 791–795.

Lynch, H. J., and Wurtman, R. J. (1979). In "Proceedings Naito International Symposium Biological Rhythms and Their Central Mechanism," (M. Suda, O. Hayaisha, and H. Nagagawa, eds.), p. 117. Elsevier/North–Holland Biomedical Press, Amsterdam.

Lynch, H. J., Wang, P., and Wurtman, R. J. (1973a). *Life Sci.* **12**, 145–151.

Lynch, H. J., Eng, P. P., and Wurtman, R. J. (1973b). *Proc. Natl. Acad. Sci. U.S.A.* **70**, 1704–1707.

Lynch, H. J., Ozaki, Y., Shakal, D., and Wurtman, R. J. (1975a). *Int. J. Biometeorol.* **19**, 267–279.

Lynch, H. J., Wurtman, R. J., Moskowitz, M. A., Archer, M. C., and Ho, M. H. (1975b). *Science* **17**, 169–171.

Lynch, H. J., Ozaki, Y., and Wurtman, R. J. (1978a). *J. Neural. Transm., Suppl.* **13**, 251–264.

Lynch, H. J., Jimerson, D. C., Ozaki, Y., Post, R. M., Bunney, W. E., and Wurtman, R. J. (1978b). *Life Sci.* **23**, 1557–1564.

Lynch, H. J., Rivest, R. W., and Wurtman, R. J. (1980). *Neuroendocrinology* **31**, 106–111.

McCord, C. P., and Allen, F. P. (1917). *J. Exp. Zool.* **23**, 207–229.

McIsaac, W., Taborsky, R., and Farrell, G. (1964). *Science* **145**, 63–64.

Maickel, R. P., and Miller, F. P. (1968). *Adv. Pharmacol.* **6**, 71–77.

Marburg, O. (1909). *Arb. Neur. Inst. Wien.* **12**, 217–279.

Marburg, O. (1930). In "Handbuch der Normalen und Pathologischen Physiologie" (A. Bethe, G. V. Bergmann, G. Embden, and A. Ellinger, eds.), Bd. 16/I., pp. 493–509. Springer-Verlag, Berlin and New York.

Marczynski, T. J., Yamaguchi, N., Ling, G. M., and Brodzinska, L. (1964). *Experientia* **20**, 435–437.

Mendlewicz, J., Linkowski, P., Branchey, L., Weinberg, U., Weitzman, E. D., and Branchey, M. (1979). *Lancet* **II**, 1362.

Miller, F. P., and Maickel, R. P. (1970). *Life Sci.* **9**, 747–752.

Minneman, K. P., and Wurtman, R. J. (1974). *Life Sci.* **15**, 1791–1796.

Minneman, K. P., and Wurtman, R. J. (1975). *Life Sci.* **17**, 1189–1200.

Minneman, K. P., and Wurtman, R. J. (1976). *Annu. Rev. Pharmacol. Toxicol.* **16**, 33–51.

Moore, D. C., Paunier, L., and Sizonenko, P. C. (1979). *Prog. Brain Res.* **52**, 517–521.

Mullen, P. E., Linsell, G. R., Leone, R. M., Silman, R. E., Smith, I., Hooper, R. J. L., Finnie, M., and Parrot, J. (1981). *Adv. Biosci.* **29**, 337.

Niles, L. P., Wong, Y. W., Mishra, R. K., and Brown, G. M. (1979). *Eur. J. Pharmacol.* **55**, 219–220.

Nordlung, J. J., and Lerner, A. B. (1977). *J. Clin. Endocrinol. Metab.* **45**, 768–774.

Ozaki, Y., and Lynch, H. J. (1976). *Endocrinology (Baltimore)* **99**, 641–644.

Ozaki, Y., Lynch, H. J., and Wurtman, R. J. (1976). *Endocrinology (Baltimore)* **98**, 1418–1424.

Pang, S. F., and Ralph, C. L. (1975). *J. Exp. Zool.* **193**, 275–280.

Pang, S. F., Brown, G. M., Grota, L. J., and Rodman, R. L. (1976). *Fed. Proc., Fed. Am. Soc. Exp. Biol.* **35**, 691.

Panke, E. S., Reiter, R. J., Rollag, M. D., and Panke, T. W. (1978). *Endocrinol. Res. Commun.* **5**, 311–324.

Panke, E. S., Rollag, M. D., and Reiter, R. J. (1979). *Endocrinology (Baltimore)* **104**, 195–197.

Papavasiliou, P. S., Cotzias, G. C., Duby, S. E., Steck, A. J., Bell, M., and Lawrence, W. H. (1972). *J. Am. Med. Assoc.* **221**, 88.

Patel, J., Marangos, P. J., Hirata, F., Skolnic, P., Paul, S. M., and Goodwin, F. K. (1981). *Abstr. 12th Meet. Am. Soc. Neurochem.*, p. 73.

Pelham, R. W. (1975). *Endocrinology (Baltimore)* **96**, 543–546.

Pelham, R. W., Ralph, C. L., and Campbell, I. M. (1972). *Biochem. Biophys. Res. Commun.* **46**, 1236–1241.

Pelham, R. W., Vaughan, G. M., Sandock, K. L., and Vaughan, M. K. (1973). *J. Clin. Endocrinol. Metab.* **37**, 341–344.

Perlow, M. J., Reppert, S. M., Tamarkin, L., Wyatt, R. J., and Klein, D. C. (1980). *Brain Res.* **182**, 211–216.

Pevet, P., Neacsu, C., Holder, F. C., Reinharz, A., Dogterom, J., Buijis, R. M., Guerne, J. M., and Vivien-Roels, B. (1981). *J. Neural. Transm.* **51**, 295–302.

Quay, W. B. (1963a). *Anal. Biochem.* **5**, 51–59.

Quay, W. B. (1963b). *Gen. Comp. Endocrinol.* **3**, 473–479.

Quay, W. B. (1964). *Proc. Soc. Exp. Biol. Med.* **115**, 710–713.

Ralph, C. L., and Lynch, H. J. (1970). *Gen. Comp. Endocrinol.* **15**, 334–338.

Ralph, C. L., Mull, D., and Lynch, H. J. (1970). *Am. Zool.* **10**, 302.

Reiter, R. J. (1980). *Endocr. Rev.* **1**, 109–131.

Reiter, R. J., and Hester, R. J. (1966). *Endocrinology (Baltimore)* **79**, 1168–1170.

Reiter, R. J., Sorrentino, S., Jr., Ralph, C. L., Lynch, H. J., Mull, D., and Jarrow, E. (1971). *Endocrinology (Baltimore)* **88**, 895–900.

Reiter, R. J., Vaughan, M. K., Vaughan, G. M., Sorrentino, S., and Donofrio, R. J. (1975). *In* "Frontiers of Pineal Physiology" (M. D. Altschule, ed.), p. 54. MIT Press, Cambridge, Massachusetts.

Reiter, R. J., Rollag, M. D., Panke, E. S., and Bank, A. F. (1978). *J. Neural. Transm., Suppl.* **13**, 209–223.

Reppert, S. M., Perlow, M. J., Tamarkin, L., and Klein, D. C. (1979). *Endocrinology (Baltimore)* **104**, 295–301.

Reppert, S. M., Perlow, M. J., and Klein, D. C. (1980). *In* "Neurobiology of Cerebrospinal Fluid" (J. H. Wood, ed.), pp. 579–589. Plenum, New York.

Richardson, S. B., Hollander, C. S., Prasad, J. A., and Hirooka, Y. (1981). *Endocrinology (Baltimore)* **109**, 602–606.

Rivest, R. W., Lynch, H. J., Ronsheim, P. M., and Wurtman, R. J. (1980). *Adv. Biosci.* **29**, 119–121.

Rollag, M. D., and Niswender, G. D. (1976). *Endocrinology (Baltimore)* **98**, 482–489.

Rollag, M. D., O'Gallaghan, P. L., and Niswender, G. D. (1978a). *Biol. Reprod.* **18**, 279–285.

Rollag, M. D., Morgan, R. J., and Niswender, G. D. (1978b). *Endocrinology (Baltimore)* **102**, 1–8.

Rollag, M. D., Panke, E. S., Trakulrungsi, W., Trakulrungsi, C., and Reiter, R. J. (1980). *Endocrinology (Baltimore)* **106**, 231–236.

Rudman, D. (1976). *Neuroendocrinology* **20**, 235–242.

Rust, C. C., and Meyer, R. K. (1961). *Science* **165**, 921–922.

Sandler, J. A., Clyman, R. I., Manganiello, V. C., and Vaughan, M. (1975). *J. Clin. Invest.* **55**, 431–435.

Scheving, L. E., Wetterberg, L., Kanabrocki, E. L., and Halberg, F. (1981). *Chronobiologica* **8**, 188.

Shein, H. M., and Wurtman, R. J. (1969). *Science* **166**, 519–520.

Silman, R. E., Leone, R. M., Hooper, R. J. L., and Preece, M. A. (1979). *Nature (London)* **282**, 301–303.

Sisak, M. E., Markey, S. P., Colburn, R. W., Zavadil, A. P., and Kopin, I. J. (1979). *Life Sci.* **25**, 803–806.

Sizonenko, P. C., Moore, D. C., Paunier, L., Beaumanoir, A., and Nahory, A. (1979). *Prog. Brain Res.* **52**, 549–551.

Smith, J. A., and O'Hara, J. (1981). *Lancet* **II**, 933.

Smith, J. A., Mee, T. J. X., Barnes, N. D., Thornburn, R. J., and Barnes, J. L. C. (1976a). *Lancet* **II**, 425.

Smith, I., Mullen, P. E., Silman, R. E., Snedded, W., and Wilson, B. W. (1976b). *Nature (London)* **260**, 718–719.

Smith, J. A., Padwick, D., Mee, T. J. X., Minneman, K. P., and Bird, E. D. (1977). *Clin. Endocrinol.* **6**, 219–225.

Smith, J. A., Barnes, J. L., and Mee, T. J. (1979). *J. Pharm. Pharmacol.* **31**, 246–248.

Smythe, G. A., and Lazarus, L. (1974). *J. Clin. Invest.* **54**, 116–121.

Tamarkin, L. T., and Goldman, B. (1978). *J. Neural. Transm., Suppl.* **13**, 393–399.

Tamarkin, L., Brown, S., and Goldman, B. (1975). *Abstr. 5th Annu. Meet. Soc. Neurosci.* p. 458.

Tamarkin, L., Westrom, W. K., Hamill, A. I., and Goldman, B. D. (1976). *Endocrinology (Baltimore)* **99**, 1534–1541.

Tamarkin, L., Reppert, S. M., and Klein, D. C. (1979). *Endocrinology (Baltimore)* **104**, 385–389.

Tamarkin, L., Danforth, D., Lichter, A., DeMoss, E., Cohen, M., Chabner, B., and Lippman, H. (1982). *Science* **216**, 1003–1005.

Tan, G. H., and Khoo, J. C. M. (1981). *Horm. Res.* **14**, 224–233.

Tapp, E. (1978). *Br. Med. J.* **II**, 636.

Tapp, E., Skinner, R. G., and Phillips, V. (1980). *J. Neural. Transm.* **48**, 137–141.

Tetsuo, M., Poth, M., and Markey, S. P. (1981). *J. Clin. Endocrinol. Metab.* **55**, 311–313.

Thoma, J. A. (1963). *J. Chromatogr.* **12**, 441–452.

Tomatis, M. E., and Orias, R. (1967). *Acta Physiol. Lat. Am.* **17**, 227–233.

Udenfriend, S., Bogdanski, D. F., and Weissbach, H. (1955). *Science* **122**, 972–974.

Vacas, M. I., and Cardinali, D. P. (1979). *Neurosci. Lett.* **15**, 259–263.

Vacas, M. I., Keller Sarmiento, M. I., and Cardinali, D. P. (1981). *Brain Res.* **225**, 207–211.

Vaughan, M. K. (1981). *In* "The Pineal Gland" (R. J. Reiter, ed.), Vol. II, pp. 125–164. CRC Press, Boca Raton, Florida.

Vaughan, G. M., Pelham, R. W., Pang, S. F., Loughlin, L. L., Wilson, K. M., Sandock, K. L., Vaughan, M. K., and Koslow, S. H. (1976). *J. Clin. Endocrinol. Metab.* **42**, 752–764.

Vaughan, G. M., Allen, J. P., Tullis, W., Siler-Khodr, T. M., de la Pena, A., and Sackman, J. W. (1978a). *J. Clin Endocrinol. Metab.* **47**, 566–571.

Vaughan, G. M., McDonald, S. D., Jordan, R. M., Allen, J. P., Bohmfalk, G. L., Abou-Samra, M., and Story, J. L. (1978b). *J. Clin. Endocrinol. Metab.* **47**, 220.

Vaughan, G. M., Allen, J. P., and de la Pena, A. (1979a). *Waking Sleeping* **3**, 169–173.

Vaughan, G. M., Bell, R., de la Pena, A. (1979b). *Neurosci. Lett.* **14**, 81–84.

Vaughan, G. M., McDonald, S. D., Jordan, R. M., Allen, J. P., Bell, R., and Stevens, E. A. (1979c). *Psychoneuroendocrinology (Oxford)* **4**, 351–362.

Vermes, I., Dull, G., Telegdy, G., and Lissak, K. (1972). *Acta Physiol. Hung.* **42**, 219–223.

Vesely, D. L. (1981). *Mol. Cell Biochem.* **35**, 55–58.

Vlahakes, G., and Wurtman, R. J. (1972). *Biochim. Biophys. Acta* **261**, 194–197.

Vollrath, L., Semm, P., and Gammel, G. (1981). *Adv. Biosci.* **29**, 327–329.

Waldhauser, F., Frisch, M., Weissenbacher, G., Zeitlhuber, U., and Toifl, K. (1981). *Pediatr. Res.* **15**, 1566.

Waring, H. (1963). "Color-Change Mechanisms of Coldblooded Vertebrates." Academic Press, New York.

Weinberg, U., D'Eletto, R. D., Weitzman, E. D., Erligh, S., and Hollander, C. (1979). *J. Clin. Endocrinol. Metab.* **48**, 114–118.

Weinberg, U., Weitzman, E. D., Fukushima, D. K., Cancel, G. F., and Rosenfeld, R. S. (1980). *J. Clin. Endocrinol. Metab.* **51**, 161–162.

Weissbach, H., and Axelrod, J. (1960). *Fed. Proc., Fed. Am. Exp. Biol.* **19**, 50.

Weitzman, E. D., Weinberg, U., D'Eletto, R., Lynch, H., Wurtman, R. J., Czeisler, C., and Erlich, S. (1978). *J. Neural. Transm., Suppl.* **13**, 325–337.

Wetterberg, L. (1977). *Nature (London)* **269**, 646.

Wetterberg, L. (1978). *J. Neural. Transm., Suppl.* **13**, 289–310.

Wetterberg, L. (1979). *Prog. Brain Res.* **52**, 523–533.

Wetterberg, L., Arendt, J., Paunier, L., Sizonenko, P. C., van Donselaar, W., and Heyden, T. (1976). *J. Clin. Endocrinol. Metab.* **42**, 185–188.

Wetterberg, L., Beck-Friis, J., Aperia, B., and Petterson, U. (1979). *Lancet* **II**, 1361.

Wetterberg, L., Aperia, B., Beck-Friis, J., Kjellman, B. F., Ljunggren, J. G., Petterson, U., Sjolin, A., Tham, A., and Unden, F. (1981a). *In* "Steroid Hormone Regulation of the Brain" (K. Fuxe, J. A. Gustafson, and L. Wetterberg, eds.). Pergamon, Oxford.

Wetterberg, L., Halberg, F., Haus, E., Kawasaki, T., Uezono, K., Ueno, M., and Oma, T. (1981b). *Chronobiologia* **8**, 188–189.

Wilkinson, M., Arendt, J., Brodtke, J., and de Ziegler, D. (1977). *J. Endocrinol.* **72**, 243–244.

Willig, R. P., and Schroder, C. (1979). *Pediatr. Res.* **13**, 1184.

Wilson, B. W., Snedden, W., Silman, R. E., Smith, I., and Mullen, P. (1977). *Anal. Biochem.* **81**, 283–291.

Wilson, B. W., Lynch, H. J., and Ozaki, Y. (1978). *Life Sci.* **23**, 1019–1024.

Winter, J. S. D., Faiman, C. H., Hobson, W. C., Prasad, A. V., and Reyes, F. I. (1975). *J. Clin. Endocrinol. Metab.* **40**, 545–551.

Wirz-Justice, A., Arendt, J., and Marston, A. (1980). *Experientia* **36**, 442–444.

Wurtman, R. J., and Anton-Tay, F. (1969). *Recent Prog. Horm. Res.* **25**, 493–522.

Wurtman, R. J., and Axelrod, J. (1965). *Sci. Am.* **213**, 50–60.

Wurtman, R. J., Altschule, M. D., and Holmgren, U. (1959). *Am. J. Physiol.* **197**, 108–110.

Wurtman, R. J., Roth, W., Altschule, M. D., and Wurtman, J. J. (1961). *Acta Endocrinol. (Copenhagen)* **36**, 617–624.

Wurtman, R. J., Axelrod, J., and Kelly, D. E. (1968). "The Pineal." Academic Press, New York.

Wurtman, R. J., Axelrod, J., and Chu, E. W. (1963a). *Science* **141**, 277–278.

Wurtman, R. J., Axelrod, J., and Phillips, L. S. (1963b). *Science* **142,** 1071–1073.
Wurtman, R. J., Axelrod, J., and Fischer, J. E. (1964a). *Science* **143,** 1329–1330.
Wurtman, R. J., Axelrod, J., and Potter, L. T. (1964b). *J. Pharmacol. Exp. Ther.* **143,** 314–318.
Wurtman, R. J., Axelrod, J., and Barchas, J. D. F. (1964c). *J. Clin. Endocrinol. Metab.* **24,** 299–301.
Wurtman, R. J., Shein, H. M., Axelrod, J., and Larin, F. (1969). *Proc. Natl. Acad. Sci. U.S.A.* **62,** 749–755.
Wurtman, R. J., Shein, H. M., and Larin, F. (1971). *J. Neurochem.* **18,** 1683–1687.
Wurtzburger, R. J., Kawashima, K., Miller, R. L., and Spector, S. (1976). *Life Sci.* **18,** 867–878.
Ying, S. Y., and Greep, R. O. (1973). *Endocrinology (Baltimore)* **92,** 333–335.
Zoia, C. (1914). *Zentralbl. Allg. Pathol. Anat.* **25,** 789.

CHAPTER 7

The *Ah* Receptor: Controlling Factor in the Induction of Drug-Metabolizing Enzymes by Certain Chemical Carcinogens and Other Environmental Pollutants

Howard J. Eisen, Rita R. Hannah,
Catherine Legraverend, Allan B. Okey,
and Daniel W. Nebert

BIOCHEMICAL ACTIONS OF HORMONES, VOL. X

I. INTRODUCTION

We are living in a sea of foreign chemicals, most likely numbering in the hundreds of thousands. An estimated 70,000 agricultural chemicals (insecticides, pesticides, and herbicides) are dumped on United States farm land each year. Between 1000 and 3000 new chemicals are synthesized each year. Vertebrates, and especially the human, are at the end of the food chain. How do our bodies recognize and detoxify these foreign substances? Understanding this recognition-and-detoxication process would have widespread applications, from the design of effective new insecticides to human survival in a world filled with increasing concentrations of noxious agents. Moreover, an increasing number of these foreign chemicals are being implicated in mutagenesis, carcinogenesis, and teratogenesis.

Many of these thousands of noxious agents are very fat soluble and would have a half-life in the organism of days, weeks, or months, were it not for Phase I and Phase II drug-metabolizing enzymes. During Phase I metabolism, polar groups (such as alcohols) are introduced into the parent molecule, thereby presenting the Phase II enzymes with a more polar substrate. The Phase II enzymes use the polar group as a "handle" for attacking other very water-soluble moieties such as glucuronide, sulfate, or glycine. Phase I products (e.g., alcohols, quinones) and especially Phase II conjugates are sufficiently polar to be easily excreted by the cell. Living organisms often respond to foreign chemical adversity by the stimulation (or induction) of both Phase I and Phase II enzymes.

Cytochrome P-450 represents the largest class of Phase I enzymes. P-450 proteins* are polypeptides ranging in molecular weight between 45,000 and 60,000; they are hemoproteins (iron is present in a porphyrin ring near

---

* Cytochrome P-450 is defined as all forms of CO-binding hemoproteins having NADPH- and sometimes NADH-dependent monooxygenase activities. P_1-450 is defined as that form of polycyclic aromatic-inducible P-450 most closely associated with polycyclic aromatic-inducible aryl hydrocarbon hydroxylase activity. P-448 is defined as that form of polycyclic aromatic-inducible P-450 most closely associated with the maximal blue shift in Soret peak of the reduced P-450·CO complex. Other abbreviations used: TCDD, 2,3,7,8-tetrachlorodibenzo-*p*-dioxin; AHH, aryl hydrocarbon (benzo[*a*]pyrene) hydroxylase (EC 1.14.14.1); B6, the C57BL/6N inbred mouse strain; D2, the DBA/2N inbred mouse strain; C3, the C3H/HeN inbred mouse strain; and EGF, epidermal growth factor.

the enzyme active site) and some appear to contain carbohydrate as well. This enzyme system is ubiquitous, existing in certain bacteria (*Pseudomonas*) and presumably all eukaryotes. Except in bacteria and certain fungi, the P-450 system is membrane bound, principally in the smooth endoplasmic reticulum and mitochondria, and has multiple components. The cofactors NADPH and/or NADH supply electrons which are passed by way of one or more membrane-bound flavoprotein reductases, ultimately to the P-450 enzymes. In some instances, an iron–sulfur protein, cytochrome b_5, or a P-450 molecule all may be involved in transferring electrons ultimately to the P-450 protein having enzymatic activity. The substrate is oxygenated, meaning that an atom of atmospheric oxygen is incorporated into the metabolite, the other oxygen atom terminating in cellular water. The catalytic activity of the P-450 system can be a monooxygenase activity, an oxidase, a peroxidase, or a reductase, depending on the substrate and the valence state of P-450 iron (reviewed in Gustafsson *et al.*, 1980; Lu and West, 1980; Mannering, 1981; Nebert *et al.*, 1981; Sato and Kato, 1982).

The P-450 systems exhibit remarkably overlapping substrate specificities which help to explain the difficulty in attempting to determine the absolute number of P-450 proteins (Nebert, 1979). The term "multisubstrate monooxygenases" has been suggested (Sato and Kato, 1982) for describing the catalytic activities of the large P-450 multigene family. Substrates for these enzymes include polycyclic hydrocarbons such as benzo[*a*]pyrene (ubiquitous in the combustion of coal and in city smog, cigarette smoke, and charcoal-cooked foods); halogenated hydrocarbons such as polychlorinated and polybrominated biphenyls, herbicides, insecticides, and ingredients in soaps and deodorants; certain fungal toxins and antibiotics; many of the chemotherapeutic agents used to treat human cancer; strong mutagens such as *N*-methyl-*N*′-nitro-*N*-nitrosoguanidine and nitrosamines; aminoazo dyes and diazo compounds; many chemicals found in cosmetics and perfumes; numerous aromatic amines, such as those found in hair dyes, nitro aromatics, and heterocyclics; *N*-acetylarylamines and nitrofurans; wood terpenes; epoxides; carbamates; alkyl halides; safrole derivatives; antioxidants, other food additives, and many ingredients of foodstuffs, fermentative alcoholic beverages, and spices; both endogenous and synthetic steroids; prostaglandins; and other endogenous compounds such as biogenic amines, indoles, thyroxine, and fatty acids.

The purpose of this review is to assess our present knowledge of the *Ah* receptor, the major regulatory gene product of the *Ah* locus. Of particular interest to endocrinologists, this receptor appears to be quite analogous to receptors for steroid hormones and retinoids. First, the *Ah* system is introduced. Second, characteristics of the cytosolic and nuclear receptor are examined. Next, recent studies with the inducer–receptor complex in tissue culture are described. Last, we speculate on which future research directions might be most profitable and on the origin and possible function of the *Ah* receptor.

II. THE *Ah* LOCUS

A. HISTORY

The *Ah* locus controls the induction of many drug-metabolizing enzyme activities by polycyclic aromatic compounds such as 3-methylcholanthrene, benzo[*a*]pyrene, β-naphthoflavone, and TCDD. The *Ah* gene encodes the *Ah* receptor protein.

Figure 1 summarizes the accomplishments of several laboratories during this past decade. Certain relatively planar polycyclic aromatic compounds are known to diffuse passively through cellular and nuclear membranes. These inducers bind avidly to the cytosolic *Ah* receptor (apparent $K_d \sim$ 1.0 nM), and nuclear translocation of the inducer–receptor complex occurs. What happens in the nucleus is not clear, but somehow the "message" is received (that these inducers of P_1-450 exist in the cell's microenvironment). The response is transcription of induction-specific mRNA's, translation of these into specific proteins such as P_1-450, and incorporation of P_1-450 into membranes, especially the smooth endoplasmic reticulum. These induced enzymes contribute both to *detoxication* and to the generation of increased amounts of reactive intermediates (*toxification*). These reactive intermediates are believed to play a role in mutagenesis, carcinogenesis, birth defects, and certain drug toxicities in laboratory animals (Nebert and Jensen, 1979). The *Ah* system has also been implicated in certain clinical diseases (Nebert, 1981).

Figure 2 shows the structures of four foreign chemicals that bind avidly to the *Ah* receptor. 3-Methylcholanthrene and benz[*a*]anthracene are regarded as strong and weak carcinogens, respectively. TCDD has been described as both a cocarcinogen (Kouri *et al.*, 1978) and a promoter of tumorigenesis (Pitot *et al.*, 1980). β-Naphthoflavone is regarded as noncarcinogenic; flavones similar in structure to β-naphthoflavone are common in such foodstuffs as cabbage and brussels sprouts. Cholanthrene-, fluorene-, and anthracene-like structures and related chemicals arise spontaneously from combustion processes such as charred foods and the burning of bituminous coal, wood, or cigarettes.

TCDD can be labeled with tritium in the 1- and 6-positions with a specific radioactivity of more than 60 Ci/mmol. Consequently, the TCDD–receptor

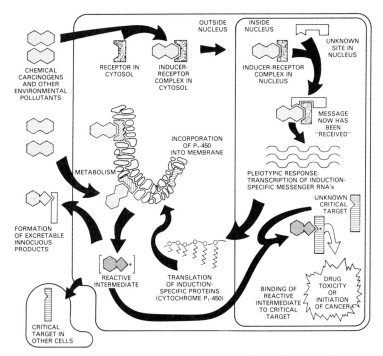

FIG. 1. Diagram of a cell and the hypothetical scheme by which a cytosolic receptor, the product of the *Ah* gene, binds to inducer (Nebert, 1979). The resultant "pleiotypic response" includes greater amounts of cytochrome P₁-450 (and numerous other forms of P-450 still being characterized), leading to enhanced steady-state levels of reactive intermediates which are associated with increases in birth defects, drug toxicity, or chemical carcinogenesis. Depending on the half-life of the reactive intermediate, important covalent binding may occur in the same cell in which metabolism took place, or in some distant cell. Although the "unknown critical target" is illustrated here in the nucleus, there is presently no experimental evidence demonstrating unequivocally the subcellular location of such a target or, for that matter, whether the target is nucleic acid or protein. Reproduced with permission from Dr. W. Junk Publishers.

complex can be followed in much the same way as the inducer–receptor complexes of steroids or retinoids. TCDD is among the most toxic small chemicals known, with an LD₅₀ in the guinea pig of about 0.6 μg/kg and marked teratogenicity in the rabbit at doses of less than 1 μg/kg (reviewed in Poland and Kende, 1976). The mechanism of TCDD toxicity is unknown, though thymic atrophy occurs in all species. The metabolism of TCDD is very slow (Guenthner *et al.*, 1979), indicating that metabolites cannot account for its extreme toxicity (Poland and Glover, 1979).

In retrospect, three different independent observations now are realized to be related. The *In* locus (differences in dimethylbenz[*a*]anthracene-induced

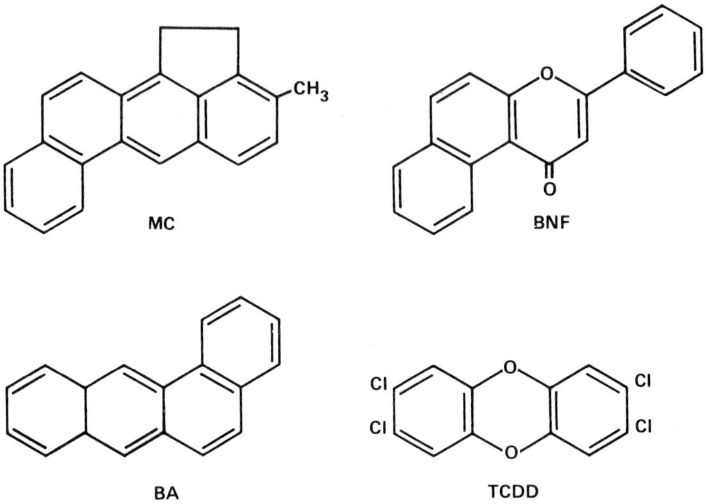

Fig. 2. Molecules that interact with the *Ah* receptor (Nebert *et al.*, 1981). MC, 3-Methyl-cholanthrene; BA, benz[*a*]anthracene; BNF, β-naphthoflavone; and TCDD, 2,3,7,8-tetra-chlorodibenzo-*p*-dioxin. Reproduced with permission from Annual Reviews, Inc.

skin *inflammation*) was described among inbred strains of mice (Taylor, 1971), though genetic linkage could not be determined. Differences in benzo[*a*]pyrene-initiated tumors on mouse skin between the C57BL/6J and DBA/2J inbred strains were reported (Kodama and Bock, 1970); no genetic crosses, however, were performed. Differences between these same two strains were described for 3-methylcholanthrene-induced AHH activity (Fig. 3) among several tissues in the intact animal (Nebert and Gelboin, 1969) and in primary and secondary fetal cell cultures (Nebert and Bausserman, 1970). The AHH induction process by 3-methylcholanthrene was found to be a dominant trait between "*Ah*-responsive" B6 and "*Ah*-nonresponsive" D2 (Nebert *et al.*, 1971, 1972; Gielen *et al.*, 1972; Nebert and Gielen, 1972). Similar data subsequently were reported with C57BL/6J and DBA/2J mice (Thomas *et al.*, 1972).

Responsiveness to *aromatic hydrocarbons* thus was designated the *Ah* locus: Ah^b for the prototype B6 mouse is the dominant allele; Ah^d for the prototype D2 mouse is the recessive allele; the Ah^b/Ah^d heterozygote phenotypically is similar to the Ah^b/Ah^b mouse in terms of AHH induction by 3-methylcholanthrene (Fig. 4). Differences in tumorigenesis, mutagenesis, drug toxicities, and birth defects among siblings of the B6D2F$_1$ × D2 backcross or of the F$_2$ generation have been reviewed (Nebert and Jensen, 1979). The *In* locus later was shown (Thomas *et al.*, 1973) to be identical to the *Ah* locus.

About this time TCDD was found to be an extremely potent inducer of

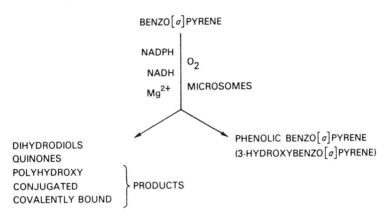

FIG. 3. Simplified scheme for measuring "AHH activity" with benzo[*a*]pyrene as substrate (Nebert, 1978). The AHH assay represents Phase I metabolism. The phenolic benzo[*a*]pyrene metabolites are determined spectrophotofluorometrically and equated with AHH activity. This assay does not detect other oxygenative metabolism occurring concomitantly.

δ-aminolevulinic acid synthetase (Poland and Glover, 1973a) and AHH activity in the chick (Poland and Glover, 1973a,b) and rat (Poland and Glover, 1974). TCDD was at least 30,000 times more effective than 3-methylcholanthrene at inducing rat liver AHH activity (Poland and Glover, 1974). The obvious question was posed: Could such a potent inducer overcome the *Ah* nonresponsiveness of D2 and other inbred strains? Such dose–response studies (Fig. 5) made it clear that all *Ah*-nonresponsive inbred strains exhibit an S-shaped curve 12–18 times farther to the right than all *Ah*-responsive inbred strains (Poland *et al.*, 1974; Niwa *et al.*, 1975b; Poland and Glover, 1975). Similar dose–response curves were also found in cell culture (Nebert and Bausserman, 1970; Niwa *et al.*, 1975a). It therefore seemed most likely that the mutation in *Ah*-nonresponsive mice represents a defective receptor molecule. If this hypothesis were true, it was proposed (Nebert *et al.*, 1975) that the mutation would be in the regulatory gene

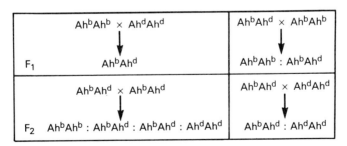

FIG. 4. Simplified genetic scheme for aromatic hydrocarbon "responsiveness" in the mouse (Nebert and Felton, 1975). Reproduced with permission from Plenum Press.

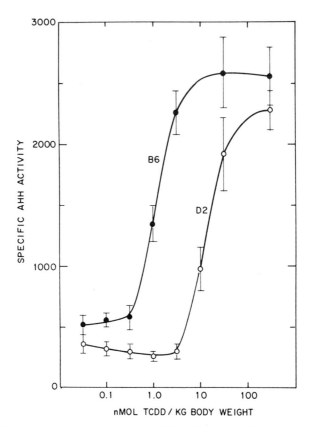

FIG. 5. Dose–response curve for hepatic AHH induction by TCDD in B6 and D2 mice (Kouri *et al.*, 1978). The enzyme activity was determined 3 days after treatment with TCDD; dosage on abscissa is on a logarithmic scale. Reproduced with permission from Williams & Wilkins.

encoding the *Ah* receptor and that D2 and other nonresponsive strains would have a normal P_1-450 structural gene. This proposal now appears to be true, in view of the characterization of immunoprecipitable P_1-450 protein from TCDD-treated D2 mice (Negishi and Nebert, 1979; Negishi *et al.*, 1981a), inducible P_1-450 mRNA from TCDD-treated D2 mice (Negishi and Nebert, 1981), and the P_1-450 structural gene from *Ah*-nonresponsive mice (Tukey *et al.*, 1981).

B. REGULATORY GENES

The simple dominant–recessive characteristics of AHH inducibility by polycyclic aromatic compounds (such as those shown in Fig. 4) turned out to be far more complicated as further experiments were performed. F_1 mice from the *Ah*-responsive C3H/HeJ crossed with the *Ah*-nonresponsive DBA/2J exhibit additive inheritance for AHH inducibility (Thomas *et al.*, 1973); the same subsequently was found for the $C3D2F_1$ (Robinson *et al.*, 1974). When *Ah*-responsive B6 and C3 are crossed, at least one in 16 of the F_2 generation is *Ah* nonresponsive (Robinson *et al.*, 1974; Nebert *et al.*, 1982c). When *Ah*-nonresponsive AKR/N or AKR/J is crossed with *Ah*-nonresponsive D2, varying numbers of the backcross and F_2 populations are *Ah* responsive (Nebert *et al.*, 1982c). The number of *Ah* regulatory genes required to explain these data must be at least two genes and at least six alleles (Robinson *et al.*, 1974; Nebert *et al.*, 1982c). Clearly the alleles at the *Ah* regulatory locus of the B6, D2, C3, and AKR inbred strains all differ from one another. Modifier genes which encode posttranslational modification (e.g., glycosylation, acetylation, phosphorylation) of the *Ah* receptor are certainly possible.

The next significant advance was the development of a dextran-coated charcoal adsorption assay similar to that designed for [³H]dexamethasone and the glucocorticoid receptor (Baxter and Tomkins, 1970). [³H]TCDD with high specific radioactivity was synthesized, and the *Ah* receptor was characterized in cell cultures (Guenthner *et al.*, 1976; Guenthner and Nebert, 1977) and in mouse liver cytosolic fractions (Poland *et al.*, 1976). More recently, other techniques, e.g., isoelectric focusing following trypsin treatment (Carlstedt-Duke *et al.*, 1978; Carlstedt-Duke, 1979), sucrose density gradient centrifugation following dextran–charcoal adsorption (Okey *et al.*, 1979, 1980; Mason and Okey, 1982), a detergent-washing procedure with purified nuclei (Greenlee and Poland, 1979), and gel permeation chromatography and anion-exchange chromatography (Hannah *et al.*, 1981), also have been used to study the *Ah* receptor.

Among 75 inbred strains and sublines of mice tested, about one-third display *Ah* nonresponsiveness (Kouri and Nebert, 1977; Nebert *et al.*, 1982a). Among four dozen inbred strains and sublines of rats examined for the *Ah* phenotype, all were responsive (Nebert *et al.*, 1982a). The reason for this difference between mice and rats is unclear.

Two males and eight females each of the *Ah*-responsive B6 and C3 strains and the *Ah*-nonresponsive D2 and AKR/N strains were allowed to breed freely and subsequent offspring were allowed to breed *ad libitum* for more than 3 years. Expression of AHH inducibility by 3-methylcholanthrene 18–22 generations later in this experiment was skewed to the left (Nebert and Atlas, 1978), indicating that, among heterogeneous randomly bred populations, "genetic drift" toward low AHH inducibility tended to be selected for. An explanation for this distribution is not known. This same sort of distribution curve has been seen for wild mice and outbred and randomly bred laboratory mice, rats, guinea pigs, and hamsters, as well as among human populations

(Nebert *et al.*, 1982c). In this context, high *Ah* receptor levels and AHH inducibility of B6 may be viewed just as unusual as *Ah* nonresponsiveness. In any event, the mutation to *Ah* nonresponsiveness (lack of detectable cytosolic *Ah* receptor) in D2 and other inbred strains is clearly not a lethal mutation, though many of these strains do exhibit some degree of problem with tendency to develop leukemia and various immunodeficient disorders.

C. Structural Genes

Aryl hydrocarbon hydroxylase activity induced by those polycyclic aromatic compounds that bind avidly to the *Ah* receptor is a P_1-450-mediated monooxygenase activity. Because the AHH fluorescent assay is relatively simple and very sensitive (Nebert, 1978), this assay with benzo[*a*]pyrene as the substrate *in vitro* is most commonly used as the biochemical marker for assessing the *Ah* locus in laboratory animal and human studies.

P_1-450 thus is regarded as one of the structural gene products controlled by the *Ah* regulatory genes. No immunoprecipitable P_1-450 protein (Negishi and Nebert, 1981; Negishi *et al.*, 1981a) or P_1-450 mRNA (Negishi and Nebert, 1981) is detectable in control B6 mouse liver. Constitutive AHH activity is thus viewed as the fortuitous metabolism of benzo[*a*]pyrene by one or more forms of endogenous P-450.

Some portion of polycyclic aromatic-induced AHH activity appears to be mediated by one or more inducible forms of P-450 other than P_1-450. Cytochrome P-448 (Negishi and Nebert, 1979) is viewed as another structural gene product controlled by the *Ah* receptor; P-448 contributes to the aggregate induced AHH activity. How many other forms of P-450 are also controlled by the *Ah* receptor is not known (Lang and Nebert, 1981; Lang *et al.*, 1981). Whatever the number of induced P-450 forms associated with the *Ah* locus, however, these proteins reflect more than two dozen induced monooxygenase activities (Nebert and Jensen, 1979; Nebert *et al.*, 1982c). Phenobarbital, pregnenolone 16α-carbonitrile, and *trans*-stilbene oxide clearly induce forms of P-450 other than P_1-450; this conclusion was reached by studies with immunoprecipitable P_1-450 protein and P_1-450 mRNA and a cloned probe (Tukey *et al.*, 1982b).

In addition to induced forms of P-450, other enzyme activities shown conclusively to be correlated with the Ah^b allele include microsomal UDP glucuronosyltransferase activity with 4-methylumbelliferone as substrate (Owens, 1977), cytosolic reduced NAD(P)H dehydrogenase (quinone) (also known as menadione oxidoreductase and DT-diaphorase) (Kumaki *et al.*, 1977), and cytosolic ornithine decarboxylase (Nebert *et al.*, 1980). These enhanced enzyme activities are believed to represent *Ah* structural gene products, i.e., part of the pleiotypic response governed by the *Ah* receptor. The extent of this response and possible reasons for this response are discussed later. Several inducible enzyme activities are known *not* to be associated with the *Ah* locus: cytochrome *c* reductase (NADPH), NADPH-P-450 reductase, epoxide hydrolase, and glutathione transferase (Nebert and Jensen, 1979; Felton *et al.*, 1980).

With the use of partially purified liver 23 S mRNA from 3-methylcholanthrene-treated B6 mice, double-stranded cDNA associated with the *Ah* locus was cloned (Lang *et al.*, 1980). By both immunological (Negishi *et al.*, 1981b) and genetic (Tukey *et al.*, 1981) criteria, clone 46 was proved to contain part of the P_1-450 structural gene. The process of P_1-450 induction was shown (Tukey *et al.*, 1981) to be under transcriptional control. With the clone 46 probe of mouse DNA, rat liver P_1-450 mRNA and the P_1-450 structural gene have been identified (Chen *et al.*, 1982a). Further characterization of the chromosomal P_1-450 structural gene (Ikeda *et al.*, 1982; Nebert *et al.*, 1982b; Nakamura *et al.*, 1983) and other P-450 structural genes should provide valuable insight into understanding the *Ah* locus, the genetic regulation of the P-450 multigene family, their evolution, and the ultimate number of possible (constitutive plus induced) forms of P-450.

D. Evidence for Possible Temporal Genes

In the apparent presence of sufficient amounts of hepatic *Ah* receptor (Kahl *et al.*, 1980), P_1-450 with its associated AHH activity is induced by 3-methylcholanthrene in the rabbit fetus and neonate, whereas P-448 is not; beyond 2 or 3 weeks postpartum, P-448 is induced by 3-methylcholanthrene whereas P_1-450 is not (Atlas *et al.*, 1977). In the rat and mouse, P_1-450 with its associated AHH activity is inducible by 3-methylcholanthrene earlier in gestation than P-448 (Guenthner and Nebert, 1978; Negishi and Nebert, 1979). Some type of temporal gene control must, therefore, be operative in order to explain these developmental findings. The mechanism of action of temporal genes (Paigen, 1979) is unclear. In view of the presumed presence of sufficient amounts of *Ah* receptor, however, most likely this temporal control affects the expression of structural gene products rather than regulatory gene products. Changes in DNA methylation appear to occur in the P_1-450 structural gene during development (Chen *et al.*, 1982b). Further studies are required in order to understand this interesting developmental system.

III. CHARACTERISTICS OF THE A*h* RECEPTOR

A. The Cytosolic Receptor

1. Velocity Sedimentation

The most potent known inducer of A*h*-associated structural gene products is TCDD. Further, TCDD is metabolized only minimally. Hence, TCDD represented the ideal ligand for characterizing the A*h* receptor. It should be emphasized that TCDD is an exceptionally toxic substance and should be handled with special care, as described by Poland and Glover (1975).

Poland and co-workers (1976) systematically studied the binding of [^{3}H] TCDD to subcellular fractions: although TCDD binding predominantly was associated with membrane fractions, this binding was not saturable; the cytosolic fraction, on the other hand, contained a small number of saturable, high-affinity TCDD-binding sites. On the basis of AHH induction as a marker, a number of TCDD congeners and other P_1-450 inducers exhibited an excellent structure–activity relationship between P_1-450 induction potency and displacement of [^{3}H]TCDD from the A*h* receptor *in vitro*. D2 and other A*h*-nonresponsive inbred strains displayed no detectable cytosolic receptor. On the basis of all these criteria (Poland *et al.*, 1976), therefore, it was concluded that the A*h* receptor had been discovered.

Greater than 99% of [^{3}H]TCDD binding to cellular macromolecules is nonspecific and nonsaturable. The dextran-coated charcoal adsorption assay, used by Poland *et al.* (1976) and used early by this laboratory (Guenthner *et al.*, 1976; Guenthner and Nebert, 1977), requires multiple treatments of cytosolic fractions with dextran–charcoal in order to decrease the nonspecific [^{3}H]TCDD-binding components. We therefore began searching for other more desirable methods to characterize the A*h* receptor. We found that rapid assays (such as dextran–charcoal, DEAE cellulose, or hydroxyapatite adsorption) in general do not satisfactorily separate the nonsaturable from the saturable TCDD-binding components.

Velocity sedimentation in sucrose density gradients was found (Okey *et al.*, 1979) to provide a satisfactory method for measuring the A*h* receptor. With this assay it was shown that the receptor binds most specifically to effective inducers of P_1-450 (Fig. 6 and Table I), is saturable, possesses high-affinity, low-capacity binding sites, and is strictly associated with the A*h*^{b} allele among individual offspring of the B6D2F$_1$ × D2 backcross. The inducer appears to be principally protein, is highly thermolabile (more so in the absence of inducer binding), and does not appear to increase during *in vivo* treatment of mice with P_1-450 inducers. Large differences in sedi-

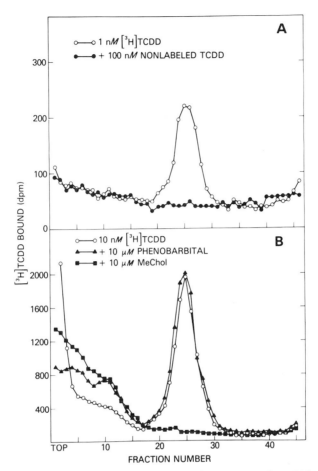

FIG. 6. Detection of specific [³H]TCDD binding of a component from B6 hepatic cytosol (Okey *et al.*, 1979). (A) Cytosol (1 mg of protein/ml) was incubated with 1 nM [³H]TCDD in the absence of competitor (○) or in the presence of 100 nM nonlabeled TCDD (●). Following dextran–charcoal treatment, gradients were centrifuged and fractionated. (B) Elimination of specific binding peak by 3-methylcholanthrene, but not by phenobarbital. Cytosol (5 mg of protein/ml) was incubated with 10 nM [³H]TCDD in the absence of competitor (○), and in the presence of 10 μM 3-methylcholanthrene (■) or 10 μM phenobarbital (▲). Reproduced with permission from American Society of Biological Chemists, Inc.

mentation properties and in the estimated number of binding sites were shown (Okey *et al.*, 1979) to depend on the choice of buffer system (especially stabilization of the receptor in the presence of glycerol), ionic strength, and protein concentration during the gradient analysis. Approximately six times less receptor, for example, was estimated with the dextran–charcoal

TABLE I

SPECIFIC [³H]TCDD BINDING TO B6 CYTOSOL RECEPTOR IN THE PRESENCE OF
COMPOUNDS THAT HAVE VARIED POTENCIES FOR HEPATIC CYTOCHROME
P_1-450 INDUCTION[a]

Compound tested	Potency as an inducer of P_1-450[b]	Binding as percentage of control by	
		Sucrose density gradient assay	Dextran–charcoal assay
Bilirubin	0	100	140
Hematin	0	100	115
Cholesterol	0	95	115
Cholic acid methyl ester	0	95	115
Phenobarbital	0	110	150
Pregnenolone-16α-carbonitrile	0	100	115
Dexamethasone	0	110	155
β-Methasone	0	90	100
Progesterone	0	110	185
Estradiol-17β	0	95	100
Dihydrotestosterone	0	100	120
p,p′-DDT	?	35	40
α-Naphthoflavone	?	70	120
β-Naphthoflavone	+ + +	25	110
Benzo[*a*]pyrene	+ + +	0	135
3-Methylcholanthrene	+ + +	0	175
Benz[*a*]anthracene	+ + +	0	85
TCDD	+ + + +	0	165
2,3-Dichlorodibenzo-*p*-dioxin	+	45	85
1,2,4-Trichlorodibenzo-*p*-dioxin	+ +	45	70
1,2,3,4,7,8-Hexachlorodibenzo-*p*-dioxin	+ + +	15	205
Octachlorodibenzo-*p*-dioxin	0	100	165

[a] Specific binding was determined by sucrose density gradient analysis after dextran–charcoal treatment using 10 n*M* [³H]TCDD (Okey *et al.*, 1979). Each compound tested (10 μ*M*) was added to cytosol 15 minutes before [³H]TCDD. The "dextran–charcoal assay" represents [³H]TCDD remaining in the cytosol after dextran–charcoal treatment (as described in Poland *et al.*, 1976) and without separation of specific binding peaks by sucrose density gradient centrifugation. Reproduced with permission from American Society of Biological Chemists.

[b] Data taken from two laboratories (Poland and Glover, 1973; Poland *et al.*, 1976; Nebert and Jensen, 1979).

adsorption assay (Poland *et al.*, 1976) than with the sucrose density gradient assay (Okey *et al.*, 1979). About 5500 *Ah* receptor molecules per hepatic cell (60 fmol/mg cytosolic protein) were estimated for B6 mice (Table II), with an apparent K_d of approximately 0.7 n*M* (Okey *et al.*, 1979). Following dextran–charcoal adsorption, the inducer–receptor complex sediments at

TABLE II

CONCENTRATION OF RECEPTOR IN HEPATIC CYTOSOL FROM VARIOUS RESPONSIVE AND
NONRESPONSIVE ANIMALS[a]

Strain	Ah phenotype	N	Specific TCDD binding[b] (fmol/mg cytosol protein)
C57BL/6N	Responsive	8	60 ± 12
C57BL/6J	Responsive	10	34 ± 16
CBA/J	Responsive	p4	20
A/J	Responsive	p4	16
C3H/HeJ	Responsive	p4	12
C3H/HeJ		1	11
C3H/HeJ		1	11
DBA/2N	Nonresponsive	6	Not detectable[c]
DBA/2J	Nonresponsive	8	Not detectable
AKR/J	Nonresponsive	p4	Not detectable
SWR/J	Nonresponsive	p4	Not detectable
RF/J	Nonresponsive	p4	Not detectable
Ah^b/Ah^d	Responsive[d]	3	35 ± 5
Ah^d/Ah^d	Nonresponsive[d]	3	Not detectable
Sprague–Dawley rat	Responsive	1	33

[a] Specific binding was measured by sucrose density gradient analysis following dextran–charcoal treatment with the use of 10 nM [^{3}H]TCDD $\pm$ 1000 nM nonlabeled TCDD (Okey *et al.*, 1979). N represents the number of individual animals assayed; p4 indicates that cytosol from four mice was pooled and used in one assay. The means for C57BL/6N mice and C57BL/6J are significantly different ($p < 0.01$ by t test). Reproduced with permission from American Society of Biological Chemists.

[b] Values are expressed as means $\pm$ SD when three or more determinations were made separately.

[c] A small peak ≤ 1.0 fmol/mg of cytosolic protein was sometimes observed.

[d] Weanlings from the B6D2F$_1$ $\times$ D2 backcross were phenotyped at age 3 to 5 weeks by the zoxazolamine paralysis test, as previously described (Robinson and Nebert, 1974). More than 1 week later these individuals then were assessed for hepatic cytosolic receptor.

about 7.5 S and 9 S on sucrose density gradients of high and low ionic strength, respectively; no statistically significant change in sedimentation size occurs during nuclear translocation in Hepa-1 cell cultures (Okey *et al.*, 1980).

2. Correlation of the Number of Ah Receptor Molecules with Inducible AHH Activity

Figure 7 illustrates the number of TCDD-binding sites per hepatic cell as a function of AHH activity in the liver of various 3-methylcholanthrene-treated inbred strains and F$_1$ hybrids. About 900 receptor molecules in the cytosolic fraction are sufficient for maximal AHH induction. The finding

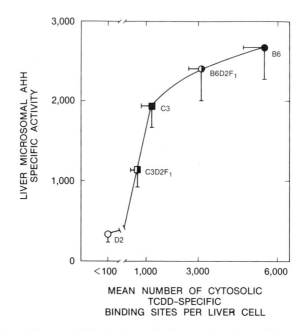

FIG. 7. Maximal hepatic AHH inducibility as a function of number of *Ah* receptor molecules per liver cell among various inbred strains of mice and F_1 hybrids. Each value is the mean of five or more individual determinations. Brackets in both directions denote standard deviations.

that the $C3D2F_1$ has about half this number explains why this hybrid exhibits additive inheritance (Thomas *et al.*, 1973; Robinson *et al.*, 1974). Of interest, just this sort of possibility was hypothesized in the 1973 paper by Thomas and co-workers.

3. Gel Permeation Chromatography

Although the sucrose density gradient assay provides a sensitive and very specific assay for the *Ah* receptor, it seemed important to us to characterize this moiety with the use of other techniques as well. By using Sephacryl S-300 column chromatography (Hannah *et al.*, 1981), for example, we were able to explain the discrepancies between the dextran–charcoal adsorption and sucrose density gradient assays.

In the liver of B6 mice (Fig. 8), [^{3}H]TCDD binds to three major components: peak I, a large aggregate which is eluted in the void volume and which sediments as a residue to the bottom of sucrose density gradient tubes; peak II, an asymmetric protein ($M_r \sim 245,000$) with a Stokes radius of about 75 Å; and peak III, a globular protein ($M_r \sim 87,000$) with an estimated

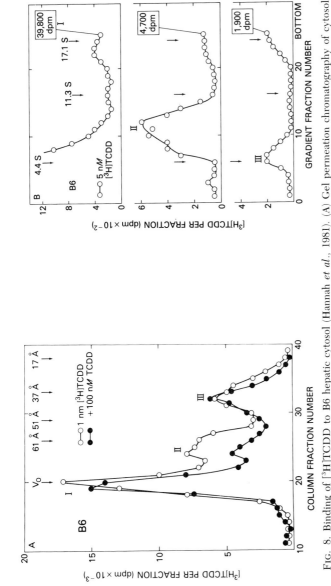

FIG. 8. Binding of [³H]TCDD to B6 hepatic cytosol (Hannah *et al.*, 1981). (A) Gel permeation chromatography of cytosol treated with [³H]TCDD. V_o, Void volumes, determined with Blue Dextran, thyroglobulin, ferritin, bovine serum albumin, and cytochrome *c*, with each of their Stokes radii indicated in Å, were used to calibrate the columns. (B) Analysis of peaks I, II, and III by velocity sedimentation. Cytosol (15 mg protein/ml) was treated with 5 n*M* [³H]TCDD for 1 hour at 4°C and then chromatographed on a Sephacryl S-300 column. Samples from the peak I (fractions 16 to 22), peak II (fractions 23 to 27), and peak III (fractions 28 to 35) regions then were added to sucrose density gradients (5–20%). In addition to the usual gradient fractions, the bottoms of the centrifuge tubes were cut off, soaked in Aquasol, and counted for radioactivity [disintegrations per minute (dpm) shown in boxes]. Approximate sedimentation values are shown for bovine serum albumin (4.4 S), bovine liver catalase (11.3 S), and ferritin (17.1 S); these standards were centrifuged in a separate gradient. [¹⁴C]Albumin (2000 dpm) was also included as an internal standard. Reproduced with permission from American Society of Biological Chemists, Inc.

Stokes radius of 40 Å. The peak I aggregate is not adsorbed by dextran-coated charcoal and therefore represents the large proportion of nonsaturable radioligand binding measured by dextran–charcoal adsorption. The peak II protein has a size of about 9.0 S in low ionic strength and 7.5 S in high ionic strength, high affinity for TCDD, and saturability at TCDD concentrations greater than about 1.0 nM. The peak II protein is not detectable in the hepatic cytosol of Ah-nonresponsive D2 mice (Fig. 9) or the Ah^d/Ah^d progeny of the B6D2F$_1$ × D2 backcross and therefore represents the Ah receptor (Hannah et al., 1981).

The peak III protein has an estimated size of 5.0 S, is not saturable with either TCDD or 3-methylcholanthrene, and is not associated with the Ah^b allele. 3-Methylcholanthrene binds to the peak III moiety much better than TCDD (Fig. 10). We estimate that peak III has an apparent K_d of about 10 nM for 3-methylcholanthrene and that the number of binding sites is >1000 fmol/mg cytosolic protein. We therefore believe peak III represents the "3-methylcholanthrene-specific binding protein" recently characterized in rat liver cytosol by Tierney and co-workers (1980). The importance of the peak III moiety is not known, although this protein is clearly not the Ah receptor (Okey and Vella, 1982). Possible functions proposed include the following: (1) movement of chemical carcinogens and/or carcinogenic metabolites into the nucleus to interact covalently with DNA (Tierney et al., 1980; Tierney and Bresnick, 1981) and (2) "carrier proteins," which function in solubilization of hydrophobic substrates and aid in P-450 mono-oxygenation (Hanson-Painton et al., 1981). The peak III protein clearly has been shown not to migrate with [^{3}H]TCDD into the nucleus (Hannah et al., 1982).

B. THE NUCLEAR RECEPTOR

1. Detection of the Nuclear Inducer–Receptor Complex in Both Ah-Responsive and Ah-Nonresponsive Mice

Greenlee and Poland (1979) and Okey et al. (1979) demonstrated by different techniques that the [^{3}H]TCDD–Ah receptor complex accumulates in the hepatocyte nucleus when B6 (Ah^b/Ah^b) or B6D2F$_1$ (Ah^b/Ah^d) mice are treated in vivo with the radioligand. Because the nuclei of untreated mice do not contain detectable Ah receptors, the nuclear inducer–receptor complexes were presumed to have resulted from translocation of these complexes formed in the cytosol.

D2 mice (Ah^d/Ah^d) and the Ah^d/Ah^d progeny of the B6D2F$_1$ × D2 backcross were also treated in vivo with [^{3}H]TCDD (Okey et al., 1979). Small quantities

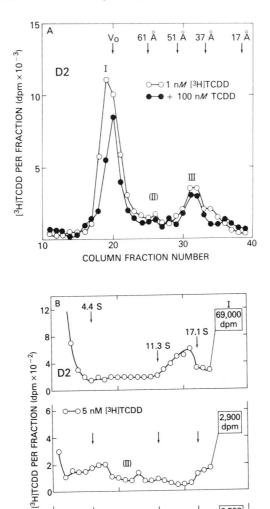

FIG. 9. Binding of [³H]TCDD to D2 hepatic cytosol (Hannah *et al.*, 1981). (A) Gel permeation chromatography of cytosol treated with [³H]TCDD. (B) Analysis of peaks I, II, and III by velocity sedimentation. These experiments with D2 mice were identical to those with B6 mice illustrated in Fig. 8. Reproduced with permission from American Society of Biological Chemists, Inc.

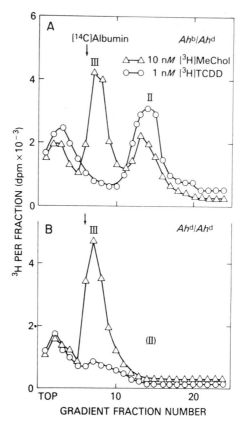

FIG. 10. Velocity sedimentation analysis of [³H]TCDD- and [³H]3-methylcholanthrene-binding moieties in hepatic cytosol of progeny from the B6D2F₁ × D2 backcross (Hannah *et al.*, 1981). Mice were from the same litter: (A) responsive *Ah*ᵇ/*Ah*ᵈ mouse; (B) nonresponsive *Ah*ᵈ/*Ah*ᵈ mouse. The backcross mice had been phenotyped by the zoxazolamine paralysis test (Robinson and Nebert, 1974) 10 days earlier. One ml of cytosol (10 mg of protein) from individual mice was treated with 1 nM [³H]TCDD or 10 nM [³H]3-methylcholanthrene for 1 hour at 4°C; following dextran-coated charcoal adsorption, the samples then were examined on sucrose density gradients. Reproduced with permission from American Society of Biological Chemists, Inc.

of specifically bound radioligand were detected in nuclear extracts analyzed on sucrose density gradients. This study demonstrated that *Ah*-nonresponsive mice contain some form of TCDD-specific binding protein (Mason and Okey, 1982; Tukey *et al.*, 1982a). Why the inducer–receptor complex is not detectable in the cytosol but can be found in the nucleus of *Ah*-nonresponsive mice is unclear. DeBoer and Notides (1981a,b) have shown that the nuclear form of the estrogen–receptor complex is more stable than the cytosolic form. Perhaps the *Ah* receptor in nonresponsive mice represents an extreme example of this phenomenon.

The stability of the nuclear estrogen–receptor complex may result from a conformational change in the protein (DeBoer and Notides, 1981a,b). Is there evidence that the *Ah* receptor undergoes an analogous change in its physicochemical properties? We have extracted [^{3}H]TCDD–*Ah* receptor complexes from hepatocyte nuclei and have compared these complexes with those from B6 liver cytosol (Tukey *et al.*, 1982a). The B6 cytosolic and the B6 and D2 nuclear *Ah* receptors have very similar hydrodynamic properties; each has a sedimentation coefficient of ~7.5 S and a Stokes radius of ~60 Å in 0.5 *M* NaCl. However, the cytosolic and nuclear inducer–receptor complexes have markedly different affinities for DNA. Whereas the cytosolic [^{3}H]TCDD–*Ah* receptor complex is not adsorbed to DNA–cellulose, both B6 and D2 nuclear [^{3}H]TCDD–*Ah* receptor complexes are adsorbed and can be eluted from DNA–cellulose as a single peak with 0.38 *M* NaCl during gradient elution. Thus, the nuclear receptors are very similar in *Ah*-responsive and *Ah*-nonresponsive mice. The major difference is the quantity of inducer–receptor molecules detectable in the nucleus following *in vivo* treatment with [^{3}H]TCDD. Over a range of 1–50 nmol of [^{3}H]TCDD per kg, nuclear inducer–receptor levels are always considerably lower in *Ah*-nonresponsive than in *Ah*-responsive mice (Tukey *et al.*, 1982a).

2. Stoichiometric Relationship between Nuclear Inducer–Receptor Complex and Appearance of P$_1$-450 mRNA

As described earlier, P$_1$-450 is an *Ah* structural gene product and clone 46 represents a portion of this structural gene (Negishi *et al.*, 1981b). It has been possible to quantitate P$_1$-450 mRNA levels by hybridization of mouse liver poly(A$^+$)-enriched RNA to nick-translated [^{32}P]DNA from clone 46 (Tukey *et al.*, 1981, 1982b). Over the range of 1 to 50 nmol of [^{3}H] TCDD per kg and during a time course after a single dose of the radioligand *in vivo*, the appearance of nuclear inducer–receptor complex is very closely related ($r = 0.99$) to the appearance of inducible P$_1$-450 mRNA. Quantitation of P$_1$-450 mRNA was made both by Northern hybridization and by R_0t analysis (Tukey *et al.*, 1982a). P$_1$-450 mRNA concentrations were determined in both B6 and D2 inbred strains as well as phenotyped *Ah*-responsive and *Ah*-nonresponsive progeny of the B6D2F$_1$ × D2 backcross. These data demonstrate clearly that the nuclear *Ah* receptor in *Ah*-nonresponsive mice is associated with an appropriate biological response.

C. The Receptor in Tissue Culture

1. Established Cell Lines

Continuous cell culture lines (such as mouse Hepa-1, rat Reuber hepatoma H-4-II-E, rat "minimal deviation" hepatoma HTC, and monkey kidney fibroblasts VERO) have been used extensively as model systems for studying the induction of AHH activity. These lines can be classified as "responsive" or "nonresponsive," on the basis of the dose of TCDD required for half-maximally inducing (ED_{50}) AHH activity (Niwa *et al.*, 1975a). Responsive lines having a low ED_{50} for TCDD include Hepa-1 (0.45 nM) and H-4-II-E (0.23 nM); nonresponsive lines having a high ED_{50} include HTC (>200 nM) and VERO (110 nM). Further, the maximally induced hydroxylase activity is more than 100 times greater in the responsive than in the nonresponsive TCDD-treated lines.

Okey *et al.* (1980) studied the *Ah* receptor in these cell lines using the sucrose density gradient assay. The two TCDD-responsive lines Hepa-1 and H-4-II-E contain *Ah* receptors. Following exposure of the cells to [^{3}H]TCDD in culture, the inducer–receptor complex is found in the cytosol and undergoes a temperature- and time-dependent translocation to the nucleus. Although the TCDD-nonresponsive VERO line did not contain detectable cytosolic or nuclear *Ah* receptors, the nonresponsive HTC line contains cytosolic inducer–receptor complexes apparently capable of undergoing nuclear translocation normally. The presence of presumably normal cytosolic and nuclear *Ah* receptors, therefore, does not guarantee that the induction process will proceed normally. The HTC cell line appears to be defective in the induction step(s) subsequent to nuclear translocation of the *Ah* receptor.

2. Benzo[a]pyrene-Resistant Mutant Clones

Benzo[*a*]pyrene induces high levels of AHH activity in Hepa-1 cells (Benedict *et al.*, 1973). The metabolites of benzo[*a*]pyrene formed by cytochrome P_1-450 are extremely toxic; exposure of these cells to concentrations of benzo[*a*]pyrene as low as 25 nM is sufficient to produce toxicity and cell death. In the presence of 4 μM benzo[*a*]pyrene, however, only a few Hepa-1 cells ($\sim 10^{-7}$ per generation) survive. These benzo[*a*]pyrene-resistant cells appear to represent somatic mutations in the pathways for AHH induction. Clones derived from such cells have been developed (Hankinson, 1979) with the intention of examining genetically the multiple steps during the process of AHH induction. By somatic cell hybridization studies (Hankinson,

1980), the clones that have been developed are known to represent at least three distinct complementation groups and therefore reflect mutations in at least three different genes.

Several clones have essentially normal *Ah* receptor levels, compared with the wild-type Hepa-1c1c7 parent, possess normal kinetics for translocation of the inducer–receptor complex into the nucleus, yet exhibit very low or nondetectable basal or inducible AHH activity. These clones could represent a mutation in the P_1-450 structural gene or other genes responsible for the induced hydroxylase activity. Other clones are receptor-deficient mutants, having no more than 10% of wild-type *Ah* receptor levels, normal kinetics of nuclear translocation of the inducer-receptor complex, and no more than 20% of wild-type hydroxylase inducibility by either TCDD or benz[*a*]anthracene. One clone has normal cytosolic levels of *Ah* receptor, is defective in nuclear translocation of the inducer–receptor complex, and lacks any detectable basal or inducible AHH activity (Legraverend *et al.*, 1982). These data are an important prelude to planned recombinant DNA experiments designed to understand better the mechanism of AHH (P_1-450) induction by polycyclic aromatic compounds.

3. Possible Interrelationship between the Cytosolic Ah and the Membrane-Bound EGF Receptors

Ivanovic and Weinstein (1981, 1982) proposed that polycyclic aromatic compounds such as 7,12-dimethylbenz[*a*]anthracene, benzo[*a*]pyrene, and β-naphthoflavone interfere with the normal turnover time for the EGF receptor in the same order of potency that these compounds displace [^{3}H]TCDD from the *Ah* receptor. If one compares the capacity of about 30 foreign chemicals and benzo[*a*]pyrene metabolites to displace [^{3}H]TCDD from the *Ah* receptor (Bigelow and Nebert, 1982), however, the order of potency in displacing the radioligand does not agree that closely with the order that these chemicals interact with the EGF receptor (or in its proximity) on the cell membrane (Ivanovic and Weinstein, 1981, 1982). For example, 7,12-dimethylbenz[*a*]anthracene metabolites are known to be among the most toxic of all polycyclic hydrocarbon metabolites in tissue culture; dimethylbenz[*a*]anthracene is the most potent in affecting EGF receptors (Ivanovic and Weinstein, 1981) yet is only intermediate in its ability to displace [^{3}H] TCDD from the *Ah* receptor (Bigelow and Nebert, 1982). Such data suggest that metabolites generated by induced P_1-450 and perhaps other forms of induced P-450 are responsible for the loss of EGF binding sites on the cell surface during a 24- or 48-hour exposure of these chemicals to cells in culture (Fig. 11). This hypothesis has been recently confirmed

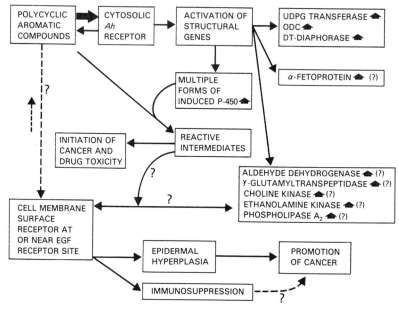

FIG. 11. The *Ah* system: A heuristic diagram showing the possible interrelationship among the pleiotropic response to polycyclic aromatic compounds, initiation of chemical carcinogenesis, drug toxicity, and promotion of cancer.

in our laboratory (Kärenlampi *et al.*, 1982) by means of studies with benzo[*a*]pyrene-resistant clones of Hepa-1. No similar effects of these polycyclic aromatic compounds on the insulin or the phorbol ester membrane-bound receptors are found (Kärenlampi *et al.*, 1982).

IV. FUTURE DIRECTIONS

A. "TRANSFORMATION" OF CYTOSOLIC TO NUCLEAR FORM OF RECEPTOR

The cytosolic and nuclear forms of the [^{3}H]TCDD–*Ah* receptor complex differ in their affinity for DNA, and these data are similar to reports of receptors for steroids and retinoids. Steroid hormone–receptor complexes can be transformed by various *in vitro* treatments, however, so that the cytosolic form subsequent to transformation now is able to bind to DNA. We have been unsuccessful with the *Ah* receptor in this regard. Heat treatment (20°C for 1 hour), exposure to increased ionic strength, and gel permeation chromatography do not change the cytosolic *Ah* receptor to its nuclear DNA-binding form (Hannah *et al.*, 1982). These data may indicate an important difference between the *Ah* receptor and the various steroid hormone receptors. Further studies of the interaction between this nuclear inducer–receptor complex and DNA or protein moieties in the nucleus should be of great interest.

B. STRUCTURE–ACTIVITY RELATIONSHIP

We and other investigators have found no exceptions to the structure–activity relationship (Poland *et al.*, 1976; Okey *et al.*, 1979; Bigelow and Nebert, 1982). If antagonists exist for the *Ah* receptor, they have not yet been discovered.

Until recently we had been unable to reconcile the observations that *Ah*-nonresponsive mice do respond, without any apparent *Ah* receptor, to high doses of TCDD with enhanced levels of induced AHH activity (Poland *et al.*, 1974), the immunoprecipitable P_1-450 protein (Negishi *et al.*, 1981a), and the P_1-450 mRNA (Tukey *et al.*, 1981). It is now realized that sufficient numbers of cytosolic *Ah* receptor exist in *Ah*-nonresponsive mice but for unknown reasons are not experimentally detectable. When sufficient amounts of [³H]TCDD are given *in vivo* (Tukey *et al.*, 1982a), the nuclear inducer–receptor complex is detectable in *Ah*-nonresponsive mice and can account for the P_1-450 induction response. The presence of sufficient amounts of the nuclear inducer–receptor complex also explains the TCDD-induced epidermal keratinization found in hairless Ah^d/Ah^d mice (Knutson and Poland, 1982). If *Ah* receptor levels are low, therefore, a response may or may not occur, depending on the potency of the chemical being studied; however, if induction or any other response is observed, there are without exception ample amounts of *Ah* receptor present in the system being studied.

The identification of an *Ah* receptor in D2 and other *Ah*-nonresponsive mice therefore has helped to resolve major discrepancies between *in vitro* radioligand binding studies and *in vivo* structure–activity studies. Several laboratories have failed to corroborate the claim (Greenlee and Poland, 1979) that the B6 cytosolic inducer–receptor is able to translocate *in vitro* to the D2 nucleus. In Ah^d/Ah^d mice, the only methods currently available to assess *Ah* receptors involve *in vivo* treatment with [³H]TCDD and subsequent isolation of nuclei. We have not found a way to distinguish clearly between nuclear receptors from *Ah*-responsive and *Ah*-nonresponsive mice. The biochemical basis for this genetic difference thus remains elusive.

C. Do Receptors Exist for Inducing Other Drug-Metabolizing Enzymes?

We do not know if the *Ah* receptor represents a unique case or is a general example of the mechanism by which foreign chemicals induce various forms of P-450 and other drug-metabolizing enzymes (Nebert *et al.*, 1981). A putative receptor of the "phenobarbital type" has been described in mice (Poland *et al.*, 1980) but now seems not to be present among several strains of rats (Poland *et al.*, 1981) that are responsive to P-450 induction by phenobarbital. More than five dozen chemicals have been listed (Nebert *et al.*, 1981) as inducers of their own metabolism; less than one dozen of these chemicals are known for certain to stimulate unique forms of P-450 which have been characterized. Does a specific receptor exist for pregnenolone 16α-carbonitrile, isosafrole, benzene, ellipticine, and each of dozens of other inducing substances? Much more work will be necessary in this area of research.

D. Recombinant DNA and Ancillary Technologies

As described above, this laboratory recently has cloned portions of the mouse genome containing the P_1-450 chromosomal structural gene plus regions upstream in the 5′ direction (Ikeda *et al.*, 1982; Nebert *et al.*, 1982b; Nakamura *et al.*, 1983). It is possible that these genomic clones contain regions involved in the regulation of P_1-450 expression. Genomic cloned DNA for rat α_{2u} globulin (Kurtz, 1981) and metallothionein (Hagar and Palmiter, 1981) has been transfected into cultured cells, and these genes have been shown to be induced by glucocorticoids in the transfected cells. It will be interesting to attempt similar experiments with the *Ah* system. The mutant Hepa-1 clones (Legraverend *et al.*, 1982) appear to be suitable target cells for such transfection experiments, since these lines are defective in various aspects of the *Ah* system.

The currently available cloned P_1-450 chromosomal gene and subclones also should prove useful for mapping the structural gene. There is no guarantee that the *Ah* regulatory gene will exist on the same chromosome. Such linkage studies are under way in this laboratory.

V. SPECULATION ON THE ORIGIN AND FUNCTION OF THE *Ah* RECEPTOR

Why does the *Ah* system enhance monooxygenase activities that often are far more important in toxification than in detoxication? The spontaneous ("background") mutation rate for organisms is higher by many orders of magnitude than what can be accounted for by cosmic irradiation. Hence, chemicals (both endogenous and exogenous) that are metabolized to reactive intermediates must account for the great majority of spontaneous mutagenesis that occurs. Hence, the *Ah* system appears to contribute to a process contrary, rather than advantageous, to survival. In terms of evolution, therefore, the *Ah* receptor must have beneficial function(s) that outweigh its disadvantageous effects.

The majority of the relatively planar chemicals that interact best with the *Ah* receptor are found in combustion processes (such as the burning of bituminous coal, cigarettes, foods, and forests) or are very similar in chemical structure to substances found in such combustion processes. These chemicals are extremely fat soluble and it might have been advantageous in terms of survival for the organism to possess enzymes capable of metabolizing these foreign chemicals to more polar products. Alternatively, organisms are known to engage in complicated forms of "chemical warfare" [e.g., alkaloids synthesized by one species of termite or ant used as a defense against another species (Spanton and Prestwich, 1981), phytoalexins, or "stress metabolites" produced by various plants (Kúc and Currier, 1976)]. Perhaps it was advantageous for organisms to develop subcellular systems for identifying and detoxifying such compounds. Hence, there may have evolved the requirement for a receptor to carry a "signal" to the cell's nucleus; the "response" having a survival advantage was to mobilize enzymes which, in turn, would break down the foreign polycyclic aromatic chemicals.

The same evolutionary mechanism might occur from the simplest to the most complex P-450-containing organisms. *Pseudomonas*, for example, are a genus of bacteria that, when grown in the presence of camphor or various benzyl or alkane derivatives, somehow "sense" the presence of these foreign substances and mobilize enzymes to metabolize and thus use these chemicals as an efficient energy source. The same has been described for alkanes and benzo[*a*]pyrene in yeast and other fungi. At some point during evolutionary phylogeny, perhaps the enzymes responsible for transforming foreign chemicals into energy became enzymes responsible for detoxication. Whether *Pseudomonas* has a specific receptor for camphor and whether yeast has a specific receptor for alkanes, however, is not known.

As mentioned earlier, in addition to an unknown number of induced forms of P-450 (Fig. 11), the induction of UDP glucuronosyltransferase, reduced NAD(P)H dehydrogenase (quinone) (menadione oxidoreductase, DT-diaphorase), and ornithine decarboxylase activities has been rigorously demonstrated to be associated with the Ah^b allele by studies of the progeny of the B6D2F$_1$ × D2 backcross. Presumably, these "activities" reflect *de novo* mRNA and protein synthesis, but this presumption still awaits experimental confirmation.

Inducers known to bind avidly to the Ah receptor also enhance α-fetoprotein levels (Becker and Sell, 1979), phospholipase A_2 (Bresnick *et al.*, 1981), cytosolic aldehyde dehydrogenase (Deitrich *et al.*, 1978; Lindahl *et al.*, 1978; Lindahl, 1980) and membrane-bound γ-glutamyltranspeptidase (Gupta *et al.*, 1981), choline kinase (Ishidate *et al.*, 1980), and ethanolamine kinase (Ishidate *et al.*, 1980) activities, although no strict correlations with the Ah^b allele have been reported yet. These last three enzymes mentioned are of particular interest because all three are involved with membrane functions such as receptor internalization and phosphatidylcholine biosynthesis. Moreover, the EGF receptor (Ivanovic and Weinstein, 1982) is a cell-surface receptor affected by inducers that bind to the Ah receptor.

The chemicals that bind most avidly to the Ah receptor (Fig. 11) also cause immunosuppression (reviewed in Nebert, 1979; Nebert *et al.*, 1981, 1982c), epidermal keratinization (Knutson and Poland, 1980), and birth defects (Shum *et al.*, 1979; Poland and Glover, 1980). Furthermore, presence of the Ah receptor and the P_1-450 induction process apparently occurs very early in gestation, even before implantation of the mouse embryo at day $3\frac{1}{2}$ (Galloway *et al.*, 1980; Filler and Lew, 1981). Why would the preimplantation embryo need this receptor? Most likely, enhancement of the embryo's capacity to metabolize benzo[*a*]pyrene is not the first and foremost requirement for this receptor. All these data therefore suggest that the Ah system may be involved in certain growth processes; our studies of the induction of drug-metabolizing enzymes might be of only secondary importance. Hence, the present state of knowledge in the Ah receptor field may be similar to the early days of the opiate receptor field, in which the receptor was well characterized with an exogenous ligand several years before the true endogenous ligand was found and the true function of the receptor was uncovered.

ACKNOWLEDGMENT

The expert secretarial assistance of Ms. Ingrid E. Jordan is greatly appreciated.

REFERENCES

Atlas, S. A., Boobis, A. R., Felton, J. S., Thorgeirsson, S. S., and Nebert, D. W. (1977). *J. Biol. Chem.* **252**, 4712.

Baxter, J. D., and Tomkins, G. M. (1970). *Proc. Natl. Acad. Sci. U.S.A.* **65**, 709.

Becker, F. F., and Sell, S. (1979). *Cancer Res.* **39**, 3491.

Benedict, W. F., Gielen, J. E., Owens, I. S., Niwa, A., and Nebert, D. W. (1973). *Biochem. Pharmacol.* **22**, 2766.

Bigelow, S. W., and Nebert, D. W. (1982). *Toxicol. Lett.* **10**, 109.
Bresnick, E., Bailey, G., Bonney, R. J., and Wightman, P. (1981). *Carcinogenesis* **2**, 1119.
Carlstedt-Duke, J. M. B. (1979). *Cancer Res.* **39**, 3172.
Carlstedt-Duke, J., Elfström, G., Snochowski, M., Högberg, B., and Gustafsson, J.-Å. (1978). *Toxicol. Lett.* **2**, 365.
Chen, Y.-T., Lang, M. A., Jensen, N. M., Negishi, M., Tukey, R. H., Sidransky, E., Guenthner, T. M., and Nebert, D. W. (1982a). *Eur. J. Biochem.* **122**, 361.
Chen, Y.-T., Negishi, M., and Nebert, D. W. (1982b). *DNA* **1**, 231.
DeBoer, W., and Notides, A. C. (1981a). *Biochemistry* **20**, 1285.
DeBoer, W., and Notides, A. C. (1981b). *Biochemistry* **20**, 1290.
Deitrich, R. A., Bludeau, P., Roper, M., and Schmuck, J. (1978). *Biochem. Pharmacol.* **27**, 2343.
Felton, J. S., Ketley, J. N., Jakoby, W. B., Aitio, A., Bend, J. R., and Nebert, D. W. (1980). *Mol. Pharmacol* **18**, 559.
Filler, R., and Lew, K. J. (1981). *Proc. Natl. Acad. Sci. U.S.A.* **78**, 6991.
Galloway, S. M., Perry, P. E., Meneses, J., Nebert, D. W., and Pedersen, R. A. (1980). *Proc. Natl. Acad. Sci. U.S.A.* **77**, 3524.
Gielen, J. E., Goujon, F. M., and Nebert, D. W. (1972). *J. Biol. Chem.* **247**, 1125.
Greenlee, W. F., and Poland, A. (1979). *J. Biol. Chem.* **254**, 9814.
Guenthner, T. M., and Nebert, D. W. (1977). *J. Biol. Chem* **252**, 8981.
Guenthner, T. M., and Nebert, D. W. (1978). *Eur. J. Biochem.* **91**, 449.
Guenthner, T. M., Poland, A. P., and Nebert, D. W. (1976). *Fed. Proc., Fed. Am. Soc. Exp. Biol.* **35**, 282 (Abstr.).
Guenthner, T. M., Fysh, J. M., and Nebert, D. W. (1979). *Pharmacology* **19**, 12.
Gupta, B. N., McConnell, E. E., Harris, M. W., and Moore, J. A. (1981). *Toxicol. Appl. Pharmacol.* **57**, 99.
Gustafsson, J.-Å., Carlstedt-Duke, J., Mode, A., and Rafter, J., eds. (1980). "Biochemistry, Biophysics and Regulation of Cytochrome P-450." Elsevier/North-Holland Biomedical Press, New York.
Hagar, L. J., and Palmiter, R. D. (1981). *Nature (London)* **291**, 340.
Hankinson, O. (1979). *Proc. Natl. Acad. Sci. U.S.A.* **76**, 373.
Hankinson, O. (1980). *In* "Microsomes, Drug Oxidation, and Chemical Carcinogenesis" (M. J. Coon, A. H. Conney, R. W. Estabrook, H. V. Gelboin, J. R. Gillette, and P. J. O'Brien, eds.), p. 1149. Academic Press, New York.
Hannah, R. R., Nebert, D. W., and Eisen, H. J. (1981). *J. Biol. Chem.* **256**, 4584.
Hanson-Painton, O., Griffin, M. J., and Tang, J. (1981). *Biochem. Biophys. Res. Commun.* **101**, 1364.
Ikeda, T., Altieri, M., Nakamura, M., Nebert, D. W., and Negishi, M. (1982). *In* "Cytochrome P-450: Biochemistry, Biophysics and Environmental Implications" (E. Hietanen, ed.). Elsevier/North Holland Biomedical Press, New York.
Ishidate, K., Tsuruoka, M., and Nakazawa, Y. (1980). *Biochim. Biophys. Acta* **620**, 49.
Ivanovic, V., and Weinstein, I. B. (1981). *J. Supramol. Struct. Cell. Biochem. Suppl.* **5**, 232 (Abstr.).
Ivanovic, V., and Weinstein, I. B. (1982). *Carcinogenesis* **3**, 505.
Kahl, G. F., Friederici, D., Bigelow, S. W., Okey, A. B., and Nebert, D. W. (1980). *Dev. Pharmacol. Ther.* **1**, 137.
Kärenlampi, S., Nebert, D. W., and Eisen, H. J. (1982). *In* "Cytochrome P-450: Biochemistry, Biophysics and Environmental Implications" (E. Hietanen, ed.). Elsevier/North Holland Biomedical Press, New York.
Knutson, J. C., and Poland, A. (1980). *Cell* **22**, 27.

Knutson, J. C., and Poland, A. (1982). *Cell* **30**, 225.

Kodama, Y., and Bock, F. G., (1970). *Cancer Res.* **30**, 1846.

Kouri, R. E., and Nebert, D. W. (1977). *In* "Origins of Human Cancer" (H. H. Hiatt, J. D. Watson, and J. A. Winsten, eds.), p. 811. Cold Spring Harbor Lab., Cold Spring Harbor, New York.

Kouri, R. E., Rude, T. H., Joglekar, R., Dansette, P. M., Jerina, D. M., Atlas, S. A., Owens, I. S., and Nebert, D. W. (1978). *Cancer Res.* **38**, 2777.

Kúc, J., and Currier, W. (1976). *In* "Mycotoxins and Other Fungal Related Food Problems— Advances in Chemistry Series" (J. V. Rodricks, ed.), Vol. 149, p. 356. American Chem. Soc., Washington, D.C.

Kumaki, K., Jensen, N. M., Shire, J. G. M., and Nebert, D. W. (1977). *J. Biol. Chem.* **252**, 157.

Kurtz (1981) *Nature (London)* **291**, 629.

Lang, M. A., and Nebert, D. W. (1981). *J. Biol. Chem.* **256**, 12058.

Lang, M. A., Nebert, D. W., and Negishi, M. (1980). *In* "Biochemistry, Biophysics and Regulation of Cytochrome P-450" (J.-Å. Gustafsson, J. Carlstedt-Duke, A. Mode, and J. Rafter, eds.), p. 415 Elsevier/North-Holland Biomedical Press, New York.

Lang, M. A., Gielen, J. E., and Nebert, D. W. (1981). *J. Biol. Chem.* **256**, 12068.

Legraverend, C., Hannah, R. R., Eisen, H. J., Owens, I. S., Nebert, D. W., and Hankinson, O. (1982). *J. Biol. Chem.* **257**, 6402.

Lindahl, R. (1980). *Biochem. Pharmacol.* **29**, 3026.

Lindahl, R., Roper, M., and Deitrich, R. A. (1978). *Biochem. Pharmacol.* **27**, 2463.

Lu, A. Y. H., and West, S. B. (1980). *Pharmacol. Rev.* **31**, 277.

Mannering, G. J. (1981). *In* "Concepts in Drug Metabolism" (P. Jenner and B. Testa, eds.), Vol. 2, p. 53. Dekker, New York.

Mason, M. F., and Okey, A. B. (1982). *Eur. J. Biochem.* **123**, 209.

Nakamura, M., Negishi, M., Altieri, M., Chen, Y.-T., Ikeda, T., Tukey, R. H., and Nebert, D. W. (1983). *Eur. J. Biochem.* (in press).

Nebert, D. W. (1978). *In* "Methods in Enzymology" (S. Fleisher, ed.), Vol. 52, pp. 226. Academic Press, New York.

Nebert, D. W. (1979). *Mol. Cell. Biochem.* **27**, 27.

Nebert, D. W. (1981). *Environ. Health Perspect.* **39**, 11.

Nebert, D. W., and Atlas, S. A. (1978). *Hum. Genet., Suppl.* **1**, 149.

Nebert, D. W., and Bausserman, L. L. (1970). *J. Biol. Chem.* **245**, 6373.

Nebert, D. W., and Felton, J. S. (1975). *In* "Cytochromes P-450 and b_5" (D. Y. Cooper, O. Rosenthal, R. Snyder, and C. Witmer, eds.), p. 127. Plenum, New York.

Nebert, D. W., and Gelboin, H. V. (1969). *Arch. Biochem. Biophys.* **134**, 76.

Nebert, D. W., and Gielen, J. E. (1972). *Fed Proc., Fed. Am. Soc. Exp. Biol.* **31**, 1315.

Nebert, D. W., and Jensen, N. M. (1979). *CRC Crit. Rev. Biochem.* **6**, p. 383.

Nebert, D. W., Goujon, F. M., and Gielen, J. E. (1971). *In* "Fonds de la Recherche Scientifique Medicale, Groups de Contact," p. 240. 11, rue d'Egmont, Bruxelles 5, Belgium.

Nebert, D. W., Goujon, F. M., and Gielen, J. E. (1972). *Nature (London), New Biol.* **236**, 107.

Nebert, D. W., Robinson, J. R., Niwa, A., Kumaki, K., and Poland, A. P. (1975). *J. Cell. Physiol.* **85**, 393.

Nebert, D. W., Jensen, N. M., Perry, J. W., and Oka, T. (1980). *J. Biol. Chem.* **255**, 6836.

Nebert, D. W., Eisen, H. J., Negishi, M., Lang, M. A., Hjelmeland, L. M., and Okey, A. B. (1981). *Annu. Rev. Pharmacol. Toxicol.* **21**, 431.

Nebert, D. W., Jensen, N. M., Shinozuka, H., Kunz, H. W., and Gill, T. J. (1982a). *Genetics* **100**, 79.

Nebert, D. W., Nakamura, M., Altieri, M., Ikeda, T., Tukey, R. H., and Negishi, M. (1982b). *J. Cell. Biochem. Suppl.* **6**, 284 (Abstr.).

Nebert, D. W., Negishi, M., Lang, M. A., Hjelmeland, L. M., and Eisen, H. J. (1982c). *Adv. Genet.* **21**, 1.

Negishi, M., and Nebert, D. W. (1979). *J. Biol. Chem.* **254**, 11015.

Negishi, M., and Nebert, D. W. (1981). *J. Biol. Chem.* **256**, 3085.

Negishi, M., Jensen, N. M., Garcia, G. S., and Nebert, D. W. (1981a). *Eur. J. Biochem.* **115**, 585.

Negishi, M., Swan, D. C., Enquist, L. W., and Nebert, D. W. (1981b). *Proc. Natl. Acad. Sci. U.S.A.* **78**, 800.

Niwa, A., Kumaki, K., and Nebert, D. W. (1975a). *Mol. Pharmacol.* **11**, 399.

Niwa, A., Kumaki, K., Nebert, D. W., and Poland, A. P. (1975b). *Arch. Biochem. Biophys.* **166**, 559.

Okey, A. B., and Vella, L. M. (1982). *Eur. J. Biochem.* **127**, 39.

Okey, A. B., Bondy, G. P., Mason, M. E., Kahl, G. F., Eisen, H. J., Guenthner, T. M., and Nebert, D. W. (1979). *J. Biol. Chem.* **254**, 11636.

Okey, A. B., Bondy, G. P., Mason, M. E., Nebert, D. W., Forster-Gibson, C., Muncan, J., and Dufresne, M. J. (1980). *J. Biol. Chem.* **255**, 11415.

Owens, I. S. (1977). *J. Biol. Chem.* **252**, 2827.

Paigen, K. (1979). *Annu. Rev. Genet.* **13**, 417.

Pitot, H. C., Goldsworthy, T., Campbell, H. A., and Poland, A. P. (1980). *Cancer Res.* **40**, 3616.

Poland, A., and Glover, E. (1973a). *Science* **179**, 476.

Poland, A., and Glover, E. (1973b). *Mol. Pharmacol.* **9**, 736.

Poland, A., and Glover, E. (1974). *Mol. Pharmacol.* **10**, 349.

Poland, A., and Glover, E. (1975). *Mol. Pharmacol.* **11**, 389.

Poland, A., and Glover, E. (1979). *Cancer Res.* **39**, 3341.

Poland, A., and Glover, E. (1980). *Mol. Pharmacol.* **17**, 86.

Poland, A., and Kende, A. (1976). *Fed. Proc., Fed. Am. Soc. Exp. Biol.* **35**, 2404.

Poland, A. P., Glover, E., Robinson, J. R., and Nebert, D. W. (1974). *J. Biol. Chem.* **249**, 5599.

Poland, A. P., Glover, E., and Kende, A. S. (1976). *J. Biol. Chem.* **251**, 4936.

Poland, A. P., Mak, I., Glover, E., Boatman, R. J., Ebetino, F. H., and Kende, A. S. (1980). *Mol. Pharmacol.* **18**, 571.

Poland, A. P., Mak, I., and Glover, E. (1981). *Mol. Pharmacol.* **20**, 442.

Robinson, J. R., and Nebert, D. W. (1974). *Mol. Pharmacol.* **10**, 484.

Robinson, J. R., Considine, N., and Nebert, D. W. (1974). *J. Biol. Chem.* **249**, 5851.

Sato, R., and Kato, R., eds. (1982). "Microsomes, Drug Oxidations, and Drug Toxicity." Japan Sci. Soc. Press, Tokyo.

Shum, S., Jensen, N. M., and Nebert, D. W. (1979). *Teratology* **20**, 365.

Spanton, S. G., and Prestwich, G. D. (1981). *Science* **214**, 1363.

Taylor, B. A. (1971). *Life Sci.* **10**, 1127.

Thomas, P. E., Kouri, R. E., and Hutton, J. J. (1972). *Biochem. Genet.* **6**, 157.

Thomas, P. E., Hutton, J. J., and Taylor, B. A. (1973). *Genetics* **74**, 655.

Tierney, B., and Bresnick, E. (1981). *Arch. Biochem. Biophys.* **210**, 729.

Tierney, B., Weaver, D., Heintz, N. H., Schaeffer, W. I., and Bresnick, E. (1980). *Arch. Biochem. Biophys.* **200**, 513.

Tukey, R. H., Nebert, D. W., and Negishi, M. (1981). *J. Biol. Chem.* **256**, 6969.

Tukey, R. H., Hannah, R. R., Negishi, M., Nebert, D. W., and Eisen, H. J. (1982a). *Cell* **31**, 275.

Tukey, R. H., Nebert, D. W., and Negishi, M. (1982b). *Mol. Pharmacol.* **22**, 779.

CHAPTER 8

Specificity of Nucleic Acid Structure for Binding Steroid Receptors

S. Anand Kumar and Herbert W. Dickerman

I. INTRODUCTION

Analogous to a neuronal response, the action of steroid hormones may be divided into afferent and efferent limbs. The afferent pathway comprises steroid diffusion into the cell, specific cytoplasmic aporeceptor binding of the hormone, translocation of the receptor complex to the nucleus, and association of the translocated holoreceptor to effector sites in the target cell's chromatin. The central question about the final step is what defines the nuclear affector sites as opposed to those that are ineffective or abortive.

BIOCHEMICAL ACTIONS OF HORMONES, VOL. X

Among the potential sites, DNA, alone or in concert with specific chromosomal proteins, appears to be of prime importance.

Early in the research on steroid receptors, their identification as DNA-binding proteins, either by association or nuclear release by selective enzymes, was exciting because of the analogy to prokaryotic gene regulatory proteins, i.e., the *lac* repressor and cAMP receptor protein of *Escherichia coli*. An initial study even reported the preferential binding of rat uterine estradiol receptors to homologous DNA (Clemens and Kleinsmith, 1972). However, subsequently it was observed that receptor binding to DNA was not saturable or specific for the source of DNA (Chamness *et al.*, 1974; André and Rochefort, 1975; Yamamoto and Alberts, 1974). Clark and Gorski (1969) had found earlier that rat uterine estradiol receptors when incubated at 25°C bound nonselectively to glass beads as well as nuclear pellets. Activated rat liver cytosol glucocorticoid receptors bound efficiently to a range of polyanions with little evidence of discrimination (Milgrom *et al.*, 1973). So, a sense of skepticism grew about the role of specific DNA sequence recognition in the nuclear action of steroid receptors. At its extreme, DNA–cellulose chromatography was considered a form of ion exchange. Conversely, a growing body of data demonstrated the importance of chromosomal nonhistone proteins at acceptor sites for the oviduct progesterone and uterine estrogen receptors (O'Malley *et al.*, 1972; Puca *et al.*, 1974; Spelsberg *et al.*, 1976).

Yet the suspicion persisted that specific recognition was a factor in steroid hormone action. Yamamoto and Alberts (1975) focused attention on the prevalence of nonspecific binding involved in the interaction of DNA-binding proteins and hypothesized that as many as 10^3 specific sequences could be hidden by assays involving unfractionated DNA. In other words, a DNA-binding protein will bind to any DNA but does so with greater avidity to selective sequences. Over the past few years, evidence accrued from several laboratories that certain steroid receptor:DNA interactions were not solely a nonspecific ionic bonding but involved structure, base recognition, and, most recently, sequence selection (Payvar *et al.*, 1981). Furthermore, certain features of prokaryotic regulators (such as the requirement of the ligand for DNA binding, separateness of the ligand- and DNA-binding sites, and the effects of certain inhibitors) have been recognized in steroid hormone receptors. It is the intent of this review to outline these studies and propose a model of productive steroid receptor:DNA interaction.

II. BIOLOGICAL SIGNIFICANCE OF DNA BINDING OF STEROID RECEPTORS

The DNA-binding property of steroid receptors seems to be physiologically significant. Yamamoto *et al.* (1974) obtained two mutant classes of glucocorticoid-resistant S49 mouse lymphoma cells. One class had depressed nuclear binding (nt^-) and the other had increased nuclear binding (nt^i) when compared to wild-type cells. The respective affinities for DNA–cellulose of the mutant receptor complexes correlated with their alterations in nuclear binding. These results suggested that a mutation affecting the polynucleotide-binding domain of the receptor resulted in a glucocorticoid-resistant phenotype. Similar observations on mouse lymphoma cells were also made by Pfahl *et al.* (1978). Khan *et al.* (1980) examined the differences in DNA binding of estrogen receptor of two sublines of a rat mammary tumor, MTW9, one of which shows ovariectomy-induced regression (OIR) and the other, MTW9-MtT, which does not. The estradiol receptor from the former binds significantly more to DNA–cellulose than that from MTW9-MtT. The MtT is a variant of MTW9, grown by coimplantation of a mammosomatotropic tumor MtTW10, but it does not show OIR. However, when the mammosomatotropic tumor (MtT) is resected, the tumor regresses and shows rapid OIR. The estradiol receptor (E_2R) from MtT resected tumors binds to DNA–cellulose as efficiently as does E_2R from MTW9-D. After implantation of MtT into animals bearing MTW9D, OIR is prevented and E_2R binding to DNA–cellulose is significantly reduced. In another study estrogen-binding components in the cytosol prepared from estrogen-independent Leydig cell tumors which could not bind to nuclei also could not bind to DNA–cellulose. Removal of a low-molecular-weight component from the cytosol converted the estrogen-binding protein to a receptor-like molecule which could bind to DNA–cellulose as well as to nuclei, suggesting that DNA binding is analogous to nuclear binding. Sato *et al.* (1981) have examined a number of human breast cancer tumors. One of the ER-positive tumors resistant to endocrine therapy contained E_2R which did not bind to DNA. The DNA-binding affinity of androgen receptors of kidneys of normal and testicular feminization (tfm) mutant rats is high for the former and low for the latter (Wieland *et al.*, 1978; Wieland and Fox, 1981). The above studies, albeit using crude receptor preparations, show that modifications of the DNA-binding activity of steroid holoreceptors correlated with alterations in steroid-modulated cellular responses.

III. SEPARATENESS OF LIGAND- AND DNA-BINDING DOMAINS

Steroid receptor proteins have distinct domains for steroid and DNA binding. Several investigations have clearly illustrated that the DNA-binding property of steroid receptors can be selectively destroyed by partial proteolysis of the receptor protein. André and Rochefort (1973) and Sala-Trepat and Vallet-Strové (1974) demonstrated that limited proteolysis either by trypsin or by a Ca^{2+}-activated cytosolic enzyme converts the calf uterine estradiol receptor to a molecular form that is unable to bind DNA or chromatin. Such a modified estradiol receptor retained the ability to bind the steroid ligand with the same affinity as the original receptor molecule. Similar studies on progesterone (Sherman *et al.*, 1978; Vedeckis *et al.*, 1979) and glucocorticoid receptors (Wränge and Gustafsson, 1978; Sherman *et al.*, 1979; Naray, 1981) have further illustrated that molecular forms resulting from partial proteolysis (referred to as "mero receptors" by Sherman and co-workers) retain their normal steroid-binding characteristics but exhibit loss of DNA or nuclear binding. Wränge and Gustafsson (1978) examined the changes in molecular dimensions of rat liver hepatic glucocorticoid receptor complexes subjected to partial proteolysis. Tryptic digestion of the rat liver hepatic glucocorticoid receptor (Stokes radius 61 Å) resulted in smaller molecules of Stokes radii 36 and 19 Å while partial digestion with chymotrypsin, papain, or an endogenous protease yielded a complex of 36 Å. The 61 and 36 Å complexes had dissociation constants of $6-9 \times 10^{-9} M$ for dexamethasone, but dissociation data for the 19 Å complex were difficult to obtain because of its lability. While both 61 and 36 Å complexes could bind DNA, the 19 Å complex could bind neither DNA nor nuclei. Digestion of DNA–cellulose or nuclei-bound dexamethasone–receptor complex with trypsin also resulted in a complex of 19 Å. The calculated molecular weights of these 61, 36, and 19 Å complexes were 102,000, 46,000, and 19,000, respectively. Treatment of the 36 Å complex with trypsin also yielded the 19 Å complex, which did not bind to DNA–cellulose. Based on these observations Wränge and Gustafsson have proposed three distinct domains for the glucocorticoid receptor: (1) the steroid-binding site, which is retained on the 19 and 36 Å complexes (2) the DNA-binding site, which is retained on the 36 Å fragment but absent in the 19 Å receptor fragment, and (3) a region of unknown function present in the original 61 Å receptor complex.

Chick oviduct progesterone receptor complexes A and B have been also probed by the endogenous Ca^{2+}-activated protease for the separateness of domains (Vedeckis *et al.*, 1979, 1980a,b). A digestion product of molecular weight 23,000 was obtained from both A and B forms of progesterone receptor. The core fragments called "mero receptors" retained the steroid hormone-binding site but lost the ability to bind DNA and/or chromatin. Higher molecular weight fragments (MW 43,000) were obtained from both the A and B forms by varying the conditions of proteolysis. These fragments were able to bind DNA and contained the steroid-binding site as well. Vedeckis *et al.* (1980a,b) have proposed a model for the large-molecular-weight form (form B) in which the MW 23,000 limit core fragment is represented as the steroid-binding site. The 43,000–45,000 fragment is presumed to be an intermediate of proteolytic digestion which consists of both steroid- and DNA-binding sites. The form A receptor (MW 79,000) presumably consists of a site with unknown function in addition to steroid- and DNA-binding sites. Form B receptor (117,000) is depicted as the native molecule consisting of the steroid-, DNA-, and chromatin-binding sites as distinct domains. [^{3}H]Progesterone-labeled A and B receptor proteins yield, upon limited digestion with *Staphylococcus aureus* V8 protease, fragments of molecular weight 43,000 which contain the DNA-binding activity (P. P. Minghetti, N. L. Wiegel, W. T. Schrader, and B. W. O'Malley, personal communication). Fragments of similar molecular weight containing both steroid- and DNA-binding sites can also be generated from partial digests of receptor A by trypsin or the endogenous Ca^{2+}-activated neutral protease. Analyses of the *S. aureus* protease-derived fragments of purified progesterone receptor A, by the two-dimensional gel system of O'Farrell (1975), the protein blotting technique (Bowen *et al.*, 1980), and assay of DNA-binding activity (P. P. Minghetti, N. L. Wiegel, W. T. Schrader, and B. W. O'Malley, personal communication), have detected three DNA-binding peptides of molecular weights 45,000, 40,000, and 15,000. More exhaustive digestion yields only the MW 15,000 polypeptide, suggesting that the higher molecular weight peptides are intermediates of enzymatic degradation. The MW 15,000 peptide is believed to be the limit digest of the DNA-binding domain of progesterone receptor, since it contains only the DNA-binding and not the steroid-binding activity. Estrogen receptors (5.3–8.6 S, dependent on ionic strength) are also converted into a smaller salt-stable form (4.4–5 S independent of ionic strength) by trypsin or by the cytosol Ca^{2+}-activated protease. The $\simeq$4 S entities generated by such treatment are incapable of binding to DNA while retaining the integrity of the estradiol binding site (André and Rochefort, 1973; Sala-Trepat *et al.*, 1974). Androgen receptor (8–9 S, 85–106 Å, M_r = 280,000–365,000), on the other hand, did not lose either the steroid- or the DNA-binding ability upon partial digestion with trypsin. The smallest fragment (3 S, 23 Å) retains both steroid- and DNA-binding properties (Wilson and French, 1979). One can speculate that in the case of androgen receptors the DNA-binding domain may be situated very close to the steroid-binding site and the trypsin-sensitive region is probably located away from these two sites.

The functional differentiation of steroid receptors is similar to the property of other DNA-binding gene regulatory proteins. Digestion of *lac* repressor with trypsin or chymotrypsin yields a resistant core which retains inducer-binding activity but has lost DNA-binding activity (Platt *et al.*, 1973). Under more restrictive incubation conditions the *lac* repressor can be dissected by trypsin into a tetrameric core and monomeric peptide fragments. The latter fragments, termed "head pieces," bind DNA (Geiser and Weber, 1977; Jovin *et al.*, 1977; Ogata and Gilbert, 1978). Similar fragmentation into two distinct functional domains is also obtained for λ repressor by papain cleavage (Pabo *et al.*, 1979). In both cases the DNA-binding fragments are the amino proximal fragments and are relatively rich in basic amino acids. However, these fragments also contain potential hydrogen-bonding amino acids such as tyrosine, threonine, and serine (Alexander *et al.*, 1977). The isolated DNA-binding fragments from both *lac* and λ repressor can also mediate positive and negative control of transcription *in vitro* (Sauer *et al.*, 1979). The cyclic AMP receptor protein (CRP), which is a positive and negative regulatory protein for gene expression in *E. coli*, also has two distinct domains, one for binding to cAMP and another for binding to DNA. In the absence of cAMP, CRP is resistant to trypsin, but with cAMP bound to CRP, trypsin treatment yields a carboxyl-proximal core fragment which retains the cAMP-binding activity (Krakow and Pastan, 1973). In a recent study Aiba and Krakow (1981) dissected CRP with chymotrypsin in the presence of sodium dodecyl sulfate (SDS) into two fragments of molecular weights 9500 and 13,000, the former being amino proximal and the latter carboxyl proximal. The carboxyl-proximal fragment could bind to DNA and contained eight of the total nine arginines present in the undegraded CRP. Other amino acids were distributed proportionately between the two fragments. The structural disposition of DNA-binding and modulator ligand-binding domains in gene regulatory proteins of prokaryotes and the steroid receptors seems to be strikingly similar.

The presence of distinct domains for steroid and DNA binding in steroid receptors is also shown by the differential sensitivities of these two sites for a number of inhibitors. Studies regarding reagents that modify specific amino acid residues have implicated lysine (Cake *et al.*, 1978; Nishigori *et al.*, 1978; Nishigori and Toft, 1979; Hiipakka and Liao, 1980; Muldoon and Cidlowski, 1980; Henrikson *et al.*, 1981) in the DNA-binding sites of glucocorticoid, androgen, progesterone, and estrogen receptors; arginine in glucocorticoid receptors (DiSorbo *et al.*, 1980); histidine in glucocorticoid (DiSorbo *et al.*, 1980) and estrogen receptors (Feldman *et al.*, 1980; Gross *et al.*, 1981); and cysteine in vitamin D (Pike, 1981). In all these studies, the effect of chemical modification is selective toward the DNA-binding property without altering the properties of the receptor-bound steroid. For example, lysine modification by the formation of Schiff base between the aldehyde group of pyridoxal phosphate and the ε-amino group of lysine residues results in the loss of DNA binding of many steroid receptors. Such a modification does not affect the dissociation constant of either the dexamethasone bound to glucocorticoid receptor (DiSorbo *et al.*, 1980) or the estrogen bound to estrogen receptor (Henrikson *et al.*, 1981). The effect of pyridoxal phosphate can be overcome by increased concentrations of the polynucleotide and the kinetics correspond to a typical competitive inhibition pattern (Henrikson *et al*., 1981). 1,2-Cyclohexanedione, a specific reagent for the guanidino group of arginine residues, also inhibits activated glucocorticoid receptor binding to DNA–cellulose without affecting ligand binding to receptor or dissociating the bound steroid from the receptor protein. The inhibition due to diethylpyrocarbonate was readily reversible by hydroxylamine, indicating that the amino acid residue involved is histidine. Photooxidation of estrogen receptor using rose bengal as a sensitizer results in a time-dependent loss of DNA-binding activity (DiSorbo *et al*., 1980; Feldman *et al*., 1980). This effect is pH dependent, suggesting the involvement of histidine residues. The estrogen-binding site is also susceptible to photooxidation but is not pH dependent. However, binding of receptor to estradiol protects the estradiol-binding site from photooxidation whereas the binding of estradiol receptor to DNA does not protect the DNA-binding site from photooxidation (Feldman *et al*., 1980).

Selective inhibition of DNA binding of steroid receptors and selective release of steroid receptors bound to DNA matrix is achieved by structural analogues of DNA, or by compounds that specifically interact with DNA-binding sites of proteins. Polyanionic compounds such as heparin, polyglutamic acid, aurintricarboxylic acid (ATA), and Cibacron Blue F3GA(CB) are known to interfere with the polynucleotide binding of DNA polymerase, RNA polymerase, polynucleotide kinase, aminoacyl-tRNA synthetase, etc. In all cases, the polyanionic compounds are presumed to mimic the anionic properties of DNA and, therefore, interact with the relatively basic DNA-binding site of these proteins. Heparin inhibits the formation of promoter·bacterial RNA polymerase complexes (Walter *et al*., 1967) and the interaction of initiation factors of protein synthesis with the ribonucleoprotein particles, particularly the 40 S ribosomal subunit (Ayuso-Parilla *et al*., 1973; Liang and Liao, 1974) of eukaryotic ribosomes. Native estradiol receptor binds with high affinity to heparin–agarose while the receptor modified by Ca^{2+}-activated protease, which has no DNA-binding activity, does not bind to heparin–agarose (Molinari *et al*., 1977). Heparin also inhibits DNA binding of estrogen, (Kumar *et al*., 1979) and of androgen receptors (Mulder *et al*., 1980). Androgen receptor bound either to DNA–cellulose, ADP–agarose, or phosphocellulose could be completely eluted with 0.2 mg/ml of heparin, indicating that heparin complexation with the steroid receptor involves mostly ionic interactions. It may be pertinent to note that nonspecific binding of bacterial RNA polymerase to DNA is more sensitive to heparin action than are specific "open promoter" complexes (Chamberlin, 1976). Aurintricarboxylic acid (Liao *et al*., 1975; Givens and Manly, 1976), rifamycin AF/013 (Meilhac *et al*., 1972; Tsai and Saunders, 1973), and Cibacron Blue F3GA (Brissac *et al*., 1976; Kumar and Krakow, 1977) also inhibit template binding of RNA and DNA polymerases. The interaction of these compounds with polymerases is mainly through nonionic forces (Stellwagen, 1977). Aurintricarboxylic acid is a polycarboxylic triphenyl methane dye and Cibacron Blue F3GA is a sulfonated polyaromatic dye. Rifamycin AF/013 is a lipophilic derivative of the ansamycin class of antibiotics. Aurintricarboxylic acid has been shown to inhibit nuclear uptake and DNA-binding properties of estrogen (Moudgil and Weekes, 1978) and progesterone receptors (Moudgil and Eessalu, 1980). Only activated progesterone receptor was sensitive to the action of ATA and not the nonactivated receptor. Rifamycin AF/013 was also a powerful inhibitor of progesterone receptor binding to nuclei and to DNA (Lohmar and Toft, 1975). Cibacron Blue F3GA has been reported to act as an inhibitor for a number of enzymes that interact with polynucleotides. Kinetic and spectral titration experiments show that the enzymes binding to oligo- and polynucleotides as well as mononucleotide substrates such as polynucleotide phosphorylase (Drocourt *et al.*, 1978), polynucleotide kinase (Nichols *et al.*, 1978), DNA polymerase (Brissac *et al.*, 1976), RNA polymerase (Kumar and Krakow, 1977), and tRNA synthetase (Moe, and Piskiewicz, 1979) bound CB primarily at the polynucleotide-binding site. Furthermore, interferon, which binds to polynucleotides, can also bind to Blue Dextran–Sepharose; when bound to the affinity matrix it was displaced by polynucleotides but not by mono- or dinucleotides. Analogous to these properties, estrogen receptor bound to oligo(dT)–cellulose was released readily by the addition of very low concentrations of CB (10 μM) (Kumar *et al.*, 1980a). Similarly, progesterone receptor was eluted from an ATP–Sepharose column with 0.25 mM ATA (Moudgil and Eessalu, 1980). Cibacron Blue, ATA, heparin, and rifamycin AF/013 did not dissociate steroid from its site on the receptor under conditions where they inhibit DNA–receptor interactions.

The selective inhibition of DNA binding of steroid receptors by CB, ATA, and rifamycin AF/013 indicates that the polynucleotide-binding domains of steroid receptors have specific structural features for which these compounds have great affinity. Thus, the interaction of steroid receptors with DNA was not an artifactual nonspecific ionic interaction, but a combination of ionic, hydrogen-binding, and hydrophobic interactions characteristic of proteins which recognize sites on the DNA for specific binding.

Another distinctive feature of proteins that regulate gene expression in prokaryotes is that the DNA-binding effect is dependent on the binding of modulator ligand to its respective site. For example, CRP is a regulatory factor for gene expression in *E. coli*. Cyclic AMP receptor protein binds to sites within the promoter loci of catabolite-repressible operons, enabling RNA polymerase to form the open promoter complex prerequisite to initiation of transcription. Cyclic AMP receptor protein is an allosteric protein in which binding of cAMP elicits a conformational transition resulting in an enhanced affinity for DNA (Krakow and Pastan, 1973; Wu *et al.*, 1974; Saxe and Revzin, 1979; Kumar *et al.*, 1980b). *Lac* repressor is another example of ligand-modulated conformational transition which alters the DNA-binding property of the protein. *Lac* repressor controls the expression of lactose genes by specifically binding to *lac* operator DNA. Binding of an inducer such as isopropyl β-ᴅ-thiogalactoside to repressor greatly reduces the affinity of the protein to the operator DNA and allows the expression of lactose genes (Müller-Hill, 1975). In the case of steroid receptors it is postulated that only the holoreceptor has the ability to migrate to the nucleus and bind to chromatin. In the absence of the steroid ligand the receptor protein is localized in the cytoplasm. The dependence on the binding of steroid ligand for the receptor molecule to form a strong complex with DNA *in vitro* was demonstrated by André and Rochefort (1973) with uterine estrogen receptors. By using a sucrose density gradient to monitor the formation of steroid receptor–DNA complex, they showed that the binding of estradiol enhanced the formation of receptor–DNA complex five- to sixfold and decreased nonspecific aggregation of the receptor protein. Estrone, a weaker estrogen, enhanced the DNA-binding ability of the receptor to a lesser degree. Nonestrogenic steroids, such as progesterone or cortisol, which did not compete with estradiol on the receptor site, were practically inactive, as was 3-deoxyestradiol. We have also demonstrated stimulation by the steroid ligand on receptor interaction with oligodeoxynucleotide–cellulose. Using oligo(dT)–cellulose as the matrix and mouse uterine cytosol as the source of estradiol receptors, the amount of binding was measured in the presence and absence of [^{3}H]estradiol (Table I). About 10% of the total available estradiol receptors bound to oligo(dT)–cellulose in the absence of estradiol, since ~90% of the available receptor was found in the unadsorbed fraction. When holoreceptor was tested, ~30% of the estradiol–receptor complex bound the oligo(dT)–cellulose matrix. Turnell *et al.* (1974) demonstrated that, while triamcinolone acetonide-bound glucocorticoid receptor in rat thymocytes forms a complex with DNA, the same receptor carrying the antiglucocorticoid cortexolone did not bind to DNA. They proposed that when agonist or antagonist steroids interact with the cytoplasmic receptor they induce a conformational change, which results in an active or inactive complex, respectively. Both of these complexes can be transported to the nucleus in a temperature-dependent step but only the agonist receptor complex will interact with chromatin and initiate the biological response.

It is clear from the above results that steroid receptors share a number of structural features with the prokaryotic gene regulatory proteins. The DNA binding is allosterically controlled by the ligand's interaction with its site. The two binding domains can be separated by controlled proteolytic digestion. The DNA-binding domain of prokaryotic gene regulatory proteins is generally rich in basic amino acids for interaction with the negative

TABLE I

EFFECT OF STEROID LIGAND ON THE BINDING OF ESTRADIOL RECEPTOR TO
OLIGO(dT)–CELLULOSE

Treatment[a]	Total available[b] estradiol receptors (fmol)	Oligo(dT)–cellulose-binding estradiol receptors[c] (fmol)
1. None	86	32
2. Passage of cytosol untreated with estradiol through oligo(dT)–cellulose	78	ND[d]
3. Same as 2 but subsequently incubated with estradiol	78	28

[a] (1) Mouse uterine cytosol was prepared according to standard procedure (Kumar et al., 1979). (2 and 3) 200 μl of the cytosol was mixed with oligo(dT)–cellulose (250 nmol organic phosphorus) and 0.15 M KCl in 0.01 M Tris–HCl, pH 7.6/0.001 M EDTA/0.001 M DTT buffer, at 4°C for 60 minutes, and centrifuged.

[b] An aliquot of the supernatant was incubated with 9 nM estradiol for 90 minutes at 4°C followed by treatment with dextran-coated charcoal. Radioactivity not adsorbed on charcoal represents the quantity of estradiol receptor complexes.

[c] An aliquot of the [³H]estradiol receptor complex was mixed with oligo(dT)–cellulose as described earlier, incubated for 60 minutes at 4°C, washed with 0.15 M KCl, and radioactivity associated with the cellulose matrix was counted. As control an equivalent amount of blank cellulose was also incubated with the [³H]estradiol receptor complex. The difference in the amount of radioactivity bound to derivatized cellulose and blank cellulose is shown.

[d] ND, Not determined.

charges of phosphate groups of DNA, but other amino acid side chains are also involved in interaction with specific DNA sequences. In the case of steroid receptors, the DNA-binding domain contains reactive basic amino acids since putative modification of lysine side chains using pyridoxal 5-phosphate led to inhibition of DNA binding of estrogen, progesterone, and glucocorticoid receptors. Arginine and histidine residues have been implicated using group specific reagents. Steroid receptor–DNA interactions involve bonding other than electrostatic and are indicated by the effect of structure-specific inhibitors such as CB, ATA, and rifamycin AF/013. The inhibitory effects of these compounds indicate that the DNA-binding domain possesses a special supersecondary structure. Thus, the striking similarities between the steroid receptors and the well-characterized gene regulatory proteins suggest that the steroid receptor may bind to discrete regions of chromosomal DNA in a manner akin to prokaryotic gene regulation. Support for this inference comes from the findings (1) that estrogen receptors are localized in transcriptionally active chromatin, and (2) that controlled digestion of chromatin by micrococcal nuclease yields mononucleosomes enriched with estradiol receptors (Hemminki, 1977; Hemminki and Vauhkonen, 1977; Massol *et al.*, 1978a; Scott and Frankel, 1980). Androgen receptors have been located in the nucleosomal linker regions (Rennie, 1979). Fractionation of mechanically sheared chromatin by sucrose density gradient centrifugation has shown that estrogen (Franceschi and Kim, 1979) and progesterone receptors (Socher *et al.*, 1976) are associated with discrete subfractions. However, no preferential distribution of the glucocorticoid nuclear receptor was found in a rat pituitary cell line (Levy and Baxter, 1976).

Although the components of the chromatin with which the steroid receptor is associated have not been established, several studies have shown that the nuclear estradiol receptor from uteri can be solubilized in a low ionic medium containing DNase in the absence of Mg^{2+} (Harris 1971; Musliner and Chader, 1971). Destruction of DNA by DNase renders the nuclear fraction refractory to subsequent binding of estradiol receptor. RNase treatment of the nuclear pellet has no effect on these reactions (Musliner and Chader, 1971). Although these findings do not exclude the participation of other nuclear components in specific binding of estradiol receptors, they suggest that the integrity of DNA is an essential component for estrogen receptor binding to chromatin. The distribution of estradiol receptor and vitellogenin gene was studied in estradiol-stimulated chick liver chromatin fractions by limited DNase II digestion and $MgCl_2$ precipitation. Estrogen receptor was enriched in the same nucleoprotein fraction as were vitellogenin gene sequences, suggesting that the receptor binds to specific sites proximal to the genes activated by it (Alberga *et al.*, 1979). Evidence suggesting that steroid receptor molecules regulate transcription by interacting directly with specific chromosomal control loci, analogous to the DNA operator sequences in prokaryotes, has come from studies on the glucocorticoid regulation of mouse mammary tumor virus (MMTV) gene expression (Varmus *et al.*, 1979). Recently, Buetti and Diggelmann (1981) cloned circular MMTV(GR) DNA, which was obtained from rat hepatoma cells in bacteriophage σ, and showed that the cloned MMTV DNA inserts were capable of expressing viral functions when transferred to L cells in culture. The MMTV gene expression in the transfectant was significantly increased by addition of dexamethasone, indicating the possibility that the recognition site for the response to glucocorticoid may reside in the MMTV DNA itself. Glucocorticoid hormones have been shown to enhance transcription from MMTV proviral DNA in cultured mammary tumor cell lines (Ringold *et al.*, 1975; Scolnick *et al.*, 1976) and in infected heterologous cells (Vaidya *et al.*, 1976; Ringold *et al.*, 1977). Recently, Payvar *et al.* (1981) have shown that extensively purified activated glucocorticoid receptor protein binds selectively *in vitro* to a cloned fragment of MMTV DNA. The DNA fragment contained about half the sequences of the intact MMTV DNA. Using an assay in which radioactively labeled DNA restriction fragments bound to receptor were retained on nitrocellulose filters, it was demonstrated that DNA restriction fragments containing the MMTV DNA sequence bind to glucocorticoid receptor, while DNA restriction fragments from *E. coli* plasmids pBR 322 and RSF 2124 or from bacteriophages σ and T4 did not bind. They also showed that specific receptor-binding sites are located only within certain subregions of the MMTV DNA since two subfragments bound the receptor and one did not. In these preliminary studies, it was of interest that one of the high-affinity subfragments was well outside of the transcriptional start site for MMTV RNA. These studies provide the best evidence by far for the presence of specific hormone receptor effector-binding sites on the DNA.

A search for specific binding sites for progesterone receptor on the ovalbumin structural gene has been made with little success. Using the rapid equilibrium filter adsorption assay of Riggs *et al.* (1970), the entire natural ovalbumin gene, containing seven intervening sequences and various ovalbumin gene fragments coding for the 5' end of the nuclear precursor RNA, intron–exon junctions, and the 3' noncoding region of the gene, was examined for high-affinity binding of purified progesterone receptor A. No DNA sequence specificity was identified; however, the structural integrity of the DNA played a significant role. Receptor affinity was lowest for supercoiled DNA and the blunt end linear duplex gene fragments. Binding to DNA containing limited nicks was saturable but binding became nonsaturable as the number of nicks increased (Hughes *et al.*, 1981).

IV. RECOGNITION OF DNA STRUCTURE BY STEROID RECEPTORS

While several studies have clearly demonstrated that steroid receptors bind to DNA, there is scarce evidence demonstrating sequence specificity. Steroid receptors interact with low affinity to a variety of homologous and heterologous DNAs. The kinetics of binding is nonsaturable (Chamness *et al.*, 1974; André and Rochefort, 1975). Nonspecific binding to DNA is not uncommon among prokaryotic gene regulatory proteins. *Lac* repressor and CRP bind with significant affinity to many nonspecific DNA sequences (Lin and Riggs, 1972a,b; Krakow and Pastan, 1973; von Hippel *et al.*, 1974). Yamamoto and Alberts (1975) have proposed that a comparable situation exists in the case of steroid receptor interactions with the genome such that nonspecific interactions mask the detection of a smaller number of specific higher affinity genome-binding sites. They determined the equilibrium dissociation constants of DNA–estradiol receptor complexes using sedimentation partition chromatography. Rat uterine estrogen 5 S receptor bound with about equal affinity (K_{rd} = 300–400 μg/ml DNA) to rat uterine DNA, *E. coli* DNA, and the synthetic copolymer poly d(A-T). A molar dissociation constant of 5 × 10^{-4} *M* DNA sites was calculated from the data when poly d(A-T) was used, since in this copolymer all the regions are equivalent and thus the concentration of binding sites corresponds to the concentration of base pairs. Interestingly, there was no binding to double-stranded reovirus RNA. Even though the binding to DNA was apparently nonspecific, the receptors could distinguish the structural differences between DNA and RNA duplexes. The binding of glucocorticoid receptors to DNA showed no differences in affinity for DNA's from rat hepatoma cells, calf thymus, and *E. coli*. However, their affinity was distinctly lower for synthetic polynucleotides such as poly d(A-T) and poly d(G-C) (Simmons, 1977). It was suggested that the differences in affinity resulted from primary effects of base sequences or the influence of heterogeneous sequences on DNA secondary structures.

Intercalative drugs, which alter the helical structure of DNA, are often used to study the contribution of secondary structure to protein–nucleic acid interaction. Ethidium bromide and 9-hydroxyellipticine are cationic dyes which at low concentrations modify the three-dimensional structure of DNA by intercalating between base pairs (LePecq and Paoletti, 1967). Both ethidium bromide and 9-hydroxyelipticine inhibited the *in vitro* binding of uterine estradiol receptor to DNA–cellulose. The drugs did not modify the concentration of steroid-binding sites in the presence or absence of DNA. The degree of inhibition obtained was the same whether the drug was first added to the receptor preparation, to DNA, or at the moment of mixing. Addition of ethidium bromide to preformed estrogen receptor–DNA complex did not cause dissociation. DNA–cellulose treated with effective concentrations of ethidium bromide fully recovered its ability to bind estrogen receptor when the drug was removed with excess of soluble DNA. Ethidium bromide did not inhibit the binding of estrogen receptor to other polyanions such as phosphocellulose or poly(A)–cellulose. These results indicated that modification of the double-stranded helical structure of DNA diminished the steroid receptor binding to DNA (André *et al.*, 1976). The binding of estrogen receptor to double-stranded DNA–cellulose was competed out efficiently by soluble double-stranded DNA, but poorly by denatured DNA and very inefficiently by poly(A). Actinomycin D intercalates into the minor groove of DNA with preference for deoxyguanosine residues (Sobell and Jain, 1972). Kallos and Hollander (1978) have demonstrated that actinomycin D inhibits the binding of estrogen receptor to DNA–cellulose; 50% inhibition was observed with 12 μ*M* actinomycin D. The inhibition was due to the drug's interaction with DNA since pretreatment of the receptor with actinomycin D, followed by Sephadex G-25 filtration, had no effect. 4',6-Diamidino-2-phenylindole, a fluorescent DNA stain that binds to d(A-T)-rich regions of DNA, also inhibited DNA binding of estrogen receptor by 80% at a 10 μM concentration (Thanki, 1980). It is apparent from these observations that binding of estrogen receptors to DNA is not solely due to nonspecific electrostatic interactions but requires a particular double-helical structure of DNA. Another approach to study the effect of change in structure on the DNA–protein interactions compared the effect of bromodeoxyuridine (BUdR) replacement of thymidine into DNA. DNA-binding proteins such as *lac* repressor, CRP, histones, and chromosomal proteins exhibit greater affinity for BUdR-substituted as compared to unsubstituted DNA (Lin and Riggs, 1972b, 1976; Lin *et al.*, 1976; Bick and Devine, 1977; Schwartz 1977). Equilibrium competition and dissociation rate studies showed that estrogen receptor binds more tightly to BUdR-substituted DNA (Kallos *et al.*, 1978). Using an assay in which the rate of transfer to DNA–cellulose of radioactively labeled estrogen receptor bound to either unsubstituted or halogen-substituted DNA was measured, Kallos *et al.* (1979) found that the rates of transfer followed an order, unsubstituted DNA > chlorodeoxyuridine > bromodeoxyuridine > iododeoxyuridine-substituted DNA. Thus, the replacement of the 5-methyl group of thymine by a halogen atom stabilized the estrogen receptor–DNA interaction. The halogen atoms in this order are decreasingly electronegative and increasingly hydrophobic. Halogen substitution also enhances base stacking (Bugg and Sternglanz, 1974). The increased affinity of estrogen receptor to halogen-substituted DNA implies that secondary structure of DNA plays a significant role in the binding. So, at least when measured by holoreceptor-binding affinity, the evidence indicates that differences in secondary structure of DNA are recognized by steroid receptors.

V. NUCLEOTIDE BASE RECOGNITION OF STEROID RECEPTORS

The studies described so far suggest that steroid receptor binding to DNA involves a combination of electrostatic, hydrophobic, and secondary structure interactions. However, steroid receptors may bind with high affinity to sequence specific sites of DNA as well as through nonspecific interactions. In order to bind to specific sequences, steroid receptors by themselves or in association with accessory factors must recognize the structures of the component bases of DNA. One approach to examine this property is to use synthetic polydeoxyribonucleotides of known base composition. Poly d(A-T) and poly d(G-C) are commonly used synthetic polymers for studying *lac* repressor, cAMP receptors, gene 32 protein, and RNA and DNA polymerases (Nissley *et al.*, 1972; Krakow and Pastan, 1973; Lin and Riggs, 1976; Kowalczykowski *et al.*, 1981). Sluyser *et al.* (1974) used poly(dT), poly(dA):poly(dT), and poly(dG):poly(dC) to study the binding efficiencies of estradiol 5 S receptors of calf uterine cytosol. The receptors were labeled with radioactive estradiol and the formation of the DNA–receptor complex was monitored by measuring the radioactivity emerging in the void volumes of a Sepharose 2B column. The method precluded the use of other synthetic polymers such as poly(dG), poly(dA), and poly d(A-T) because these polymers were retarded on Sepharose 2B columns. In this limited study, poly(dT) and poly(dG):poly(dC) bound significantly more 5 S receptor than calf thymus DNA. Poly(dA):poly(dT) also bound approximately the same amount of 5 S receptor as poly(dT). Kallos and Hollander (1978) employed a competition assay in which [³H]estradiol receptor was allowed to form a complex with DNA–cellulose in the presence or absence of synthetic polydeoxynucleotide or soluble DNA. Only estradiol holoreceptor was active since neither free estradiol alone nor estradiol in presence of heat-denatured cytosol complexed with DNA–cellulose. Several natural DNAs could compete with DNA–cellulose for estradiol holoreceptor but tRNA was ineffective. The experiments confirmed earlier observations on the preference of estrogen receptors for DNA rather than RNA. Among the polynucleotides, poly d(A-T) and poly d(C-G), which have alternating bases and homopolymers, poly(dA), poly(dT), and the duplex poly(dA):poly(dT) were compared for their efficiency in the competition assay. Poly d(A-T) and poly d(G-C) were effective competitors; the former was better than the latter while the single-stranded homopolymers or the homopolymer duplex [poly(dA):poly(dT)] were very poor competitors (Fig. 1). The bindings of dihydrotestosterone–receptor to poly d(A-T) and poly d(G-C) were compared by the competition assay. Androgen receptor bound more to poly d(G-C) than to poly d(A-T) (Lin and Ohno, 1981). These data showed that estradiol receptor could discriminate between synthetic DNA duplexes differing in their base composition.

Another method of examining the base recognition properties of steroid receptors employs oligodeoxynucleotide–celluloses in which the oligomer is attached covalently to cellulose through its 5'-phosphate. Thrower *et al.* (1976) first reported that estradiol receptor complexes bind to oligo(dT)–cellulose and the reaction conditions were similar to DNA–cellulose binding. In our laboratory, oligodeoxynucleotide–celluloses were used as probes of the polynucleotide-binding domains of steroid receptor proteins. These affinity matrixes have certain characteristics that are advantageous for this use as they are relatively homogeneous in length, unlike polynucleotides or DNA which are heterogeneous with respect to their size. The oligonucleotides are attached through their 5'-terminus giving them a directional

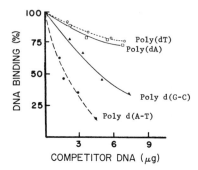

FIG. 1. Competition for rabbit uterine [³H]estradiol receptor (E₂R) by soluble synthetic polynucleotides [poly d(A-T), poly d(C-G), poly (dA), and poly(dT) from PL-Biochemicals]. DNA–cellulose (0.2 ml; 7 μg DNA) was incubated with 0.2 ml [³H]E₂R containing increasing amounts of soluble synthetic polynucleotide for 2 hours at 25°C and DNA-bound radioactivity was assayed as described in Kallos et al. (1978). Results are expressed as percentage of binding without competitor (100% value was about 3500–3600 cpm per 7 μg DNA; triplicate determinations). With permission from Nature (London) (Kallos et al., 1978).

polarity. The covalent attachment improves the stability of the ligand attachment compared to DNA adsorbed to cellulose (Alberts and Herrick, 1971) which can dissociate at low ionic strength. Initial studies with estradiol receptor showed that oligodeoxynucleotide binding was a characteristic property of the steroid receptor since neither the high-capacity, low-affinity steroid-binding protein, bovine serum albumin, nor the low-capacity high-affinity estradiol binder, α-fetoprotein, were capable of binding to oligo(dT)–cellulose (Fig. 2) (Thanki et al., 1978). Similar selectivity is observed with DNA–cellulose; estradiol receptor bound avidly but nonreceptor steroid-binding proteins did not adhere to DNA–cellulose (Wieland and Fox, 1981). Oligodeoxynucleotide binding was not restricted to estradiol receptors; other steroid receptors that also bind will be discussed later.

A. Salt Dependence for Binding of Steroid Receptors to Oligodeoxynucleotide Cellulose

The interaction of DNA-binding proteins with DNA lattices involves large electrostatic contributions and the binding properties are expected to be highly sensitive to changes in ionic strength. This is the case for a number of prokaryotic gene regulatory proteins. Association and dissociation rates of lac repressor binding to DNA were highly sensitive to changes in ionic strength (de Haseth et al., 1977; Revzin and von Hippel, 1977; Barkley, 1981). The formation of DNA–cAMP receptor complex was reduced by increased concentrations of potassium chloride (Takahashi et al., 1979).

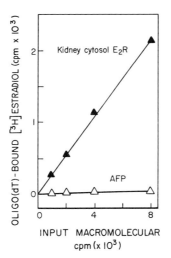

FIG. 2. Comparison of oligo(dT)–cellulose binding of mouse uterine estradiol receptor (E_2R) and of mouse α-fetoprotein–estradiol complex. The α-fetoprotein (AFP) was partially purified from mouse amniotic fluid and [³H]estradiol was exchanged for α-fetoprotein-bound estrone. The kidney E_2R used was a 0–30% ammonium sulfate fraction of [³H]estradiol-charged cytosol. Binding conditions were as described in Thanki et al. (1978).

Interactions of bacteriophage T4-coded gene 32 protein with polynucleotides revealed that binding is highly salt dependent and essentially stoichiometric at salt concentrations less than 0.2 M. Binding became much weaker and the binding isotherms were typically sigmoid in protein concentration at higher salt concentrations (Kowalczykowski et al., 1981). Generally, changes in ionic strength did not appreciably alter the cooperativity parameter or the site size. Instead, the intrinsic binding constant (a measure of affinity) appeared sensitive to changes in ionic strength (Takahashi et al., 1979; Barkley et al., 1981; Kowalczykowski et al., 1981). The salt dependence of the binding constant is generally interpreted on the basis of Manning's counterion condensation model (Manning, 1978). In the model, binding of protein to polynucleotides is presumed to be entropically driven by the counterion diffusion potential.

While the kinetics of association of steroid receptors to DNA or oligo-deoxynucleotide–celluloses have not been analyzed, a typical bell-shaped dependence on salt concentration for steroid receptor binding to oligo-deoxynucleotide–cellulose is generally observed. With estradiol receptor an optimal concentration (0.05–0.15 M KCl) of monovalent cations was required for binding to oligo(dT)–cellulose (Fig. 3A). Similarly, temperature-activated mouse liver dexamethasone receptor binding showed an optimal stimulation at 0.1 M KCl followed by a sharp decrease at higher salt con-

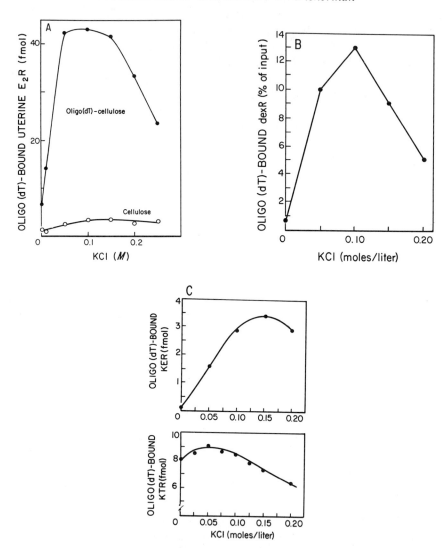

Fig. 3. (A) Effect of KCl on binding of uterine cytosol [³H]estradiol receptor. Reaction mixtures contained 0.2 ml of uterine cytosol (9460 cpm of macromolecular bound [³H]estradiol), 0.2 ml of TED buffer (10 mM Tris–HCl pH 7.5, 1.5 mM EDTA, 1 mM dithiothreitol), and the cellulose in a final volume of 0.6 ml. The conditions of the binding reaction were as described in Thanki et al. (1978). At the optimal salt concentrations 42% of input radioactivity was selectively bound. (B) Binding of dexamethasone receptor (dexR) to oligo(dT)–cellulose as a function of KCl concentration. Aliquots of mouse liver dexR were incubated for 30 minutes at 23°C and centrifuged through columns of Sephadex G-25. Samples containing 275 fmol of dexR were then tested for their ability to bind oligo(dT)–cellulose in the presence of 0–0.2 M KCl. Following incubation at 4°C for 1 hour, the celluloses were washed with TED buffer

centrations (Fig. 3B). In the absence of KCl there was virtually no binding of dexamethasone receptor and very little binding of estrogen receptor to oligo(dT)–cellulose. In the case of mouse kidney testosterone receptors, binding occurred even without the addition of KCl and there was not a distinctive optimal concentration (Fig. 3C). Binding was maximal at very low concentrations of KCl ($\leq 0.05\ M$) for dihydrotestosterone receptor from cultured genital skin fibroblasts (Rothwell *et al.*, 1981; C. J. Migeon, personal communication). These results indicated that salt dependency of steroid receptor–oligodeoxynucleotide interaction varies significantly among different holoreceptors. However, with all receptors there was decreased binding at KCl concentrations in excess of 0.2 M. The salt dependence of steroid receptor–oligodeoxynucleotide–cellulose interactions is qualitatively similar to the binding properties of *lac* repressor to nonoperator DNA and of nonspecific interactions of a variety of DNA-binding proteins. Detailed kinetic analyses of the association and dissociation rates of steroid–oligodeoxynucleotide complexes are required for a more critical interpretation.

The binding of estradiol receptor to oligodeoxynucleotide–cellulose was insensitive to the type of monovalent cation. The binding in the presence of chloride salts of Cs^+, K^+, Na^+ showed negligible differences, but the effects of monovalent anions were large and variable (Table II). Generally, the lyotropic nature of the anion and the binding affinity were correlated. Acetate, fluoride, chloride, and bromide ions, which promote ordered water structure, were favorable for the formation of the complex while SO_4^-, NO_3^-, ClO_4^-, and SCN^-, which disrupt the water structure, were unfavorable. A comparison of binding of estradiol receptor to oligo(dT)– and oligo(dG)–celluloses revealed that there were significant differences between the two interactions as binding decreases 10- to 30-fold in the order, $CH_3CO_2^- \geq Cl^- > F^- > Br^- > NO_3^- > SO_4^{2-} > SCN^- > I^- > ClO_4^-$ for oligo(dT), and $Cl^- > F^- > CH_3CO_2 \geq Br^- > NO_3^- > I^- > SO_4^{2-} > ClO_4^- > SCN^-$ for oligo(dG). The formation of estradiol receptor·oligo(dG)–cellulose complex was less sensitive to I^-, ClO_4^-, and SCN^- ions than was the complex with oligo(dT)–cellulose. The binding of *lac* repressor to DNA is

---

containing the same concentration of KCl as that used in the binding incubation. Results are expressed as percentage of input radioactivity (dexR) bound specifically to oligo(dT)–cellulose. (C) Binding of kidney estradiol receptor (KER) and kidney testosterone receptor (KTR) to oligodeoxynucleotides as a function of KCl concentration. Aliquots of KER and KTR were centrifuged through columns of Sephadex LH-20 to remove free steroid. KER samples containing 38 fmol of macromolecular [³H]estradiol were tested in the standard binding assay containing 200 nmol of oligonucleotide phosphorus (top frame). Similarly, KTR samples containing 41 fmol of [³H]testosterone were assayed for binding to 0.2 ml of oligo(dT)–cellulose containing 420 nmol of oligonucleotide phosphorus (bottom frame). In both cases, incubation was for 1 hour at 4°C and each cellulose pellet was washed with the indicated concentration of KCl in TED buffer. Figure 3A from Thanki *et al.* (1978); Fig. 3B and C from Gross *et al.* (1982).

TABLE II

EFFECT OF CHAOTROPIC SALTS ON BINDING OF MOUSE UTERINE ESTRADIOL RECEPTOR
TO OLIGO(dT)– AND OLIGO(dG)–CELLULOSES[a]

| Salt (0.15 M) | Oligodeoxynucleotide-bound estrogen receptor (fmol) | | Ratio (2)/(1) |
	oligo(dT)–cellulose (1)	oligo(dG)–cellulose (2)	
NaSCN	0.99	3.92	3.9
NaClO$_4$	0.54	4.38	8.1
NaNO$_3$	9.48	16.69	1.8
KI	0.64	8.05	12.6
KBr	14.14	21.26	1.5
KCl	26.41	34.07	1.3
K$_2$SO$_4$	5.57	7.98	1.4
KOOCCH$_3$	27.81	21.35	0.8
KF	22.87	25.45	1.1

[a] Oligodeoxynucleotide–cellulose containing 195 nmol of nucleotide phosphorus and 88 fmol of mouse uterine cytosol [³H]estradiol receptor were used in each assay. Radioactivity bound specifically to the oligodeoxynucleotide–cellulose was measured and the nonnucleotide binding was measured by substituting the corresponding quantity of blank cellulose. In each case oligonucleotide binding refers to the difference between the amount bound to derivatized cellulose and blank cellulose.

also sensitive to chaotropic anions. The association and dissociation rates are both affected by a factor of 40, the former decreasing and the latter increasing in the following order: $CH_3CO_2^- > F^- > SO_4^{2-} > Cl^- > Br^- > NO_3^- > SCN^- \geq I^-$ (Barkley et al., 1981). It is believed that the observed effect of anions is caused by conformational changes in the DNA-binding domain of lac repressor. The differences observed between formation of complexes of estradiol receptor with the two oligodeoxynucleotide–celluloses support the view that the subsites in the DNA-binding domain with different deoxynucleotide affinities vary in their response to perturbations in the ionic environment.

B. REQUIREMENT OF ACTIVATION FOR STEROID RECEPTORS TO BIND OLIGODEOXYNUCLEOTIDE CELLULOSES

As a general mechanism for steroid hormone action, cytosol steroid receptors upon binding to the steroid ligand are believed to undergo a temperature-mediated conformational change that facilitates their migration into the nucleus where the receptors bind to the chromatin and exert specific biological action. In some cases such as the glucocorticoid receptor, an obligatory requirement for activation to bind *in vitro* to DNA can be demonstrated. With other steroid receptors, activation is not obligatory but an enhancement of net binding may be observed (Higgins *et al.*, 1973; Park and Witliff, 1977). In our studies with estradiol receptor, no requirement for prior activation to bind oligodeoxynucleotide celluloses was observed. At either high or low ionic strength, a decrease in the extent of binding to oligo(dT)–cellulose occurred when the temperature was increased above 15°C either prior to binding or during the binding reaction (Thanki *et al.*, 1978; Kumar *et al.*, 1980a). Similar observations were made by Thrower *et al.* (1976) for chromatography of rat uterine estradiol receptor using oligo(dT)–cellulose where greater uptake was obtained at 4° than at 18°C. Metzger *et al.* (1977) also found loss of DNA-binding ability on short-term incubation at 30°C of partially purified rat uterine receptors. Similarly, testosterone receptors from mouse kidney showed no significant enhancement of binding to oligodeoxynucleotides following exposure to increased salt or temperature (Gross *et al.*, 1982). Mouse liver glucocorticoid receptors, however, required prior activation by exposure to elevated temperature or to salt concentration. Mouse liver dexamethasone receptors, unexposed to 0.5 M KCl for 30 minutes, bound slightly to oligodeoxynucleotide–cellulose and this did not increase with time if the binding temperature was held at 4°C. A shift to 22°C for 30 minutes resulted in doubling of binding to oligo(dT)–cellulose. Maximal activation also occurred by exposure to 0.4–0.5 M KCl for 30 minutes at 4°C. The increased binding of dexamethasone receptor to oligo(dT)–cellulose by either elevation in temperature or ionic strength is consistent with an activation process described for binding of the rat liver glucocorticoid receptor to nuclei and DNA. Figure 4 illustrates the effect of activation of glucocorticoid, estrogen, and androgen receptors of liver, uterine, and kidney cytosols, respectively, from adrenalectomized mice (Gross *et al.*, 1982). Only in the case of the mouse liver glucocorticoid receptor was there a clear requirement for activation in order to bind to oligo(dT)–cellulose. However, C. J. Migeon (personal communication) claims that androgen receptor from skin fibroblasts shows a slight increase in the percentage of the receptor bound to oligo(dT)–cellulose following a 30-minute incubation at 24°C, although there was loss of intact receptor molecules.

C. Oligodeoxynucleotide Binding Specificities of Dexamethasone, Testosterone, and Estradiol Receptors

A study employing homologous oligodeoxynucleotides of equal average chain length revealed that steroid receptors bound different oligodeoxy-

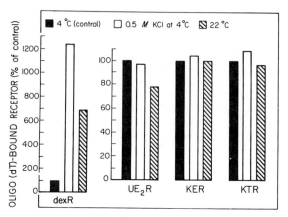

FIG. 4. Activation requirements for binding of mouse liver dexamethasone receptor (dexR), uterine estradiol receptor (E_2R), kidney E_2R, and testosterone receptor to oligo(dT)–cellulose. Each cytosol receptor preparation was incubated for 30 minutes at 4°C in TED buffer alone (dark bar) or in TED plus 0.5 M KCl (open bar) or at 22°C in TED (hatched bar). Free steroid was removed by sedimentation through charcoal-coated Sephadex G-25, and the quantity of macromolecular bound steroid was determined by counting an aliquot of the void volume. Each receptor preparation was tested for binding to oligo(dT)–cellulose containing 420 nmol of nucleotide phosphorus. KCl was added for the binding reaction: dexR, 0.1 M; uterine E_2R, 0.1 M; kidney E_2R, 0.15 M; and kidney testosterone receptor, 0.05 M. The duration of the binding reaction was 10 minutes for dexR, 20 minutes for uterine E_2R, and 60 minutes for kidney E_2R and testosterone receptor. The holoreceptor inputs (in fmol) were dexR, 162; uterine E_2R, 105; kidney E_2R, 38; and kidney testosterone receptor, 39. Control receptor bound to oligo(dT)–cellulose (in fmol) was dexR, 1.6; uterine E_2R, 50.2; kidney E_2R, 9.1; and kidney testosterone receptor, 6.5. From Gross *et al.* (1982).

nucleotide–celluloses to varying extents. Our initial study with mouse uterine cytosol estradiol receptor indicated that binding to oligodeoxynucleotide–celluloses followed an order of preference such that oligo(dG) > oligo(dT) ≥ oligo(dC) ≫ oligo(dA) > oligo(dI) (Table III). The difference between oligo(dG) and oligo(dI) was indeed surprising, since except for an amino group at position 2 in guanine they are identical, yet the receptor molecules could discriminate between them (Kumar *et al.*, 1980a). Similar binding preferences have been observed with calf uterine cytosol estradiol receptor complexes (K. T. Henrikson, T. A. Beach, S. A. Kumar, and H. W. Dickerman, unpublished data). Testosterone and dexamethasone receptors also showed the same relative order of binding but there were quantitative variations. Binding of activated liver dexamethasone receptor to oligo(dT)–cellulose was markedly greater than to oligo(dC)–cellulose while the testosterone receptors showed no clear preference between the oligodeoxypyrimidine nucleotide celluloses. Estradiol receptor from mouse kidney and uterus also did not show a marked preference between oligo(dT) and

TABLE III
RELATIVE E_2R BINDING EFFICIENCY OF DIFFERENT
OLIGODEOXYNUCLEOTIDE–CELLULOSES[a]

Cellulose	Oligodeoxynucleotide binding (fmol)	Percentage bound of input E_2R
Oligo(dG)	20.1	37
Oligo(dT)	15.1	28
Oligo(dC)	10.7	20
Oligo(dA)	2.3	4
Oligo(dI)	0.67	1

[a] From Kumar *et al.* (1980a).

oligo(dC). The relative binding to oligo(dA)–cellulose was better for kidney testosterone receptors than observed with liver dexamethasone and the estradiol receptors (Fig. 5) (Gross *et al.*, 1982). Androgen receptor from skin fibroblasts showed a greater preference for oligo(dT) and significantly less for oligo(dC), oligo(dG), oligo(dA), and oligo(dI). However, this receptor preparation showed very negligible binding to DNA–cellulose (Rothwell *et al.*, 1981; C. J. Migeon, personal communication). Several years ago, King (1972) reported that uterine estradiol receptor binds to polyribonucleotides with an order of preference such that poly(rG) > poly(rC) > poly(rA) > poly(rI). Recently, Feldman and co-workers (1981) studied the effect of synthetic polyribonucleotides on the rate of release of rabbit uterine estrogen receptor from DNA–cellulose. They also examined the inhibition of estrogen receptor binding to DNA–cellulose by synthetic homopolymers of ribonucleotides. By both procedures they observed a definite order of specificity: poly G > poly U ≫ poly A ≥ poly C. Liao *et al.* (1980) investigated the differences in the effectiveness of polyribonucleotides in releasing steroid receptor complexes from DNA in an effort to determine the relative receptor binding affinities for these polymers. It is apparent from their data (Table IV) that polyriboguanylate and polyribouridylate were effective while polyribocytidylate was ineffective. They also tested heteropolyribonucleotides for their effectiveness in promoting the release of androgen receptor complex from DNA–cellulose. They found that poly(U,G), regardless of size, was much more effective than poly(G), poly(U), or a mixture of equivalent amounts of poly(G) and poly(U). When poly(U,G) of different U/G ratios were used, the ability of the polymer to release DNA–cellulose-bound androgen receptor decreased as the ratio increased. These investigators suggest that receptors may bind to specific sequences of RNA and thus play a role in posttranscriptional control. However, it is interesting to note that by different experimental approaches (Kumar *et al.*, 1980a; Liao *et al.*, 1980; Dickerman and Kumar, 1981; Feldman *et al.*, 1981), it was clearly

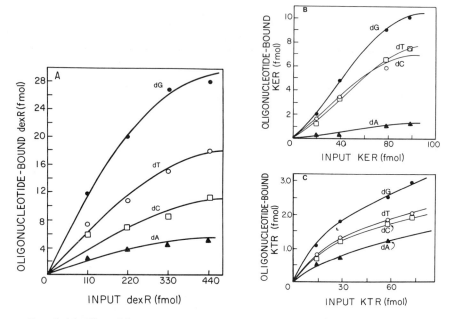

F<small>IG</small>. 5. (A) Effect of the concentration of activated dexamethasone receptor on binding to oligodeoxynucleotide–celluloses. Activation of dexamethasone receptor (dexR) was accomplished by incubation at 22°C for 1 hour. Free steroid was removed by treatment with dextran-coated charcoal. Aliquots containing 110–140 fmol dexR were tested for binding to oligo(dG) (●), oligo(dT) (○), oligo(dC) (□), and oligo(dA) (▲) (containing 200 nmol of oligonucleotide phosphorus) in the standard assay. Incubations were for 20 minutes at 4°C. (B) Binding of kidney estradiol receptor (KER) and kidney testosterone receptor (KTR) to oligodeoxynucleotides as a function of input receptor concentration. Kidney estradiol receptor and KTR were each prepared by the standard procedure from the same mouse kidney cytosol and were treated with dextran-coated Sephadex G-25. Various quantities of each eluate were tested by the standard binding technique containing oligo(dG) (●), oligo(dT) (○), oligo(dC) (□), and oligo(dA) (▲), containing 200 nmol of oligonucleotide phosphorus. Both assays were identical with the exception that KER binding was assayed at 0.15 M KCl (top frame), while KTR binding was assayed at 0.05 M KCl (bottom frame). From Gross et al. (1982).

established that steroid receptors distinguished different nucleotide base structures. In these experiments, guanine appears to be the base with highest affinity, adenine to be the base with lowest affinity, and the pyrimidines have intermediate affinities.

The nucleotide base preferences of steroid receptors are also reflected in the stabilities of the complexes. For example, estradiol receptor complexes bound to oligo(dG)–cellulose were more stable to salt than those bound to other oligodeoxynucleotide–celluloses. The association of estradiol receptor with oligodeoxynucleotide ligands was maximal between 0.1 and 0.2 M

TABLE IV

Polymer (150 μM)	Percentage elution			
	Androgen receptor	Estrogen receptor	Glucocorticoid receptor	Progesterone receptor
Poly(rG)	76	98	90	54
Poly(rU)	57	54	41	17
Poly(rC)	4	5	8	6
Poly(rA)	2	2	0	2

[a] From Liao *et al.* (1980).

KCl, while elution of bound estradiol receptor required higher salt concentrations. Estradiol receptor·oligo(dG)–cellulose complexes, suspended
in various KCl concentrations at 4°C for 60 minutes and subsequently
assayed for residual radioactivity associated with the matrices, showed greater
retention than those bound to oligo(dT)– and oligo(dC)–cellulose (Fig. 6A).
Similarly, preformed estradiol receptor·oligo(dG)–cellulose complexes were
relatively more stable to elution by Cibacron Blue, while estradiol receptor
complexes with oligo(dC)–celluloses were of intermediate stability and
oligo(dT)–cellulose receptor complexes were very sensitive (Fig. 6B). Inhibition of estradiol receptor association to oligodeoxynucleotide celluloses
by Cibacron Blue also showed that higher concentrations of the dye were
necessary for 50% inhibition of complex formation with oligo(dG)–cellulose
followed by oligo(dC)– and oligo(dT)–celluloses. The effect of pyridoxal
phosphate concentration on the inhibition of estradiol receptor binding to
oligodeoxynucleotide celluloses showed that inhibition was greatest for
oligo(dC)–, least for oligo(dG)–, and intermediate for oligo(dT)–cellulose
complex formation (Fig. 7A). Fifty percent inhibition of binding to oligo(dG)–,
oligo(dT)–, and oligo(dC)–celluloses occurred at 3, 1.5, and 0.8 mM
pyridoxal phosphate, respectively (Henrikson *et al.*, 1981). Diethyl pyro-
carbonate inhibition also followed a similar pattern (Gross *et al.*, 1981) (Fig.
7B). Preliminary studies in our laboratory have shown that association constants
for estradiol receptor·oligonucleotide–cellulose complexes can be determined
using the technique described by de Haseth *et al.* (1977). The method
involves loading a small column (1 ml) of oligodeoxynucleotide–cellulose
with cytosol estradiol receptor and subsequently eluting the protein with
buffer at a constant salt concentration (0.15 M NaCl). From the shape of
the elution profile the binding constant for the interaction is calculated.
K_{rd}, the observed association constant is determined as follows: since the
percentage of the total protein eluted in fraction i (P_{fi}) is a linear function

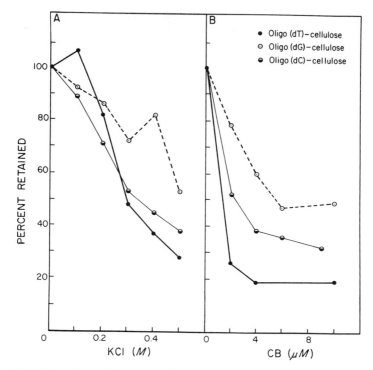

FIG. 6. Stability of estradiol receptor (E_2R)–oligodeoxynucleotide–cellulose complexes in the presence of increasing concentrations of (A) KCl or (B) Cibracon Blue F3GA (CB). E_2R–oligodeoxynucleotide–cellulose complexes were formed under standard binding conditions. Then, either KCl or CB was added at the indicated concentration in 0.01 M Tris–HCl buffer, pH 7.6, containing 1 mM EDTA. Incubation was at 4°C for 90 minutes. Cellulose-bound E_2R was measured as described in Kumar et al. (1980a); 100% represents bound E_2R remaining in control experiments in which E_2R–oligodeoxynucleotide–cellulose complex was incubated at 4°C for 90 minutes with Tris–HCl/EDTA buffer alone. From Kumar et al. (1980a).

of the total protein remaining on the column after elution of fraction i (P_{ci}), the two parameters can be related in a manner analogous to the linear isotherms with a proportionality constant k, which is determined from the slope of a semilogarithmic plot of P_{ci} versus fraction number, and K_{rd} is derived from the relation $K_{rd}(\text{obsd}) = V_f/kD_t$ where V_f is the volume of the fraction and D_t is the total molar amount of nucleotides on the column. The $K_{rd}(\text{obsd})$ values at 0.15 M NaCl for mouse uterine estradiol receptor·oligodeoxynucleotides are given in Table V. These values are in agreement with the association constant determined by Yamamoto and Alberts (1975) for estradiol receptor interactions with DNA. The affinity for oligo(dG) is

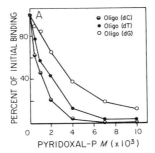

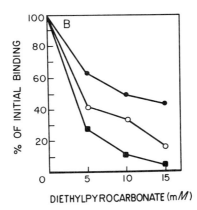

FIG. 7. (A) Effect of pyridoxal phosphate concentration on mouse uterine estradiol receptor (E_2R) binding to oligodeoxynucleotide–celluloses. The designated concentrations of pyridoxal phosphate were incubated with mouse uterine cytosol E_2R for 7 minutes at 4°C. Samples of E_2R (100 fmol) were then assayed for binding to oligo(dG)– (○), oligo(dT)– (●), and oligo(dC)–cellulose (◓). The final concentration of pyridoxal phosphate in the preincubation. Initial bindings (100%) were oligo(dG)–, 40 fmol; oligo(dC)–, 26 fmol; and oligo(dT)–cellulose, 32 fmol. (B) Modification of calf uterine estradiol receptor by various concentrations of diethylpyrocarbonate (DEP). Aliquots of E_2R were incubated in the presence or absence of DEP (at indicated concentrations) for 10 minutes at 4°C. The reaction was then terminated by the addition of a 5.7-fold excess of histidine. Aliquots containing 124 fmol E_2R were tested immediately for the ability to bind oligodeoxynucleotide– and unmodified celluloses in the standard assay. Results are expressed as percentage of E_2R bound in the absence of DEP and have been corrected by subtracting E_2R bound to unmodified cellulose. Unmodified E_2R binding was 10.2 fmol to oligo(dG)– (●), 9.1 fmol to oligo(dT)– (○), and 5.9 fmol to oligo(dC)–cellulose (■). Figure 7A from Henrikson *et al.* (1981); Fig. 7B from Gross *et al.* (1981).

TABLE V

APPARENT ASSOCIATION CONSTANTS FOR MOUSE UTERINE ESTRADIOL RECEPTOR
OLIGODEOXYNUCLEOTIDE COMPLEXES

Oligodeoxynucleotide	Apparent K_{rd} at 0.15 M NaCl
oligo(dG)	$3.7 \times 10^4\ M^{-1}$
oligo(dT)	$1.75 \times 10^4\ M^{-1}$
oligo(dC)	$1.49 \times 10^4\ M^{-1}$

greater than the affinities for oligo(dT) and oligo(dC). The association constants are very low for specific binding, but large differences in the magnitude of affinity between binding to oligodeoxynucleotides and polynucleotides have been reported for backteriophage T4-induced gene 32 protein. These differences have been attributed to alteration in the binding mode of the protein (Newport *et al.*, 1981; von Hippel *et al.*, 1981). Such a change in conformation of the protein might be operative in the steroid receptor DNA interactions.

Although the experiments indicated increased stability of binding of estradiol receptors to oligo(dG) in relation to other ligands, there were no clear qualitative differences among the receptor oligodeoxynucleotide interactions. Perturbation of structure by elevated temperature was tested for differences in the oligodeoxynucleotide-binding properties of estradiol receptors. Incubation at 37°C resulted in rapid loss of binding of uterine estradiol receptor to oligo(dC)–cellulose and, to a slightly lesser extent, oligo(dT)–cellulose. However, binding to oligo(dG)–cellulose remained unchanged over the same period of incubation (Fig. 8). In this experiment, the amount of estradiol receptor used in the binding reactions was normalized for the loss of macromolecular bound steroid. The stability of oligo(dG)–cellulose binding was also observed in a study of differential binding following partial purification of uterine estradiol receptor. Perturbations of the environment, such as exposure to elevated temperature or the adsorption–elution from affinity matrix, resulted in qualitative differences in the oligodeoxynucleotide-binding activities. These data, together with differences in stability to ionic strength, inhibitors, and in affinity constants, suggest that the polynucleotide-binding domain of estradiol receptor is composed of two classes of subsites: stable sites, involved in deoxyguanylate recognition (G sites), and labile sites, which interact with other nucleotides (N sites). Presence of high-affinity G-binding sites are indicated in competition experiments with soluble oligodeoxynucleotides. For example, preincubation of estradiol receptor with oligo(dT) of homogeneous chain length followed by an assay for the receptor binding to oligo(dT)–cellulose resulted in an inhibition of binding to the immobilized oligonucleotide. Competition was efficient if the soluble oligomer contained

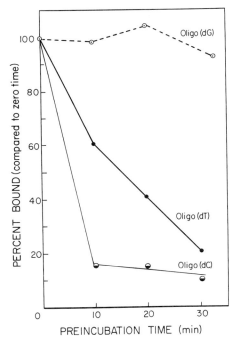

FIG. 8. Effect of preincubation of mouse uterine cytosol estradiol receptor (E_2R) at 37°C on binding to oligodeoxynucleotide–celluloses. E_2R was incubated for times indicated at 37°C. At the end of the incubation, free estradiol was removed by treatment with charcoal/dextran and binding assays with oligo(dG)–, oligo(dC)–, and oligo(dT)–cellulose were carried out, using aliquots representing equivalent quantities of E_2R. Incubations were at 4°C for 90 minutes. In each case the amount of bound E_2R that had not been preincubated (0-minute controls) represents 100%. From Kumar *et al.* (1980a).

eight or more nucleotides. Inhibition by oligo(dT) was more pronounced with the homologous oligo(dT)–cellulose than with the heterologous oligo(dG)–cellulose (Fig. 9). These findings confirm that the polynucleotide-binding domain consists of subsites with different specificities and stabilities and suggest that a minimum chain length is required for stable interaction to occur (Dickerman and Kumar, 1981).

VI. POTENTIAL MODULATORS OF STEROID
HOLORECEPTOR:DNA INTERACTION

Although studies of specific chromosomal proteins as components of putative acceptor sites for steroid receptors were reviewed recently (Thrall *et al.*,

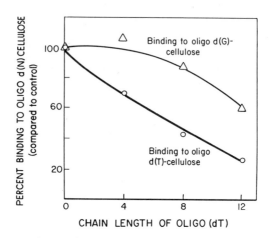

FIG. 9. Competition for estradiol receptor (E_2R) binding between soluble and immobilized oligodeoxynucleotides. E_2R (94 fmol) was incubated with 200 nmol of oligo(dT) of indicated chain length in 10 mM Tris–HCl, pH 7.6, containing 1.5 mM EDTA, 0.15 M KCl, and 1 mM DTT at 4°C for 30 minutes on a multipurpose rotator. Then, oligo(dT)– or oligo(dG)–cellulose (representing 20 nmol oligodeoxynucleotide) was added and incubation continued for another 30 minutes. Buffer and other components were also added to obtain the same final concentrations as described above in total volume of 0.6 ml. The reaction mixture was filtered through GF/C filter discs, washed three times with 10 ml each of 10 mM Tris–HCl, pH 7.6, containing 1.5 mM EDTA and 1 mM DTT. Estradiol receptor bound to the oligodeoxynucleotide cellulose matrix was determined by measuring the radioactivity retained on the filters. From Dickerman and Kumar (1981).

1978; Spelsberg, 1981), little attention has been paid to factors within target cell cytoplasm which alter DNA binding of holoreceptors. Immobilized templates like DNA–cellulose or oligodeoxynucleotide–celluloses provide a means to study the effect of different variables, including endogenous cytosol proteins, on these binding reactions. Thrower *et al.* (1976) indicated that such factors exist. When using rat uterine cytosol estrogen receptors, depleted by gel filtration, they could stimulate binding to oligo(dT)–cellulose by an unfractionated uterine cytosol. Conversely, Goidl *et al.* (1977) removed a low-molecular-weight inhibitor of rat liver glucocorticoid receptor activation assessed by binding to DNA–cellulose.

Recently, Thampan and Clark (1981) fractionated rat uterine cytosol containing labeled estrogen receptor into a DEAE-bound (II) and -unbound (I) fraction. Fraction II, eluted with 0.3 M KCl, had an S value of 3.85, did not bind to either immobilized or soluble DNA, and showed a small, transitory binding to homologous nuclei. Addition of fraction I to fraction II led to a shift in sedimentation profile detected by sucrose density centrifugation with two peaks of bound estrogen at 4.8 and 3.8 S. Following a lag phase, nuclear binding of fraction II was stimulated by addition of fraction I, as was binding to DNA–cellulose and soluble DNA. All the binding reactions were done at 30°C, which may represent a contrast to unpublished results of our laboratory. Fractionation of mouse uterine cytosol holoreceptor on DEAE–cellulose led to recovery of two column-bound peaks of [³H]estradiol-labeled protein, neither of which required accessory factors for binding to oligo(dT)–cellulose. In our case, the binding reactions were performed at 4°C. So temperature and species may be responsible for the differences in the requirement for the stimulatory factor found in the DEAE–cellulose-unbound fraction of rat uterine cytosol. Factor I has been further identified as a 3 S protein, probably basic in isoelectric point.

Another cytosol accessory factor was detected during efforts to purify the mouse kidney estrogen receptor using oligo(dT)–cellulose chromatography (Thanki *et al.*, 1979). Following adsorption of the holoreceptor at 0.15 *M* KCl and desorption at 0.5 *M* KCl, there was an 80-fold increase in receptor specific activity (macromolecular bound [³H]estradiol). Yet, there was the same or less efficiency of holoreceptor binding to oligo(dT)–cellulose despite the use of this putative affinity matrix in the purification. It appeared that an accessory factor(s) bound to the ligand but resisted desorption at the higher salt concentration. Using stimulation of oligodeoxynucleotide binding of the partially purified estrogen receptor as an assay, a cytosol factor was identified which was heat stable, nondialyzable, sensitive to Pronase, proteinase K, pepsin, and *Staphylococcus aureus* protease V. It was resistant to inactivation by trypsin or chymotrypsin. Similar activity was identified in uterine and lung cytosols but not in those of brain or skeletal muscle or in serum. The heat-stable factor was effective with oligo(dC)–, oligo(dA)–, or DNA–celluloses as the binding matrices and stimulated binding if incubated with the oligodeoxynucleotide ligands prior to addition of the receptor. There was no evidence that the factor interacted directly with the holoreceptor so the conclusion was drawn that the factor was a small cytosol polypeptide that promoted binding of holoreceptors by modulation of the ligand structure in a manner not specific to receptor:DNA interaction.

An interesting by-product of the studies on the mouse kidney cytosol factor was obtained when specificity of the stimulation was examined. Basic proteins including calf thymus histones and, to a lesser extent, lysozyme, actively increased the rebinding of partially purified holoreceptor to oligo(dT)–cellulose. Fox *et al.* (1979) also demonstrated a significant effect of lysozyme on the DNA–cellulose elution patterns of estrogen and androgen receptors indicative of an interaction between these proteins. Among the histones, slightly lysine rich H2A and H2B, and arginine rich H3 were most effective, while the very lysine rich H1 was much less so. A comparison of the activities of H2A and H1 is depicted in Fig. 10. Polylysine, M_r 140,000,

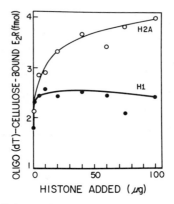

FIG. 10. The effect of calf thymus histones H1 (●——●) and H2A (○——○) on binding of estradiol receptor (E_2R) to oligo(dT)–cellulose. The commercially obtained histones were analyzed by acid–urea gel electrophoresis and found to be essentially uncontaminated. From Thanki *et al*. (1979).

was inhibitory and γ-globulin was without effect. It seemed that the active histones stabilized the oligodeoxynucleotide ligand in a preferred binding structure but an additional factor might be a direct interaction with the receptor complex as well as with the oligodeoxynucleotide. This was tested by addition of the individual histones to a 200-fold-purified kidney estrogen receptor followed by sucrose density centrifugation in a 5–20% gradient containing 0.15 *M* KCl at 4° and 12°C. In the absence of added histones, there was a significant dissociation of steroid from the receptor, more so at the higher temperature. Preincubation with the histones led to increases in the area of the 4 S holoreceptor peak, with less steroid dissociation. The stabilization was greatest with H2A and H2B, less so with H1 and H3, and not at all with lysozyme or γ-globulin.

There is an asymmetry in the distribution of basic charges within histones so it was possible to determine if the effects on holoreceptor binding and/ or stability were correlated with those parts of the histone molecules with a higher or lower basic charge density. H2B has an uneven distribution of lysine/arginine residues and is cleaved by cyanogen bromide into an N-terminal half molecule containing residues 1–58 with 32% of the residues basic and a C-terminal half molecule with 20% of its residues basic (Iwai *et al.*, 1970). Following cleavage and recovery of the H2B half molecules, they were tested for their ability to stimulate the oligo(dT)–cellulose binding of purified kidney estrogen holoreceptor and the results are shown in Fig. 11. Both the half molecules were active but the N-terminal fragment was more effective while combinations of the N- and C-terminal half molecules produced additive effects.

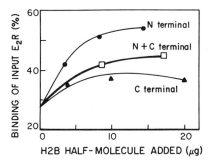

Fig. 11. The effect of N- and C-terminal half molecules of H2B on oligo(dT)–cellulose binding of estradiol receptor (E₂R). The fragments were generated and recovered as described by Adler *et al.* (1974). The input of [³H]E₂R was 6 fmol. The symbols represent the N-terminal half molecule (●), the C-terminal half molecule (▲), and equal mixtures of the fragments (□). From Thanki *et al.* (1979).

The half molecules were tested for their ability to stabilize purified holoreceptors during sucrose gradient sedimentation and the results are shown in Fig. 12. Both at 4° and 12°C, the parent H2B molecule stabilized the holoreceptor 4 S peak, an effect that was clearly reproduced with the N-terminal half molecule but not with the C-terminal one. Addition of the latter led to marked aggregation of the holoreceptor. These results indicated that the mouse kidney estrogen holoreceptor contained a reactive site, presumably for cationic amino acid-rich polypeptides, which affects steroid retention. However, while the N-terminal half molecule of H2B was more active, there probably are necessary structural determinants other than basic charge densities, as neither lysine-rich H1 nor polylysine were especially effective.

The evidence that estrogen receptors interact selectively with histones was strengthened by the work of Kallos *et al.* (1981). In binding to immobilized histones, rabbit uterine cytosol receptors had the highest affinity for H2B and H2A, moderate affinity for H4 and H3, with little avidity for H1. Following interaction with either H2A or H2B, the isoelectric focusing pattern of holoreceptor shifted to higher pH values, suggesting complex formation between the proteins. The separateness of the histone-binding site from that of DNA was detected following limited proteolysis; DNA binding of the holoreceptor was markedly reduced while steroid and histone binding were unaffected. The receptor–histone–DNA–cellulose complex was more stable than that formed between the receptor and naked DNA–cellulose. These results, coupled with the study of Thanki *et al.* (1979), indicate that a site on estrogen receptors exists which selectively interacts

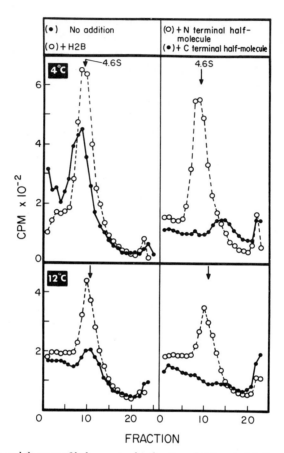

FIG. 12. The stabilization of holoreceptor by the N- and C-terminal half molecules of H2B during sedimentation. [³H]Estradiol receptor was enriched and concentrated using (NH₄)₂SO₄ as described in Thanki et al. (1979). The 5–20% linear sucrose gradients were equilibrated at the temperature used in the subsequent centrifugation for 4 hours. The amount of [³H]E₂R applied to the gradients was 8000 cpm, 4°C, and 5100 cpm, 12°C. Fifty μg of the histones or H2B half molecules were incubated with E₂R for 30 minutes at 0°C prior to transfer to the gradients. The 4.6 S position was identified by the peak of [¹⁴C]-labeled bovine serum albumin. From Thanki et al. (1979).

with nucleosomal histones or, more generally, certain cationic proteins. What is the physiological importance of these *in vitro* binding studies? First, they may provide a molecular basis for the observed chromatin localization of estrogen receptors. In two separate studies (Massol *et al.*, 1978b; Senior and Frankel, 1978), limited digestion of nuclei containing [³H]estradiol-labeled receptor followed by density sedimentation indicated that the radioactivity was largely associated with the mononucleosomal peak which contains H2A and H2B, H3, and H4, but is deficient in H1. The observed *in vitro* affinity of holoreceptors with H2A and H2B may be a factor in the nuclear positioning and stability of these molecules.

Beyond the structure of the chromatin supramolecular complex, the histone interaction provides an insight into the modulation of the DNA-binding sites of steroid holoreceptors by neighboring chromosomal proteins. As described in an earlier section, the DNA-binding domain of the mouse uterine estrogen holoreceptor is composed of at least two subsites; a stable group which recognizes oligo(dG) and labile sites which interact with oligo(dT), oligo(dC), and oligo(dA). This distinction was also apparent following partial purification of the receptor (Table VI). When cytosol holoreceptors are bound at 0.15 M KCl to either oligo(dT)– or oligo(dG)–cellulose and then eluted with 0.5 M KCl, the holoreceptors no longer bind to oligo(dT)–, oligo(dC)–, or oligo(dA)–celluloses. Although diminished, binding to oligo(dG)–cellulose was retained. However, addition of H2B to the partially purified receptor fully restored the binding activities of the labile sites and increased the oligo(dG) binding. It did not matter whether the initial nucleotide-binding matrix contained oligo(dG) or oligo(dT). This indicates that H2B modulated the recognition capabilities of the DNA-binding domain. Whether H2A and H2B retain this function *in vivo* and/or are successfully mimicking the function of other chromosomal proteins remains to be seen. But it does indicate that the DNA-binding domain is malleable and can be altered by interaction with other proteins.

TABLE VI

Rebinding of E_2R Eluted from Oligo(dT)– and Oligo(dG)–Cellulose Complexes to Oligodeoxynucleotide–Celluloses[a]

| | Percentage bound of input E_2R | | | |
| | E_2R off oligo(dT)–cellulose | | E_2R off oligo(dG)–cellulose | |
Cellulose	− H2B	+ H2B	− H2B	+ H2B
Oligo(dG)	18	33	21	32
Oligo(dA)	0	6	0	6
Oligo(dC)	0	12	0	14
Oligo(dT)	0	22	1	23

[a] Estradiol receptor oligo(dG)– or oligo(dT)–cellulose complexes were formed under standard binding assay conditions. Elution of bound E_2R was achieved by using 0.5 M KCl. Samples (0.2 ml) of the eluates were used in the rebinding assay with fresh oligodeoxynucleotide–celluloses in a total volume of 0.6 ml so that the final concentration of KCl was 0.15 M. H2B was added to the rebinding assay at 50 μg where indicated. From Kumar *et al.* (1980a).

VII. AN ALLOSTERIC MODEL OF STEROID
RECEPTOR:DNA INTERACTION

What insights are gained into the nuclear action of steroid receptors from the preceding studies on receptor binding to DNA, polynucleotides, and oligonucleotides? First, a note of caution that the overwhelming majority of these experiments was done with impure receptors, nonspecific nucleotide ligands, and ignorance about nonreceptor molecules which may potentially affect receptor binding and activity. However, a pattern emerges about those aspects of receptor molecules involved in binding to chromosomal DNA. Although far less is known about the structure of steroid receptors, they share some common features with the well-delineated bacterial gene regulatory proteins. These include (1) separateness of the DNA and small ligand-binding domains, (2) modulation of DNA binding by association with the small ligand molecules, (3) sensitivity to inhibitors that modify cationic amino acid residues, and (4) sensitivity to inhibitors that restrict the secondary structure at the template-binding site.

While these factors provide suggestions about the topographical organization of the receptor molecules, they do not help much in developing concepts about the selective interaction of the receptor and DNA. The problem has been stated lucidly by Record and his colleagues (1981): "to an approaching ligand, the phosphate lattice appears relatively homogeneous, affording sites for nonspecific interactions. The lattice(s) of base pairs, which exhibit both sequence heterogeneity and consequently local conformation heterogeneity, may bind ligands through intercalation or by specific interactions with accessible functional groups on the bases." Underlying the use of sequence heterogeneity is the ability of the ligands to discriminate among the deoxynucleotide bases within the helix. This property was demonstrated for different steroid holoreceptors using both ribonucleotide and deoxyribonucleotide polymers. Again, a feature shared with bacterial regulators; *lac* repressor bound more avidly to poly d(A-T) than to other synthetic polynucleotides (Linn and Riggs, 1970). However, affinity for poly d(A-T) was many orders of magnitude below that for the *lac* operon. Perhaps, in the same way, the hierarchy of steroid receptor nucleotide recognition is a harbinger of higher affinity binding to specific sequences within DNA. Furthermore, receptor nucleotide recognition is a measurable phenomenon, and information may be obtained about the process, albeit of an indirect nature. We use such information about the mouse uterine cytosol estradiol receptor to propose a model of nonspecific and specific binding of receptors to DNA.

The experimental observations underlying the proposed model are the following:

1. The estradiol receptor possesses structural features capable of dis-criminating between deoxynucleotide bases with a preference for oligo(dG) > oligo(dT) ≥ oligo(dC) ≫ oligo(dA) > oligo(dI). The distinction between the oligodeoxypurines emphasizes the importance of receptor binding to accessible functional groups of the bases rather than their dependence on stacking properties of the bases.

2. The DNA-binding domain of the estradiol receptor contains at least two classes of subsites: those that bind to dG residues and those that bind to dT, dC, and dA residues. The former (G sites) are more stable to increased temperature, disruption by chaotropic salts, and to inhibitors, while the latter (N sites) are labile to all these perturbations.

3. In addition to steroid- and DNA-binding domains, estradiol receptors have binding site(s) for histones. The interaction is selective since H2A and H2B are more efficacious than the others. Furthermore, the H2B effect was duplicated by the N-terminal half molecule generated by cyanogen bromide cleavage of the parent molecule. These experiments indicated that estradiol receptors can engage in protein:protein interactions with functional consequences for the binding of estradiol to the receptor.

4. The association with H2A and H2B influenced not only the steroid binding of the holoreceptor but also the oligodeoxynucleotide recognition pattern of the receptor. Following holoreceptor purification, there was a loss of N-site binding but retention of G-site activity at a reduced level. Addition of H2B resulted in full restoration of the N-site and an increase in G-site activity. Since limited proteolysis of the holoreceptor eliminated the H2B response, the effect probably involved the DNA-binding domain of the holoreceptor and was not an adventitious result of histone:DNA interaction (S. A. Kumar and H. W. Dickerman, unpublished results).

In the proposed model (Fig. 13), it is assumed that estradiol receptors bind to prevalent nonspecific and rarer specific sites on DNA by recognizing a common feature of both types of sites. This feature is the spatial disposition of two deoxyguanylate residues along one surface of the helix so that these residues could be derived from either of the two strands. The distinction of specific from nonspecific sites resides in the nucleotide sequence com-position around the "anchor" dG residues. Binding to the dG residues alone leads to a nonproductive association. There are two principal determinants of effective binding: (1) a nucleotide sequence of modestly greater affinity than its neighboring residues, and (2) the direct effect of neighboring chro-mosomal proteins on the DNA-binding domain of the chromatin-associated holoreceptor. The N subsites of the domain are apparently malleable, labile under potentially denaturing conditions, yet restructured in the presence of H2B. We postulate that the restoration is due to direct interaction at

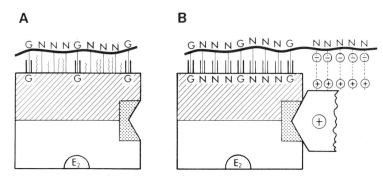

FIG. 13. Allosteric modulation of steroid receptor:DNA interaction. Mouse uterine estrogen holoreceptor is depicted in a (A) nonspecific, abortive and (B) specific, productive complex with a limited DNA sequence. The sequence represents one helical surface with nucleotide contributions possible from either strand. The receptor has three facets: the steroid-binding domain with a bound estradiol (E_2) (open region), the polynucleotide-binding domain (hatched region), and the binding site for histones and/or other cationic proteins (dotted region). In the polynucleotide-binding domain are two classes of subsites, G and N. The former bind to dG residues while the latter bind to dT, dC, and dA residues. In the absence of an associated cationic protein, the N sites are labile (wavy vertical lines) but are restructured to effective binding sites in the presence of the cationic protein (thin vertical lines). The G sites are active in either condition (thick vertical lines).

the cationic protein-binding site and is a form of allosteric control in which the binding repertoire of the DNA-binding domain can be altered. In the absence of an effective neighboring DNA-bound protein, only the anchor dG residues are efficiently bound; in the presence of an effective neighbor, the N-site activity is enhanced. Although our results were observed with histones, it is possible that nonhistone proteins may act in a similar manner, possibly through localized cationic amino acid residue-rich areas. This represents an alternative to the concept that the nonhistone protein itself is the acceptor component within target cell chromatin.

The value of a model is its aid in designing future experiments as well as in systematizing past results. Two aspects of the proposed model which may aid in research design are (1) the malleable property of the N subsites of the DNA-binding domain of the estradiol and perhaps other steroid holoreceptors, and (2) the reduced necessity of the putative DNA-specific sequences to exhibit markedly greater binding affinity than nonrelevant sequences. To attribute an allosteric mechanism to alteration of the binding capacities of the holoreceptors imputes nothing about the underlying structural changes in the receptor molecule. With sufficient purified receptor, the DNA or oligodeoxynucleotide interaction as effected by accessory proteins should be an object of study. Are there nonhistone components of chromatin which restore N sites at lower concentrations than H2B? A basic nonhistone chromatin component that might be effective is the high-mobility group of proteins, associated with active transcriptional fractions. Do modulator proteins require binding to DNA in order to alter receptor activity? In regard to the putative specific sequences within DNA, the model provides a cautionary note that enhanced binding of dG-rich fractions must be scrutinized carefully before designation as effector sites. It also reduces the necessity that effector sites must have comparable affinities for receptor that the *lac* operon has for the repressor. A more modest interaction, such as that demonstrated by the cAMP-binding protein, may suffice if the receptor is modulated by neighboring proteins. Ultimately, these questions will be answered by the correct reconstruction of purified receptor, accessory proteins, and DNA sequences of enhanced affinity.

ACKNOWLEDGMENTS

The authors thank Dr. Kantilal Thanki, Mrs. Thaisa Beach, Dr. Katherine P. Henrikson, Dr. Sharon C. Gross, and Mr. Arthur Bass for their contributions, without which our studies would have not been possible. In addition, they thank Miss Donna O'Connor for her generous help in the editing of this review.

The studies from the authors' laboratory were supported in part by National Institutes of Health Research Grant number AM23075-02 awarded by the National Institute of Arthritis, Metabolic and Digestive Diseases, PHS/DHHS.

REFERENCES

Adler, A. J., Ross, D. G., Chen, K., Stafford, P. A., Woiszwillo, M. J., and Fasman, G. D. (1974). *Biochemistry* 13, 616–623.
Aiba, H., and Krakow, J. S. (1981). *Biochemistry* 16, 4774–4780.
Alberga, A., Tran, A., and Baulieu, E.-E. (1979). *Nucleic Acids Res.* 7, 2031–2044.
Alberts, B., and Herrick, G. (1971). In "Methods in Enzymology" (L. Grossman, ed.), Vol. 21, pp. 198–217. Academic Press, New York.
Alexander, M. E., Burgum, A. A., Noall, R. A., Shaw, M. D., and Matthews, K. G. (1977). *Biochim. Biophys. Acta* 493, 367–379.
André, J., and Rochefort, H. (1973). *FEBS Lett.* 29, 135–140.
André, J., and Rochefort, H. (1975). *FEBS Lett.* 50, 319–323.
André, J., Pfeiffer, A., and Rochefort, H. (1976). *Biochemistry* 15, 2964–2969.
Ayuso-Parilla, M., Henshaw, E. C., and Hirsch, A. C. (1973). *J. Biol. Chem.* 248, 4386–4393.
Barkley, M. D. (1981). *Biochemistry* 20, 3833–3842.
Barkley, M. D., Lewis, P. A., and Sullivan, G. E. (1981). *Biochemistry* 20, 3842–3851.
Bick, M., and Devine, E. (1977). *Nucleic Acids Res.* 4, 3687–3700.
Bowen, B., Steinberg, H., Laemmli, U. K., and Weintraub, H. (1980). *Nucleic Acids Res.* 8, 1–20.
Brissac, C., Rucheton, M., Brund, C., and Jeanteur, P. (1976). *FEBS Lett.* 61, 38–40.
Buetti, E., and Diggelmann, H. (1981). *Cell* 23, 335–345.

Bugg, C. D., and Sternglanz, H. (1974). In "Molecular and Quantum Pharmacology" (E. Bergmann and B. Pullman, eds.), pp. 473–500. Reidel Publ., Netherlands.

Cake, M. H., DiSorbo, D. M., and Litwack, G. (1978). J. Biol. Chem. 253, 4886–4891.

Chamberlin, M. J. (1976). In "RNA Polymerase" (R. Losick and M. J. Chamberlin, eds.), pp. 159–191. Cold Spring Harbor Lab., Cold Spring Harbor, New York.

Chamness, G. C., Jennings, A. W., and McGuire, W. L. (1974). Biochemistry 13, 327–331.

Clark, J. H., and Gorski, J. (1969). Biochim. Biophys. Acta 192, 508–515.

Clemens, L. E., and Kleinsmith, L. J. (1972). Nature (London), New Biol. 237, 204–206.

de Haseth, P. L., Lohman, T. M., and Record, M. T., Jr. (1977). Biochemistry 16, 4783–4790.

Dickerman, H. W., and Kumar, S. A. (1981). Adv. Exp. Med. Biol. 138, 1–18.

DiSorbo, D. M., Phelps, D. S., and Litwack, G. (1980). Endocrinology (Baltimore) 106, 922–929.

Drocourt, J.-L., Thang, D.-C., and Thang, M.-N. (1978). Eur. J. Biochem. 82, 355–362.

Feldman, M., Kallos, J., and Hollander, V. P. (1980). J. Biol. Chem. 255, 8776–8779.

Feldman, M., Kallos, J., and Hollander, V. P. (1981). J. Biol. Chem. 256, 1145–1148.

Fox, T. O., Bates, S. E., Vito, C. C., and Wieland, S. J. (1979). J. Biol. Chem. 254, 4963–4966.

Franceschi, R. T., and Kim, K.-H. (1979). J. Biol. Chem. 254, 3637–3646.

Geiser, N., and Weber, K. (1977). Biochemistry 16, 938–943.

Givens, J. F., and Manly, K. F. (1976). Nucleic Acids Res. 3, 405–418.

Goidl, J. A., Cake, M. H., Dolan, K. P., Parchman, L. G., and Litwack, G. (1977). Biochemistry 16, 2125–2130.

Gross, S. C., Kumar, S. A., and Dickerman, H. W. (1981). Mol. Cell. Endocrinol. 22, 371–384.

Gross, S. C., Kumar, S. A., and Dickerman, H. W. (1982). J. Biol. Chem. 257, 4738–4745.

Harris, G. S. (1971). Nature (London), New Biol. 231, 246–248.

Hemminki, K. (1977). Acta Endocrinol. (Copenhagen) 84, 215–224.

Hemminki, K., and Vauhkonen, M. (1977). Biochim. Biophys. Acta 474, 109–116.

Henrikson, K. P., Gross, S. C., and Dickerman, H. W. (1981). Endocrinology (Baltimore) 109, 1196–1202.

Higgins, S. J., Rousseau, G. G., Baxter, J. D., and Tomkins, G. M. (1973). J. Biol. Chem. 248, 5866–5872.

Hiipakka, R. A., and Liao, S. (1980). J. Steroid Biochem. 13, 841–846.

Hughes, M. R., Compton, J. G., Scharder, W. T., and O'Malley, B. W. (1981). Biochemistry 20, 2481–2491.

Iwai, K., Ishikawa, K., and Hayashi, H. (1970). Nature (London) 226, 1056–1058.

Jovin, J. M., Geisler, N., and Weber, K. (1977). Nature (London) 269, 668–672.

Kallos, J., and Hollander, V. P. (1978). Nature (London) 272, 177–179.

Kallos, J., Fasy, T. M., Hollander, V. P., and Bick, M. D. (1978). Proc. Natl. Acad. Sci. U.S.A. 75, 4896–4900.

Kallos, J., Fasy, T. M., Hollander, V. P., and Bick, M. D. (1979). FEBS Lett. 98, 347–349.

Kallos, J., Fasy, T. M., and Hollander, V. P. (1981). Proc. Natl. Acad. Sci. U.S.A. 78, 2874–2878.

Khan, S., Feldman, M., and Hollander, V. P. (1980). Cancer Res. 40, 1050–1053.

King, R. J. B. (1972). In "Effects of Drugs on Cellular Control Mechanisms" (B. R. Rabin, and R. B. Freedman, eds.), pp. 11–26. Univ. Park Press, Baltimore, Maryland.

Kowalczykowski, S. C., Lonberg, N., Newport, J. W., and von Hippel, P. H. (1981). J. Mol. Biol. 145, 75–104.

Krakow, J. S., and Pastan, I. (1973). Proc. Natl. Acad. Sci. U.S.A. 70, 2529–2533.

Kumar, S. A., and Krakow, J. S. (1977). *J. Biol. Chem.* **252**, 5724–5728.
Kumar, S. A., Beach, T. A., and Dickerman, H. W. (1979). *Proc. Natl. Acad. Sci. U.S.A.* **76**, 2199–2203.
Kumar, S. A., Beach, T. A., and Dickerman, H. W. (1980a). *Proc. Natl. Acad. Sci. U.S.A.* **77**, 3341–3345.
Kumar, S. A., Murthy, N. S., and Krakow, J. S. (1980b). *FEBS Lett.* **109**, 121–124.
LePecq, J. B., and Paoletti, C. (1967). *J. Mol. Biol.* **27**, 87–106.
Levy, W. B., and Baxter, J. D. (1976). *Biochem. Biophys. Res. Commun.* **68**, 1045–1051.
Liang, T., and Liao, S. (1974). *J. Biol. Chem.* **249**, 4671–4678.
Liao, L.-L. S., Horwitz, S. B., Huang, M. T., and Grollman, A. P. (1975). *J. Med. Chem.* **18**, 117–120.
Liao, S., Smythe, S., Tymoczko, J. L., Rossini, G. P., Chen, C., and Hiipakka, R. A. (1980). *J. Biol. Chem.* **255**, 5545–5551.
Lin, S., and Ohno, S. (1981). *Biochim. Biophys. Acta* **654**, 181–186.
Lin, S., and Riggs, A. D. (1970). *Nature (London)* **228**, 1184–1186.
Lin, S., and Riggs, A. D. (1972a). *J. Mol. Biol.* **72**, 671–690.
Lin, S., and Riggs, A. D. (1972b). *Proc. Natl. Acad. Sci. U.S.A.* **69**, 2574–2576.
Lin, S., and Riggs, A. (1976). *Biochim. Biophys. Acta* **432**, 185–191.
Lin, S., Lin, D., and Riggs, A. (1976). *Nucleic Acids Res.* 3, 2183–2191.
Lohmar, P. H., and Toft, D. O. (1975). *Biochem. Biophys. Res. Commun.* **67**, 8–15.
Manning, G. S. (1978). *Q. Rev. Biophys.* **11**, 179–246.
Massol, N., Lebeau, M.-C., and Baulieu, E.-E. (1978a). *Nucleic Acids Res.* **5**, 723–738.
Massol, N., LeBeau, M.-C., and Baulieu, E.-E. (1978b). *Nucleic Acids Res.* **4**, 3158–3173.
Meilhac, M., Tysper, Z., and Chambon, P. (1972). *Eur. J. Biochem.* **28**, 291–300.
Metzger, D. A., Clark, J. H., Schrader, W. T., and Peck, E. J., Jr. (1977). *Abstr. 59th Annu. Meet. Endocr. Soc.*, New York Abstr. No. 160.
Milgrom, E., Atger, M., and Baulieu, E.-E. (1973). *Biochemistry* **12**, 5198–5205.
Moe, J. G., and Piszkiewicz, D. (1979). *Biochemistry* **13**, 2810–2814.
Molinari, A. M., Medici, N., Moncharmont, B., and Puca, G. A. (1977). *Proc. Natl. Acad. Sci. U.S.A.* **74**, 4886–4890.
Moudgil, V. K., and Eessalu, T. E. (1980). *Biochim. Biophys. Acta* **627**, 301–312.
Moudgil, V. K., and Weekes, G. A. (1978). *FEBS Lett.* **94**, 324–326.
Mulder, E., Vrij, L., and Foekens, J. A. (1980). *Steroids* **36**, 633–645.
Muldoon, T. G., and Cidlowski, J. A. (1980). *J. Biol. Chem.* **255**, 3100–3107.
Müller-Hill, B. (1975). *Prog. Biophys. Mol. Biol.* **30**, 227–252.
Musliner, T. A., and Chader, G. J. (1971). *Biochem. Biophys. Res. Commun.* **45**, 998–1003.
Naray, A. (1981). *J. Steroid Biochem.* **14**, 71–76.
Newport, J. W., Lonberg, N., Kowalczykowski, S. C., and von Hippel, P. H. (1981). *J. Mol. Biol.* **145**, 105–121.
Nichols, B. N., Lindell, T. D., Stellwagen, E., and Donelson, J. E. (1978). *Biochim. Biophys. Acta* **526**, 410–417.
Nishigori, H., and Toft, D. (1979). *J. Biol. Chem.* **254**, 9155–9161.
Nishigori, H., Moudgil, V. K., and Toft, D. (1978). *Biochem. Biophys. Res. Commun.* **80**, 112–118.
Nissley, P., Anderson, W. B., Gallo, M., Pastan, I., and Perlman, R. L. (1972). *J. Biol. Chem.* **247**, 4264–4269.
O'Farrell, P. H. (1975). *J. Biol. Chem.* **250**, 4007–4021.
Ogata, R. T., and Gilbert, W. (1978). *Proc. Natl. Acad. Sci. U.S.A.* **75**, 5851–5854.
O'Malley, B. W., Spelsberg, T. C., Schrader, W. T., Chytel, F., and Steggles, A. W. (1972). *Nature (London)* **235**, 141–144.

Pabo, C. D., Sauer, R. I., Sturtevant, J. M., and Ptashne, M. (1979). *Proc. Natl. Acad. Sci. U.S.A.* **76**, 1603–1612.

Park, D. C., and Witliff, J. L. (1977). *Biochem. Biophys. Res. Commun.* **78**, 251–258.

Payvar, F., Wrange, Ö., Carlstedt-Duke, J., Okret, S., Gustafsson, J.-Å, and Yamamoto, K. R. (1981). *Proc. Natl. Acad. Sci. U.S.A.* **78**, 6628–6632.

Pfahl, M., Kelleher, R. J., and Bourgeois, S. (1978). *Mol. Cell. Endocrinol.* **10**, 183–191.

Pike, J. W. (1981). *Biochem. Biophys. Res. Commun.* **100**, 1713–1719.

Platt, T., Files, J. G., and Weber, K. (1973). *J. Biol. Chem.* **248**, 110–121.

Puca, G. A., Sica, V., and Nola, E. (1974). *Proc. Natl. Acad. Sci. U.S.A.* **71**, 979–983.

Record, M. T., Jr., Mazur, S. J., Melancon, P., Roe, J.-H., Shaner, S. L., and Unger, L. (1981). *Annu. Rev. Biochem.* **50**, 997–1024.

Rennie, P. S. (1979). *J. Biol. Chem.* **254**, 3947–3952.

Revzin, A., and Von Hippel, P. H. (1977). *Biochemistry* **16**, 4769–4776.

Riggs, A. D., Suzuki, H., and Bourgeois, S. (1970). *J. Mol. Biol.* **48**, 67–83.

Ringold, G. M., Yamamoto, K. R., Tomkins, G. M., Bishop, J. M., and Varmus, H. E. (1975). *Cell* **6**, 299–305.

Ringold, G. M., Cardiff, R. D., Varmus, H. E., and Yamamoto, K. R. (1977). *Cell* **10**, 11–18.

Rothwell, S. W., Brown, T. R., and Migeon, C. J. (1981). *Abstr. 63rd Annu. Meet. Endocr. Soc., Cincinnati, Ohio* Abstr. No. 717.

Sala-Trepat, J. M., and Vallet-Strové, C. (1974). *Biochim. Biophys. Acta* **371**, 186–202.

Sato, B., Nomura, Y., Nakao, K., Ochi, H., and Matsumoto, K. (1981). *J. Steroid Biochem.* **14**, 295–303.

Sauer, R. T., Pabo, C. D., Meyer, B. J., Ptashne, M., and Backman, K. C. (1979). *Nature (London)* **279**, 396–400.

Saxe, S. A., and Revzin, A. (1979). *Biochemistry* **18**, 255–263.

Schwartz, S. A. (1977). *Biochemistry* **16**, 4101–4108.

Scolnick, E. M., Young, H. A., and Parks, W. P. (1976). *Virology* **69**, 148–156.

Scott, R. W., and Frankel, F. R. (1980). *Proc. Natl. Acad. Sci. U.S.A.* **77**, 1291–1295.

Senior, M. B., and Frankel, F. R. (1978). *Cell* **13**, 629–642.

Sherman, M. R., Pickering, L. A., Rollwagen, F. M., and Miller, L. K. (1978). *Fed. Proc., Fed. Am. Soc. Exp. Biol.* **37**, 167.

Sherman, M. R., Barzilai, D., Pine, P. R., and Tuazon, F. B. (1979). *Adv. Exp. Med. Biol.* **117**, 357–375.

Simmons, S. S. (1977). *Biochim. Biophys. Acta* **496**, 349–358.

Sluyser, M., Evers, S. G., and Nijsen, T. (1974). *Biochem. Biophys. Res. Commun.* **61**, 380–388.

Sobell, H. M., and Jain, S. C. (1972). *J. Mol. Biol.* **68**, 21–34.

Socher, S. H., Krall, J. F., Jaffe, R. C., and O'Malley, B. W. (1976). *Endocrinology (Baltimore)* **99**, 891–900.

Spelsberg, T. C. (1981). *In* "Biochemical Actions of Hormones" (G. Litwack, ed.), Vol. 9, pp. 142–204. Academic Press, New York.

Spelsberg, T. C., Webster, R. A., and Pikler, G. M. (1976). *Nature (London)* **262**, 65–67.

Stellwagen, E. (1977). *Acc. Chem. Res.* **10**, 92–98.

Takahashi, M., Blazy, B., and Baudras, A. (1979). *Nucleic Acids Res.* **7**, 1699–1712.

Thampan, T. N. R. V., and Clark, J. H. (1981). *Nature (London)* **290**, 152–154.

Thanki, K. H. (1980). *Abstr. 62nd Annu. Meet. Endocr. Soc. Washington, D.C.* Abstr. No. 716, p. 253.

Thanki, K. H., Beach, T. A., and Dickerman, H. W. (1978). *J. Biol. Chem.* **253**, 7744–7750.

Thanki, K. H., Beach, T. A., Bass, A. I., and Dickerman, H. W. (1979). *Nucleic Acids Res.* **6**, 3859–3877.

Thrall, C. L., Webster, R. A., and Spelsberg, T. C. (1978). *In* "The Cell Nucleus" (H. Busch, ed.), Vol. VI, pp. 461–529. Academic Press, New York.

Thrower, S., Hall, C., Lin, L., and Davidson, A. N. (1976). *Biochem. J.* **160**, 271–280.

Tsai, M. J., and Saunders, G. (1973). *Proc. Natl. Acad. Sci. U.S.A.* **70**, 2072–2076.

Turnell, R. W., Kaiser, N., Milholland, R. J., and Rosen, F. (1974). *J. Biol. Chem.* **249**, 1133–1138.

Vaidya, A. B., Lasfargues, E. Y., Heubel, G., Lasfargues, J. C., and Moore, D. H. (1976). *J. Virol.* **18**, 911–917.

Varmus, H. W., Ringold, G., and Yamamoto, K. R. (1979). *Monogr. Endocrinol.* **12**, 253–278.

Vedeckis, W. V., Schrader, W. T., and O'Malley, B. W. (1979). *In* "Steroid Hormone Receptor Systems" (W. W. Leavitt and J. H. Clark, eds.), pp. 309–327. Plenum, New York.

Vedeckis, W. V., Freeman, M. R., Schrader, W. T., and O'Malley, B. W. (1980a). *Biochemistry* **19**, 335–343.

Vedeckis, W. V., Schrader, W. T., and O'Malley, B. W. (1980b). *Biochemistry* **19**, 343–349.

von Hippel, P. H., Revzin, A., Gross, C. A., and Wang, A. C. (1974). *Proc. Natl. Acad. Sci. U.S.A.* **71**, 4808–4812.

von Hippel, P. H., Newport, J. W., Kowalczykowski, S. C., Lonberg, N., and Paul, L. S. (1981). *Abstr. 7th Int. Biophys. Congr., 3rd Pan Am. Biochem. Congr. Mexico City*, p. 214.

Walter, G., Zillig, W., Palm, P., and Fuchs, E. (1967). *Eur. J. Biochem.* **3**, 194–201.

Wieland, S. J., and Fox, T. O. (1981). *J. Steroid Biochem.* **14**, 409–414.

Wieland, S. J., Fox, T. O., and Savakis, C. (1978). *Brain Res.* **140**, 159–164.

Wilson, E. M., and French, F. S. (1979). *J. Biol. Chem.* **254**, 6310–6319.

Wränge, Ö., and Gustafsson, J.-Å (1978). *J. Biol. Chem.* **253**, 856–865.

Wu, F. H., Nath, K., and Wu, C. W. (1974). *Biochemistry* **13**, 2567–2572.

Yamamoto, K. R., and Alberts, B. M. (1975). *Cell* **4**, 301–310.

Yamamoto, K. R., Stampfer, M. R., and Tomkins, G. M. (1974). *Proc. Natl. Acad. Sci. U.S.A.* **71**, 3901–3905.

CHAPTER 9

Mammary Tumor Growth and Response to Ovariectomy

Mark Feldman, Albert Volchek, and Vincent P. Hollander

I. INTRODUCTION

Induction of tumor remission by endocrine treatment occurs in about 60% of patients with advanced breast cancers that contain estradiol receptor. The failure of remission in the remaining patients represents an important clinical problem and is the stimulus for this review, which will attempt to bring our own studies with transplantable rat mammary cancer into perspective with the clinical and experimental studies of others. Rather than attempt an exhaustive review, we will examine specific hypotheses in the light of our own studies. Particular emphasis is placed on ovariectomy-induced regression (OIR), because more clinical and experimental data are available

BIOCHEMICAL ACTIONS OF HORMONES, VOL. X
Copyright © 1983 by Academic Press, Inc.
All rights of reproduction in any form reserved.
ISBN 0-12-452810-4

for this modality of endocrine treatment. When appropriate, other modalities will be included in our analysis of the chemical significance of such regression. First, we will present the evidence that suggests that tumor estradiol receptor is the cardinal indicator for hormonal sensitivity of breast cancers to all modalities of endocrine treatment. We then will analyze an experimental approach to the concept that chemical differences exist between estradiol receptors which correlate with hormonal sensitivity or resistance. Finally, we will attempt to correlate what is known about the control of OIR in man and experimental animals with the literature on growth factors for mammary cancer cells. The role of insulin in the growth of mammary cancer *in vitro* and *in vivo* is well established (Harmon and Hilf, 1979; Shafie, 1980). This area of research is rapidly developing but will not be covered in this review.

II. EARLY STUDIES

The effect of ovariectomy on advanced breast cancer was discovered before ovarian hormones had been isolated, but was not widely used as treatment until put into perspective with modern endocrinology. Successful ablative therapy was reported first by Beatson, a surgeon working at the end of the nineteenth century who found significant regression of advanced breast cancer in two ovariectomized patients (Beatson, 1896). Pearson *et al.* (1954) utilized the degree of hypercalciuria in women suffering from advanced breast cancer with bone metastases as a rapid measure of the effect of ovariectomy. The patients could be divided into those with rhythmic surges in hypercalciuria and hypercalcemia which matched the menstrual cycle, and those who showed no such rhythmicity in the rate of bone destruction by tumor. The data contrasted calcium excretion in the two types of patients and it demonstrated the abrupt cessation of hypercalciuria after ovariectomy in patients with cyclical hypercalciuria and the lack of improvement in hypercalciuria in those patients with calcium excretion uncorrelated with the menstrual cycle. When small doses of estrogen were administered to patients whose tendency to hypercalciuria and hypercalcemia had vanished after ovariectomy, the hypercalciuria promptly recurred. When progesterone was given to such subjects, no change in calcium balance was noted. This study was the first to allow separation of human mammary cancer into estrogen-dependent and estrogen-independent tumors. In a larger study Pearson *et al.* (1955) showed that about 40% of premenopausal women with advanced breast cancer might be expected to achieve remission after ovariectomy, and as a result of this study there was greatly increased interest in such treatment. Ovariectomy would be expected to lower serum estrogen and progesterone concentrations and very likely to affect the concentration of various peptide hormones such as growth hormone, soma-tomedin, prolactin, gonadotropin, and relaxin. The relapse demonstrated by administration of physiological doses of estrogen and the lack of a clear response to progesterone administration suggest that the removal of estrogen is an important factor in the mechanism of OIR. However, this certainly does not prove that the effect of estrogen is direct and that it is uninfluenced by other hormonal factors (Sterental *et al.*, 1963). In contrast to the metabolic evidence of transient relapse during estrogen administration to patients with tumors in OIR, administration of human growth hormone or estradiol to women with tumors in hypophysectomy-induced regression did not show any evidence of growth (Pearson and Ray, 1959).

III. ESTRADIOL RECEPTOR AS AN INDEX OF HORMONAL RESPONSIVENESS

A major advance in the understanding of hormonal regulation of breast cancer was obtained when Jensen *et al.* (1971) demonstrated the usefulness of tumor estrogen receptor measurement for the prediction of the response of human breast cancer to ovariectomy. These findings were rapidly confirmed by other investigators (Pearson *et al.*, 1975; Saez *et al.*, 1978). When human mammary cancer was analyzed for progesterone receptor in addition to estradiol receptor, it was noted that the presence of both estradiol and progesterone receptors enhanced the probability of endocrine-induced re-mission (Horwitz *et al.*, 1975; McGuire *et al.*, 1978). These observations suggested that the progesterone receptor might serve as a marker of func-tionally active estradiol receptor. However, almost 20% of human tumors bearing both receptors still fail to respond, while some tumors that are estradiol receptor positive, progesterone receptor negative, do respond to hormonal treatment (McGuire *et al.*, 1978). Moreover, estradiol may have a specific effect on progesterone receptor yet not affect the growth of a mammary tumor. For example, Ip *et al.* (1979), studying MTW9B, an autonomous tumor, found that although the tumor responded to ovariectomy by major reduction in the amount of progesterone receptor (which could be reversed by estrogen treatment), the ovariectomy had no effect on the rate of tumor growth.

Various endocrine therapies in addition to ovariectomy (both additive and ablative) have been used in the treatment of mammary cancer, and in almost all instances estradiol receptor analysis was a useful indicator for the probability of tumor remission, since in the absence of receptor, remissions were very low (McGuire *et al.*, 1975; Pearson *et al.*, 1975; Jensen *et al.*, 1975; Wittliff and Savlov, 1975; Singhakowinta *et al.*, 1975; Stoll, 1980).

However, these data also showed that at least a third of all patients with tumor that has estrogen receptor will fail to benefit from endocrine treatment. The similarity in results afforded by all the endocrine modalities raises the possibility that a common locus is responsible for all endocrine effects, and it is conceivable that the central agent might be some estrogenic hormone. Ovariectomy would remove the main source of estrogen; adrenalectomy might also remove residual estrogen, while hypophysectomy might remove gonadotropic hormones, resulting in a diminished secretion of estrogen. Tamoxifen works at least partly as an antiestrogen; possibly androgens, progestins, and glucocorticoids also act in this manner, but high-dose estrogen therapy represents a real problem to hypotheses involving a simple, direct action of estrogen on stimulation of tumor growth. Accordingly, to better understand the mechanism(s) of hormonal regulation of tumor growth, it is necessary to turn to experimental systems involving either mammary tumor cells growing in culture or in rodent hosts that can be manipulated at will.

IV. MTW9 RAT MAMMARY TUMOR MODEL

MTW9 is a transplantable mammary tumor developed by Kim and Furth (1960) by intragastric administration of methylcholanthrene to a Wistar–Furth (W/Fu) rat bearing a mammosomatotrophic tumor (MtT). The mammary tumor requires high prolactin for growth which is obtained by either coimplantation of host W/Fu females with MtT or by administration of dopamine antagonist drugs (Hollander and Diamond, 1978). Despite the fact that prolactin levels are high in both cases, the drug-supported tumor (designated MTW9-D) regresses following host ovariectomy, whereas the tumor supported by MtT implantation (MTW9-MtT) does not regress following ovariectomy. This suggests that the MtT tumor might be secreting some factor that prevents OIR of MTW9.

A. Studies on Steroid Receptors

Since estrogen receptor analysis is so useful in predicting tumor response to hormone therapy, we have been analyzing the sublines of MTW9 for possible differences in receptor content. Table I shows that both MTW9-D and MTW9-MtT contain cytosolic estrogen and progesterone receptors, although the concentration of the receptors (unoccupied sites) is significantly higher in the drug-supported tumor. Prolactin membrane receptors are also higher in MTW9-D (Powell *et al.*, 1977). The crude estradiol receptors

TABLE I

STEROID RECEPTOR LEVELS IN MTW9-D AND MTW9-MtT CYTOSOLS[a]

Tumor	Estrogen	Progesterone
MTW9-D (8)	180 ± 70.4	304 ± 99.9
MTW9-MtT (7)	90.8 ± 39.4	147 ± 56.2
	$p < 0.025$	$p < 0.005$

[a] The values represent femtomoles specifically bound steroid per milligram cytosolic protein expressed as the mean ± SD. The number of samples analyzed in each group is given in parentheses.

from both tumors have similar sedimentation coefficients, Stokes radii, and association constants for estradiol. However, the receptor populations differ in their ability to bind to DNA–cellulose, with a greater percentage of the estrogen receptor from MTW9-D binding to DNA–cellulose than that from MTW9-MtT (Khan *et al.*, 1980); this difference in binding correlates with the biological status of the animal in that resection of the mammosomatotrophic tumor from MTW9-MtT-bearing animals increases the amount of receptor which binds to DNA to that from MTW9-D (Khan *et al.*, 1980), and also makes the MTW9 responsive to ovariectomy (Diamond *et al.*, 1976). Conversely, implantation of the MtT into MTW9-D-bearing animals reduces tumoral receptor binding to DNA (Khan *et al.*, 1980) while preventing OIR (Diamond *et al.*, 1978). The difference in binding might reflect some intrinsic physical difference in the receptor molecules or could be due to the presence (or absence) of some modulating compounds in the cytosol which might influence receptor·DNA interaction. Such "inhibitors" and "activators" of receptor binding to DNA have been described in a number of systems (Chamness *et al.*, 1974; Milgrom and Atger, 1975; Simons *et al.*, 1976; Cake *et al.*, 1978; Shyr and Liao, 1978; Thanki *et al.*, 1979). We have found that in the MTW9 system, cytosolic RNA could effectively inhibit the binding of estrogen receptor to DNA (Feldman *et al.*, 1981). Whether some difference in RNA content of the tumor cytosols could explain the difference in receptor binding to DNA remains to be determined. It also remains to be established whether DNA·receptor interaction has any physiological relevance or, if not, whether the interaction can be used as some practical test of tumor responsiveness to hormonal therapy.

In addition to a difference in DNA-binding ability, the estrogen receptors from MTW9-D and MTW9-MtT differ in the rate of steroid dissociation when analyzed by an exchange assay done in the presence of 2% (v/v) ether (Giladi-Josowitz and Hollander, 1977; Hollander and Khan, 1980). Under normal conditions of exchange (at 20°C in the absence of 2% ether) both tumor receptors display a single dissociation rate constant with a mean half-time of 55 minutes for the MTW9-MtT receptor and 61 minutes for receptor from MTW9-D. However, the rate of exchange is greatly enhanced when the same experiment is done in the presence of 2% ether, and can be resolved into two components. The slower exponential rate is not significantly different between the tumor receptors; however, the fast dissociation rate is significantly greater for MTW9-MtT receptor, with a mean half-time of 2.9 minutes compared with 9.2 minutes for MTW9-D receptor. This difference might indicate different subpopulations of receptor which could conceivably be involved in the response of tumor to ovariectomy. The existence of biphasic dissociation kinetics has also been implicated in the conversion of receptor from an inactive to an activated form (Sala-Trepat and Reti, 1974; Weichman and Notides, 1977).

B. Studies on Growth Requirements

1. Growth of Tumor Transplants

When MTW9 is transplanted into W/Fu rats, no outgrowth of tumor occurs unless a high serum prolactin is produced in recipient hosts and the ovaries are present (MacLeod *et al.*, 1964). High serum prolactin may be produced by administration of ovine prolactin (Diamond *et al.*, 1980a), by administration of dopamine antagonists such as perphenazine (Diamond *et al.*, 1976), or by coimplantation of a mammosomatic tumor such as MtTW5 which secretes large amounts of prolactin and growth hormone (Kim and Furth, 1960). The resulting tumors are similar in gross and microscopic appearance but differ in estrogen receptor content (Diamond *et al.*, 1977), estrogen receptor properties (Kahn *et al.*, 1980; Giladi-Josowitz and Hollander, 1977), and response to ovariectomy (Diamond *et al.*, 1976). Coimplantation of hosts with MtTW10 also produces high serum prolactin and MTW9 growth. Coimplantation with MtT-OM, a subline developed in our laboratory which secretes growth hormone but not prolactin (Hollander and Hollander, 1971), does not produce growth of MTW9 transplants.

All MTW9 tumors grown by giving various dopamine antagonist drugs to transplant recipients are similar to those produced by administration of perphenazine; they all show OIR. Administration of these drugs subcutaneously, at a dose of 2 mg two times per week, allows good tumor growth with maximal serum prolactin levels of 500–1200 ng/ml obtained within 2 hours after injection, and decreasing to 200–450 ng/ml 24 hours after injection. Normal pretreatment levels of prolactin are usually below 100 ng/ml. This is in contrast to serum prolactin levels of 5–30 μg/ml in rats bearing MtTW10. High serum prolactin is not the sole requirement for growth of MTW9 from a transplant, since ovariectomized recipients of both MTW9 and MtTW5 allow only MtT growth (with high prolactin secretion), and administration of various combinations of steroids to ovariectomized recipients produced high prolactin concentrations but did not allow growth (Murota and Hollander, 1971).

2. Growth following Ovariectomy

MTW9-D tumors neither grow nor regress following drug withdrawal, but do regress after ovariectomy regardless of whether or not drug treatment is continued. In contrast, MTW9-MtT tumors do not regress after ovariectomy, but only stop growing (Diamond *et al.*, 1976, 1978). However, significant regression does occur following MtT resection in intact animals and almost complete regression after combined MtT resection and ovariectomy. The resection is accompanied by rapid decline of prolactin to normal levels. It has been shown in our laboratory (Diamond *et al.*, 1980b) that daily administration of 4 or 10 mg progesterone can totally prevent OIR of MTW9-D tumors and restore growth of MTW9-MtTW10 tumors which had been stopped by ovariectomy (Figs. 1 and 2). However, another active progestin, hydroxyprogesterone caproate, was not effective at all in OIR prevention. Estrogens had more complicated effects on OIR and tumor growth. Low doses of estradiol valerate (15 μg, one time per week) allowed only partial OIR, after which 60–70% of initial tumor volume remained. Very low doses of estradiol valerate (10, 5, or 2 μg, one time per week) were more effective in preventing OIR. However, very high doses of estradiol valerate (50 or 100 μg daily) not only were ineffective in OIR prevention, but were able to induce regression in intact MTW9-D rats. Moreover, the stimulatory effect of progesterone on tumor growth in ovariectomized rats bearing MTW9-MtT was completely prevented by combining progesterone injections with 5 μg estradiol benzoate daily (Diamond *et al.*, 1980b).

The prevention of OIR by progesterone and low-dose estradiol does not involve stimulation of prolactin secretion or pituitary hypertrophy (A. Volchek, C. de la Torre, and V. P. Hollander, unpublished observations). In addition, very high doses of estradiol valerate, which could not prevent OIR, did stimulate prolactin secretion and pituitary hypertrophy. These data suggest a direct effect of estradiol on tumor cells and exclude the assumption that estrogens always act on tumors through stimulation of prolactin secretion. MTW9-D cells, after ovariectomy, are sensitive not only to progesterone and estrogens, but possibly to other hormonally active steroids and even some nonsteroidal compounds. Thus, norethindrone, well known as a contraceptive steroid, prevented OIR (Fig. 3). In addition, we have found that testosterone, medroxiprogesterone acetate, and the nonsteroidal antiandrogen

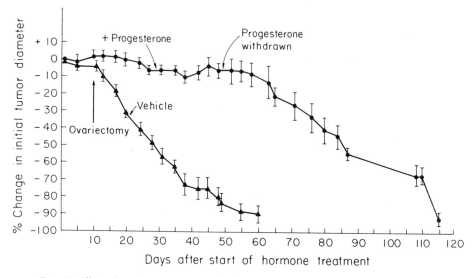

FIG. 1. Effect of ovariectomy on growth of MTW9-D in rats receiving daily injections of progesterone (10 mg/day). Rats bearing MTW9-D (following drug withdrawal) received 2 daily sc injections of progesterone (10 mg/day; $n = 8$) or equal volumes of steroid-suspending vehicle ($n = 8$). After treatment for 10 days, all rats were ovariectomized as indicated, and progesterone administration continued. Change in average tumor diameter (three diameters/ 3) is expressed as a percentage of the average diameter at start of treatment (initial tumor diameter). Mammary tumors were 1.0–1.5 cm in average diameter before start of treatment. Points represent mean values; bars, SE. On day 50, progesterone-treated rats were taken off progesterone, and tumor measurement continued as indicated. From Diamond *et al.* (1980b).

flutamide could all retard OIR (A. Volchek, M. Feldman, and V. P. Hollander, unpublished observations).

Although the ability of estradiol to prevent OIR of MTW9-D suggests a direct action of the steroid on tumor cells, the absence of OIR of MT-MtT tumors cannot be readily explained by estrogen secretion by MtT since serum estrogen levels in rats bearing MtTW10 are less than in MTW9-D-bearing animals (Diamond *et al.*, 1977). This suggests that some nonsteroidal hormonal factor secreted by the MtT tumor is responsible for prevention of OIR. However, administration of growth hormone, prolactin, or adrenocorticotropin (ACTH), known secretory products of MtT, either alone or in combination to MTW9-D-bearing rats failed to prevent OIR (Diamond *et al.*, 1978). In addition, serum from MtT-bearing rats could effectively stimulate DNA synthesis in MTW9 explants, whereas normal rat sera, prolactin, growth hormone, or a mixture of hormones simulating MtT serum could not (Mayer *et al.*, 1980). It would appear, therefore, that some other hormonal product of MtT is the actual mammatotroph, although it is also

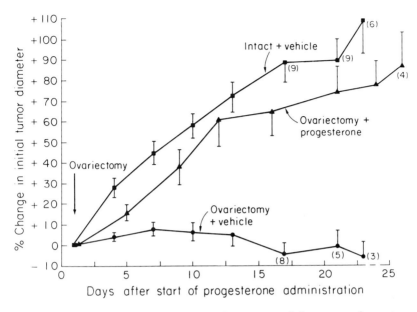

FIG. 2. Growth of MTW9-MtT in ovariectomized rats receiving daily injections of progesterone. Rats bearing MTW9-MtT were ovariectomized and received sc injections of progesterone (4 mg/day in steroid-suspending vehicle; $n = 8$) or vehicle ($n = 9$). Intact tumor-bearing rats received sc injections of vehicle ($n = 10$). Change in average tumor diameter (three diameters/ 3) is expressed as a percentage of the average diameter on the day of ovariectomy (initial tumor diameter). Mammary tumors measured 1.0–2.0 cm at the start of the experiment. Points represent mean values; bars, SE. Numbers in parentheses represent number of remaining animals. From Diamond *et al.* (1980b).

conceivable that the extremely high levels of prolactin obtained in rats bearing MtT tumors (up to 30 μg/ml) might selectively stimulate a sub-population of tumor cells having a high dependency on prolactin.

3. Regrowth of Nodules following OIR

When MTW9-D tumors are regressed to nodules by ovariectomy, effective regrowth can be achieved by treating animals with various steroids; differences in growth rate, latent periods preceding growth, and other indices of growth dynamics were obtained depending on the compound used. For most compounds that are active in OIR prevention, regrowth starts within 2–4 weeks after beginning treatment and continues at a steady rate of 1–2 mm/10 days over a period of several months. Thus, 2 and 10 μg estradiol valerate given once a week, norethindrone (5 mg given daily; Fig. 3), or testosterone (5 mg given daily) were very active in stimulating tumor regrowth. Micro-

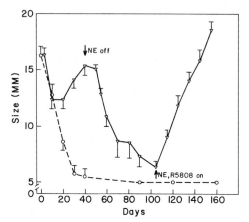

FIG. 3. Effect of norethindrone (NE) on the prevention of OIR and regrowth of MTW9-D. MTW9 tumors were grown by sc injection of the dopamine antagonist R5808 (2 mg/day). When tumors reached an average diameter of 1.5–1.8 cm, animals were ovariectomized (day 0), and R5808 replaced with daily injections of 5 mg NE in steroid-suspending vehicle (△, $n = 6$) or steroid-suspending vehicle alone (○, $n = 7$). Norethindrone treatment was discontinued on day 40 after ovariectomy; following regression of these tumors, regrowth was obtained by combined treatment with R5808 (5 mg/day) and NE (2 mg/day). Similar regrowth rates were achieved with NE alone.

scopically, these tumors had the appearance of adenocarcinomas and contained cytosolic estrogen and progestin receptors, although the levels of receptors varied significantly between different groups (Table II).

The dopamine antagonist R5808, or very high doses of estradiol valerate, both ineffective in OIR prevention, were also able to stimulate tumor

TABLE II

Steroid Receptor Levels in MTW9 Tumors Regrown from Nodules By Different Treatments[a]

Treatment	Number analyzed	Estrogen	Progesterone
+NE[b]	5	26.7 ± 9.43	93.4 ± 38.7
+R5808[c]	2	86.0 ± 12.7	57.0 ± 17.0
+NE + R5808	4	30.0 ± 10.3	61.6 ± 42.7
+EB (low dose)[d]	6	151.0 ± 34.8	414.0 ± 49.5
+EB (high dose)[e]	5	32.4 ± 4.95	294.0 ± 75.0

[a] The values represent femtomoles specifically bound steroid per milligram cytosolic protein expressed as the mean ± SD.

[b] Norethindrone (5 mg/rat, 5 times per week).

[c] 8-[3-(p-Fluorophenoxy)propyl]-1-phenyl-1,3,8-triazaspiro-4,5-decan-4-one hydrochloride (2 mg/rat, five times per week). This dopamine antagonist was provided by Janssen R & D, Inc.

[d] Estradiol benzoate (10 μg/rat, one time per week).

[e] Estradiol benzoate (10 μg/rat, five times per week).

regrowth. However, the latent period for regrowth was at least 6–8 weeks followed by a period of very rapid growth. Such growth dynamics are surprising in light of the inability of these treatments to prevent OIR, and might indicate stimulation of a small part of the total cell population resulting in a tumor with a different cell composition. When these regrown tumors are transplanted into ovariectomized rats, growth is obtained only when the same drug regimen is continued; R5808 tumors grow in response to R5808 and estradiol-induced tumors grow in response to high doses of estradiol. The receptor levels in these "second-generation" tumors were similar to the parent tumors (see Table II). Although these data are not yet published, the utility of the MTW9 system as a model to study mammary tumor growth is clearly indicated.

V. GROWTH FACTORS FOR MAMMARY TUMOR CELLS

In vivo studies in the rat indicate that MTW9 and primary dimethyl-benzanthracene (DMBA) tumors are stimulated to grow by a direct action of prolactin (Kim and Furth, 1960; MacLeod *et al.*, 1964; Welsch and Meites, 1978). The effect of estrogen on tumor growth is more complex (Leung *et al.*, 1975; Leung and Sasaki, 1975) and may involve stimulation of prolactin secretion (Manni *et al.*, 1977). In contrast, human mammary cancer appears to utilize estrogen rather than prolactin as a principal means of growth support, although other hormonal factors may be involved (Nagasawa, 1979; Leung and Shiu, 1981). These discrepancies might be resolved by the use of tumor cells in culture, which should allow simple direct testing of mitogenic factors in a defined environment. Studies could then be carried out on hosts inoculated with the cultured cells under experimental conditions that would allow testing of hormones for tumor-growth stimulation.

A. NONHUMAN CELL LINES

Some interesting studies have been done with MTW9/PL, an epithelial cell line derived from MTW9 which requires serum for growth (Sirbasku, 1978a,b; Sirbasku and Benson, 1979). Mitogenic factors were evaluated by removing serum from the cultures after 24 hours' growth in Dulbecco's modified Eagle's medium containing 10% fetal calf serum, and then adding the hormones or organ extracts to be tested. Only the extracts of uterus, kidney, and liver from estrogen-treated rats were active in stimulating cell growth and proliferation; although estradiol was necessary for this effect, addition of estradiol or prolactin directly to cell culture medium did not stimulate growth. Tumor growth *in vivo*, however, was highly dependent on estrogen. The tumors grew well in intact female rats but poorly in intact males or castrated male or female hosts; estradiol, progesterone, or testosterone, but not hydrocortisone, restored growth in ovariectomized females. Estradiol and/or testosterone restored the growth in castrated males but dihydrotestosterone had only a modest restorative effect. Testosterone or dihydrotestosterone administration to intact male hosts resulted in only modest tumor growth in contrast to the excellent growth obtained in castrated males treated with testosterone. The antiestrogen U11,100A also stimulated the growth of tumor in castrated males, but less well than estradiol. Tumor dependence on estrogens *in vivo*, with no mitogenic effect of estrogens on tumor cells in culture, suggested that the steroid might be acting through some target tissue to produce an intermediate ("estromedin") that would be the actual growth factor.

Sirbasku also demonstrated that MTW9/PL cells did not grow well in ovariectomized females implanted with a prolactin-secreting tumor as had been demonstrated for the original MTW9 tumor by MacLeod *et al.* (1964); prolactin in the absence of estrogen does not stimulate the early growth of MTW9. However, a reduction of tumor growth was obtained in female hosts when prolactin secretion was inhibited by administration of the dopamine agonist CB-154, showing that prolactin and estradiol are both of importance in the maintenance of tumor growth. One unexpected finding was a decrease in estrogen-mediated growth in rats rendered hypothyroid by administration of propylthiouracil. Further study of thyroid hormone effects on mammary cancer sensitivity toward steroid hormones may be revealing (Eskin, 1979).

B. Human Cell Lines

1. Estrogenic Stimulation

A role for estrogen in the growth of the human cell line MCF-7 *in vivo* is persuasive. Soule and McGrath (1980) have shown that inoculation of MCF-7 into nude mice given supplementary estrogen resulted in tumor growth in 70% of hosts; tumors had human karyotype and markers for MCF-7. Shafie and Grantham (1981) inoculated intact BALB/c nude mice with 2×10^6 MCF-7 cells and within 7 days all hosts developed tumors. No tumors developed in ovariectomized or streptozotocin-induced diabetic hosts but were induced with 100% frequency when the estrogen or insulin deficit was replaced by hormone administration. Estrone, estradiol, and estriol were active, but no effect was observed with testosterone, progesterone, or hydrocortisone.

The role of estrogen in the growth of MCF-7 in culture is less clear. Although all strains possess estradiol and progesterone receptors (Engle and Young, 1978), only some demonstrate estrogen-mediated growth (Jozan *et al.*, 1979; Sonnenschein and Soto, 1980). For example, Shafie (1980) has done a study demonstrating that MCF-7 cells fail to respond to estrogen *in vitro* yet require the hormone *in vivo*. He examined the growth of MCF-7 in a continuous culture line and in a line derived from a nude mouse passage. MEM–Hanks' balanced salt solution supplemented with 2 mM L-glutamine, 10 μg bovine insulin/ml, penicillin, streptomycin, and 10% fetal calf serum, which constituted the initial medium, was inoculated with 5×10^6 MCF-7 cells. After 3 days of growth, the cells were transferred to serum-free medium and hormones were added. Media were changed daily for 6 days and cell growth estimated by hemocytometer. Both sublines showed an impressive increase in growth when insulin was added, but estradiol was ineffective over a range of 10^{-11}–10^{-8} M. Moreover, estradiol had no effect on growth in the presence of fetal calf serum or serum stripped by adsorption to dextran-coated charcoal. However, since the initial growth of cells was in 10% fetal calf serum, which contains variable amounts of steroids, one must examine evidence for the capacity of MCF-7 cells to store either estrogen or the intermediates involved in hormonal action. Such a study has been done by Strobl and Lippman (1979), who demonstrated that the half-life of specifically bound [^{3}H]estradiol in MCF-7 cells, measured over a 78-hour period with three media changes, was about 24 hours.

Butler *et al.* (1979) grew MCF-7 cells in MEM–Hanks' supplemented with nonessential amino acids, glutamine, 12 μg/ml insulin, penicillin, streptomycin, and 10% calf serum. Cells were plated, transferred to a serum-free defined medium for 5 days with one medium change, and the effect of estradiol on growth and on the secretion of plasminogen activator were determined. No effect on growth was seen, but as little as 10^{-10} M estradiol increased the secretion of activator. If functional retention of estradiol from the original serum supplement could explain the absence of a growth response to added estradiol, the ready response to 10^{-10} M hormone by plasminogen activator synthesis would not have been predicted.

Since resolution of the direct or indirect nature of growth stimulation of mammary cancer by estrogen is of such importance, it is necessary to examine other evidence for direct growth effects of estrogen on mammary cancer cell lines. Lippman *et al.* (1976a) studied the effect of estradiol on the growth of MCF-7 cells cultured on medium containing estrogen-depleted serum (less than 10^{-12} M estradiol). When 5×10^4 cells were plated in MEM, containing glutamine and 10% depleted fetal calf serum, growth was retarded within 6 days in plates without added hormone but continued in those containing 10^{-8} M estradiol. The difference after 8 days of growth appeared significant and is a result of growth cessation of the controls following 6 days of excellent growth. It is not clear why growth stimulation was seen in these studies but not in the studies of Shafie (1980) or Jozan *et al.* (1979). Allegra and Lippman (1978) have studied estradiol growth stimulation in the human breast cancer line ZR-75-1. Growth studies were done by attaching the cells in steroid-depleted medium and then changing to serum-free medium containing estradiol, transferrin, T_3, dexamethasone, and insulin, which allowed good growth. Depletion of estradiol from this defined medium, which had been present at 10^{-8} M, caused retardation of growth by the seventh day.

Discrepancies regarding effects of estrogens on cell growth *in vitro* may be resolved by the observation that antiestrogens inhibit the growth of rat mammary cancer cells *in vitro*, regardless of whether estrogens are present in the medium or not. Horwitz *et al.* (1978) studied the effect of tamoxifen and nafoxidine on growth and induction of progesterone receptors in MCF-7 cells transferred 2 days after plating to MEM supplemented with nonessential amino acids, glutamine, insulin, hydrocortisone, prolactin, gentamycin, and added test hormones. At low concentrations (less than 0.1 μM), tamoxifen acts as an estrogen, rapidly inducing progesterone receptor with only slight inhibition of cell growth. At higher concentrations (1 μM) both growth and progesterone receptor induction are suppressed and the suppression is reversed by estradiol. Nafoxidine failed to induce progesterone receptor at any concentration tested but at high concentrations (10^{-6} M) inhibited cell growth. Under the conditions of this experiment, 10 nM estradiol had no effect on growth but readily induced receptor. The distinction between effects on growth and receptor induction are difficult to reconcile with either a single cytosol estrogen receptor molecule or a single effective nuclear site for this receptor. The observations are compatible with the possibility of a small amount of estradiol receptor in MCF-7 nuclei being occupied by a substance other than estradiol which is stable under *in vitro* (but not *in vivo*) conditions. This complex would permit maximal growth, but could exchange with antiestrogens to form a growth-inhibitory complex; this in turn can exchange with estradiol to form a growth-stimulating complex. *In vivo*, the estradiol receptor would be occupied by estradiol, and therefore stimulate growth.

Lippman *et al.* (1976b) studied the effects of tamoxifen on MCF-7 and Zr-75-1 human breast cancer cell lines in the presence or absence of estradiol. Unfortunately, this chapter does not examine growth effects but only thymidine incorporation; 10^{-9} M estradiol stimulated incorporation whereas 10^{-7} M tamoxifen inhibited the process. Addition of 10^{-9} M estradiol reversed the inhibition caused by 10^{-6} M tamoxifen. In addition, these authors showed that exposure of cells to tamoxifen for 3 days led to irreversible damage to cell growth and that tamoxifen caused greater inhibition of macromolecular synthesis than did exposure to hormone-free media; these studies suggest that tamoxifen not only competes for estradiol receptor sites (Hahnel *et al.*, 1973), but may also interact with receptors for some other estrogen-like substance which may have a capacity to stimulate growth.

2. Prolactin Stimulation

Shafie and Grantham (1981) examined the effect of prolactin on the growth of MCF-7 *in vivo*. Administration of perphenazine to intact mice produced excellent growth of tumor, comparable to that observed in hypophysectomized mice bearing an estradiol implant. Perphenazine administration to ovariectomized mice yielded modest but significant growth; no palpable growth was obtained in untreated ovariectomized mice. Ovine prolactin administration to intact tumor-inoculated hosts (300 μg/day) produced about a 20% increase in tumor growth, and palpable tumor developed in ovariectomized mice treated with prolactin. Pituitary grafts beneath the renal capsule also caused tumor growth.

These results are of great interest. Although MCF-7 cells have prolactin membrane receptor (Shiu, 1979) and respond to prolactin in culture by increased production of estradiol receptor (Shafie and Brooks, 1977), there is no convincing evidence that prolactin stimulates growth of human tumor cells in culture. From Shafie's data it is not clear whether perphenazine administration gives comparable prolactin concentrations to those obtained with ovine prolactin administration or pituitary transplants; there is a possibility that perphenazine has some action on tumor growth independent of an increase in serum prolactin since it is more active than ovine prolactin. The increased growth of human tumor produced by an estrogen pellet in hypophysectomized mouse hosts is of importance since it is believed that rat mammary gland or tumor cannot be stimulated by estrogens in the absence of pituitary hormones (Lyons *et al.*, 1958; Sterental *et al.*, 1963). However, Manni *et al.* (1979) note that estrone, estradiol, and estriol were detectable at low concentrations in the serum of completely hypophysectomized patients after a variable remission; since tamoxifen treatment of some of these patients could induce a second remission, it is possible that estrogens may stimulate some mammary tumors *in vivo* in the absence of pituitary hormones. Shafie's observations are compatible with this concept.

3. Other Factors

Barnes and Sato (1979) succeeded in growing MCF-7 in a serum-free medium supplemented with physiological concentrations of insulin, transferrin, epidermal growth factor, prostaglandin $F_2\alpha$, and cold-insoluble globulin. The growth rate in this medium was identical to that of cells grown in serum-supplemented medium; however, the cells grew as rounded clumps and attached poorly to the culture dish. When the α-1 serum protein purified by Holmes (1967) was added to this defined medium, the morphology of the cells was similar to that of MCF-7 grown by the addition of 10% serum. Addition of L-triiodothyronine or estradiol in concentrations as low as 10^{-10} M produced morphological changes in MCF-7 grown in media supplemented by the five growth factors although no effect on cell number was noted. However, when α-1 protein alone was present as supplement, in a medium that therefore did not support growth, 10^{-9} M estradiol did increase cell number. One can conclude from this work that, with optimal nonsteroidal supplements in the media, MCF-7 can grow well and addition of estrogen does not stimulate further growth.

Some recent studies suggest that glucocorticoids might be of major importance in mammary tumor growth. Aylsworth *et al.* (1980) demonstrated that administration of dexamethasone (50 μg/day) to rats bearing dimethyl-benzanthracene-induced mammary tumors caused a substantial regression of the tumors even though serum prolactin levels were very high due to chronic administration of haloperidol, a dopamine antagonist. Haloperidol alone gave good tumor growth. This effect of dexamethasone might be directly on tumor cells, since Osborne *et al.* (1979) found that glucocorticoids inhibit the growth of human breast cancer in culture and oppose the growth-stimulating action of insulin.

Leung and Shiu (1981) studied the growth of another human breast cancer cell line, T-47D, in nude mice. Tumor growth did not occur in control mice or in those coimplanted with GH_3 cells, a pituitary-derived clonal line that secretes prolactin and growth hormone. However, rapid growth of T-47D was obtained in animals bearing GH_3 tumor which were given 500 μg estradiol valerate every 2 weeks. In the absence of GH_3, estradiol valerate administration resulted in only moderate tumor growth and produced only a modest increase in serum growth hormone and no increase in serum prolactin. Animals bearing GH_3 tumor had high serum values of both pituitary factors and coincident estrogen administration gave rise to even higher concentrations in a single surviving mouse. Mammary tumor growth correlated better with serum growth hormone than prolactin concentration. These data, in conjunction with data from the MTW9 tumor model, suggest that an unidentified pituitary factor acting in consort with estrogen is responsible for mammary tumor growth. Indeed, synergism between estrogen and peptide hormones has recently been demonstrated in the estrogen-mediated induction of ovalbumin gene transcription in oviduct explant cultures (Evans *et al.*, 1981).

VI. SUMMARY

The growth of mammary cancer is a complex phenomenon which is dependent on the interplay of ovarian and pituitary factors, and possibly involves substances derived from other organs as well. Although it is far from clear why some tumors respond to hormonal therapy and some do not, the presence of estrogen receptor in a tumor is a useful indicator for predicting the biological behavior of that tumor. By combining studies on estrogen receptor characterization and regulation with tumor growth requirements, it should be possible to gain some insight into why tumors respond as they do. The MTW9 rat mammary tumor model we have described represents an interesting and useful system for studying differences between responsive and nonresponsive tumor cells.

REFERENCES

Allegra, J. C., and Lippman, M. E. (1978). *Cancer Res.* 38, 3823–3829.
Aylsworth, C. F., Sylvester, P. W., Leung, F. C., and Meites, J. (1980). *Cancer Res.* 40, 1863–1866.
Barnes, D., and Sato, G. (1979). *Nature (London)* 281, 388–389.
Beatson, G. T. (1896). *Lancet* 2, 104–107.
Butler, W. B., Kirkland, W. L., and Jorgensen, T. L. (1979). *Biochem. Biophys. Res. Commun.* 90, 1328–1334.
Cake, M. H., DiSorbo, D. M., and Litwack, G. (1978). *J. Biol. Chem.* 253, 4886–4891.
Chamness, G. C., Jennings, A. W., and McGuire, W. L. (1974). *Biochemistry* 13, 327–331.
Diamond, E. J., Koprak, S., Shen, S. K., and Hollander, V. P. (1976). *Cancer Res.* 36, 77–80.
Diamond, E. J., Giladi, M., Khan, S., and Hollander, V. P. (1977). *Cancer Res.* 37, 1852–1856.
Diamond, E. J., Khan, S., Koprak, S., and Hollander, V. P. (1978). *Cancer Res.* 38, 2239–2245.
Diamond, E. J., Khan, S., Paul, M. A., Koprak, S., and Hollander, V. P. (1980a). *Endocrinology (Baltimore)* 106, 952–958.
Diamond, E. J., Koprak, S., and Hollander, V. P. (1980b). *Cancer Res.* 40, 1091–1096.
Engle, L. W., and Young, N. A. (1978). *Cancer Res.* 38, 4327–4339.
Eskin, B. A. (1979). *In* "Influences of Hormones in Tumor Development" (J. A. Kellen and R. Hilf, eds.), Vol. II, pp. 129–156. CRC Press, Boca Raton, Florida.
Evans, M. I., Hager, L. J., and McKnight, G. S. (1981). *Cell* 25, 187–193.
Feldman, M., Kallos, J., and Hollander, V. P. (1981). *J. Biol. Chem.* 256, 1145–1148.
Giladi-Josowitz, M., and Hollander, V. P. (1977). *Endocr. Res. Commun.* 4, 183–193.
Hahnel, R., Twaddle, E., and Ratajczak, T. (1973). *J. Steroid Biochem.* 4, 687–695.
Harmon, J. T., and Hilf, R. (1979). *In* "Influences of Hormones in Tumor Development" (J. A. Kellen and R. Hilf, eds.), Vol. II, pp. 111–128. CRC Press, Boca Raton, Florida.
Hollander, V. P., and Diamond, E. J. (1978). *In* "Endocrine Control in Neoplasia" (R. K. Sharma and W. E. Criss, eds.), pp. 93–119. Raven, New York.
Hollander, V. P., and Hollander, N. (1971). *Proc. Soc. Exp. Biol. Med.* 137, 1157–1162.
Hollander, V. P., and Khan, S. (1980). *J. Steroid Biochem.* 12, 131–134.

Holmes, R. (1967). *J. Cell Biol.* **32**, 297–308.

Horwitz, K. B., McGuire, W. L., Pearson, O. H., and Segaloff, A. (1975). *Science* **189**, 726–727.

Horwitz, K. B., Koseki, Y., and McGuire, W. L. (1978). *Endocrinology (Baltimore)* **103**, 1742–1751.

Ip, M., Milholland, R. J., Rosen, F., and Kim, U. (1979). *Science* **203**, 361–363.

Jensen, E. V., Block, G. E., Smith, S., Kyser, K., and DeSombre, E. R. (1971). *Natl. Cancer Inst. Monogr.* **34**, 55–70.

Jensen, E. V., Polley, T. Z., Smith, S., Block, G. E., Ferguson, D. J., and DeSombre, E. R. (1975). *In* "Estrogen Receptors in Human Breast Cancer" (W. L. McGuire, P. P. Carbone, and E. P. Vollmer, eds.), pp. 37–56. Raven, New York.

Jozan, S., Moure, C., Gillois, M., and Bayard, F. J. (1979). *J. Steroid Biochem.* **10**, 341–342.

Khan, S., Feldman, M., and Hollander, V. P. (1980). *Cancer Res.* **40**, 1050–1053.

Kim, U., and Furth, J. (1960). *Proc. Soc. Exp. Biol. Med.* **103**, 640–642.

Leung, B. S., and Sasaki, G. H. (1975). *Endocrinology (Baltimore)* **97**, 564–572.

Leung, C. K. H., and Shiu, R. P. C. (1981). *Cancer Res.* **41**, 546–551.

Leung, B. S., Sasaki, G. H., and Leung, J. S. (1975). *Cancer Res.* **35**, 621–627.

Lippman, M., Bolan, G., and Huff, K. (1976a). *Cancer Res.* **36**, 4595–4601.

Lippman, M., Bolan, G., and Huff, K. (1976b). *Cancer Treat. Rep.* **60**, 1421–1429.

Lyons, W. R., Li, C. H., and Johnson, R. E. (1958). *Recent Prog. Horm. Res.* **14**, 219–248.

McGuire, W. L., Carbone, P. P., Sears, M. E., and Escher, G. C. (1975). *In* "Estrogen Receptors in Human Breast Cancer" (W. L. McGuire, P. P. Carbone, and E. P. Vollmer, eds.), pp. 1–7. Raven, New York.

McGuire, W. L., Horwitz, J. B., Zava, D. T., Garola, R. E., and Chamness, G. C. (1978). *Metabolism* **27**, 487–501.

MacLeod, R. M., Allen, M. S., and Hollander, V. P. (1964). *Endocrinology (Baltimore)* **75**, 249–258.

Manni, A., Trujilli, J. E., and Pearson, O. H. (1977). *Cancer Res.* **37**, 1216–1219.

Manni, A., Pearson, O. H., Brodkey, J., and Marshall, J. S. (1979). *Cancer (Philadelphia)* **44**, 2330–2337.

Mayer, R. M., Diamond, E. J., and Hollander, V. P. (1980). *J. Natl. Cancer Inst.* **65**, 1033–1038.

Milgrom, E., and Atger, M. (1975). *J. Steroid Biochem.* **6**, 487–492.

Murota, S., and Hollander, V. P. (1971). *Endocrinology (Baltimore)* **89**, 560–564.

Nagasawa, H. (1979). *Eur. J. Cancer* **15**, 267–279.

Osborne, C. K., Monaco, M. E., Kahn, C. R., Huff, K., Bronzert, D., and Lippman, M. E. (1979). *Cancer Res.* **39**, 2422–2428.

Pearson, O. H., and Ray, B. S. (1959). *Cancer (Philadelphia)* **12**, 85–92.

Pearson, O. H., West, C. D., Hollander, V. P., and Treves, N. E. (1954). *J. Am. Med. Assoc.* **154**, 234–239.

Pearson, O. H., West, C. D., McLean, J. P., Li, M. C., and Lipsett, M. B. (1955). *Am. Surg.* **21**, 1075–1083.

Pearson, O. H., McGuire, W. L., Brodkey, J., and Marshall, J. (1975). *In* "Estrogen Receptors in Human Breast Cancer" (W. L. McGuire, P. P. Carbone, and E. P. Vollmer, eds.), pp. 31–36. Raven, New York.

Powell, B. L., Diamond, E. J., Koprak, S., and Hollander, V. P. (1977). *Cancer Res.* **37**, 1328–1332.

Saez, S., Brunat, M., Cheix, F., Colon, J., and Mayer, M. (1978). *In* "Hormone Deprivation in Breast Cancer" (M. Mayer, S. Saez, and B. A. Stoll, eds.), pp. 37–50. Imperial Chemical Industries Limited, Cheshire, England.

Sala-Trepat, J. M., and Reti, E. (1974). *Biochim. Biophys. Acta* **338**, 92–103.

Shafie, S. M. (1980). *Science* **209**, 701–702.

Shafie, S. M., and Brooks, S. C. (1977). *Cancer Res.* **37**, 792–799.

Shafie, S. M., and Grantham, F. H. (1981). *J. Natl. Cancer Inst.* **67**, 51–56.

Shiu, R. P. C. (1979). *Cancer Res.* **39**, 4381–4386.

Shyr, C. I., and Liao, S. (1978). *Proc. Natl. Acad. Sci. U.S.A.* **75**, 5969–5973.

Simons, S. S., Jr., Martinez, H. M., Garcea, R. L., Baxter, J. D., and Tomkins, G. M. (1976). *J. Biol. Chem.* **251**, 334–343.

Singhakowinta, A., Mohindra, R., Brooks, S. C., Vaitkevicius, V. K., and Brennan, M. J. (1975). *In* "Estrogen Receptors in Human Breast Cancer" (W. L. McGuire, P. P. Carbone, and E. P. Vollmer, eds.), pp. 131–155. Raven, New York.

Sirbasku, D. A. (1978a). *Cancer Res.* **38**, 1154–1165.

Sirbasku, D. A. (1978b). *Proc. Natl. Acad. Sci. U.S.A.* **75**, 3786–3790.

Sirbasku, D. A., and Benson, R. H. (1979). *Cold Spring Harbor Conf. Cell Proliferation* **6**, 477–497.

Sonnenschein, C., and Soto, A. M. (1980). *J. Natl. Cancer Inst.* **64**, 211–215.

Soule, H. D., and McGrath, C. M. (1980). *Cancer Lett.* (*Shannon, Irel.*) **10**, 177–189.

Sterental, A., Dominguez, J. M., Weissman, C., and Pearson, O. H. (1963). *Cancer Res.* **23**, 481–484.

Stoll, B. A. (1980). *In* "Endocrine Treatment of Breast Cancer" (B. Henningsen, F. Linder, and C. Steichele, eds.), pp. 207–211. Springer–Verlag, Berlin and New York.

Strobl, J. S., and Lippman, M. E. (1979). *Cancer Res.* **39**, 3319–3327.

Thanki, K. H., Beach, T. A., Bass, A. I., and Dickerman, H. W. (1979). *Nucleic Acids Res.* **6**, 3859–3877.

Weichman, B. M., and Notides, A. C. (1977). *J. Biol. Chem.* **252**, 8856–8863.

Welsch, C. W., and Meites, J. (1978). *In* "Endocrine Control in Neoplasia" (R. K. Sharma and W. E. Criss, eds.), pp. 71–92. Raven, New York.

Witliff, J. L., and Savlov, E. D. (1975). *In* "Estrogen Receptors in Human Breast Cancer" (W. L. McGuire, P. P. Carbone, and E. P. Vollmer, eds.), pp. 73–91. Raven, New York.

CHAPTER 10

Hormonal Regulation of Estrogen and Progesterone Receptor Systems

Wendell W. Leavitt, Richard G. MacDonald, and William C. Okulicz

BIOCHEMICAL ACTIONS OF HORMONES, VOL. X

I. INTRODUCTION

The mammalian uterus is exquisitely sensitive to the ovarian steroid hormones, estrogen and progesterone, and uterine structure and function are controlled to a large extent by the combined action of these hormones during the female reproductive cycle and pregnancy (Wynn, 1977). It is now generally accepted that hormone action is mediated by specific receptor systems. Steroid hormone binding by specific cytoplasmic receptors causes receptor activation and the intracellular translocation of hormone–receptor complex to responsive acceptor sites in the target cell nucleus. This mechanism is depicted in Fig. 1.

The last decade was a period when investigators characterized the physicochemical properties of the steroid receptor proteins present in various reproductive organs (Leavitt and Clark, 1979; O'Malley and Birnbaumer, 1978). In addition, we began to gain an understanding of the underlying mechanisms controlling receptor site availability in the target organs (Brenner

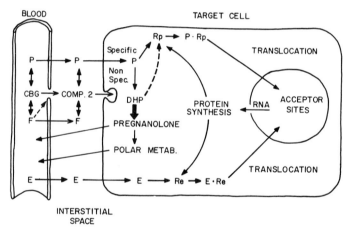

Fig. 1. Schematic representation of steroid hormone action in a uterine target cell. Estrogen (E) and progesterone (P) bind to specific receptors in the cell cytoplasm, and hormone–receptor complexes are translocated to the cell nucleus where they interact with high-affinity acceptor sites on the chromatin. Interaction of hormone–receptor complex with acceptor sites mediates a change in hormone-dependent gene expression which is manifest by alteration of RNA and protein synthesis. In the case of E action, synthesis of estrogen receptor (Re) and progesterone receptor (Rp) is stimulated, while P action blocks E-dependent Re and Rp production. Other abbreviations: CBG, corticosteroid-binding globulin; comp. 2, component 2 (Do and Leavitt, 1978); DHP, dihydroprogesterone (5α-pregnan-3,20-dione; Leavitt and Grossman, 1974); F, cortisol (hydrocortisone); Non Spec., nonspecific binding; polar metab., polar metabolites. Adapted from Leavitt et al. (1978).

and West, 1975). Progestin and estrogen exert opposing effects on both the estrogen receptor and progesterone receptor systems. As is shown in Fig. 1, estradiol action up regulates the estrogen and progesterone receptor systems by stimulation of macromolecular synthesis leading to accumulation of available receptor sites in the target cell cytoplasm (Clark *et al.*, 1978; Leavitt *et al.*, 1978). In contrast, progesterone down regulates both the estrogen and progesterone receptor systems by processes that are not fully understood (Clark *et al.*, 1977; Leavitt *et al.*, 1974; Milgrom *et al.*, 1973). Interaction of progesterone with its receptor causes loss of sites by an unknown mechanism in conjunction with receptor translocation to the target cell nucleus (Isomaa *et al.*, 1979; Leavitt *et al.*, 1979). Furthermore, progesterone inhibits or modifies many estrogen-dependent responses, including progesterone receptor synthesis (Leavitt *et al.*, 1974; Milgrom *et al.*, 1973) and estrogen receptor replenishment (Hseuh *et al.*, 1976). Thus, while we have learned much about the up regulation of uterine steroid receptors, we still do not know how the receptor systems are down regulated. In addition, we need to determine whether these and perhaps other mechanisms are operative under normal physiological conditions such as occur during the female cycle and pregnancy. Information is available on the cyclic variation of uterine receptor levels for a number of species, including the rat (Feherty *et al.*, 1970; VuHai *et al.*, 1978), hamster (Leavitt *et al.*, 1974; West *et al.*, 1978), mouse (Feil *et al.*, 1972), sheep (Miller *et al.*, 1977), monkey (Flickinger *et al.*, 1977), and human (Robel *et al.*, 1981). However, less is known about uterine receptor patterns during pregnancy and lactation (Alexandrova and Soloff, 1980a,b; VuHai *et al.*, 1978). While it has been informative to correlate serum steroid and uterine receptor levels during the cycle and pregnancy, in fact such correlations fail to establish cause and effect relationships. Experimental approaches are needed to reveal what happens to the number and subcellular distribution of receptors when serum steroids are varied within the physiological limits imposed during the cycle and pregnancy, but unfortunately few studies have approached or answered this question. The work to be reviewed in this article was aimed at determining serum steroid–uterine receptor relationships in different reproductive states. Our recent experiments revealed a novel mechanism by which progesterone regulates the nuclear retention of estrogen receptors under physiological conditions. Whatever success we have had in these studies can be attributed in large part to the golden hamster which has remarkably efficient and predictable reproductive processes and to the development of reliable methods for the simultaneous measurement of estrogen and progesterone receptors in the cytosol and nuclear fractions derived from individual tissue samples.

II. METHODS

Although several methods have been developed for the study of uterine steroid receptors, few of these procedures permit the simultaneous analysis of estrogen and progesterone receptors in cell nucleus and cytosol. The original assay developed for estrogen receptor utilized a Tris–ethylenedi-aminetetraacetate (Tris-EDTA or TE) buffer, which does not permit adequate progesterone receptor recovery. Progesterone receptor stability is improved by addition of glycerol and monothioglycerol to the TE buffer system (Feil *et al.*, 1972; Leavitt *et al.*, 1974). In addition, the nuclear exchange procedure developed for the assay of total estrogen receptor is performed with nuclear suspensions (Anderson *et al.*, 1972), and this approach is not suitable for the assay of nuclear progesterone receptor in that hormone–receptor complex is lost from nuclei even at low temperature (Chen and Leavitt, 1979; Walters and Clark, 1978; Walters *et al.*, 1980). Nuclear estrogen receptor can be measured after KCl extraction from the nuclear fraction (Zava *et al.*, 1976) and this procedure gives good receptor recovery and assay precision. Furthermore, maximum recovery of nuclear progesterone receptor can be achieved by extraction from nuclei with Tris buffer containing glycerol and 0.5 M KCl (Chen and Leavitt, 1979; Chen *et al.*, 1981). Based on these considerations, we developed and validated an assay that is appropriate for studying the subcellular distribution of estrogen and progesterone receptors in uterine tissues during the estrous cycle and pregnancy (Evans *et al.*, 1980; Leavitt *et al.*, 1979). As is shown in Fig. 2, cytosol and nuclear KCl extract are prepared from a fresh tissue homogenate. Cytosol receptors are assayed at 0°C for 16–18 hours which provides the total progesterone receptor (Leavitt *et al.*, 1974) and the unoccupied estrogen receptor (Katzenellenbogen *et al.*, 1973). Total estrogen receptor can be determined by exchange assay at 30°C for 1 hour, and occupied receptor is estimated from the difference between total and unoccupied receptor (Okulicz *et al.*, 1981a). The solubilized nuclear receptors are measured by exchange assay performed at 30°C for 1 hour in the case of estrogen receptor (Evans *et al.*, 1980) and at 0°C for 16–18 hours for progesterone receptor (Chen and Leavitt, 1979). The nuclear exchange assays determine total receptor and also permit estimation of unlabeled steroid in the nuclear KCl extract (Fig. 3). The slope of the Scatchard relationship varies as a function of the unlabeled steroid content of nuclear KCl extract (Chen and Leavitt, 1979; Leavitt *et al.*, 1979). The amount of steroid associated with nuclear receptor can be estimated if the equilibrium association constant (K_A) is known, and the true K_A can be derived from the equation for slope (Fig. 3) when steroid content is known. In practical terms, this means that there is enough unlabeled steroid present in nuclear KCl extract to affect the slope of the Scatchard relationship.

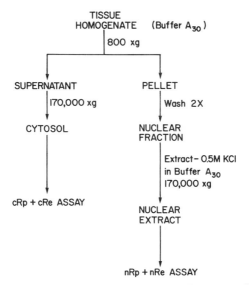

FIG. 2. Flow diagram of cytosol and nuclear receptor isolation procedure. Buffer A_{30} [50 mM Tris–HCl, 1 mM ethylenediaminetetraacetate (EDTA), 12 mM monothioglycerol, 30% glycerol, v/v, pH 7.5] was used throughout; see text for details. Abbreviations: c, cytosol; n, nuclear; Re, estrogen receptor; Rp, progesterone receptor.

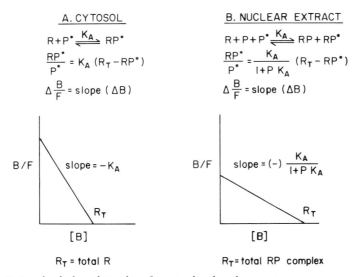

FIG. 3. Scatchard plot relationships for cytosol and nuclear progesterone receptor assays. (A) The relationship for cytosol receptor assay is as previously described (Leavitt *et al.*, 1978). (B) The exchange assay for nuclear progesterone receptor produces a more complex Scatchard relationship, and the assay results permit calculation of total receptor (R_T), K_A if P is known, and P if K_A is known. Adapted from Chen and Leavitt (1979). Abbreviations: B, bound; B/F, bound/free; K_A, equilibrium association constant; P, unlabeled steroid; P*, labeled steroid; R, receptor; RP, unlabeled complex; RP*, labeled complex; R_T, total receptor.

Thus, the K_A can only be derived from the slope after correction for the influence of endogenous steroid.

Recently, two types of estrogen-binding sites have been demonstrated in the nuclear fraction of rat uterus using the [³H]estradiol exchange assay (Clark *et al.*, 1979; Eriksson *et al.*, 1978). The type I binding site possessed properties of the classical estrogen receptor whereas the type II binding site had a greater binding capacity and a lower affinity than the type I site. Type I and II sites have also been detected in hamster uterine nuclei (Fig. 4). However, only the type I site (estrogen receptor) was solubilized by KCl extraction, and the type II site lacked estrogen-binding specificity (Okulicz *et al.*, 1981b). The properties of type II sites (high capacity, low affinity, and lack of estrogen specificity) indicate that these latter sites do not participate in receptor-mediated estrogen action. Therefore, the true nuclear estrogen receptor can be separated from type II sites by KCl extraction and measured by exchange assay as described above (Okulicz *et al.*, 1981b).

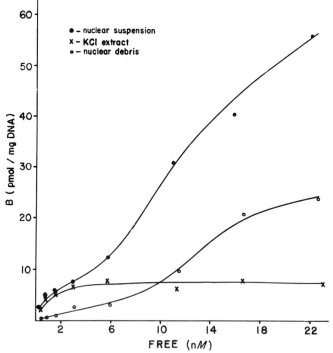

FIG. 4. Estrogen-binding sites in hamster uterine nuclei. Two types of binding sites are detected in a nuclear suspension (●). The estrogen receptor (type I site, X) is extracted with 0.5 *M* KCl. The type II site (O) is not extracted by 0.5 *M* KCl and remains associated with the nuclear debris. Thus, the estrogen receptor can be separated from type II sites by KCl extraction. From Okulicz *et al.* (1981b).

III. SERUM STEROID–UTERINE RECEPTOR RELATIONSHIPS

A. THE ESTROUS CYCLE

Our previous studies with the golden hamster established that estrogen secretion during the follicular phase of the estrous cycle stimulates the synthesis and accumulation of progesterone receptor in uterine cytosol (Leavitt *et al.*, 1974, 1977, 1979). Uterine nuclear estrogen receptor levels increase during the follicular phase of the cycle in association with the elevation of serum estradiol (Evans *et al.*, 1980; West *et al.*, 1978). Thus, a positive relationship among serum estradiol, nuclear estrogen receptor, and cytosol progesterone receptor levels has been documented for the follicular phase of the hamster cycle (Fig. 5).

Serum steroid–uterine receptor relationships during the ovulatory phase of the cycle are less well understood (Fig. 6). This is a period of rapid

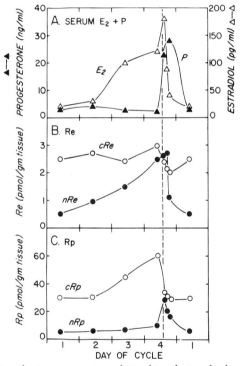

FIG. 5. Serum steroid–uterine receptor relationships during the hamster estrous cycle. Data are taken from Chen and Leavitt (1979) and Evans *et al.* (1980). The dashed vertical line indicates the time of the critical period for the ovulatory surge of gonadotropin. Abbreviations: c, cytosol; E_2, estradiol-17β; n, nuclear; P, progesterone; Re, estrogen receptor; Rp, progesterone receptor.

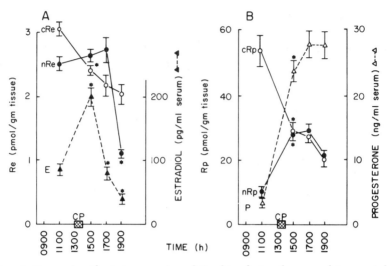

FIG. 6. Serum steroid–uterine receptor relationships during the preovulatory period on day 4 (proestrus) of the hamster estrous cycle. Each point represents the mean ± SE ($n = 5$). The critical period (CP) for the ovulatory surge of gonadotropin is indicated by hatched box below. Abbreviations are as in Fig. 5. *$p < 0.05$. From Evans et al. (1980).

change in ovarian steroid secretion, so the relationships between serum estrogen and progesterone and the subcellular distribution of uterine estrogen and progesterone receptors were examined at frequent intervals during the preovulatory period on cycle day 4 (Evans et al., 1980). Following the critical period for gonadotropin release on the afternoon of proestrus, there was a transient surge of serum estradiol and a sustained elevation of serum progesterone (Fig. 6). Cytosol progesterone receptor was translocated to the nucleus in conjunction with preovulatory progesterone secretion (Fig. 6B). However, cytosol estrogen receptor depletion during the estradiol surge did not result in a significant increase in nuclear receptor (Fig. 6A). Nuclear estrogen receptor levels remained constant up to 1700 hours, after which time they declined as serum estradiol fell. Total estrogen receptor declined at 1500 hours in association with cytosol receptor depletion, and the sharp fall of nuclear receptor at 1900 hours accounted for a further reduction in total uterine estrogen receptor (Evans et al., 1980). Experimental studies (see Section IV) revealed that the rapid decline of nuclear estrogen receptor during the ovulatory phase of the cycle was the result of progesterone action and not estrogen withdrawal (Evans et al., 1980). Cytosol estrogen and progesterone receptors dropped during the ovulatory phase of the cycle in association with the preovulatory surge of estradiol and progesterone secretion, respectively (Fig. 5). However, by the next morning (day 1), cytosol estrogen receptor levels had recovered, but cytosol progesterone receptor had not. These results are consistent with the idea that progesterone causes degradation of its receptor (Leavitt *et al.*, 1974; Milgrom *et al.*, 1973) but at odds with the suggestion that progesterone blocks cytosol estrogen receptor replenishment during the estrous cycle (West *et al.*, 1978). Apparently, cytosol estrogen receptor levels are not altered appreciably by hormone action during the cycle whereas cytosol progesterone receptor waxes and wanes in response to estrogen and progestin action, respectively. Two pools of progesterone receptor have been identified, one that is independent of hormonal support and one that is dependent on estrogen stimulation (Allen and Leavitt, 1981; Leavitt *et al.*, 1977). It would appear that hormone action regulates the estrogen-dependent pool of progesterone receptor during the estrous cycle.

B. PREGNANCY AND PSEUDOPREGNANCY

The hamster, like other rodent species, depends on ovarian progesterone for pregnancy maintenance (Weitlauf and Greenwald, 1967), and parturition is triggered by the prepartum decline in luteal progesterone secretion (Csapo and Wiest, 1969; Leavitt and Blaha, 1970). During hamster pregnancy, estrogen secretion follows a pattern similar to that observed for progesterone, dropping before term (Baranczuk and Greenwald, 1974). This is in contrast to the pregnant rat, which has a prepartum increase in estrogen secretion (Shaikh, 1971; Labhsetwar and Watson, 1974). Thus, the hamster maintains a rather constant ratio of estrogen to progesterone throughout pregnancy (Fig. 7), while the rat exhibits a dramatic increase in the estrogen: progesterone ratio at term (Alexandrova and Soloff, 1980a). As in the pregnant rat (Alexandrova and Soloff, 1980a; VuHai *et al.*, 1978), myometrial estrogen and progesterone receptors remain low until ovarian steroid secretion changes before term in the hamster (Fig. 7). Cytosol estrogen and progesterone receptors increase in the myometrium in association with the decrease in serum estradiol and progesterone levels prior to parturition. Of interest is the prepartum elevation of nuclear estrogen receptor which occurs in the face of falling serum estrogen levels. Thus, the prepartum increase in nuclear estrogen receptor in hamster myometrium appears to be correlated with progesterone withdrawal rather than with a change in serum estradiol.

In the pseudopregnant hamster, ovarian progesterone secretion is maintained for 7 or 8 days depending on the condition of the uterus (Greenwald and Bast, 1978; Terranova, 1975). When the uterus is decidualized, progesterone drops and estrogen rises on days 8 and 9 (Fig. 8), and the

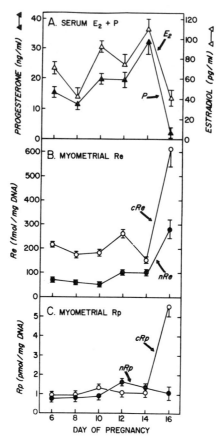

FIG. 7. Serum steroid–myometrial receptor relationships during pregnancy in the hamster. Parturition occurs on day 16. Abbreviations are as in Fig. 5. From Leavitt *et al.* (1983).

deciduoma, which requires progesterone for its growth and differentiation, involutes on day 9 (Leavitt *et al.*, 1979). Progesterone and estrogen receptors in myometrium are reduced to low levels until day 9. Then progesterone receptor increases in myometrial cytosol in conjunction with progesterone withdrawal, and cytosol and nuclear estrogen receptors increase as estradiol titers rise. In comparing the myometrial receptor responses to the change in ovarian steroid secretion at the end of pregnancy (Fig. 7) and pseudo-pregnancy (Fig. 8), it is evident that nuclear estrogen receptor increases to the same extent in both cases. This observation suggests that the rise in nuclear estrogen receptor may be a response to progesterone withdrawal. However, when serum estrogen is kept high, as in pseudopregnancy, the tendency is for lower cytosol estrogen receptor and higher cytosol progesterone

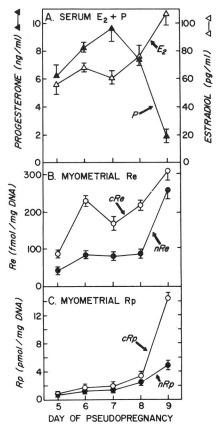

FIG. 8. Serum steroid–myometrial receptor relationships during pseudopregnancy in the hamster. Deciduoma were induced on day 4, and deciduomal involution occurred on day 9. Abbreviations are as in Fig. 5. From Leavitt *et al.* (1983).

receptor. Apparently, estrogen exposure promotes depletion of its cytosol receptor and stimulates progesterone receptor production.

IV. PROGESTERONE REGULATION OF NUCLEAR ESTROGEN RECEPTOR DURING THE ESTROUS CYCLE

A. Estrogen Withdrawal versus Progesterone Action in Hamster and Rat Uterus

Comparable patterns of uterine nuclear estrogen receptor are observed during the rat and hamster estrous cycles (Clark *et al.*, 1972; Evans *et al.*,

1980) (Fig. 5). There is general agreement that nuclear estrogen receptor
increases during the follicular phase of the cycle in response to the elevation
of circulating estradiol levels, but experimental evidence was lacking as to
the cause of the nuclear receptor decline during the ovulatory phase of the
cycle. To distinguish between the effect of estrogen withdrawal and progesterone action on uterine estrogen receptor during the ovulatory period,
hamsters were ovariectomized at 0800 hours on cycle day 3 (diestrus) and
given subcutaneous estradiol implants for 24 hours (Evans *et al.*, 1980).
The estradiol implants maintained serum estradiol at approximately 200 pg/
ml and stimulated uterine weight gain, luminal fluid accumulation, and
cytosol progesterone receptor synthesis to levels comparable to those observed
at proestrus. Removal of the estradiol implants resulted in the rapid decline
($t_{1/2}$ = 20–30 minutes) of serum estradiol. Following estrogen withdrawal,
cytosol estrogen receptor rose and nuclear estrogen receptor decreased by
an approximately equal increment, such that total receptor did not decline
during the 8-hour period studied (Fig. 9). However, when estradiol implants
were left in place and progesterone administered, nuclear estrogen receptor

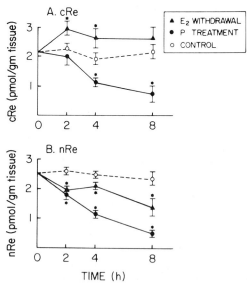

FIG. 9. The time course of cytosol (A) and nuclear (B) estrogen receptor response to estrogen
withdrawal or progesterone treatment. Hamsters were ovariectomized and given estradiol
implants subcutaneously at 0800 hours on cycle day 3 (diestrus). Treatments were administered
24 hours later: estradiol implant removed (E$_2$ withdrawal, ▲); progesterone treatment (2.5
mg/100 gm body weight) with estradiol implant retained (P treatment, ●); and control (estradiol
implant retained, ○). Receptors were measured at the times indicated. Each point represents
the mean ± SE (n = 6). *p < 0.05. Abbreviations are as in Fig. 5. From Evans *et al.* (1980).

dropped at 2 hours and continued to fall progressively from 2 to 8 hours (Fig. 9B). Although serum estradiol was maintained by the estradiol implant, progesterone treatment caused a large reduction in total uterine estrogen receptor.

A second experiment was done in which the preovulatory changes in serum steroids on cycle day 4 were approximated by combining estrogen withdrawal and progesterone treatment; estrogen receptor was measured 4 hours later (Fig. 10). Again estradiol withdrawal altered estrogen receptor distribution between the cytosol and nuclear fractions, and progesterone treatment with circulating estradiol maintenance caused a large decrease in both nuclear and cytosol estrogen receptor. When estrogen withdrawal was combined with progesterone treatment, nuclear estrogen receptor was again greatly reduced but cytosol receptor did not fall (Fig. 10). Thus, progesterone treatment selectively reduced nuclear estrogen receptor, and cytosol receptor depletion following progesterone treatment was dependent on exposure to serum estradiol. Of interest was the observation that nuclear and cytosol estrogen receptor levels 4 hours after combined estrogen withdrawal and progesterone treatment (Fig. 10) were equivalent to those measured at 1900 hours on day 4, approximately 4 hours after serum estradiol began to fall and serum progesterone became elevated (see Fig. 6). These

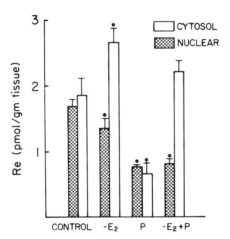

FIG. 10. Uterine estrogen receptor (Re) response to progesterone action with and without estrogen withdrawal. Hamsters were prepared as described in Fig. 9. Treatments: estradiol implant retained (control); estrogen withdrawal ($-E_2$); progesterone treatment (P) with estradiol implant retained; and combined estrogen withdrawal and progesterone treatment ($-E_2 + P$). Receptors were measured 4 hours after treatment. Values represent the mean ± SE ($n = 6$). *$p < 0.05$. From Evans *et al.* (1980).

results demonstrate that (1) estrogen withdrawal does not account for either the decline of total estrogen receptor or the extent of nuclear estrogen receptor reduction observed during the ovulatory phase of the estrous cycle, and (2) progesterone action was responsible for the rapid and selective reduction of nuclear estrogen receptor.

Inhibition of cytosol estrogen receptor replenishment has been suggested as a mechanism of progesterone antagonism of estrogen action in the rat uterus (Clark *et al.*, 1977). We designed an experiment to examine the short-term effects of progesterone on nuclear estrogen receptor levels in rat uterus (Okulicz *et al.*, 1981c) using the same approach employed previously with the hamster (Evans *et al.*, 1980). One week after combined ovariectomy and adrenalectomy and placement of estradiol implants, groups of rats were assayed for uterine nuclear and cytosol estrogen receptor at 2, 4, and 8 hours following estrogen withdrawal, progesterone treatment, and combined estrogen withdrawal and progesterone treatment. Rats with the estradiol implants left in place served as controls. All groups not receiving progesterone were treated with corn oil vehicle.

Progesterone treatment under conditions that promote translocation of estrogen receptor (implants retained) caused a significant reduction in total estrogen receptor compared to control at 4 and 8 hours after treatment (Okulicz *et al.*, 1981c). In contrast, estrogen withdrawal caused a significant increase in total receptor at each time examined (Fig. 11). When estrogen withdrawal was combined with progesterone treatment, at 2 hours there was an increase in total receptor similar to hormone withdrawal alone, and subsequently (4 and 8 hours) total receptor returned to control levels.

The decrease in total estrogen receptor observed with progesterone treatment can be attributed to a reduction in nuclear receptor levels at 4 and 8 hours since cytosol receptor levels did not change significantly (Fig. 11). Thus, progesterone rapidly and selectively reduced nuclear estrogen receptor retention in the rat uterus. The nuclear receptor level did not change in response to estrogen withdrawal until 8 hours after the hormone implants were removed, reflecting a prolonged nuclear receptor retention. However, when progesterone treatment was combined with estrogen withdrawal, nuclear receptor retention was reduced at 4 hours, which was the same result as progesterone treatment with estradiol maintenance.

The increase in total estrogen receptor observed in the estrogen withdrawn group was due to an elevation of cytosol estrogen receptor at all time periods examined (Fig. 11B). Thus, interruption of receptor translocation led to a rapid (<2 hours) accumulation of cytosol receptor which was also apparent at 4 and 8 hours after estrogen withdrawal. The accumulation of cytosol receptor at 2 hours in the combined treatment group ($-E + P$) accounted for the elevation of total estrogen receptor at this time. However, in contrast to estrogen withdrawal ($-E$), accumulation of cytosol receptor did not lead

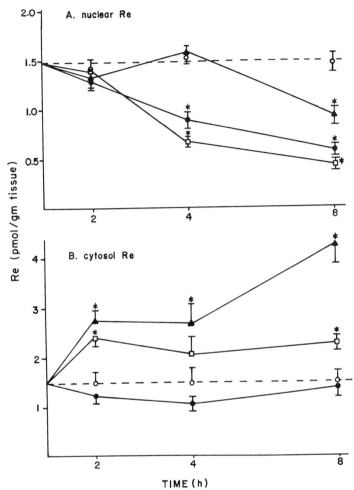

FIG. 11. Time course of nuclear (A) and cytosol (B) estrogen receptor (Re) responses in rat uterus to progesterone action and estrogen withdrawal. Ovariectomized, adrenalectomized rats were given estradiol implants for 1 week prior to treatment: estrogen withdrawal (implants removed, − E, ▲); progesterone treatment (10 mg progesterone/rat with implants retained, + P, ●); combined estrogen withdrawal and progesterone treatment (implants removed and 10 mg progesterone/rat, − E + P, □); control (implants retained, ○). Receptors were measured at the times indicated. Each point represents the mean ± SE (n = 5 or more). *p < 0.05. From Okulicz *et al.* (1981c).

to an increase in total receptor at 4 and 8 hours after − E + P treatment apparently because progesterone action reduced nuclear estrogen receptor at these later times. In addition, progesterone inhibited accumulation of cytosol receptor at 8 hours following estrogen withdrawal (compare − E and − E + P, Fig. 11B).

These experiments clearly demonstrate an early and selective action of progesterone on nuclear estrogen receptor in the hamster and rat uterus (Evans *et al.*, 1980; Okulicz *et al.*, 1981c). As to whether the fall in nuclear estrogen receptor during the ovulatory period of the estrous cycle could be ascribed to progesterone action or estrogen withdrawal, progesterone action was shown to reduce total estrogen receptor within 2–4 hours by selective inhibition of nuclear receptor (Figs. 9 and 11). In contrast, estrogen withdrawal altered the subcellular distribution of estrogen receptor without decreasing total receptor levels. Thus, it can be concluded that progesterone action is responsible for the rapid clearance of nuclear estrogen receptor, while estrogen withdrawal interrupts cytosol receptor translocation to the nuclear fraction. The responses of cytosol estrogen receptor during pro-gesterone action with or without maintenance of circulating estradiol indicate that cytosol receptor depletion is regulated primarily by estrogen-induced receptor translocation rather than progesterone inhibition of cytosol receptor replenishment.

B. Dose–Response and Specificity Studies

The progesterone dose dependency and steroid specificity of progesterone receptor translocation in the hamster uterus have been established (Chen and Leavitt, 1979; Leavitt *et al.*, 1979). In order to evaluate the nuclear estrogen receptor response to progesterone action, animals were ovariec-tomized at 0800 hours on cycle day 4, given 1 μg estradiol, and either various doses of progesterone or a 1-mg dose of different steroids (Evans *et al.*, 1980). Estrogen receptor response was measured 4 hours after steroid treatment. Nuclear estrogen receptor was reduced in a dose-dependent manner, and a dose of 1 mg progesterone/100 gm body weight lowered nuclear estrogen receptor by 50%, which was the maximum response. A 1-mg dose of deoxycorticosterone caused a maximum nuclear receptor response; testosterone was somewhat effective; and dihydroprogesterone (5α-preg-nanedione) and cortisol were inactive (Evans *et al.*, 1980). Thus, nuclear estrogen receptor depletion is a sensitive and specific end point of progestin action. This is particularly evident when the dose–response curves for progesterone and estrogen receptor responses to progesterone action are compared (Fig. 12). There is a good correlation between progesterone receptor translocation to the nuclear fraction and the subsequent decline of nuclear estrogen receptor. Thus, the progesterone receptor system appears to mediate the nuclear estrogen receptor response to progestin action, but the mechanism remains to be clarified.

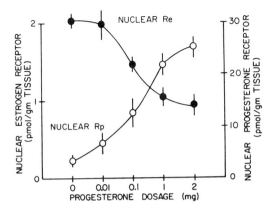

FIG. 12. Comparison of nuclear estrogen receptor (Re) and progesterone receptor (Rp) responses to graded doses of progesterone (mg/100 gm body weight). The progesterone receptor response was measured at 2 hours after progesterone treatment, and the nuclear estrogen receptor response was at 4 hours after progesterone. Each point represents the mean ± SE (*n* = 5 or more). Data are taken from Chen and Leavitt (1979) and Evans *et al.* (1980).

C. [³H]ESTRADIOL RETENTION

In this study, the effect of progesterone on uterine uptake and retention of [³H]estradiol was examined (Evans and Leavitt, 1980a). Hamsters were ovariectomized and given subcutaneous estradiol implants. At the time of [³H]estradiol injection (0.1 μg/100 gm body weight), the estradiol implants were removed and either progesterone (2.5 mg/100 gm body weight) or corn oil vehicle (control) were injected. At 1, 2, and 4 hours after treatment, blood, uteri, and segments of the small intestine (control tissue) were collected. Cytosol and nuclear KCl-extract fractions were prepared, and bound radioactivity was measured after dextran–charcoal adsorption of free steroid. Specifically bound [³H]estradiol was limited to the cytosol and nuclear fractions of the uterus. Progesterone had no influence on blood or cytosol radioactivity, or the initial (1–2 hours) uptake of radioactivity by the uterine nuclear fraction (Fig. 13). However, at 4 hours after treatment, the amount of radioactivity retained by the uterine nuclear fraction was reduced in progesterone-treated animals. Bound radioactivity that was lost from the nuclear fraction did not appear in the cytosol fraction. KCl-resistant nuclear radioactivity was monitored and, though present at much lower levels (ca. 10% of total nuclear radioactivity), it followed the pattern of KCl-extractable radioactivity. These results indicate that reduction of uterine nuclear estrogen receptor stems from the progesterone-stimulated loss of

Wendell W. Leavitt et al.

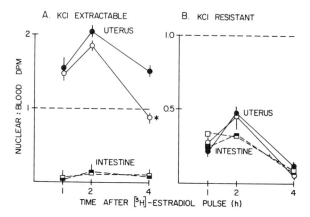

FIG. 13. Nuclear retention of [³H]estradiol in hamster uterus and small intestine. (A) KCl-extractable radioactivity is the radioactivity bound in the nuclear KCl extract. (B) KCl-resistant radioactivity is that extracted by ethanol from the KCl-extracted nuclear pellet. Nuclear radioactivity is expressed relative to blood radioactivity at various intervals after [³H]estradiol injection with (open symbols) or without (closed symbols) progesterone treatment. *$p < 0.01$ progesterone versus control treatment. From Evans and Leavitt (1980a).

receptor from the nuclear fraction and not from the inhibition of cytosol receptor translocation.

D. Occupied versus Unoccupied Nuclear Receptor

An experiment was done to determine whether the progesterone-induced loss of nuclear estrogen receptor was accounted for by either the occupied or unoccupied forms of receptor in proestrous hamster uterus. In previous studies (Evans et al., 1980), the total nuclear estrogen receptor was measured by [³H]estradiol exchange assay performed at an elevated incubation temperature (30°C). The exchange assay does not distinguish between receptor that is bound to hormone (occupied) from receptor that is not (unoccupied). The difference between total receptor measured under exchange conditions and unoccupied receptor assayed at 0°–4°C provided the estimate of the hormone–receptor complex (Okulicz et al., 1981a).

Following progesterone administration (5 mg/100 gm body weight), there was no change in occupied cytosol estrogen receptor during the 4-hour period of observation (Fig. 14). At all time periods, unoccupied receptor accounted for 75–80% of the total cytosol receptor. Consistent with results obtained previously, total nuclear estrogen receptor dropped between 2

and 4 hours after progesterone treatment (Fig. 14). Although unoccupied
estrogen receptor constituted a large proportion (50–60%) of the total nuclear
receptor, progesterone did not significantly alter the amount of this form
of estrogen receptor. However, occupied nuclear receptor was reduced
dramatically to the limit of detection between 2 and 4 hours following
progesterone treatment. These results demonstrate that progesterone acts
selectively on the occupied form of nuclear estrogen receptor with no effect
on the level of the unoccupied form.

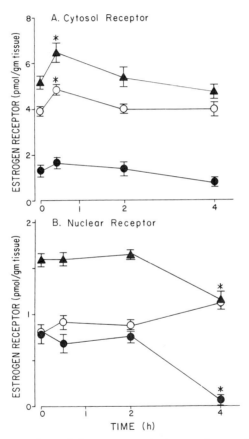

FIG. 14. The response of occupied estrogen receptor to progesterone action in the proestrous
hamster uterus. Total receptor (▲) was determined by exchange assay performed at 30°C for
1 hour. Unoccupied receptor (○) was measured at 0°C for 18 hours, and occupied receptor
(●) was the difference between the total and unoccupied level. Values represent the mean
± SE ($n = 6$). *$p < 0.05$. From Okulicz et al. (1981a). Science 213, 1503–1505. Copyright
1981 by the American Association for the Advancement of Science.

E. Involvement of RNA and Protein Synthesis

It was next of interest to investigate the mechanism of progesterone action in the regulation of uterine nuclear estrogen receptor (Evans and Leavitt, 1980b). According to the receptor hypothesis for steroid hormone action, translocation of the hormone–receptor complex from the cytoplasm to the nucleus alters gene expression with consequent changes in RNA and protein synthesis (Fig. 1). If progesterone acts through such a mechanism to cause the decline of nuclear estrogen receptor, then inhibitors of RNA and protein synthesis would be expected to block the response of nuclear estrogen receptor to progesterone action. A previously characterized *in vitro* uterine strip system (Leavitt *et al.*, 1977, 1980) was used to test this possibility. In this *in vitro* system, estrogen action stimulates the synthesis of cytoplasmic progesterone receptor, and progesterone treatment causes progesterone receptor translocation to the nucleus (Leavitt *et al.*, 1980). The responsiveness of uterine strips to progesterone action was established first by demonstrating that progesterone-induced progesterone receptor depletion was correlated with a rapid decline of nuclear estrogen receptor (Evans and Leavitt, 1980b). Second, through the use of the inhibitors actinomycin D, puromycin, and cycloheximide, it was determined that the progesterone-induced decline of nuclear estrogen receptor was dependent on RNA and protein synthesis (Fig. 15).

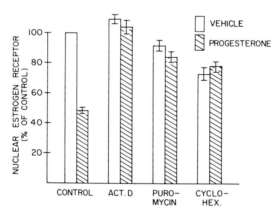

FIG. 15. Effect of RNA and protein synthesis inhibitors on nuclear estrogen receptor response to progesterone action *in vitro*. Uterine strips were pretreated with 30 nM estradiol to stimulate synthesis of progesterone receptor (Leavitt *et al.*, 1977). After 11.5 hours of incubation, inhibitor (10 µg/ml medium) or a vehicle control treatment was given, and 30 minutes later either 0.1 µM progesterone (hatched bars) or vehicle (open bars) was added to the strips for the next 4 hours. Values are the mean ± SE ($n = 6$). Abbreviations: ACT.D, actinomycin D; CYCLOHEX., cycloheximide. From Evans and Leavitt (1980b).

F. Characterization of Estrogen Receptor-Regulatory Factor

Collectively, the previous results suggested that progesterone might induce a factor, estrogen receptor-regulatory factor (ReRF), that acts on the occupied form of estrogen receptor in the target cell nucleus. To test this hypothesis, we determined whether a progesterone-induced ReRF could be demonstrated in a cell-free system (Okulicz *et al.*, 1981d). When uterine nuclear suspensions from progesterone-treated proestrous hamsters were incubated at 37°C (Fig. 16), nuclear estrogen receptor was lost more rapidly in nuclear suspension prepared at 2 hours after progesterone treatment than at 30 minutes or at zero time. In addition, the occupied form of nuclear estrogen receptor decayed more rapidly than the unoccupied form (Fig. 16B). Thus, a progesterone-induced activity capable of degrading estrogen receptor was associated with the nuclear fraction. This activity could be extracted from the uterine nuclei using 0.5 M KCl in buffer A_{30} (see Fig. 2). Nuclear KCl extract from progesterone-treated animals showed an enhanced estrogen receptor loss at 37°C, and the occupied receptor appeared to be the preferred substrate (Fig. 17). The presence of the putative ReRF activity and its

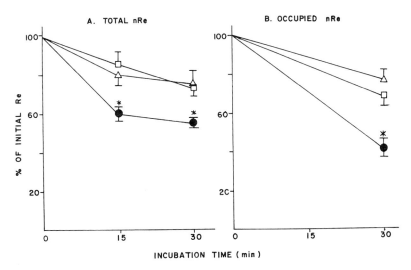

FIG. 16. Nuclear estrogen receptor (nRe) loss from uterine nuclei incubated at 37°C in a cell-free system. Proestrous hamsters were treated with progesterone, and uterine nuclei were prepared at 0 time, 30 minutes, and 2 hours later. Nuclear suspensions were incubated for the indicated times at 37°C in buffer A_{30} (see Fig. 2). Nuclear receptor is expressed as a percentage of the initial level (0 time). Control (□); 30 minutes after progesterone (△); and 2 hours after progesterone (●) *$p < 0.05$. From Okulicz *et al.* (1981d).

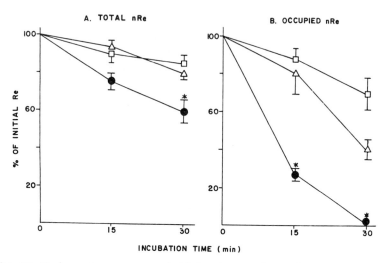

FIG. 17. Nuclear estrogen receptor (nRe) loss from nuclear KCl extract at 37°C. The experimental conditions were identical to those described in Fig. 16. Nuclei were obtained at 0 time (□), 30 minutes (△), and 2 hours (●) after progesterone treatment of proestrous hamsters. *$p < 0.05$. From Okulicz *et al.* (1981d).

receptor substrate in the nuclear KCl extract permitted a preliminary characterization of the factor. It appears unlikely that ReRF is a protease because various protease inhibitors [including N-ethylmaleimide, phenylmethylsulfonyl fluoride (PMSF), pepstatin, leupeptin, and soybean trypsin inhibitor] failed to block progesterone-induced estrogen receptor loss in the cell-free assay system (R. G. MacDonald, W. C. Okulicz, and W. W. Leavitt, unpublished results). It is pertinent that ReRF activity is diminished by phosphate (Okulicz *et al.*, 1981d) and that it is blocked by the phosphatase inhibitors molybdate and vanadate (Fig. 18). These results suggest that ReRF could be a phosphatase or an activator of phosphatase activity. Currently, studies are under way to isolate and identify ReRF.

V. ESTROGEN RECEPTOR RECOVERY IN THE PROGESTERONE-DOMINATED UTERUS

A. RESPONSE TO PROGESTERONE WITHDRAWAL

Progesterone is known to suppress the estrogen receptor system (Brenner *et al.*, 1979; Clark *et al.*, 1977), and estrogen receptors are reduced to low

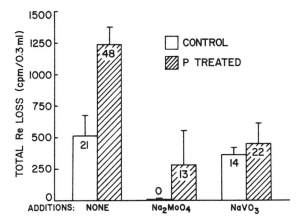

FIG. 18. Inhibition of nuclear estrogen receptor (Re) loss by phosphatase inhibitors. Uterine nuclear KCl extract was prepared from hamsters treated for 2 hours with progesterone (hatched bars) or vehicle (control, open bars). Nuclear extract was pretreated with 10 mM sodium molybdate or 10 mM sodium vanadate for 30 minutes at 0°C and then incubated at 37°C for 30 minutes. The bars represent the mean ± SE estrogen receptor loss, and the number in each bar is the percentage of receptor lost at 37°C relative to that at 0°C. Abbreviations: Na_2MoO_4, sodium molybdate; $NaVO_3$, sodium vanadate; P, progesterone. From Okulicz *et al.* (1981d).

levels during pregnancy (Fig. 7) and pseudopregnancy (Fig. 8). We reasoned that information pertinent to the mechanism involved might be obtained by studying the recovery of the estrogen receptor system following progesterone withdrawal. Of interest are recent results obtained with the pseudopregnant decidualized hamster (Leavitt *et al.*, 1983) which demonstrate a rapid recovery of nuclear and cytosol estrogen receptors in myometrium within 4 to 8 hours after progesterone withdrawal. Animals were ovariectomized, and serum hormone titers were maintained constant by subcutaneous implants of estradiol and progesterone until the time of progesterone withdrawal. Serum estradiol levels were maintained at 100 pg/ml by an estradiol implant while serum progesterone falls rapidly after removal of the progesterone implant (Fig. 19). It is noteworthy that nuclear estrogen receptor increased within 4–8 hours and cytosol estrogen receptor rose at 8 hours following progesterone withdrawal despite the fact that serum estradiol remained unchanged. Since estrogen action stimulates the synthesis of progesterone receptor (Leavitt *et al.*, 1977) and oxytocin receptor (Nissenson *et al.*, 1978; Soloff, 1975) in myometrium, it was of interest to correlate changes in these end points of estrogen action with the recovery of the estrogen receptor system (Fig. 19). Oxytocin receptor concentration in the myometrial membrane fraction began to increase at 8 hours and rose dra-

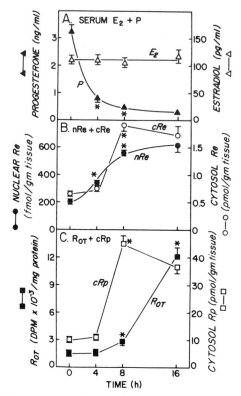

FIG. 19. Myometrial receptor response to progesterone withdrawal in the pseudopregnant decidualized hamster. Pseudopregnant hamsters were ovariectomized at the time of deciduomal induction (day 4), and Silastic estradiol and progesterone implants were placed subcutaneously. Progesterone implants were removed on day 8, and receptor responses were measured at the indicated times thereafter. R_{OT}, oxytocin receptor; other abbreviations are as in Fig. 5. $*p < 0.05$.

matically by 16 hours of progesterone withdrawal. Although progesterone receptor levels are influenced by the decline in serum progesterone in addition to estrogen stimulation, the first significant response of cytosol progesterone receptor was noted at 8 hours. Thus, these studies demonstrate that the earliest response that can be detected upon progesterone withdrawal is the recovery of nuclear estrogen receptor. Cytosol estrogen receptor also increases greatly, but the cytosol receptor response appears to follow temporally the change in nuclear estrogen receptor. In addition, estrogen-dependent proteins such as oxytocin receptor and progesterone receptor respond after nuclear estrogen receptor has increased. These results suggest the hypothesis that progesterone action inhibits nuclear estrogen receptor levels and that this leads to suppression of estrogen-dependent protein synthesis including the production of progesterone receptor, oxytocin receptor, and the estrogen receptor itself. This hypothesis is supported by observations made in a companion experiment which was done to compare the effects of estrogen and progesterone withdrawal on myometrial receptor levels in the pseudopregnant decidualized hamster (Fig. 20). Again, progesterone withdrawal caused an elevation in nuclear estrogen receptor at 4 hours whether or not serum estrogen levels were maintained. However, the nuclear estrogen receptor response at 8 hours following progesterone withdrawal was dependent on the presence of serum estradiol, and the cytosol estrogen and progesterone receptor responses at 8 hours were enhanced when serum estradiol was maintained. From this, it would appear that although nuclear estrogen receptor recovery is a rapid response to progesterone withdrawal, serum estrogen is required to sustain nuclear receptor levels. Furthermore, it appears significant that total estrogen receptor levels increased to the same extent after progesterone withdrawal with and without serum

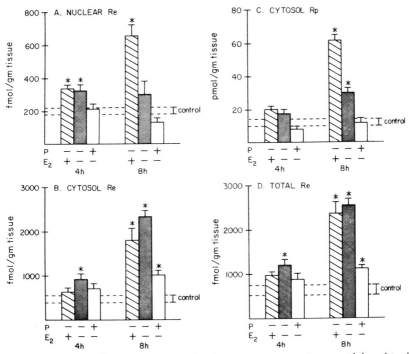

FIG. 20. Myometrial receptor response to estrogen versus progesterone withdrawal in the pseudopregnant decidualized hamster. Animals were prepared as described in Fig. 19. Hormone implants were removed on day 8, and receptor responses were measured at 4 and 8 hours thereafter. Abbreviations are as in Fig. 5. *$p < 0.05$.

estradiol maintenance, but estrogen receptor distribution between nucleus and cytosol was a function of estrogen exposure (Fig. 20).

B. Effect of Cycloheximide

In order to determine whether protein synthesis was required for the myometrial receptor responses to progesterone withdrawal (Figs. 19 and 20), the inhibitor cycloheximide was used (Leavitt *et al.*, 1983). Pseudo-pregnant decidualized hamsters were prepared with subcutaneous estradiol and progesterone implants as before. Progesterone withdrawal occurred at time 0; cycloheximide (10 mg/animal) or saline vehicle were injected intraperitoneally at 4 hours; and myometrial receptors were measured at 8 hours after progesterone withdrawal. The estrogen receptor, oxytocin receptor, and progesterone receptor responses to progesterone withdrawal were all blocked by cycloheximide treatment (Fig. 21). Although other interpretations are possible, these results suggest that the recovery of the estrogen receptor system from suppression by progesterone is dependent on protein synthesis. Whether this involves sequential production of estrogen receptor followed by progesterone and oxytocin receptors remains to be determined.

VI. SUMMARY AND CONCLUSIONS

A. Mechanism of Progesterone Action

Our experiments demonstrate for the first time an early and selective action of progesterone on nuclear estrogen receptor retention in the hamster and rat uterus (Evans *et al.*, 1980; Okulicz *et al.*, 1981c). Progesterone-induced loss of nuclear estrogen receptor appears to proceed through progesterone receptor translocation (Fig. 12) and the stimulation of RNA and protein synthesis (Evans and Leavitt, 1980b) (see Fig. 22). The nuclear estrogen receptor response to progesterone action is rapid and may be an important first step in the control of estrogen action in the uterus (Leavitt *et al.*, 1979). Although it is clear that progesterone and estrogen exert opposing effects on nuclear estrogen receptor, the mechanisms involved are less certain. Estrogen-induced translocation of estrogen receptor to the nuclear fraction is well documented, and nuclear retention of receptor–hormone complex is required to maintain the uterotrophic response to estrogen (Anderson *et al.*, 1974, 1975). Prolonged nuclear retention of receptor–estrogen complex is presumably the result of high affinity binding

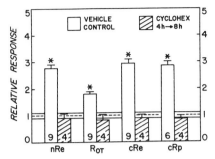

FIG. 21. Effect of cycloheximide in myometrial receptor response to progesterone withdrawal. Pseudopregnant decidualized hamsters were prepared as described in Fig. 19, and progesterone implants were removed at 0 time. Cycloheximide (10 mg/animal, hatched bars) and vehicle control (open bars) were given at 4 hours, and receptor levels were measured at 8 hours after progesterone withdrawal. The horizontal bar represents results from sham withdrawn preparations which served as a control for progesterone withdrawal. Abbreviations: CYCLOHEX., cycloheximide; R_{OT}, oxytocin receptor; others are as in Fig. 5. *$p < 0.05$. From Leavitt *et al.* (1983).

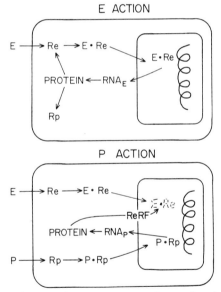

FIG. 22. Proposed mechanism of progesterone regulation of nuclear estrogen receptor. During estrogen action, estradiol–receptor complex interacts with chromatin to stimulate estrogen-dependent RNA and protein synthesis, the products of which are estrogen receptor and progesterone receptor. Progesterone action is mediated by the progesterone receptor system resulting in progesterone-dependent RNA and protein synthesis. A product of progesterone action is proposed to be the estrogen receptor-regulatory factor responsible for the degradation or inactivation of estrogen–receptor complex in the target cell nucleus. Abbreviations: E, estrogen; P, progesterone; Re, estrogen receptor; Rp, progesterone receptor; RNA_E, estrogen-dependent RNA; RNA_p, progesterone-dependent RNA. Adapted from Evans and Leavitt (1980b).

of the complex by nuclear acceptor sites (Clark and Peck, 1976). There is general agreement as to the number of nuclear estrogen receptor sites per cell which exhibit long-term nuclear retention in hamster and rat uterus during estrogen action, and progesterone appears to interrupt the retention of a biologically active population of nuclear receptors (Evans *et al.*, 1980; Okulicz *et al.*, 1981a,b).

Earlier studies suggest that progesterone antagonism of estrogen action may result from inhibition of cytosol estrogen receptor replenishment (Bhakoo and Katzenellenbogen, 1977; Hseuh *et al.*, 1976; West *et al.*, 1976, 1978). A major portion of uterine estrogen receptor replenishment is dependent on RNA and protein synthesis (Sarff and Gorski, 1971). Actinomycin D blocks estrogen receptor replenishment when administered within 6 hours of estrogen treatment, suggesting that early RNA synthesis is required for later cytosol receptor production (Sarff and Gorski, 1971). Similarly, progesterone inhibition of estrogen receptor replenishment diminishes with time after estrogen treatment, falling rapidly after 8 hours (Bhakoo and Katzenellenbogen, 1977; Clark *et al.*, 1977). Thus, antagonism of cytosol estrogen receptor replenishment seems to involve progesterone-induced modification of estrogen-dependent RNA synthesis (Fig. 22). Furthermore, progesterone inhibition of cytosol estrogen receptor replenishment is not observed until 12–24 hours after treatment of the estrogen-primed animal (Clark *et al.*, 1977; Hseuh *et al.*, 1976). From this it would appear that the progesterone effect on cytosol receptor replenishment occurs secondarily to an earlier primary action of progesterone at the nuclear level.

In assessing various possibilities that might account for the mechanism of progesterone action, it was found that progesterone had no effect on [^{3}H]estradiol uptake by the nuclear fraction, but the amount of hormone retained by the nuclear fraction at 4 hours after progesterone was reduced (Evans and Leavitt, 1980a). Thus, progesterone neither blocked estrogen receptor translocation to the nucleus nor stimulated recycling of nuclear receptor to the cytoplasm. Of interest is the finding that progesterone induced the preferential loss of receptor–estrogen complex from the target cell nucleus, suggesting a selective effect on the biologically active form of nuclear estrogen receptor. Occupied and unoccupied forms of estrogen receptor possess distinctive physicochemical properties (Jensen, 1979). In addition to the presence of steroid, other features that differentiate occupied from unoccupied receptor include conformational changes in the protein acquired during transformation to the nuclear form (Notides *et al.*, 1981). One or more of these unique physiocochemical properties may account for the substrate specificity of progesterone action.

The mechanism by which progesterone appears to selectively regulate nuclear estrogen receptor is summarized in Fig. 22. We discovered that inhibitors of RNA and protein synthesis block the inhibitory effect of progesterone on nuclear receptor *in vitro* (Evans and Leavitt, 1980b). We postulate that the mechanism of progesterone modulation of nuclear estrogen receptor retention may involve the induction or stimulation of a factor (ReRF) that directly alters nuclear receptor (Okulicz *et al.*, 1981d). The presence of a progesterone-induced modulator capable of altering the occupied form of estrogen receptor within the target cell nucleus would provide a novel mechanism for regulation of cellular response to hormone action. Our studies *in vitro* have demonstrated a progesterone-induced activity associated with the uterine nuclear fraction which causes the loss of nuclear estrogen receptor (Okulicz *et al.*, 1981d). These results confirm the existence of ReRF in that this factor can be extracted from the nuclear fraction with high salt (0.5 M KCl) and appears to act preferentially on the occupied form of nuclear estrogen receptor (Figs. 16 and 17). Inhibition of ReRF activity by molybdate, vanadate, and phosphate suggests that it may be a phosphatase or an activator of phosphatase activity.

Enzymes have been described which are capable of altering estrogen receptor (Auricchio *et al.*, 1981a,b; Puca *et al.*, 1977). We have shown for the first time under physiological conditions that progesterone stimulates an enzymatic mechanism that controls the retention of nuclear estrogen receptor. Estrogen receptor-regulatory factor appears to be an enzyme that is specific for the hormone–receptor complex, and its action may involve dephosphorylation of the receptor protein. It is still not certain whether steroid receptors are phosphoproteins, but there is evidence that they are (Auricchio *et al.*, 1981a; Weigel *et al.*, 1981; Wheeler *et al.*, 1981). The activation of estrogen receptor appears to be enhanced by a phosphorylation mechanism (Auricchio *et al.*, 1981b; Moudgil and Eessalu, 1980). Thus, estrogen receptor dephosphorylation is an attractive possibility for the mechanism of nuclear receptor inactivation and attenuation of estrogen-dependent gene expression.

Our ability to extract ReRF from uterine nuclei and assay its activity in a cell-free system will permit the further characterization and purification of this factor. It will be of particular interest to examine the regulation of ReRF in the progesterone-dominated uterus since our studies of the pregnant and pseudopregnant animal suggest that ReRF activity should be high. Furthermore, the regulation of such a modulator by exogenous agents could provide a specific and selective means of controlling hormone-induced responses. In this regard, progestin therapy is useful in the management of certain types of endometrial cancer. Our studies suggest that occupied nuclear receptor or ReRF responses to progestin action could provide a new approach for selection of patients with hormone-dependent endometrial cancer.

B. Receptor Regulation During the Cycle

There is ample evidence to document the positive relationship that exists between the rise in estrogen secretion during the follicular phase of the estrous cycle and the elevation of uterine nuclear estrogen receptor and cytosol progesterone receptor levels (Leavitt *et al.*, 1978, 1979) (Fig. 5). However, the factors contributing to receptor changes during the ovulatory phase of the cycle are less certain. Preovulatory progesterone secretion causes progesterone receptor depletion and translocation to the nuclear fraction, but the duration of the nuclear progesterone receptor response is short (Chen and Leavitt, 1979). In experiments designed to determine whether the precipitous fall in nuclear estrogen receptor during the ovulatory period of the hamster estrous cycle could be ascribed to progesterone action or estrogen withdrawal, progesterone action was found to reduce total estrogen receptor within 2–4 hours by selective inhibition of nuclear receptor (Evans *et al.*, 1980). In contrast, estrogen withdrawal altered the subcellular distribution of estrogen receptor with no change in total receptor levels. Thus, progesterone action is responsible for the rapid clearance of nuclear estrogen receptor, whereas estrogen withdrawal interrupts cytosol receptor translocation to the nuclear fraction. It should be pointed out that the changes observed in cytosol estrogen receptor levels during progesterone action with or without serum estradiol maintenance (Figs. 10 and 11) indicate that cytosol receptor depletion is regulated primarily by estrogen-induced receptor translocation rather than progesterone-induced inhibition of cytosol receptor replenishment.

The cause-and-effect relationships established by our experiments support the following interpretation of uterine estrogen receptor levels during the ovulatory period of the cycle. The ovulatory surge of gonadotropin stimulates a transient rise in serum estradiol causing translocation of cytosol receptor to the nucleus, but nuclear estrogen receptor fails to accumulate because preovulatory progesterone acts to suppress nuclear receptor retention. When serum estradiol declines, cytosol estrogen receptor translocation diminishes and nuclear receptor levels fall precipitously in response to unopposed progesterone action. Thus, the changes in cytosol and nuclear estrogen receptor levels observed during the ovulatory phase of the cycle are proposed to result first from combined progesterone and estrogen action, and second from continued progesterone action during estrogen withdrawal.

During the hamster cycle, cytosol estrogen receptor remains fairly constant except during the ovulatory period on day 4 when ovarian estrogen secretion increases abruptly. However, by the morning of the next day, cytosol estrogen receptor levels return to diestrous values. This result is at odds with the suggestion that cytosol estrogen receptor replenishment is compromised by progesterone action during the ovulatory phase of the cycle (West *et al.*, 1978). Although estrogen receptor levels are suppressed during chronic exposure to progesterone action such as in pregnancy, progesterone secretion during the cycle is not sufficient to inhibit cytosol estrogen receptor levels.

That cytosol progesterone receptor is not limiting during the estrous cycle was shown by the ability of exogenous progesterone treatment to cause nuclear translocation of progesterone receptor on successive days of the cycle (Chen and Leavitt, 1979). An estrogen-dependent and an estrogen-independent pool of progesterone receptor have been characterized (Allen and Leavitt, 1981; Leavitt *et al.*, 1977). Apparently, the estrogen-dependent pool of progesterone receptor is regulated by estrogen and progesterone secretion during the cycle, but the independent pool is sufficient to mediate hormone action (Isotalo *et al.*, 1981).

C. Receptor Regulation during Pregnancy

There have been few studies of uterine receptor regulation during pregnancy. The consensus is that estrogen and progesterone receptor systems are suppressed during pregnancy in the rat (Alexandrova and Soloff, 1980a; VuHai *et al.*, 1978), guinea pig (Alexandrova and Soloff, 1980b), and other animals (Brenner *et al.*, 1979). Our studies with the pregnant and pseudopregnant hamster support this conclusion (Figs. 7 and 8) (Leavitt *et al.*, 1979, 1983). Furthermore, our experiments on the recovery of myometrial receptors to progesterone withdrawal show that progesterone suppression of the estrogen receptor system is short-lived. Nuclear estrogen receptor recovered within 4–8 hours of progesterone withdrawal, and augmentation of estrogen-dependent protein synthesis was evident at 8 hours in the form of oxytocin receptor, progesterone receptor, and cytosol estrogen receptor responses. As a working hypothesis, we speculate that progesterone action during pregnancy chronically induces an ReRF, which functions to inactivate nuclear estrogen receptor, and thus blunts estrogen action. The ReRF has a short half-life and depends on continued progesterone stimulation for sustained activity. Withdrawal of progesterone leads to the rapid loss of ReRF and the recovery of nuclear estrogen receptor levels. Such an hypothesis would apply to the mechanism of parturition in the rat and hamster. The prepartum decline in ovarian progesterone secretion would be expected to interrupt ReRF production and to restore estrogen action. This proposition can be approached experimentally with the advent of an ReRF assay.

Finally, the hypothesis that progesterone regulates estrogen action by means of ReRF induction is certainly not the only possibility to be considered.

Recent results with the chick oviduct system support the idea that estrogen modulates gene transcription at multiple sites on the genome, and progesterone action is proposed to regulate some but not all of these sites (Palmiter *et al.*, 1981; Thomas *et al.*, 1981). However, other studies with chick oviduct indicate that progesterone can attenuate estrogen-induced nuclear receptor response (Seaver *et al.*, 1980; Sutherland *et al.*, 1980). Therefore, it is reasonable at this point to speculate that the underlying mechanism of progesterone control of estrogen action may be similar in avian oviduct and mammalian uterus. Clearly, only future work can determine the merits and generality of the ReRF hypothesis of progesterone action, and we forward it solely to stimulate additional study of the processes that regulate nuclear receptor retention and hormone-dependent gene expression.

ACKNOWLEDGMENTS

The studies reported here were supported by NSF grant PCM 77-25630 and NIH grants CA 23362, HD 13152, and HD 15452. We thank William F. Robidoux, Jr., and Lois Hager and Dot Jamieson for assistance in preparation of the manuscript.

REFERENCES

Alexandrova, M., and Soloff, M. S. (1980a). *Endocrinology (Baltimore)* **106**, 730–735.
Alexandrova, M., and Soloff, M. S. (1980b). *Biol. Reprod.* **22**, 1106–1111.
Allen, T. C., and Leavitt, W. W. (1981). *J. Steroid Biochem.* **14**, 29–36.
Anderson, J., Clark, J. H., and Peck, E. J., Jr. (1972). *Biochem. J.* **126**, 561–567.
Anderson, J. N., Peck, E. J., Jr., and Clark, J. H. (1974). *Endocrinology (Baltimore)* **95**, 174–178.
Anderson, J. N., Peck, E. J., Jr., and Clark, J. H. (1975). *Endocrinology (Baltimore)* **96**, 160–166.
Auricchio, F., Migliaccio, A., and Rotondi, A. (1981a). *Biochem. J.* **194**, 569–574.
Auricchio, F., Migliaccio, A., Castoria, G., Lastoria, S., and Schiavone, E. (1981b). *Biochem. Biophys. Res. Commun.* **101**, 1171–1178.
Baranczuk, R., and Greenwald, G. S. (1974). *J. Endocrinol.* **63**, 125–135.
Bhakoo, H., and Katzenellenbogen, B. S. (1977). *Mol. Cell. Endocrinol.* **8**, 121–134.
Brenner, R. M., and West, N. B. (1975). *Annu. Rev. Physiol.* **37**, 273–302.
Brenner, R. M., West, N. B., Norman, R. L., Sandow, B. A., and Verhage, H. G. (1979). *In* "Steroid Hormone Receptor Systems" (W. W. Leavitt and J. H. Clark, eds.), pp. 173–196. Plenum, New York.
Chen, T. J., and Leavitt, W. W. (1979). *Endocrinology (Baltimore)* **104**, 1588–1597.
Chen, T. J., MacDonald, R. G., Robidoux, W. F., Jr., and Leavitt, W. W. (1981). *J. Steroid Biochem.* **14**, 1023–1028.
Clark, J. H., and Peck, E. J., Jr. (1976). *Nature (London)* **260**, 635–636.
Clark, J. H., Anderson, J. N., and Peck, E. J., Jr. (1972). *Science* **176**, 528–530.
Clark, J. H., Hseuh, A. J. W., and Peck, E. J., Jr. (1977). *Ann. N. Y. Acad. Sci.* **286**, 161–179.

Clark, J. H., Peck, E. J., Jr., Hardin, J. W., and Eriksson, H. (1978). *In* "Receptors and Hormone Action" (B. W. O'Malley and L. Birnbaumer, eds.), Vol. II, pp. 1–31. Academic Press, New York.

Clark, J. H., Markaverich, B., Upchurch, S., Eriksson, H., and Hardin, J. W. (1979). *In* "Steroid Hormone Receptor Systems" (W. W. Leavitt and J. H. Clark, eds.), pp. 17–46. Plenum, New York.

Csapo, A. I., and Wiest, W. G. (1969). *Endocrinology (Baltimore)* **85**, 735–746.

Do, Y. S., and Leavitt, W. W. (1978). *Endocrinology (Baltimore)* **102**, 443–451.

Eriksson, H., Upchurch, S., Hardin, J. W., Peck, E. J., Jr., and Clark, J. H. (1978). *Biochem. Biophys. Res. Commun.* **81**, 1–7.

Evans, R. W., and Leavitt, W. W. (1980a). *Endocrinology (Baltimore)* **107**, 1261–1263.

Evans, R. W., and Leavitt, W. W. (1980b). *Proc. Natl. Acad. Sci. U.S.A.* **77**, 5856–5860.

Evans, R. W., Chen, T. J., Hendry, W. J. III, and Leavitt, W. W. (1980). *Endocrinology (Baltimore)* **107**, 383–390.

Feherty, P., Robertson, D. M., Waynforth, H. B., and Kellie, A. E. (1970). *Biochem. J.* **120**, 837–844.

Feil, P. D., Glasser, S. R., Toft, D. O., and O'Malley, B. W. (1972). *Endocrinology (Baltimore)* **91**, 738–746.

Flickinger, G. L., Elsner, C., Illingworth, D. V., Muechler, E. K., and Mikhail, G. (1977). *Ann. N. Y. Acad. Sci.* **286**, 180–189.

Greenwald, G. S., and Bast, J. D. (1978). *Biol. Reprod.* **18**, 658–662.

Hseuh, A. J. W., Peck, E. J., Jr., and Clark, J. H. (1976). *Endocrinology (Baltimore)* **98**, 438–444.

Isomaa, V., Isotalo, H., Orava, M., and Janne, O. (1979). *Biochim. Biophys. Acta* **585**, 24–33.

Isotalo, H., Isomaa, V., and Janne, O. (1981). *Endocrinology (Baltimore)* **109**, 868–873.

Jensen, E. V. (1979). *Pharmacol. Rev.* **30**, 477–491.

Katzenellenbogen, J., Johnson, H. J., Jr., and Carlson, K. E. (1973). *Biochemistry* **12**, 4092–4099.

Labhsetwar, A. P., and Watson, D. J. (1974). *Biol. Reprod.* **10**, 103–110.

Leavitt, W. W., and Blaha, G. C. (1970). *Biol. Reprod.* **3**, 353–361.

Leavitt, W. W., and Clark, J. H., eds. (1979). "Steroid Hormone Receptor Systems." Plenum, New York.

Leavitt, W. W., and Grossman, C. J. (1974). *Proc. Natl. Acad. Sci. U.S.A.* **71**, 4341–4345.

Leavitt, W. W., Toft, D. O., Strott, C. A., and O'Malley, B. W. (1974). *Endocrinology (Baltimore)* **94**, 1041–1053.

Leavitt, W. W., Chen, T. J., Allen, T. C., and Johnston, J. O. (1977). *Ann. N. Y. Acad. Sci.* **286**, 210–225.

Leavitt, W. W., Chen, T. J., Do, Y. S., Carlton, B. D., and Allen, T. C. (1978). *In* "Receptors and Hormone Action" (B. W. O'Malley and L. Birnbaumer, eds.), Vol. II, pp. 157–188. Academic Press, New York.

Leavitt, W. W., Chen, T. J., and Evans, R. W. (1979). *In* "Steroid Hormone Receptor Systems" (W. W. Leavitt and J. H. Clark, eds.), pp. 197–222. Plenum, New York.

Leavitt, W. W., Chen, T. J., Allen, T. C., and Kessell, B. (1980). *In* "Steroid Induced Uterine Proteins" (M. Beato, ed.), pp. 153–170. Elsevier/North-Holland Biomedical Press, New York.

Leavitt, W. W., Robidoux, W. F., Jr., Evans, R. W., Do, Y. S., MacDonald, R. G., and Roberts, J. S. (1983). *Endocrinology (Baltimore)* (submitted).

Milgrom, E., Luu Thi, M. T., Atger, M., and Baulieu, E. E. (1973). *J. Biol. Chem.* **248**, 6366–6374.

Miller, B. G., Murphy, L., and Stone, G. M. (1977). *J. Endocrinol.* **73**, 91–98.

Moudgil, V. K., and Eessalu, T. E. (1980). *FEBS Lett.* **122**, 189–192.

Nissenson, R., Flouret, G., and Hechter, O. (1978). *Proc. Natl. Acad. Sci. U.S.A.* **75**, 2044–2048.

Notides, A. C., Lerner, N., and Hamilton, D. E. (1981). *Proc. Natl. Acad. Sci. U.S.A.* **78**, 4926–4930.

Okulicz, W. C., Evans, R. W., and Leavitt, W. W. (1981a). *Science* **213**, 1503–1505.

Okulicz, W. C., Evans, R. W., and Leavitt, W. W. (1981b). *Biochim. Biophys. Acta* **677**, 253–256.

Okulicz, W. C., Evans, R. W., and Leavitt, W. W. (1981c). *Steroids* **37**, 463–470.

Okulicz, W. C., MacDonald, R. G., and Leavitt, W. W. (1981d). *Endocrinology (Baltimore)* **109**, 2273–2275.

O'Malley, B. W., and Birnbaumer, L., eds. (1978). "Receptors and Hormone Action," Vol. II. Academic Press, New York.

Palmiter, R. D., Mulvihill, E. R., Shepherd, J. H., and McKnight, G. S. (1981). *J. Biol. Chem.* **56**, 7910–7916.

Puca, G. A., Nola, E., Sica, V., and Bresciani, F. (1977). *J. Biol. Chem.* **252**, 1358–1366.

Robel, P., Mortel, R., and Baulieu, E. E. (1981). *In* "Biochemical Actions of Hormones" (G. Litwack, ed.), Vol. VIII, pp. 493–514. Academic Press, New York.

Sarff, M., and Gorski, J. (1971). *Biochemistry* **10**, 2557–2563.

Seaver, S. S., Hoffmann, J. F., and Coulson, P. B. (1980). *J. Steroid Biochem.* **13**, 1269–1276.

Shaikh, A. A. (1971). *Biol. Reprod.* **5**, 297–307.

Soloff, M. S. (1975). *Biochem. Biophys. Res. Commun.* **65**, 205–212.

Sutherland, R. L., Geynet, C., Binart, N., Catelli, M. G., Schmelck, P. H., Mester, J., Lebeau, M.-C., and Baulieu, E. E. (1980). *Eur. J. Biochem.* **107**, 155–164.

Terranova, P. F. (1975). *Proc. Soc. Exp. Biol. Med.* **148**, 1111–1113.

Thomas, P. S., Shepherd, J. H., Mulvihill, E. R., and Palmiter, R. D. (1981). *J. Mol. Biol.* **150**, 143–166.

VuHai, M. T., Logeat, F., and Milgrom, E. (1978). *J. Endocrinol.* **76**, 43–48.

Walters, M. R., and Clark, J. H. (1978). *Endocrinology (Baltimore)* **103**, 152–155.

Walters, M. R., Hunziker, W., and Clark, J. H. (1980). *J. Steroid. Biochem.* **13**, 1129–1132.

Weigel, N. L., Tash, J. S., Means, A. R., Schrader, W. T., and O'Malley, B. W. (1981). *Biochem. Biophys. Res. Commun.* **102**, 513–519.

Weitlauf, H. M., and Greenwald, G. S. (1967). *J. Reprod. Fertil.* **14**, 489–491.

West, N. B., Verhage, H. G., and Brenner, R. M. (1976). *Endocrinology (Baltimore)* **99**, 1010–1016.

West, N. B., Norman, R. L., Sandow, B. S., and Brenner, R. M. (1978). *Endocrinology (Baltimore)* **103**, 1732–1741.

Wheeler, R. H., Leach, K. L., LaForest, A. C., O'Toole, T. E., Wagner, R., and Pratt, W. B. (1981). *J. Biol. Chem.* **256**, 434–441.

Wynn, R. M. (1977). "Biology of the Uterus." Plenum, New York.

Zava, D. T., Harrington, N. Y., and McGuire, W. L. (1976). *Biochemistry* **15**, 4292–4297.

CHAPTER 11

Genetic and Biochemical Studies on Glucocorticoid-Induced Cleft Palate

David L. Gasser and Allen S. Goldman

I. INTRODUCTION

The induction of cleft palate by glucocorticoids has been a favorite model system of developmental biologists and teratologists for a number of years, and recently some interesting advances have been made in our understanding of the genetics and biochemistry of this disorder. This review will focus on specific genes which are now known to be involved in susceptibility, on the possibility that a biochemical pathway that is known to be involved in

BIOCHEMICAL ACTIONS OF HORMONES, VOL. X

glucocorticoid effects on inflammation may also play a role in glucocorticoid-induced cleft palate, and on the possible sites *in vivo* and *in vitro* of teratogenic action of glucocorticoids.

II. NORMAL SECONDARY PALATAL DEVELOPMENT

The normal development of the secondary palate involves a converging movement of the palatal shelves and their subsequent fusion at the line of contact. The palatine shelves initially hang vertically from the roof of the mouth, but then change to a horizontal position. In the mouse, this change starts with a bulging of the medial wall at the posterior end and proceeds anteriorly in a wavelike manner until the whole shelf lies dorsal to the tongue (Walker and Fraser, 1956). There are genetic differences in the rate at which this shelf elevation occurs, and these differences could eventually be useful in elucidating the biochemical bases of this movement. Walker and Fraser (1956) observed that the palate in C57BL embryos closed from early to late day 14, but that it did not close until late day 14 to early day 15 in A/J embryos. Considerable research has been performed concerning the mechanisms of normal shelf elevation, but there is little agreement on the mechanism by which the vertical embryonic palatal shelves reorient horizontally. On the one hand, a force external to the embryonic palate has been postulated. Possible examples of this external force include straightening of the cranial base (Verussio, 1970), nonpalatal muscular movement, swallowing, and descent of the tongue and lower jaw (Humphrey, 1969; Walker, 1969). On the other hand, embryonic shelf movement was postulated by Walker and Fraser (1956) to result from an internal shelf force. One possibility of an internal shelf force is that derived from the expansion of the embryonic palatal shelves (Lazzaro, 1940; Diewert and Tate, 1979), possibly from the rapid synthesis of glycosaminoglycans in the embryonic palate (Larsson, 1962; Ferguson, 1978). Hyaluronic acid, which is rapidly synthesized in the palate (Pratt *et al.*, 1973), is hydrophilic, binds considerable quantities of water, and causes an increase in osmotic pressure (Laurent, 1970). As a result, a force is thought to be produced to elevate the shelves, although this hypothesis is not universally accepted.

Zimmerman and colleagues (1980) have proposed that palate elevation is regulated by neurotransmitters such as serotonin, acetylcholine, and γ-aminobutyric acid (GABA). In their experiments several cholinergic agents stimulated elevation of the posterior end of the palate in embryo cultures, and this effect was inhibited by hexamethonium. These authors concluded that the cholinergic ganglion in the posterior palate may play a role in regulating shelf rotation (Wee *et al.*, 1980).

Much more is known about fusion of the embryonic palatal shelves primarily because this developmental process has been more amenable than shelf elevation to *in vitro* studies. Angelici and Pourtois (1968) have described four independent events involved in this process: (1) differentiation of the cell layers at the edges of the shelves, (2) fusion of the differentiated epithelial cells, (3) rupture of the partition, and, finally, (4) degeneration of the epithelial remains. Midline epithelial cells cease cell proliferation (Jelinek and Dostal, 1973, 1974) and DNA synthesis (Hassell *et al.*, 1974) 24–36 hours before shelf elevation and contact. Prior to and during elevation, the embryonic palatal shelves synthesize sulfated proteoglycans (Larsson *et al.*, 1959; Larsson, 1961; Walker, 1961), chondroitin sulfate and/or hyaluronic acid (Andersen and Mathiessen, 1967), and collagen (Pratt and King, 1971). Once contact between the two apposing shelves occurs, a tight adhesion develops, and attempts to separate the shelves after contact produce tearing of epithelial cell membranes (Zeiler *et al.*, 1964; Farbman, 1968). Initial adhesion may be mediated by cell surface carbohydrates. A carbohydrate-rich surface coat increases dramatically on the medial edge epithelial cell surface as shown at the ultrastructural level by the binding of the plant lectin concanavalin A (Pratt *et al.*, 1973; Pratt and Hassell, 1975) and by staining with ruthenium red (Greene and Kochhar, 1974). Concanavalin A binds to mannosyl and glucosyl residues of glycolipids and glycoproteins and ruthenium red binds to glycosaminoglycans and glycoproteins. In the medial edge epithelium of rat and mouse embryonic palatal shelves, a transient increase in the level of cyclic AMP has been shown by immunohistochemical procedures to occur 18–24 hours prior to epithelial contact, suggesting that activation of medial edge epithelial cells to mature *in vivo* may be mediated through cyclic nucleotides (Greene and Pratt, 1979; Greene *et al.*, 1980).

Angelici and Pourtois (1968) demonstrated acid phosphatase activity in the epithelial cells of palatal shelves in contact, and this was presumed to represent an active lysosomal system. The same enzymatic activity also occurred in epithelial cells of an unfused A/J mouse palate, suggesting that development of the lysosomal system was not dependent on contact of the palatal processes. Subsequent experiments demonstrated that selective death of the medial edge epithelium occurs on schedule when shelves are cultured singly (Smiley and Koch, 1972) or when the isolated palatal epithelium is cultured (Tyler and Koch, 1974). Thus, the cells in the palatal epithelium are programmed to die, and this event is not dependent on contact with epithelium of an apposing palatal shelf. The possibility that glucocorticoids induce cleft palate by interfering with programmed cell death is discussed in Section VI.

III. EFFECT OF GLUCOCORTICOIDS

It was established during the 1950s that glucocorticoids administered to pregnant mice during a sensitive period induced varying frequencies of cleft palate among the fetuses of various inbred strains (Baxter and Fraser, 1950; Fraser and Fainstat, 1951; Kalter, 1954; Fraser et al., 1957). The fact that some strains were more sensitive than others was most useful, since this allowed genetic studies to be made. In Table I is a summary of strain susceptibilities that have been reported in the literature. Nongenetic factors such as the type of food used (Miller, 1977) or the amount of stress the mothers receive (Hemm et al., 1977) are known to influence this trait, but in spite of these effects, there is general agreement among investigators as to the relative levels of susceptibility of various inbred strains. There are several conclusions that can be drawn from these genetic data: (1) The frequency of cleft palate among F_1 hybrid fetuses is strongly dependent on the genotype of the mother. Kalter (1954) observed that (A/J × C57BL/6J)F_1 fetuses (derived from A/J mothers) had a frequency of cortisone-induced cleft palate that was 10 times as great as that observed among (C57BL/6J × A/J)F_1 fetuses (derived from C57BL/6J mothers). This difference has been attributed to physiological differences in the mothers, although Francis (1973) has reported evidence for an effect of X-linked genes in these crosses. According to this hypothesis, the male fetuses derived from the A/J female × C57BL/6J male mating would be expected to be more sensitive than the male fetuses from the reciprocal mating since their X chromosome was derived from the A/J parent. The data obtained by testing reciprocal backcrosses were in agreement with this model (Francis, 1973). (2) At least two of the genes involved in determining susceptibility are closely linked to the H-2 complex, which is a group of genes on the chromosome 17 controlling transplantation antigens and several other functions, as discussed below. The role of the H-2 region in cleft palate susceptibility was first shown by Bonner and Slavkin (1975), and has been confirmed in several other laboratories (Biddle and Fraser, 1977; Tyan and Miller, 1978; Gasser et al., 1981). Thus, the B10.A congenic strain, which has the same H-2 haplotype as the highly susceptible A/J strain but the genetic background of the C57BL/10 (or B10) strain, is significantly more susceptible than the B10 strain. Bonner and Slavkin have also shown that the H-2 region is related to the maternal environment effect described above. They reported that 64% of the (B10.A × B10)F_1 fetuses had cleft palate if the B10.A

TABLE I

GENETIC DIFFERENCES IN SUSCEPTIBILITY OF MICE TO CORTISONE-INDUCED CLEFT PALATE

Strain or hybrid	H-2	H-3	Cortisone dose[a]	Cleft palate (%)	Reference
A/J	a	Not a or b	2.5 mg	100	Kalter (1954)
A/J			2.5 mg	99	Bonner and Slavkin (1975)
C57BL/6	b	a	2.5 mg	19	Kalter (1954)
C57BL/6			2.5 mg	25	Bonner and Slavkin (1975)
C57BL/6			100 mg/kg	21	Gasser et al. (1981)
(A/J × C57BL/6J)F₁	a/b	?/a	2.5 mg	43	Kalter (1954)
(C57BL/6 × A/J)F₁	b/a	a/?	2.5 mg	4	Kalter (1954)
C57BL/10Sn (B10)	b	a	2.5 mg	22	Bonner and Slavkin (1975)
C57BL/10Sn (B10)			100 mg/kg	22	Gasser et al. (1981)
B10.A	a	a	2.5 mg	81	Bonner and Slavkin (1975)
B10.A			2.5 mg	92	Tyan and Miller (1978)
B10.A			100 mg/kg	83	Gasser et al. (1981)
(B10.A × B10)F₁	a/b	a	2.5 mg	64	Bonner and Slavkin (1975)
(B10 × B10.A)F₁	b/a	a	2.5 mg	31	Bonner and Slavkin (1975)
DBA/1J	q	b	2.5 mg	92	Kalter (1965)
DBA/1J			2.5 mg	94	Tyan and Miller (1978)
SWR/FR	q	?	2.5 mg	100	Salomon and Pratt (1979)
SWR/NIH	q	?	2.5 mg	100	Salomon and Pratt (1979)
SWR/J	q	b	2.5 mg	100	Salomon and Pratt (1979)
C3H/HeJ	k	b	2.5 mg	68	Kalter (1965)
CBA/J	k	Not a or b	2.5 mg	12	Kalter (1965)
A.BY	b	Not a or b	2.5 mg	85	Salomon and Pratt (1979)
A.BY			100 mg/kg	100	Gasser et al. (1981)
A.BY			50 mg/kg	36	Gasser et al. (1981)
B10.LP	b	b	100 mg/kg	56	Gasser et al. (1981)
B10.LP-H-3[b]	b	b	100 mg/kg	50	Gasser et al. (1981)

[a] In all of the experiments shown in this table, the pregnant mothers received an injection of cortisone on days 11, 12, 13, and 14. The amount per injection is shown in the column.

mother had been injected with cortisone, but only 31% of the (B10 ×
B10.A)F$_1$ fetuses were affected when the B10 mother had been injected.
Thus, even if there is an X-linked gene which contributes to the maternal
effect (Francis, 1973), a substantial portion of this effect can be attributed
to the *H-2* region. (3) Another gene involved in determining susceptibility
is closely linked to the *H-3* locus on the second chromosome (Gasser *et
al.*, 1981). The evidence for this is that two congenic strains, B10.LP and
B10.LP-*H-3^b*, were significantly more susceptible than their inbred partner
strain, B10. These congenic lines have the same genetic background as
B10, but possess a short chromosomal segment from LP/J which includes
the *H-3* histocompatibility locus and the *Ir-2* immune response gene.

An important question to consider is whether the levels of fetal or maternal
glucocorticoids can account for these genetic differences. Corticosterone is
the major glucocorticoid in the mouse, and the levels of this hormone in
the fetus and maternal plasma during midgestation have been measured
by Salomon *et al.* (1979). The A/J and C57BL/6J strains, which differ
markedly in cleft palate susceptibility, were found to have no significant
differences in the endogenous concentrations of maternal plasma or fetal
corticosterone. However, there is evidence that genetic differences in susceptibility to glucocorticoid-induced cleft palate may be related to differences
in the quantity of glucocorticoid receptor. The first indication of genetic
differences in cortisone binding was reported by Levine *et al.* (1968), who
demonstrated that [^{14}C]cortisone injected into pregnant mice on day 11 of
gestation was retained in greater quantities by the A/J strain than by CBA.
Reminga and Avery (1972) then demonstrated that 30 minutes after injection
of [^{14}C]cortisol on day 12.5, the amount of tightly bound label was significantly
higher in A/J fetuses than in C57BL fetuses. These observations led to
experiments by Goldman *et al.* (1977), who measured the amounts of cytosolic
cortisol-binding proteins in fetal palatal tissues of various strains. The A/J
and DBA/1J strains, which are highly susceptible to cortisone-induced cleft
palate, had a prominent peak of cortisol-binding protein at a p*I* of approximately
6.9–7.0. Other strains which are less susceptible had significantly lower
amounts of activity at this peak. Since the B10.A congenic strain had approximately twice the amount of material in this peak as the parental B10
strain, it was suggested that the cortisol-binding protein observed was either
coded by a gene closely linked to *H-2*, or was coded elsehwere in the
genome but was affected in some way by an *H-2*-linked gene. It was
subsequently shown that the locus for the major glucocorticoid receptor is
on chromosome 18 (Francke and Gehring, 1980). Therefore, the *H-2*-linked
gene on chromosome 17 either codes for a different receptor or, what is
more likely, has an indirect effect on the major receptor.

This work was extended by experiments with [^{3}H]dexamethasone, since dexamethasone is more tightly bound to the receptor and binds poorly to ligandin (Litwack *et al.*, 1973), does not bind to transcortin (Rousseau *et al.*, 1972), and stabilizes the receptor (Schmid *et al.*, 1976). In this experiment, cytosols were incubated with various concentrations of [^{3}H]dexamethasone in the presence or absence of 20 μM nonradioactive dexamethasone. By this method, the fetal palatal preparations from B10.A and B10.A(2R) were shown to have significantly greater quantities of specifically bound dexamethasone than those from B10 or B10.A(5R) mice (Katsumata *et al.*, 1981). This difference was not observed in the liver, in agreement with the observations of Butley *et al.* (1978), but the genetic difference was apparent in primary cell cultures derived from maxillary processes. It was also shown that the p*I* 7.0 peak bound to DNA–cellulose but not cellulose, suggesting that this protein has the DNA-binding characteristic expected of a biologically active receptor.

Evidence in agreement with these findings was reported independently by Salomon and Pratt (1976), who demonstrated that embryonic A/J facial mesenchyme cells contain about twice as much saturable [^{3}H]dexamethasone receptors as those in C57 cells obtained either directly or in primary culture. These investigators have also shown that the levels of specific binding of [^{3}H]dexamethasone to embryonic maxillary cytosols in several inbred strains are in agreement with the degrees of susceptibility to glucocorticoid-induced cleft palate in those strains, but they did not investigate the role of *H-2* (Salomon and Pratt, 1979).

Some results with triamcinolone acetonide have not been in agreement with our findings. Although Zimmerman and Bowen (1972) showed that embryos of the CBA strain retained unmetabolized [^{3}H]triamcinolone acetonide to about 60% of the level of the more sensitive strains C3H and A/J, Hackney (1980) reported that receptor binding of [^{3}H]triamcinolone acetonide in mouse embryo heads was lower in the A/J strain than in C3H and CBA. Hackney also showed that the dose–response curves for triamcinolone acetonide-induced cleft palate were not parallel in these strains as they were for cortisone, suggesting that cleft palate induction by triamcinolone acetonide involves slightly different mechanisms than those involved in cortisone-induced cleft palate.

It is not clear at this point how important the receptor level is in determining the *H-2*-linked susceptibility difference, but it is interesting that *H-2* seems to be involved in both of these traits. It may also be relevant that other hormone receptors are apparently influenced by the *H-2* region. As discussed below, it has been reported that *H-2* affects the level of glucagon receptors (Lafuse and Edidin, 1980) and several other hormone-associated phenomena. Even if the high susceptibility of A/J and B10.A mice is related to a higher level of glucocorticoid receptor than what is present in less sensitive strains, this clearly is not the only mechanism involved in the genetic determination of susceptibility. Mice that are homozygous for the *brachymorph* (*bm*) mutation are as susceptible to cortisone-induced cleft palate as A/J mice, but the level of glucocorticoid receptor in the *bm*/*bm* palate on day 14 was the same as the amount found in the C57 palate (Pratt *et al.*, 1980).

IV. GENETICS OF THE *H-2* AND *H-3* REGIONS

The discoveries that genes affecting cleft palate susceptibility are linked to *H-2* and *H-3* are not as helpful as one might think, since *H-2* is enormously complex and *H-3* is becoming increasingly complicated. Genetic information about the *H-2* region is still in a state of flux, but our current understanding is summarized in Fig. 1. Each of these loci will be discussed briefly, since it is not yet clear which of them are involved in cleft palate susceptibility.

The strong transplantation antigens discovered by Gorer (1937) and Snell (1948) are now referred to as K and D, and are known to be 45,000-dalton molecules associated on the cell surface with a 12,000-dalton molecule known as β_2-microglobulin (Vitetta and Capra, 1978). The complete sequence of one H-2K molecule has been reported (Coligan *et al.*, 1981). The K and D molecules are important biologically, as they are known to control target cell recognition by cytotoxic T cells (Doherty *et al.*, 1976). The more recently discovered L molecule is biochemically similar to K and D (Hansen *et al.*, 1977; Krakauer *et al.*, 1980), and has similar biological activity (Levy and Hansen, 1980).

The discovery that *H-2*-linked genes control specific immune responses led to the identification of the *A* region (McDevitt and Tyan, 1968; McDevitt and Chinitz, 1969; McDevitt *et al.*, 1972). It was later shown that these genes code for lymphocyte antigens which are concentrated predominantly on the surfaces of bone marrow-derived cells, and these antigens were called Ia, or "Immune response-associated," antigens (Shreffler and David, 1975). The antigens identified as A and E products are both dimers consisting of α and β chains, with molecular weights of 32,000 and 28,000, respectively. The genes for both chains of the A molecule are known to map in the *A* region, but only the α chain of the E molecule maps in the *E* region. The

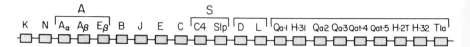

Fig. 1. Current map of the mouse *H-2* region. Loci of uncertain order are bracketed.

E β chain maps in the A region (Cook *et al.*, 1979), which leads to genetic complementation for what appears to be a single gene product. This explains why some immune responses (Dorf and Benacerraf, 1975), the precipitated E-region antigen (Jones *et al.*, 1978), and E-region serological specificities (Lafuse *et al.*, 1980) are each controlled by two complementing genes. It is possible that the N (Hayes and Bach, 1980) and U (O'Neill and Parish, 1981) gene products are biochemically and functionally similar to A and E, but little information is available about these recently discovered loci.

The C locus was originally thought to control serologically detectable Ia antigens (Shreffler and David, 1975), but more recent evidence indicates that the Ia products that were thought to map in C are coded by the A and E loci (Cullen *et al.*, 1980). Although it has been argued that C does not exist (Klein *et al.*, 1981), there is a suppressor cell function which maps in C (Rich and Rich, 1976). Biochemical products have not been identified so far for the J locus, but the evidence is well established that this region controls several aspects of suppressor cell function (Murphy *et al.*, 1976; Tada *et al.*, 1976; Greene *et al.*, 1977; Streilein and Klein, 1979; Czitrom *et al.*, 1980).

The B locus is the most problematic of the H-2 region genes. An H-2-linked gene was shown to control the response of mice to IgG allotypes, and this gene seemed to map to the right of A (Lieberman *et al.*, 1972). A gene controlling responsiveness to the B subunits of lactate dehydrogenase also appeared to map in the same position (Melchers *et al.*, 1973). However, no Ia antigens have yet been identified which map in B, suggesting that responsiveness to IgG and LDH may be determined by the interaction of A and E loci (Shreffler *et al.*, 1976). Evidence for this hypothesis has been reported by Baxevanis *et al.* (1981), who demonstrated that nonresponder $H\text{-}2^a$ lymphocytes could be made to respond to LDH and IgG if the cells were treated with an antibody directed to the E molecule, Ia.m7. However, the suppressive effect of E-region molecules has not yet been demonstrated with the response to staphylococcal nuclease, which also maps in the B region (Lozner *et al.*, 1974).

The S region was identified by its control over the quantitative level of a serum substance (Ss) which was eventually shown to be the C4 component of complement (Shreffler, 1976). Reciprocal immunizations of mice with different Ss genotypes led to the identification of a sex-limited protein (Slp) in males with certain H-2 types (Passmore and Shreffler, 1970). It is now known that the C4 molecules are negative for Slp antigen, and evidence indicates that C4 and Slp are coded by discrete but closely linked loci (Shreffler *et al.*, 1981). A gene that codes for a protein that binds C4 (C4-BP) is known to map in a short segment to the right of H-2D (Kaidoh *et al.*, 1981).

The *Tla* locus has been known for a number of years to code for antigens that occur on thymocytes and leukemia cells (Klein, 1975). Careful studies on this genetic region led to the realization that a number of additional loci occur between *H-2* and *Tla*, and that some of these loci code for antigens which are similar in some respects to some of the *II-2* antigens. The *Qa-1* (Stanton and Boyse, 1976) and *Qa-2* (Flaherty, 1976) antigens occur on the surfaces of various lymphocytes. *Qa-1* at least is related in some way to lymphocyte function, as cells that are positive or negative for *Qa-1* are known to have different functional properties (Stanton *et al.*, 1978). The gene products of the *Tla*, *Qa-1*, and *Qa-2* loci all have molecular weights of approximately 45,000, and all are associated with β_2-microglobulin (Michaelson *et al.*, 1977; Vitetta *et al.*, 1975; Stanton and Hood, 1980). Two loci which code for T-cell antigens, *Qat-4* and *Qat-5*, are known to be closely linked to *Qa-2* and *Qa-3* (Hammerling *et al.*, 1979).

The *H-2T* locus codes for an antigen that was detected in the cell-mediated lympholysis assay (Klein and Chiang, 1978). Other *H-2*-linked loci which code for products that can be identified by cytotoxic killer cells are *K*, *A*, *E*, *D*, *Qa-2*, and, possibly, *L*. Two minor histocompatibility loci, *H-31* and *H-32*, have also been identified in the *Qa/H-2T* region (Klein *et al.*, 1978).

There are several enzymes which also map in the *H-2* region. Their positions are not known precisely, and they are presumably unrelated to the immunological functions of the neighboring genes, but they are important from our point of view because *H-2*-linked effects on glucocorticoid sensitivity could be the result of these enzymes. A short segment to the right of *H-2D* is known to include genes for phosphoglycerate kinase (VandeBerg and Klein, 1978), kidney catalase (Hoffman and Grieshaber, 1976; Klein *et al.*, 1978), and superoxide dismutase (Novak *et al.*, 1980). The SM/J strain is also known to carry an *H-2*-linked neuraminidase mutation, which not only leads to a drastic reduction in the quantity of liver neuraminidase, but also affects posttranscriptional processing of acid phosphatase, α-mannosidase, arylsulfatase-B, and α-glucosidase (Womack *et al.*, 1981).

In the case of humans, it is known that the gene for 21-hydroxylase is closely linked to HLA (Dupont *et al.*, 1977). Since this enzyme converts 17-hydroxyprogesterone to 11-desoxycortisol (Bongiovanni, 1958), variations in 21-hydroxylase activity could possibly affect glucocorticoid-induced cleft palate.

Genes linked to *H-2* are known to affect the levels of cyclic AMP in the liver (Meruelo and Edidin, 1975), and this is now known to be the result of an *H-2*-linked effect on glucagon receptors (Lafuse and Edidin, 1980). The *H-2* region has been shown to affect various other hormone-associated phenomena such as the sizes of the seminal vesicles, testes, thymus, and lymph nodes, as well as the levels of testosterone and testosterone-binding globulin (Ivanyi, 1978). It has been suggested that histocompatibility antigens could mimic hormone receptors and could interfere with hormone binding (Svejgaard and Ryder, 1976). The only direct evidence in favor of this hypothesis so far is the report that binding of both insulin and glucagon could be inhibited by anti-*H-2* sera (Meruelo and Edidin, 1980).

Experiments have been done to determine which part of the *H-2* region might be involved in affecting cleft palate susceptibility. Tyan and Miller (1978) proposed that a gene that maps in *H-2D* affects a food-associated difference in susceptibility. Several strains that possess the *H-2D^b* allele had a greater sensitivity to cortisone when fed Breeder Chow than when maintained on Laboratory Chow, which had a lower vitamin A content. Other strains which did not have the *H-2D^b* allele did not show this difference. We confirmed that the type of chow that is fed does indeed affect cleft palate susceptibility, but we did not find any evidence that *H-2D* was responsible for the food-associated effect (Gasser *et al.*, 1981). For example, two strains with the *H-2D^d* allele, B10.A and B10.A(5R), were significantly more sensitive when fed Purina Mouse Chow (with high vitamin A content) than when fed Wayne Lablox, and the difference was of the same magnitude as that observed with *H-2D^b* strains. Our findings did support the conclusion of Tyan and Miller that at least two *H-2*-linked loci are involved in controlling susceptibility. One of these genes appeared to map in the *H-2B* region, since B10.A(4R) and B10.A(5R) had low susceptibilities, whereas B10.A and B10.A(2R) had high susceptibility levels. If the *B* locus does not exist, as discussed above, our results can only be explained by complementary effects of at least two genes. High susceptibility would be determined by a *k* gene in the *K/A* region in combination with a *d* gene in the *C/S/D* region. Even if the *B* locus does exist, our comparison of the B10.BR, B10.D2, and B10.A strains can only be explained by the action of two complementary genes, one to the left of *C* and the other to the right of *E*.

One possible explanation for these results would be that they represent pleiotropic effects of *H-2*-linked enzyme genes. The major problem with this explanation is that four different levels of susceptibility have been identified among *H-2* congenic strains of mice. The strains B10.D2, B10, B10.BR, and B10.A all differ significantly from one another in their levels of susceptibility (Gasser *et al.*, 1981). If this effect were caused by a closely linked enzyme locus, the implication is that the locus would have at least four alleles, each of which is associated with a different *H-2* haplotype. Furthermore, susceptibility to cortisone-induced cleft palate seems to be determined by *H-2*-linked genes which act by complementation, a characteristic that is well documented for the antigen-coding genes in the central regions of *H-2*. The most parsimonious explanation for the results obtained so far would seem to be that the antigen-coding genes themselves are responsible for the effects on susceptibility to cortisone-induced cleft palate. Whether this results from an effect of these antigens on hormone binding (Svejgaard and Ryder, 1976), or perhaps derives from the concept that the ancestral function of MHC gene products is the regulation of cell interactions (Snell, 1981) has not been determined. The levels of a number of hormone receptors may be affected by a variety of genes that do not code for the receptors themselves. For example, the quantity of insulin receptor sites per cell is affected by genes closely linked to the *albino* locus in mice, although the insulin receptor itself does not seem to map in this region (Goldfeld *et al.*, 1981).

Although the genetic map of the *H-3* region is not yet as complex as that of *H-2*, a number of interesting genes are now known to map in this region. Snell (1958) first recognized the *H-3* histocompatibility locus during the derivation of an extensive series of congenic lines. The LP/DiSn strain was crossed with C57BL/10ScSn (B10), and heterozygotes were backcrossed repeatedly to the B10 parental strain with selection for the *white-bellied agouti* (A^w) coat color allele. A minor histocompatibility locus, *H-13*, was identified in the same region (Snell *et al.*, 1967). *H-13* is 1.6 centimorgans from *agouti*, and there is approximately 17% recombination between *agouti* and *H-3*. Either *H-3* or a closely linked gene affects segregation ratios (Hull, 1969).

A number of additional genes are known to map in the *H-3* region. (a) A gene regulating responsiveness to the *Ea-1* erythrocyte alloantigen was shown to map between *H-3* and *agouti*, and has been designated *Ir-2* (Gasser, 1969, 1976a). The most unusual feature of this *Ir* gene is that (YBR × HTG)F_1 hybrids are unresponsive to *Ea-1*, despite the fact that both the YBR and HTG parental strains are very good responders (Gasser and Shreffler, 1974). It was demonstrated in F_2 and backcross generations that the gene for unresponsiveness was linked to *agouti* and was derived from the HTG strain. Thus, the HTG strain is a good responder, despite the fact that it is homozygous for a dominant gene for unresponsiveness. Complementation with an unidentified gene from YBR apparently occurs, resulting either in the synthesis of an antigen that induces cross-tolerance for *Ea-1*, or in the type of suppression which the *J* region of *H-2* is known to control. (b) Either *H-3* or a closely linked gene affects responsiveness to the *H-13* histocompatibility antigen (Gasser, 1976b). (c) The delayed hypersensitivity reaction to *Leishmania donovani* is associated with a dominant gene that is either identical or closely linked to *Ir-2* (DeTolla *et al.*, 1980). (d) An antigen defined by cytotoxic lymphocytes is *H-3* linked (Roopenian and Click, 1980). (e) The *Ly-4* lymphocyte antigen, which is predominantly present on B lymphocytes, is closely linked to *H-3* (McKenzie *et al.*, 1977). (f) The Ly-m11 lymphocyte antigen, which has been defined by a monoclonal antibody, is either identical or closely linked to *H-3* (Tada *et al.*, 1980). (g) The gene for β_2-microglobulin, which is associated on the cell surface with a number of *H-2*-linked antigens, is also linked to *H-3* (Michaelson, 1981). (h) Susceptibility to radiation-induced leukemia is strongly influenced by a gene (*Ril-1*) which is closely linked to *H-3* (Meruelo *et al.*, 1981). (i) The *Ly-6* lymphocyte antigen locus, which also regulates the expression of multiple allospecificities (Takei and Horton, 1981), maps in the *H-3* region (Meruelo *et al.*, 1981).

It has not yet been possible to map all of these genes in the correct order since the recombinants that would be needed have not been identified. What is emerging from these studies, however, is the general conclusion that both the *H-2* and *H-3* regions include a number of genes which control lymphocyte antigens and immunologic responsiveness. The fact that both regions also include genes for susceptibility to glucocorticoid-induced cleft palate could be coincidental, or it could have biological significance. Which of these alternatives is correct can only be determined by future investigations.

V. BIOCHEMICAL EFFECTS OF GLUCOCORTICOIDS

A. CLEFT PALATE STUDIES

A number of studies have been done which attempted to identify biochemical events that were specifically correlated with the various events involved in palatal differentiation. A correlation has been reported between the time of maximum sulfated glycosaminoglycan (GAG) accumulation in embryonic palatal mesenchyme and time of shelf elevation. Maximum ^{35}S incorporation was delayed 16 hours in cortisone-treated mouse fetuses (Jacobs, 1964), and cortisone delayed elevation in susceptible strains of mice (Fraser *et al.*, 1954; Walker and Fraser, 1957; Ross and Walker, 1967). However, much evidence exists that induction of cleft palate by glucocorticoids is not related to inhibition of GAG synthesis. Larsson (1962), using histochemical methods, demonstrated that GAG synthesis in a glucocorticoid-susceptible strain of mice (A/J) and a resistant strain (CBA) were equally inhibited by cortisone. Similar conclusions were reached by Andrew and Zimmerman (1971) based on measurements of ^{35}S incorporation into palatal GAG of glucocorticoid-treated embryos. Moreover, there was no difference in the degree of cleft palate produced by triamcinolone acetonide, which inhibited GAG synthesis to 74% of normal, and cortisol acetate, which inhibited GAG synthesis to 35% of normal, and a nonteratogenic dose of cortisol acetate, which inhibited GAG synthesis to 68% of normal (Andrew and Zimmerman, 1971). Thus, these authors concluded that glucocorticoid-induced cleft palate is not related to inhibition of GAG synthesis.

A potential role of inhibition of collagen synthesis by glucocorticoids in the induction of cleft palate was considered by Shapira and Shosan (1972), who reported a considerable increase in the proline/hydroxyproline ratio of cortisone-treated fetal mouse palates compared with controls. This suggests that cortisone inhibits the hydroxylation of proline in collagen synthesis in the palate.

Transient increases in rodent embryonic palatal epithelial cAMP during the period just prior to fusion have suggested a role of cyclic nucleotides in medial edge epithelial differentiation (Olson and Massaro, 1977; Greene and Pratt, 1979; Greene *et al.*, 1981). Maternal administration of teratogenic levels of glucocorticoids resulted in decreased levels of cAMP on day 14 of gestation in both sensitive A/J and resistant C57 embryos (Erickson *et al.*, 1979). Dibutyryl-cAMP given to the immature day 14 rat shelf *in vitro* produced a precocious decrease in medial edge epithelial DNA synthesis and an increase in glycoprotein synthesis (Pratt and Martin, 1975). These induced changes normally occur on days 15 to 16. Dibutyryl cAMP prevented epidermal growth factor-induced inhibition of epithelial cell death (Pratt *et al.*, 1975). The A/J and C57 strains were compared to determine whether glucocorticoids affected the transient peak in cAMP differentially, but it was shown that palatal cAMP levels were depressed equally in the two strains by maternal administration of teratogenic doses of glucocorticoids (Greene *et al.*, 1981). The transient peak of palatal cAMP was not evident in steroid-treated embryonic palates of each strain and the decrease in cAMP *in vivo* was confined to the epithelium *in vivo* as demonstrated by immunohistochemical localization. Thus, although glucocorticoids may affect palatal epithelial differentiation by inhibiting the transient rise in cAMP, differential susceptibility to cortisone-induced cleft palate in A/J and C57 does *not* appear to involve a differential effect on palatal cAMP levels.

B. Glucocorticoids and Inflammation

A number of important advances have been made recently in the biochemistry of inflammation, and in the hormonal mechanisms by which glucocorticoids affect inflammatory reactions. Since the cleft palate teratogenicity of glucocorticoids is known to be correlated with their antiinflammatory potency (Pinsky and Di George, 1965; Walker, 1971), the possibility should be considered that the teratogenic and antiinflammatory effects of glucocorticoids could involve some of the same reactions. It was proposed by Lewis and Piper (1975) that at least some of the actions of antiinflammatory corticosteroids could be explained by the inhibition of prostaglandin release. Hong and Levine (1976) extended this hypothesis by proposing that corticosteroids bring about this effect by inhibiting arachidonic acid release from phospholipids, since arachidonic acid is the limiting precursor for prostaglandin biosynthesis and there is little free arachidonic acid in most cells. Hong and Levine's conclusion was based on a study of MC5-5 mouse cells which accumulate prostaglandins E_2 (PGE$_2$) and $F_{2\alpha}$ (PGF$_{2\alpha}$) in the medium. Hydrocortisone and other antiinflammatory steroids inhibited this release of prostaglandins, whereas exogenously supplied arachidonic acid stimulated prostaglandin production. The authors labeled the phospholipids of MC5-5 cells with [^{3}H]arachidonic acid, and showed that 96% of the radioactivity that was released into the medium appeared as arachidonic acid and 4% as PGE$_2$. Hydrocortisone inhibited the release of labeled arachidonic acid, but did not inhibit prostaglandin synthetase. The latter conclusion was based on the observation that hydrocortisone did not inhibit prostaglandin production in the presence of exogenously supplied arachidonic acid.

On the basis of studies with rabbit platelets, Blackwell and colleagues (1977) suggested that phospholipase A$_2$ plays a key role in arachidonic acid release from phospholipids, and that drugs such as mepacrine could act by blocking this enzyme. This concept was supported and extended by experiments in which perfused guinea pig lungs were stimulated by various agents such as histamine to release rabbit aorta contracting substance (RCS) (Blackwell *et al.*, 1978). Rabbit aorta contracting substance is a mixture of prostaglandin endoperoxides and thromboxane A$_2$ (TXA$_2$), and the release of these substances was blocked by antiinflammatory steroids. Evidence for a second messenger which mediates the antiphospholipase effects of steroids was obtained, and this factor, designated macrocortin, was shown to be an intracellular polypeptide with molecular weight of approximately 15,000 (Blackwell *et al.*, 1980). Its activity was measured by inhibition of prostaglandin formation by test leukocytes. Hydrocortisone induced the release of macrocortin from leukocytes, so that by 150 minutes virtually all the inhibitory activity was extracellular. Macrocortin was not released by leukocytes incubated with cycloheximide or without hydrocortisone.

This pathway was studied in rabbit neutrophils by Hirata *et al.* (1979, 1980). When rabbit peritoneal neutrophils were treated with the chemoattractant fMet-Leu-Phe, a decrease in the incorporation of L-[*methyl*-^{3}H] methionine into lipids occurred as a result of increased phospholipid degradation, and this was paralleled by an increase in arachidonic acid release. This suggested that phospholipase A$_2$ was activated by the chemoattractant. Mepacrine and hydrocortisone inhibited both chemotaxis and phospholipase A$_2$ activity.

The inhibition of both chemotaxis and phospholipase A$_2$ by glucocorticoids required an incubation period of 5–10 hours, and the inhibitory effect was diminished by actinomycin D. When the cells were incubated with Pronase, there was an increase in arachidonic acid release. These results suggested that an inhibitor of phospholipase A_2 was being synthesized during the incubation period. The cells were then incubated with [^{3}H]lysine, lysed in distilled water, and centrifuged. Precipitates were solubilized with NP-40 and the supernatants were applied to a Sephadex G-200 column. An inhibitor of phospholipase A_2 was identified with a molecular weight of approximately 40,000. It was suggested that the antiinflammatory effects of glucocorticoids might be attributable to their ability to stimulate synthesis of this protein, designated lipomodulin (Hirata *et al.*, 1981), which would decrease the availability of arachidonic acid, and hence, of prostaglandins. This hypothesis was extended by studies with the sera of patients with autoimmune diseases such as rheumatoid arthritis and systemic lupus erythematosus. A substantial proportion of such sera were found to include antibodies against lipomodulin (Hirata *et al.*, 1981). Although lipomodulin seems to have the same biological effects as macrocortin, the fact that different masses have been reported for the two factors suggests that they are different molecules.

These studies demonstrated that glucocorticoids can induce the synthesis of phospholipase A_2 inhibitory proteins. This induction can be blocked by inhibitors of RNA and protein synthesis, such as actinomycin D and cycloheximide. The induction of a phospholipase A_2 inhibitory protein is mediated through cytosolic glucocorticoid receptors which can be blocked by receptor antagonists, such as the antiglucocorticoid cortexolone and/or progesterone. Phospholipase A_2 hydrolyzes phosphatidylcholine to generate lysophosphatidylcholine and arachidonic acid. Arachidonic acid serves as a substrate for two important enzymes, cyclooxygenase for prostaglandin synthesis and lipoxygenase for hydroxy- or hydroperoxyeicosatetraenoic acid and leukotriene formation (Kuehl and Egan, 1980). The products of these enzymes are known to have many physiological functions. The presence of phospholipase A_2 inhibitory proteins might provide a regulatory mechanism for the activity of phospholipase A_2 and the subsequent availability of its metabolic products. The hormonal effects of glucocorticoids could result from the capacity of cells to synthesize these phospholipase A_2 inhibitory proteins, as recently proposed for the guinea pig lung perfusion system (Danon and Assouline, 1978; Flower and Blackwell, 1979), rabbit neutrophil system (Hirata *et al.*, 1980), and the inhibition of induction of rat paw edema (Tsurufuji *et al.*, 1979). Phopholipase A_2-mediated events may include lymphocyte mitogenesis (Hirata *et al.*, 1980), chemotaxis of leukocytes (Hirata *et al.*, 1979), histamine release of mast cells (Hirata *et al.*, 1979), desensitization of β-adrenergic receptors in C6 astrocytoma cells (Mallorga *et al.*, 1980), production of bronchoconstrictor slow-reacting substance of anaphylaxis (Burka and Flower, 1979), macrophage phagocytosis (Higgs *et al.*, 1975), inhibition of electrically induced ileal contractions (Farnaly *et al.*, 1975), smooth muscle contracting activity of what had been known as G-acid, but now known to be arachidonic acid (Bates and Sih, 1979), lymphocyte migration (Van Epps, 1981), modulation of phagocytic release of lysosomal enzymes from neutrophils (Smith, 1977), stimulation of glycosaminoglycans (Chang *et al.*, 1977), initiation of cell proliferation (de Asua *et al.*, 1975), and modulation of adenylate cyclase (Gorman *et al.*, 1977).

A positive correlation has been demonstrated between the antiinflammatory potency of glucocorticoids and the degree of their ability to inhibit prostaglandin biosynthesis (Tam *et al.*, 1977), which occurs primarily through inhibition of the release of arachidonic acid rather than through inhibition of cyclooxygenase (Hirata *et al.*, 1980; Blackwell *et al.*, 1980). Exogenous arachidonic acid reverses the glucocorticoid-induced depression of prostaglandin production in anaphylactic lungs (Gryglewski *et al.*, 1975) and inflamed synovia (Floman and Zor, 1976), and reverses the inhibition of glucocorticoids of rat paw edema induced by carrageenin (Hicks *et al.*, 1979). Because of these relationships, and the correlation between the antiinflammatory potency of glucocorticoids and their capacity to induce cleft palate in rodents (Pinsky and Di George, 1965; Walker, 1971), it has been proposed that glucocorticoids may also induce cleft palate by blocking the release of arachidonic acid (Tzortzatou *et al.*, 1981).

C. ARACHIDONIC ACID RELEASE AND CLEFT PALATE

Three different types of observations support the hypothesis that glucocorticoids induce palatal clefting by blocking the release of arachidonic acid (Tzortzatou *et al.*, 1981). (1) Exogenous arachidonic acid given at the same time as dexamethasone produced a significant reduction in the percentage of fetuses with cleft palate. (2) The effect of exogenous arachidonic acid on dexamethasone-induced cleft palate can be reversed by treatment with indomethacin. Since this drug is an inhibitor of cyclooxygenase (Vane, 1971; Flower *et al.*, 1973), this observation supports the proposal that reduction in the quantities of prostaglandins and/or thromboxanes is teratogenic in the palate. (3) Dexamethasone was also shown to inhibit the release of labeled free arachidonic acid from the precipitable fraction of embryonic jaws, suggesting that there was less arachidonic acid available to the microsomal cyclooxygenase in the supernatant fraction. These experiments were all done in rats, but it has also been shown that arachidonic acid reduces the clefting action of cortisone in sensitive strains of mice (Goldman *et al.*, 1981b).

The proposal that the clefting action of dexamethasone leads to a reduction in the products of cyclooxygenase activity raises the question of whether prostaglandins and/or thromboxanes may be involved in normal palatal differentiation. Primary cultures of mouse embryo palatal mesenchymal cells can be stimulated to produce several prostaglandins from labeled arachidonic acid *in vitro* (Chepenik and Greene, 1981). If prostaglandins or thromboxanes are involved in normal palatal differentiation, one would expect palatal clefting to be produced by indomethacin and other nonsteroidal antiinflammatory inhibitors of cyclooxygenase, such as aspirin and phenylbutazone (Vane, 1971; Flower *et al.*, 1973). Indomethacin does not produce cleft palate in mice *in vivo* (Kalter, 1973), but only blocks the corrective action of arachidonic acid on dexamethasone-induced clefting (Tzortzatou *et al.*, 1981). Aspirin and phenylbutazone, two other inhibitors of cyclooxygenase, do produce cleft palate in rodents (Trasler, 1965; Montenegro *et al.*, 1976), and aspirin also increases the frequency of clefting induced by cortisone (Fritz, 1976). Thus, it is quite possible that prostaglandins do participate in normal palatal development, and that indomethacin produces an inhibition of embryonic cyclooxygenase sufficient to block the effects of exogenous arachidonic acid, but not sufficient to produce cleft palate by itself.

VI. GLUCOCORTICOIDS, SHELF ELEVATION, AND PROGRAMMED CELL DEATH

Glucocorticoids are known to affect at least two aspects of palatal differentiation: they induce a delay in the elevation of palatal shelves (Walker and Fraser, 1957; Walker and Patterson, 1978), and they affect programmed cell death. It was once thought that the delay in shelf elevation was sufficient to explain cortisone induction of cleft palate, since it was assumed that when the palatal shelves finally do become horizontal they are too far apart to meet in the midline and fuse. However, an *in vivo* study by Greene and Kochhar (1973) using frozen, cryostat-sectioned fetal heads from glucocorticoid-treated ICR mice showed that, in addition to showing a delay in elevation, palatal shelves made contact but then failed to undergo epithelial breakdown and fusion. This is consistent with studies mentioned in Section II which showed that epithelial cell death can occur in the absence of shelf contact (Smiley and Koch, 1972; Tyler and Koch, 1974). Thus, the cells of the normal palatal epithelium are programmed to die and this is independent of the contact between the palatal shelves, but both of these events can be influenced by glucocorticoids.

In a recent report by Walker and Patterson (1978), fetuses from cortisone-treated CD-1 mice were released from the uterus and amnion and chorion and allowed to develop for 8 hours in a fluid medium with the umbilical cord left intact. Removal of these tissues permits shelves from glucocorticoid-treated fetuses as well as controls to move without delay to the horizontal and fuse, indicating that fetal membranes and tongue are major obstacles to shelf elevation in glucocorticoid-treated mice. However, even under these conditions, shelves exposed to glucocorticoids appeared to fuse less readily than controls. The *in vivo* studies of frozen cryostat sections were extended to include the highly sensitive strain A/J and the less sensitive strain, B10 (Goldman *et al.*, 1981b). Shelf contact occurred in A/J subsequent to a lengthy steroid-promoted delay in shelf elevation; the percentage of cortisone-treated fetal heads with shelves in contact peaks was about 30% during this period. The lysosomal activity in the steroid-treated A/J shelves in contact was limited to the superficial epithelial cells along the medial edge and was apparently reduced in amount as well. In the less sensitive strain, B10, shelf contact occurred simultaneously in 60–70% of both control and cortisone-treated fetal heads, and lysosomal activity was virtually unaffected. In an *in vitro* culture model the actions of cortisol on medial edge epithelium have been examined in the highly sensitive strains A/J, CD-1, and ICR, and the more resistant strains B6 and B10 (Herold and Futran, 1980; Goldman *et al.*, 1981b). In this culture model, cortisol prevented the programmed breakdown of the medial edge epithelium and inhibited in this epithelial population the synthesis and/or release of lysosomal enzymes such as acid phosphatase or trimetaphosphatase. These changes were produced by cortisol only in shelves of the susceptible strains which have high levels of glucocorticoid receptors, suggesting that cortisol–receptor interactions may be involved in the steroid inhibition of programmed cell death in this palatal epithelium.

These results provide further evidence for the hypothesis that inhibition of programmed cell death is also important in glucocorticoid-promoted clefting. The inhibition of programmed cell death, like the delay of shelf elevation, is related to genetic differences in susceptibility to steroid-induced cleft palate.

The *in vitro* model may be useful in helping to examine the biochemical mechanisms underlying the teratogenic action of glucocorticoids in inhibiting programmed cell death in the absence of the mother. This method has been used to compare the effect of exogenous arachidonic acid on programmed cell death *in vitro* and *in vivo* in sensitive and resistant mouse strains (Goldman *et al.*, 1981a). Exogenous arachidonic acid significantly reduced the frequency of palatal clefting in both A/J and CD-1 strains *in vivo*. Arachidonic acid *in vitro* (1 ng to 1 μg/ml) reversed the inhibition of medial edge epithelial breakdown by cortisol in palatal shelves of CD-1 and A/J mice. Thus, arachidonic acid reversed the teratogenic effect of glucocorticoids both in the fetus and in organ cultures.

VII. GENETICS OF CLEFTING IN HUMANS

At this time there is no way of knowing how much of the preceding information applies to cleft palate in humans. Although cleft palate is one of the most common congenital malformations in human populations, there is no information as to how many of these cases could be attributed to glucocorticoids. There are over 50 recognized syndromes that include cleft lip and/or palate as one feature (Fraser, 1970), and a variety of mechanisms are undoubtedly involved in these conditions. It has been proposed that clefting can be explained by Falconer's threshhold model of polygenic inheritance, in which an abnormal phenotype occurs when a number of unspecified genetic and environmental factors accumulate beyond a certain threshhold (Carter, 1976). This has been disputed by Melnick *et al.* (1980), who proposed an alternative model involving single gene-dependent susceptibility to a variety of teratogens. It may be relevant to point out that diabetes was once considered the classic example of a disorder determined by a polygenic mode of inheritance, but after the important role of the HLA region was recognized, it began to look more and more like a single-gene disorder (Spielman *et al.*, 1980). In the case of glucocorticoid-induced cleft palate in the mouse, major genes on the second and seventeenth chromosomes have now been identified as being involved, but the human counterparts of these genes may not be important in the "spontaneous" human cleft palate. In one study the HLA haplotypes Aw24 and Aw28 appeared in higher than normal frequencies among patients with cleft lip and palate, but the differences were not statistically significant (Bonner *et al.*, 1978). In another study, there was no association between craniofacial anomalies and the A or B products of the HLA complex, but there was a relatively high incidence of sharing of the HLA-D haplotypes among affected family members (Rapaport *et al.*, 1979). In a third study, there was no association between HLA and clefting in 8 families in which two sibs were affected (Van Dyke *et al.*, 1980). Obviously a great deal of work remains to be done before the genetic and biochemical mechanisms involved in human cleft palate will be understood. Hopefully the murine studies will be useful in guiding these investigations.

VIII. SUMMARY

The induction of cleft palate by glucocorticoids is a very complex process that involves a number of genetic and biochemical factors. Inbred strains of mice show wide variations in their susceptibility to this condition, and the susceptibility of F_1 hybrids is strongly influenced by the maternal environment. The *H-2* histocompatibility region includes genes which affect glucocorticoid susceptibility, and these genes also influence the maternal effect. A gene linked to a minor histocompatibility locus (*H-3*) on the second chromosome also influences susceptibility to glucocorticoid-induced cleft palate.

The capacity of glucocorticoids to induce cleft palate is correlated with their antiinflammatory potency. At least some of the antiinflammatory effects of glucocorticoids can be explained by the inhibition of prostaglandin release, which in turn could be caused by inhibition of arachidonic acid release from phospholipids. Similar mechanisms may be involved in cleft palate induction, as exogenous arachidonic acid injected into pregnant rats and mice at the same time as glucocorticoids reduces the teratogenic potency of the steroids.

Glucocorticoids cause a delay in shelf elevation, and this delay is promoted by fetal membranes and the tongue. However, the cells of the medial edge epithelium are programmed to die whether contact is made with the apposing shelf or not. Glucocorticoids interfere with this programmed cell death, and this interference seems to be related to arachidonic acid release.

ACKNOWLEDGMENTS

We thank Drs. Robert P. Erickson, Robert M. Greene, Ronald L. Piddington, Harold C. Slavkin, and Zeev Davidovitch for critically reading the manuscript and making helpful suggestions. Studies in the authors' laboratories were supported by grants DE-05008 and DE-4622 from the National Institutes of Health.

REFERENCES

Andersen, H., and Mathiessen, M. E. (1967). *Acta Anat.* **68**, 473–508.

Andrew, F. D., and Zimmerman, E. F. (1971). *Teratology* **4**, 31–38.

Angelici, D. R., and Pourtois, M. (1968). *J. Embryol. Exp. Morphol.* **20**, 15–23.

Bates, H. A., and Sih, C. J. (1979). *Proc. Natl. Acad. Sci. U.S.A.* **76**, 2712–2714.

Baxevanis, C. N., Nagy, Z. A., and Klein, J. (1981). *Proc. Natl. Acad. Sci. U.S.A.* **78**, 3809–3813.

Baxter, H., and Fraser, F. C. (1950). *McGill Med. J.* **19**, 245–249.

Biddle, F. G., and Fraser, F. C. (1977). *Genetics* **85**, 289–302.

Blackwell, G. J., Duncombe, W. G., Flower, R. J., Parsons, M. F., and Vane, J. R. (1977). *Br. J. Pharmacol.* **59**, 353–366.

Blackwell, G. J., Flower, R. J., Nijkamp, F. P., and Vane, J. R. (1978). *Br. J. Pharmacol.* **62**, 79–89.

Blackwell, G. J., Carnuccio, R., DiRosa, M., Flower, R. J., Parente, L., and Persico, P. (1980). *Nature (London)* **287**, 147–149.

Bongiovanni, A. M. (1958). *J. Clin. Invest.* **37**, 1342–1347.

Bonner, J. J., and Slavkin, H. C. (1975). *Immunogenetics (N. Y.)* **2**, 213–218.
Bonner, J. J., Terasaki, P. I., Thompson, P., Holve, L. M., Wilson, L., Ebbin, A. J., and Slavkin, H. C. (1978). *Tissue Antigens* **12**, 228–232.
Burka, J. F., and Flower, R. J. (1979). *Br. J. Pharmacol.* **65**, 35–41.
Butley, M. S., Erickson, R. P., and Pratt, W. B. (1978). *Nature (London)* **275**, 136–138.
Carter, C. O. (1976). *Br. Med. Bull.* **32**, 21–26.
Chang, W. C., Abe, M., and Murota, S. (1977). *Prostaglandins* **13**, 15–63.
Chepenik, K. P., and Greene, R. M. (1981). *Biochem. Biophys. Res. Commun.* **100**, 951–958.
Coligan, J. E., Kindt, T. J., Uehara, H., Martinko, J., and Nathenson, S. G. (1981). *Nature (London)* **291**, 35–39.
Cook, R. C., Vitetta, E. S., Uhr, J. W., and Capra, J. D. (1979). *J. Exp. Med.* **149**, 981–986.
Cullen, S. E., Shreffler, D. C., Kindle, C. S., and David, C. S. (1980). *Immunogenetics (N. Y.)* **11**, 535–547.
Czitrom, A. A., Sunshine, G. H., and Mitchison, N. A. (1980). *Immunogenetics (N. Y.)* **11**, 97–102.
Danon, A., and Assouline, G. (1978). *Nature (London)* **273**, 552–554.
de Asua, J., Clingan, D., and Rudland, P. S. (1975). *Proc. Natl. Acad. Sci. U.S.A.* **72**, 2724–2728.
De Tolla, L. J., Semprevivo, L. H., Palczuk, N. C., and Passmore, H. C. (1980). *Immunogenetics (N. Y.)* **10**, 353–361.
Diewert, V. M., and Tait, B. (1979). *J. Anat.* **128**, 609–618.
Doherty, P. C., Blanden, R. V., and Zinkernagel, R. M. (1976). *Transplant. Rev.* **29**, 89–123.
Dorf, M. E., and Benacerraf, B. (1975). *Proc. Natl. Acad. Sci. U.S.A.* **72**, 3671–3675.
Dupont, B., Oberfield, E. E., Smithwick, E. M., Lee, T. D., and Levine, L. S. (1977). *Lancet* **2**, 1309–1312.
Erickson, R. P., Butley, M. S., and Sing, C. F. (1979). *J. Immunogenet.* **6**, 253–262.
Farbman, A. I. (1968). *Dev. Biol.* **18**, 93–116.
Farnaly, J. P., Fontaine, J., and Reuse, J. (1975). *Agents Actions* **5**, 354–358.
Ferguson, M. W. J. (1978). *J. Anat.* **125**, 555–577.
Flaherty, L. (1976). *Immunogenetics (N. Y.)* **3**, 533–539.
Floman, Y., and Zor, U. (1976). *Prostaglandins* **12**, 403–413.
Flower, R. J., and Blackwell, G. J. (1979). *Nature (London)* **278**, 456–459.
Flower, R. J., Cheung, H. S., and Cushman, D. W. (1973). *Prostaglandins* **4**, 325–341.
Francis, B. M. (1973). *Teratology* **7**, 119–126.
Francke, U., and Gehring, U. (1980). *Cell* **22**, 657–664.
Fraser, F. C. (1970). *Am. J. Hum. Genet.* **22**, 336–352.
Fraser, F. C., and Fainstat, T. D. (1951). *Pediatrics* **8**, 527–533.
Fraser, F. C., Kalter, H., Walker, B. E., and Fainstat, T. D. (1954). *J. Cell. Comp. Physiol.* **43**(Suppl. 1), 237–259.
Fraser, F. C., Walker, B. E., and Trasler, D. G. (1957). *Pediatrics* **19**, 782–787.
Fritz, H. (1976). *Experientia* **32**, 721–722.
Gasser, D. L. (1969). *J. Immunol.* **103**, 66–70.
Gasser, D. L. (1976a). *Immunogenetics (N. Y.)* **3**, 271–276.
Gasser, D. L. (1976b). *In* "The Role of Products of the Histocompatibility Gene Complex in Immune Responses" (D. H. Katz and B. Benacerraf, eds.), pp. 289–295. Academic Press, New York.
Gasser, D. L., and Shreffler, D. C. (1974). *Immunogenetics (N. Y.)* **1**, 133–140.

Gasser, D. L., Mele, L., Lees, D. D., and Goldman, A. S. (1981). *Proc. Natl. Acad. Sci. U.S.A.* **78**, 3147–3150.

Goldfeld, A. E., Rubin, C. S., Siegel, T. W., Shaw, P. A., Schiffer, S. G., and Waelsch, S. G. (1981). *Proc. Natl. Acad. Sci. U.S.A.* **78**, 6359–6361.

Goldman, A. S., Katsumata, M., Yaffe, S. J., and Gasser, D. L. (1977). *Nature (London)* **265**, 643–645.

Goldman, A. S., Herold, R. C., and Piddington, R. (1981a). *Proc. Soc. Exp. Biol. Med.* **166**, 418–424.

Goldman, A. S., Piddington, R. L., and Herold, R. C. (1981b). *Teratology* **23**, 36A.

Gorer, P. A. (1937). *J. Pathol. Bacteriol.* **44**, 691–697.

Gorman, R. R., Bunting, S., and Miller, D. V. (1977). *Prostaglandins* **13**, 377–388.

Greene, M. I., Dorf, M. E., Pierres, M., and Benacerraf, B. (1977). *Proc. Natl. Acad. Sci. U.S.A.* **74**, 5118–5121.

Greene, R. M., and Kochhar, D. M. (1973). *Teratology* **8**, 153–166.

Greene, R. M., and Kochhar, D. M. (1974). *J. Embryol. Exp. Morphol.* **31**, 683–692.

Greene, R. M., and Pratt, R. M. (1979). *J. Histochem. Cytochem.* **27**, 924–931.

Greene, R. M., Shanfeld, J. L., Davidovitch, Z., and Pratt, R. M. (1980). *J. Embryol. Exp. Morphol.* **60**, 271–281.

Greene, R. M., Goldman, A. S., Lloyd, M., Baker, M., Brown, K. S., Shanfeld, J. L., and Davidovitch, Z. (1981). *J. Craniofacial Genet. Dev. Biol.* **1**, 31–44.

Gryglewski, R., Panczenko, B., Korbrit, R., Grodzinska, L., and Ocetkiewicz, A. (1975). *Prostaglandins* **10**, 343–355.

Hackney, J. F. (1980). *Teratology* **21**, 39–70.

Hammerling, G., Hammerling, U., and Flaherty, L. (1979). *J. Exp. Med.* **150**, 108–116.

Hansen, T. H., Cullen, S. E., and Sachs, D. H. (1977). *J. Exp. Med.* **145**, 438–442.

Hassell, J. R., King, C. T. G., and Cohen, S. (1974). *J. Dent. Res.* **53**, 65.

Hayes, C. E., and Bach, F. H. (1980). *J. Exp. Med.* **151**, 481–485.

Hemm, R. D., Arslanoglou, L., and Pollock, J. J. (1977). *Teratology* **15**, 243–248.

Herold, R. C., and Futran, N. (1980). *Arch. Oral Biol.* **25**, 423–429.

Hicks, J., Hillier, M., Sibley, P., Skidmore, I. F., and White, B. (1979). *Br. J. Pharmacol.* **68**, 126P.

Higgs, G. S., McCall, E., and Youlten, L. J. F. (1975). *Br. J. Pharmacol.* **53**, 539–546.

Hirata, F., Corcaran, B. A., Venkatasubramanian, K., Schiffman, E., and Axelrod, J. (1979). *Proc. Natl. Acad. Sci. U.S.A.* **76**, 2640–2643.

Hirata, F., Schiffman, E., Venkatasubramanian, K., Salomon, D., and Axelrod, J. (1980). *Proc. Natl. Acad. Sci. U.S.A.* **77**, 2533–2536.

Hirata, F., Carmine, R. D., Nelson, C. A., Axelrod, J., Schiffman, E., Warabi, A., De Blac, A. L., Nirenberg, M., Monganiello, V., Vaughan, M., Kumagai, S., Green, I., Decker, J. L., and Steinberg, A. D. (1981). *Proc. Natl. Acad. Sci. U.S.A.* **78**, 3190–3194.

Hoffman, H. A., and Grieshaber, C. K. (1976). *Biochem. Genet.* **14**, 59–66.

Hong, S.-C. L., and Levine, L. (1976). *Proc. Natl. Acad. Sci. U.S.A.* **73**, 1730–1734.

Hull, P. (1969). *Heredity* **24**, 203–209.

Humphrey, T. (1969). *Am. J. Anat.* **125**, 317–344.

Ivanyi, P. (1978). *Proc. R. Soc. London, Ser. B* **202**, 117–158.

Jacobs, R. M. (1964). *Anat. Rec.* **150**, 271–277.

Jelinck, R., and Dostal, M. (1973). *Acta Chir. Plast.* **15**, 216–222.

Jelinck, R., and Dostal, M. (1974). *Folia Morphol. (Praha)* **22**, 94–101.

Jones, P. P., Murphy, D. B., and McDevitt, H. O. (1978). *J. Exp. Med.* **148**, 925–939.

Kaidoh, T., Shunnosuke, N. S., and Takahashi, M. (1981). *Proc. Natl. Acad. Sci. U.S.A.* **78**, 3794–3798.

Kalter, H. (1954). *Genetics* **39**, 185–196.

Kalter, H. (1965). *In* "Teratology: Principles and Techniques" (J. B. Wilson and J. Warkany, eds.), pp. 57–80. Univ. of Chicago Press, Chicago, Illinois.

Kalter, H. (1973). *Teratology* **7**, A19.

Katsumata, M., Baker, M. K., Goldman, A. S., and Gasser, D. L. (1981). *Immunogenetics (N. Y.)* **13**, 319–325.

Klein, J. (1975). "Biology of the Mouse Histocompatibility-2 Complex." Springer-Verlag, Berlin and New York.

Klein, J., and Chiang, C. L. (1978). *Immunogenetics (N. Y.)* **6**, 235–243.

Klein, J., Flaherty, L., VandeBerg, J. L., and Shreffler, D. C. (1978). *Immunogenetics (N. Y.)* **6**, 489–512.

Klein, J., Juretic, A., Baxevanis, C. N., and Nagy, Z. A. (1981). *Nature (London)* **291**, 455–460.

Krakauer, T., Hansen, T. H., Camerini-Otero, R. D., and Sachs, D. H. (1980). *J. Immunol.* **124**, 2149–2156.

Kuehl, F. A., Jr., and Egan, R. W. (1980). *Science* **210**, 978–984.

Lafuse, W., and Edidin, M. (1980). *Biochemistry* **19**, 49–54.

Lafuse, W. P., McCormick, J. F., and David, C. S. (1980). *J. Exp. Med.* **151**, 709–715.

Larsson, K. S. (1961). *Acta Morphol. Neerl. Scan.* **4**, 349–367.

Larsson, K. S. (1962). *Acta Odontol. Scand.* **20**, Suppl. 31, 1–35.

Larsson, K. S., Bostrom, H., and Carlsoo, S. (1959). *Exp. Cell Res.* **16**, 379–383.

Laurent, T. C. (1970). *In* "Chemistry and Molecular Biology of the Intercellular Matrix" (E. A. Balazs, ed.), pp. 703–732. Academic Press, New York.

Lazarro, C. (1940). *Monitore Zool. Ital.* **51**, 249–273.

Levine, A., Yaffe, S. J., and Back, N. (1968). *Proc. Soc. Exp. Biol. Med.* **129**, 86–88.

Levy, R. B., and Hansen, T. H. (1980). *Immunogenetics (N. Y.)* **10**, 7–17.

Lewis, G. P., and Piper, P. J. (1975). *Nature (London)* **254**, 308–311.

Lieberman, R., Paul, W. E., Humphrey, W., and Stimpfling, J. H. (1972). *J. Exp. Med.* **136**, 1231–1240.

Litwack, G., Filler, R., Rosenfield, S. A., Lichtash, N., Wishman, C. A., and Singer, S. (1973). *J. Biol. Chem.* **248**, 7481–7486.

Lozner, E. C., Sachs, D. H., and Shearer, G. M. (1974). *J. Exp. Med.* **139**, 1204–1214.

McDevitt, H. O., and Chinitz, A. (1969). *Science* **163**, 1207–1208.

McDevitt, H. O., and Tyan, M. L. (1968). *J. Exp. Med.* **128**, 1–11.

McDevitt, H. O., Deak, B. D., Shreffler, D. C., Klein, J., Stimpfling, J. H., and Snell, G. D. (1972). *J. Exp. Med.* **135**, 1259–1278.

McKenzie, I. F. C., Gardiner, J., Cherry, M., and Snell, G. D. (1977). *Transplant. Proc.* **9**, 667–669.

Mallorga, J., Tallman, J. F., Henneberry, D. C., Hirata, F., Strittmatter, W. J., and Axelrod, J. (1980). *Proc. Natl. Acad. Sci. U.S.A.* **77**, 1341–1345.

Melchers, I., Rajewsky, K., and Shreffler, D. C. (1973). *Eur. J. Immunol.* **3**, 754–761.

Melnick, M., Bixler, D., Fogh-Anderson, P., and Conneally, P. M. (1980). *Am. J. Med. Genet.* **6**, 83–97.

Meruelo, D., and Edidin, M. (1975). *Proc. Natl. Acad. Sci. U.S.A.* **72**, 2644–2648.

Meruelo, D., and Edidin, M. (1980). *Contemp. Top. Mol. Immunol.* **9**, 231–233.

Meruelo, D., Offer, M., and Flieger, N. (1981). *J. Exp. Med.* **154**, 1201–1211.

Michaelson, J. (1981). *Immunogenetics (N. Y.)* **13**, 167–171.

Michaelson, J., Flaherty, L., Vitetta, E., and Paulik, M. (1977). *J. Exp. Med.* **145**, 1066–1070.

Miller, K. K. (1977). *Teratology* **15**, 249–252.

Montenegro, M. A., Cubrillo, P., and Palonimo, H. (1976). *Rev. Med. Chile* **104**, 606–609.

Murphy, D. B., Herzenberg, L. A., Okumura, K., Herzenberg, L. A., and McDevitt, H. O. (1976). *J. Exp. Med.* **144**, 699–712.

Novak, R., Bosze, Z., Matkovics, B., and Fachet, J. (1980). *Science* **207**, 86–87.

Olson, F. C., and Massaro, E. J. (1977). *Fed. Proc., Fed. Am. Soc. Exp. Biol.* **36**, 928a.

O'Neill, H. C., and Parish, C. R. (1981). *Immunogenetics (N. Y.)* **13**, 247–259.

Passmore, H. C., and Shreffler, D. C. (1970). *Biochem. Genet.* **4**, 351–365.

Pinsky, L., and Di George, A. M. (1965). *Science* **147**, 402–403.

Pratt, R. M., and Hassell, J. R. (1975). *Dev. Biol.* **45**, 192–198.

Pratt, R. M., and King, C. T. G. (1971). *Arch. Oral Biol.* **16**, 1181–1185.

Pratt, R. M., and Martin, G. R. (1975). *Proc. Natl. Acad. Sci. U.S.A.* **72**, 874–877.

Pratt, R. M., Goggins, J. F., Wilk, A. L., and King, C. T. G. (1973). *Dev. Biol.* **32**, 230–237.

Pratt, R. M., Greene, R. M., Hassell, J. R., and Greenberg, J. (1975). *In* "Extracellular Matrix Influences on Gene Expression" (H. C. Slavkin and R. C. Greulich, eds.), pp. 561–566. Academic Press, New York.

Pratt, R. M., Salomon, D. S., Diewert, V. M., Erickson, R. P., Burns, R., and Brown, K. S. (1980). *Teratogen. Carcinogen. Mutagen.* **1**, 15–23.

Rapaport, F. T., Bach, F. H., Bachvaroff, R. J., McCarthy, J. G., Raisheck, A. P., Egelanfsdal, B., and Converse, J. M. (1979). *Tissue Antigens* **14**, 407–421.

Reminga, T., and Avery, J. K. (1972). *J. Dent. Res.* **51**, 1426–1430.

Rich, S. S., and Rich, R. R. (1976). *J. Exp. Med.* **143**, 672–677.

Roopenian, D. C., and Click, R. E. (1980). *Immunogenetics (N. Y.)* **10**, 333–341.

Ross, L. M., and Walker, B. E. (1967). *Am. J. Anat.* **121**, 509–522.

Rousseau, G. G., Baxter, J. D., and Tomkins, G. M. (1972). *J. Mol. Biol.* **67**, 99–115.

Salomon, D. S., and Pratt, R. M. (1976). *Nature (London)* **264**, 174–177.

Salomon, D. S., and Pratt, R. M. (1979). *Differentiation (Berlin)* **13**, 141–154.

Salomon, D. S., Gift, V. D., and Pratt, R. M. (1979). *Endocrinology (Baltimore)* **104**, 154–156.

Schmid, W., Grote, H., and Sekeris, C. E. (1976). *Mol. Cell. Endocrinol.* **5**, 223–241.

Shapira, Y., and Shosan, S. (1972). *Arch. Oral Biol.* **17**, 1699–1703.

Shreffler, D. C. (1976). *Transplant. Rev.* **32**, 140–167.

Shreffler, D. C., and David, C. S. (1975). *Adv. Immunol.* **20**, 125–195.

Shreffler, D. C., Meo, T., and David, C. S. (1976). *In* "The Role of Products of the Histocompatibility Gene Complex in Immune Responses" (D. H. Katz and B. Benacerraf, eds.), pp. 3–29. Academic Press, New York.

Shreffler, D. C., Atkinson, J. P., Brown, L. J., Parker, K. L., and Roos, M. H. (1981). *In* "Immunobiology of the Major Histocompatibility Complex" (M. B. Zaleski, C. J. Abeyounis, and K. Kano, eds.), pp. 78–88. Karger, Basel.

Smiley, G. R., and Koch, W. E. (1972). *Anat. Rec.* **173**, 405–416.

Smith, R. J. (1977). *J. Pharmacol. Exp. Ther.* **200**, 647–657.

Snell, G. D. (1948). *J. Genet.* **49**, 87–108.

Snell, G. D. (1958). *J. Natl. Cancer Inst.* **21**, 843–877.

Snell, G. D. (1981). *Science* **213**, 172–178.

Snell, G. D., Cudkowicz, G., and Bunker, H. P. (1967). *Transplantation* **5**, 492–503.

Spielman, R. S., Baker, L., and Zmijewski, C. M. (1980). *Ann. Hum. Genet.* **44**, 135–150.

Stanton, T. H., and Boyse, E. A. (1976). *Immunogenetics (N. Y.)* **3**, 525–531.

Stanton, T. H., and Hood, L. (1980). *Immunogenetics (N. Y.)* **11**, 309–314.

Stanton, T. H., Calkins, C. E., Jandinski, J., Schendel, D. J., Stutman, O., Cantor, H., and Boyse, E. A. (1978). *J. Exp. Med.* **148**, 963–973.

Streilein, J. W., and Klein, J. (1979). *Transplant. Proc.* **11**, 732–735.

Svejgaard, A., and Ryder, L. P. (1976). *Lancet* **2**, 547–549.

Tada, T., Taniguchi, M., and David, C. S. (1976). *J. Exp. Med.* **144**, 713–725.
Tada, N., Kimura, S., Hatzfeld, A., and Hammerling, U. (1980). *Immunogenetics (N. Y.)* **11**, 441–449.
Takei, F., and Horton, M. A. (1981). *Immunogenetics (N. Y.)* **13**, 435–441.
Tam, S., Hong, S.-C. L., and Levine, L. (1977). *J. Pharmacol. Exp. Ther.* **203**, 162–168.
Trasler, D. G. (1965). *Lancet* **1**, 606–607.
Tsurufugi, S., Sugio, K., and Takemasa, F. (1979). *Nature (London)* **280**, 408–410.
Tyan, M. L., and Miller, K. K. (1978). *Proc. Soc. Exp. Biol. Med.* **158**, 618–621.
Tyler, M. S., and Koch, W. E. (1974). *J. Dent. Res.* **53**, 64 (Abstr.).
Tzortzatou, G. G., Goldman, A. S., and Boutwell, W. C. (1981). *Proc. Soc. Exp. Biol. Med.* **166**, 321–324.
VandeBerg, J. L., and Klein, J. (1978). *J. Exp. Zool.* **203**, 319–324.
Van Dyke, D. C., Goldman, A. S., Spielman, R. S., Zmijewski, C. M., and Oka, S. W. (1980). *Cleft Palate J.* **17**, 189–193.
Vane, J. R. (1971). *Nature (London), New Biol.* **231**, 232–235.
Van Epps, D. E. (1981). *Inflammation (N. Y.)* **5**, 81–87.
Verrusio, A. C. (1970). *Teratology* **3**, 17–20.
Vitetta, E. S., and Capra, J. D. (1978). *Adv. Immunol.* **26**, 148–193.
Vitetta, E. S., Uhr, J. W., and Boyse, E. A. (1975). *J. Immunol.* **14**, 252–254.
Walker, B. E. (1961). *J. Embryol. Exp. Morphol.* **9**, 22–31.
Walker, B. E. (1969). *Teratology* **2**, 191–198.
Walker, B. E. (1971). *Teratology* **4**, 39–42.
Walker, B. E., and Fraser, F. C. (1956). *J. Embryol. Exp. Morphol.* **4**, 176–189.
Walker, B. E., and Fraser, F. C. (1957). *J. Embryol. Exp. Morphol.* **5**, 201–209.
Walker, B. E., and Patterson, A. (1978). *Teratology* **17**, 51–56.
Wee, E. L., Philips, N. J., Babriarz, B. S., and Zimmerman, E. F. (1980). *J. Embryol. Exp. Morphol.* **58**, 177–193.
Womack, J. E., Lu Shun Yam, D., and Potier, M. (1981). *Science* **212**, 63–65.
Zeiler, K. B., Weinstein, S., and Gibson, R. D. (1964). *Arch. Oral Biol.* **9**, 545–554.
Zimmerman, E. F., and Bowen, D. (1972). *Teratology* **5**, 335–344.
Zimmerman, E. F., Wee, E. L., Clark, R. L., and Venkatasubramanian, K. (1980). *In* "Current Research Trends in Prenatal Craniofacial Development" (R. M. Pratt and R. L. Christiansen, eds.), pp. 187–202. Elsevier/North-Holland, New York.

CHAPTER 12

Molecular Basis of Glucocorticoid Resistance in Experimental and Human Leukemia

John Stevens, Yee-Wan Stevens, and Harriette Haubenstock

BIOCHEMICAL ACTIONS OF HORMONES, VOL. X

I. INTRODUCTION

The suppressive action of glucocorticoids on lymphoid tissue has been known for many years (for a historic review, see Stevens *et al.*, 1979a) and forms the basis for the widespread use of this class of steroid in the treatment of various kinds of leukemia and lymphoma. Until the 1960's, the glucocorticoids were frequently used as single agents (Cline, 1974). During this period it became clear that patients who initially responded favorably to steroid administration later became refractory to this form of treatment. It was also observed that certain classes of leukemia and lymphoma were resistant to glucocorticoids from the outset. With the advent of combination chemotherapy, glucocorticoids were incorporated into many of the successful multiagent protocols. Under such circumstances resistance to steroid might be masked by the therapeutic efficacy of the other lympholytic drugs. However, administration of glucocorticoids is far from innocuous (Melby, 1977). It would obviously be desirable to spare patients with corticoid-resistant (CR) disease from receiving an ineffective agent (glucocorticoid) that could give rise to serious complications. Hence, the importance of establishing criteria that would permit rapid distinction between corticoid-sensitive (CS) and CR lymphocytes. In spite of considerable effort by many investigators, the exact mechanism by which glucocorticoids kill CS lymphocytes remains to be established. Current knowledge in this area was discussed recently (Stevens *et al.*, 1979a; Lippman, 1980; Thompson *et al.*, 1980; Munck and Crabtree, 1981) and will only be touched on briefly here. This chapter will focus on the problem of resistance to glucocorticoids and the possible biochemical and molecular basis of this phenomenon.

II. GLUCOCORTICOID EFFECTS ON CORTICOID-SENSITIVE LYMPHOCYTES

One of the earliest steps in glucocorticoid action on CS lymphocytes is binding of the hormone to specific intracellular receptor proteins. After undergoing a temperature-dependent process called "activation" or "transformation," the resulting hormone–receptor (HR) complexes bind to the nucleus (Munck and Crabtree, 1981) where they presumably initiate the events that ultimately lead to cell death and dissolution. In addition to their lethal action, corticosteroids also cause a variety of biochemical changes in CS lymphocytes such as inhibition of glucose transport (Munck, 1968), suppression of nucleoside and amino acid uptake, and incorporation into macromolecules (Makman *et al.*, 1968; Baran *et al.*, 1972; Rosen *et al.*, 1972; Stevens *et al.*, 1974), reduced oxidation of free fatty acids (Turnell and Burton, 1975), decreased incorporation of [^{14}C]acetate into lipids (Foley *et al.*, 1980; Picard *et al.*, 1980), and inhibition of choline incorporation into phosphatidylcholine (Story *et al.*, 1973).

However, no clear relationship has been demonstrated between these effects and hormone-induced cell death. The mechanism by which nuclear binding of glucocorticoid–receptor complexes is linked to these and other biochemical changes, and possibly to cell death, also remains to be established. The observation that many of these metabolic alterations can be prevented if steroid-treated lymphocytes are exposed at appropriate times to inhibitors of RNA and protein synthesis has led to the suggestion that hormone action is dependent on the transcription of specific mRNA(s) that code for effector protein(s) which mediate the biological response (Makman *et al.*, 1971; Mosher *et al.*, 1971; Young *et al.*, 1974; Stevens and Stevens, 1975b).

No direct evidence for the existence of steroid-induced "lethal" proteins or for the mRNA that codes for them has yet been obtained in glucocorticoid-treated, CS lymphocytes. However, exposure of rat thymus cells to dexamethasone resulted in a rapid (within 10 minutes) rise of RNA polymerase B activity, with no detectable change in RNA polymerase A activity at this time. After 30 minutes, there was a parallel decline in the activity of both enzymes (Bell and Borthwick, 1979). RNA polymerase B appears to be responsible for the transcription of mRNA in eukaryotic cells. After a 1-hour exposure of thymocytes to dexamethasone, there was increased incorporation of radioactive amino acids into three nonhistone chromosomal protein fractions. Analysis of cytosolic proteins or of solubilized plasma membranes revealed no differences in amino acid incorporation between control and dexamethasone-treated cells (Bell and Borthwick, 1979). More recently, Voris and Young (1981) demonstrated rapid (within 15 to 45 minutes) dexamethasone-induced increases in the rate of radioactive amino acid incorporation into several rat thymus proteins using giant two-dimensional gel electrophoresis. One of these proteins may be associated with the plasma membrane. None of them appeared to be identical to the dexamethasone-induced proteins described by Bell and Borthwick (1979).

Munck and Crabtree (1981) recently suggested that steroid killing of CS lymphocytes may result from the progressive accumulation of a wide variety of glucocorticoid-induced alterations that ultimately overwhelm the cell's ability to survive and continue multiplying. These alterations may include not only the metabolic changes alluded to earlier, but also increased nuclear fragility (Nicholson and Young, 1978), activation of an endogenous, non-lysosomal endonuclease that excises nucleosome chains from chromatin (Wyllie, 1980), and increased rates of protein degradation (Sutherland and Haynes, 1967; Stevens *et al.*, 1973; MacDonald *et al.*, 1980). Resistance to glucocorticoid-induced lymphocytolysis could be due to defects at any point along these complex and converging pathways.

III. RESISTANCE TO GLUCOCORTICOIDS IN ANIMAL MODEL SYSTEMS

A. RESISTANCE ASSOCIATED WITH ALTERATIONS IN GLUCOCORTICOID BINDING LEVELS

So far, there has been no exception to the observation that all CS lymphocytes contain receptor proteins that bind glucocorticoids in a specific and saturable manner. Together with the finding that absence of specific glucocorticoid binding is invariably associated with resistance to steroid, this has led to the generally held view that formation of HR complexes is a key step in glucocorticoid-induced lymphocytolysis. Indeed, severely reduced levels, or complete lack of glucocorticoid-binding activity, appear to be the most frequent mechanisms of resistance of murine lymphoma cells to the lethal action of glucocorticoids (Sibley and Tomkins, 1974b; Pfahl *et al.*, 1978b).

Hollander and Chiu (1966) were the first to show that resistance of tumor lymphocytes to glucocorticoid action was associated with decreased glucocorticoid binding. The model system used by these authors was mouse lymphoma P1798, a transplantable, estrogen-induced thymoma which is available in CS and CR strains (McCain-Lampkin and Potter, 1958). Corticoid-sensitive P1798 regresses dramatically when tumor-bearing animals are injected with pharmacological doses of glucocorticoid, whereas growth of CR P1798 is unaffected by steroid administration (Stevens *et al.*, 1974). Hollander and Chiu (1966) found that cytosol from CR P1798 tumors bound markedly less cortisol than cytosol from CS tumors. This observation was confirmed and extended by Kirkpatrick *et al.* (1971, 1972) who used both cortisol and the potent synthetic glucocorticoid triamcinolone acetonide (TA) as the radioactive ligands.

Markedly diminished levels of glucocorticoid binding were subsequently found in steroid-resistant tissue culture lines of mouse lymphoma S49 (Baxter *et al.*, 1971; Rosenau *et al.*, 1972). Sibley and Tomkins (1974b) tested 42 steroid-insensitive S49 clones for their ability to bind [³H]dexamethasone and found that 33 of these clones retained 60% or less steroid than wild-type (wt), sensitive cells. In many of the clones, specific binding was reduced to 20% or less of the sensitive level. Interestingly, some of the 42 CR clones displayed binding levels in the same range as wild-type cells. Possible mechanisms of resistance in receptor-positive lymphocytes will be discussed later. Inasmuch as steroid binding was measured with a whole cell assay, decreased glucocorticoid binding by the CR clones could have been due to impermeability of the cells to steroid. However, this was not the case, since CR lymphocytes that retained little or no [^{3}H]dexamethasone in the whole cell assay displayed similarly reduced levels of specific glucocorticoid binding when tested in a cell-free binding system (Sibley and Tomkins, 1974b).

The fact that many CR lymphocytes have lower levels of glucocorticoid binding than their CS counterparts does not necessarily mean that the CR cells contain reduced levels of receptor protein. Some classes of CR lymphocytes might contain altered binding components with very low affinity for steroid. One mechanism that could result in resistance to glucocorticoid action and decreased steroid binding without actual loss of receptor protein has been suggested by the work of Munck (1968), who found that the metabolic effects of cortisol on rat thymocytes could be abolished under anaerobic conditions. Munck and Brinck-Johnson (1968) subsequently showed that levels of specific binding of cortisol by intact thymocytes at 37°C depended on the metabolic state of the cells and, more specifically, on the intracellular level of ATP. Based on these observations, Munck *et al.* (1972) suggested that, in the absence of ATP, glucocorticoid receptors may exist in forms that are unable to bind cortisol at 37°C and that these forms are converted to the "normal" receptor in an ATP-dependent manner. These results were confirmed and extended by Wheeler *et al.* (1981), who demonstrated that the loss of glucocorticoid-binding ability by cultured human lymphoblastoid cells (IM-9) roughly paralleled the decline in intracellular ATP caused by incubation of the cells under nitrogen in glucose-free medium. Exposure of the metabolically deprived cells to air and glucose restored glucocorticoid binding and ATP levels in the cytosol. Restoration of binding was not blocked by prior incubation of the cells with cycloheximide and therefore did not seem to depend on continuing protein synthesis. Since the cytosol was prepared from cells that had not been previously exposed to steroid, it was the ligand-free receptor that was rapidly losing and regaining its glucocorticoid-binding ability according to the metabolic state of the cell. In other work, Nielsen and associates (1977) showed that highly purified calf intestinal alkaline phosphatase inactivated the glucocorticoid-binding capacity of high-speed supernatants from mouse fibroblasts and rat liver. Thus, certain classes of steroid-resistant lymphoma cells might display reduced levels of glucocorticoid binding because they contain altered receptor proteins that cannot be adequately phosphorylated, or because the putative receptor phosphorylation–dephosphorylation mechanisms do not function normally. The use of antibodies that specifically recognize glucocorticoid receptors (Okret *et al.*, 1981; Eisen, 1982) may help to shed light on this problem.

B. Genetic Analysis of Resistance

In the course of studies on steroid sensitivity of S49 lymphoma cells in culture, Sibley and Tomkins (1974a) noticed that the fraction of steroid-resistant cells in recently cloned populations was orders of magnitude lower than in populations that had not been cloned for several years. A Luria–Delbruck fluctuation test was carried out to determine whether resistance was caused by a random mutational event or whether it might have resulted from a heritable steroid-induced phenotypic change. The results indicated that resistant clones emerged randomly at the rate of 3.5×10^{-6} cell/generation. This frequency is consistent with a mutational origin and it was increased 20-fold by 9-aminoacridine and 50- to 100-fold by N-methyl-N'-nitro-N-nitrosoguanidine (MNNG). Both these compounds are known to be mutagenic in other systems.

The genetic approach pioneered by Sibley and Tomkins was also used by Bourgeois and Newby (1977) to study steroid resistance in the S49 lymphoma system and in the W7 mouse thymoma cell line. These authors confirmed the high frequency of transition to resistance of S49 cells, whereas they found that CS cultures of W7 cells gave rise to CR variants at a much lower rate (less than 3×10^{-9} cell/generation). This frequency was increased severalfold by exposing the W7 cells to MNNG.

Based on the fact that wild-type W7 cells were more sensitive to the growth-inhibitory effects of lower concentrations of dexamethasone (10^{-9}–10^{-8} M) than wild-type S49 cells, Bourgeois and Newby (1977) selected W7 variants that were partially resistant to dexamethasone. The partially resistant clones arose at frequencies ranging from 6.5×10^{-8} to 2×10^{-6} cell/generation. In the presence of high concentrations of dexamethasone, these partially resistant variants gave rise to cells that were fully resistant to glucocorticoid at the relatively high frequency of 4×10^{-6} to 1.5×10^{-5} cell/generation. This frequency was reasonably close to that obtained by Sibley and Tomkins (1974a) for S49 cells.

Whole cell assay of glucocorticoid binding levels revealed that fully sensitive, wild-type W7 cells contained approximately 30,000 receptor sites per cell, whereas wild-type S49 lymphocytes and partially resistant W7 cells contained approximately half that number of sites. There was no difference in the dissociation constant of dexamethasone binding among the various CS and partially CR lines that were tested ($K_d = 1.3 \times 10^{-8}$ M). Based on these results, Bourgeois and Newby (1977) postulated that development of this type of resistance proceeded in two steps. The first step would correspond to extinction of one of the two functional alleles of the receptor gene ($r^+/r^+ \rightarrow r^+/r^-$). The second step would involve extinction of the remaining allele ($r^+/r^- \rightarrow r^-/r^-$). The observed rates of appearance of partially resistant and fully resistant variants were consistent with a single genetic event at each step. According to this model, wild-type W7 cells were assumed to be homozygous at the r gene (receptor gene) locus whereas wild-type S49 lymphocytes and the partially CR W7 variants of equivalent sensitivity were presumed to be heterozygous or functionally hemizygous (r^+/r^-). The fact that wild-type W7 cells contained twice as many glucocorticoid-binding sites per cell as wild-type S49 lymphocytes or partially resistant W7 thymoma cells was suggestive of a gene dosage effect. Further evidence was obtained by fusing homozygous (r^+/r^+ or r^-/r^-) or heterozygous (r^+/r^-) W7 cells and analyzing the hybrid clones for glucocorticoid receptor content and cytolytic response to dexamethasone (Bourgeois and Newby, 1979). The levels of [^{3}H]dexamethasone binding per cell of the parental lines and of the hybrids are summarized in Table I. The response of the

TABLE I

RECEPTOR CONTENT OF PARENTAL LINES AND HYBRIDS[a]

Cell line	Selective marker	Receptor alleles	Number of r^+ alleles/ cell	Receptor sites/ cell	$K_d \times 10^8$
W7TB	BUdR[b]	r^+/r^+	2	28,000 ± 300[c]	1.4 ± 0.2[c]
W7TG	TG[d]	r^+/r^+	2	30,100 ± 1,100	1.3 ± 0.1
MS1	BUdR	r^+/r^-	1	14,700 ± 1,100	1.5 ± 0.4
EO24	TG	r^+/r^-	1	13,200 ± 200	1.2 ± 0.2
AN6	BUdR	r^-/r^-	0	<100	
SL3	TG	r^-/r^-	0	<100	
W7TB × W7TG		$r^+/r^+ \times r^+/r^+$	4	57,500 ± 3,900[e]	1.4 ± 0.2[e]
W7TB × EO24		$r^+/r^+ \times r^+/r^-$	3	44,600[f]	1.7[f]
W7TG × MS1		$r^+/r^+ \times r^+/r^-$	3	41,000[f]	1.8[f]
W7TB × SL3		$r^+/r^+ \times r^-/r^-$	2	33,700 ± 1,700	1.5 ± 0.4
MS1 × EO24		$r^+/r^- \times r^+/r^-$	2	33,200 ± 1,500	1.7 ± 0.2
W7TG × AN6		$r^+/r^+ \times r^-/r^-$	2	30,700[f]	1.2[f]
MS1 × SL3		$r^+/r^- \times r^-/r^-$	1	12,700 ± 1,500[g]	1.5 ± 0.3[g]

[a] From Bourgeois and Newby (1979) with permission.
[b] BUdR, 5-bromodeoxyuridine.
[c] Mean ± SE.
[d] TG, thioguanine.
[e] Mean ± SE for two independent hybrid clones.
[f] Single determinations.
[g] Mean ± SE for four independent hybrid clones.

cell lines to varying concentrations of dexamethasone is shown in Fig. 1. Although there was a clear correlation between receptor content and ploidy of the *r* gene, the correlation between number of receptor sites/cell and cytolytic response to dexamethasone was not as clear. For example, both

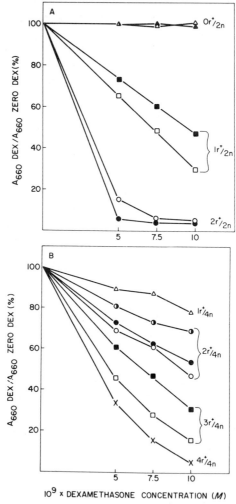

FIG. 1. Sensitivity to dexamethasone of parental and hybrid cell lines. The cellular material present in culture after eight doublings was monitored by turbidity at 660 nm (Bourgeois and Newby, 1977). The results obtained for the cultures with dexamethasone are expressed as percentages of the A_{660} reached in the control without steroid. (A) Parental lines: ●, W7TB; ○, W7TG; □, E024; ■, MS1; ▲, AN6; △, SL3. (B) Hybrid lines: X, W7TB × W7TG; □, W7TB × EO24; ■, W7TG × MS1; ○, W7TG × AN6; ●, MS1 × EO24; ◑, W7TB × SL3; △, MS1 × SL3. From Bourgeois and Newby (1979) with permission.

$1r^+/2n$ cell lines (diploid lines with one functional receptor allele) were much more sensitive to steroid than the $1r^+/4n$ hybrid (a tetraploid line with one functional receptor allele) even though all three lines contained the same number of dexamethasone-binding sites/cell (13,000–15,000). Similarly, the $4r^+/4n$ (a tetraploid line with four functional receptor alleles) hybrid with 60,000 sites/cell was considerably less sensitive than either of the $2r^+/2n$ wild-type lines (diploid lines with two functional receptor alleles) with 30,000 binding sites/cell. It is important to note that nuclear transfer of steroid–receptor complexes took place normally in all the hybrid lines. However, when the diploid and tetraploid cell lines were considered as separate groups, there was good correlation between number of binding sites per cell and sensitivity to dexamethasone.

If receptor-positive [r(+)] CR lymphoma cells were resistant to steroid because they contained an inhibitor to one or more of the steps between formation of HR complexes and the onset of cell death, fusion of such cells with CS lymphocytes might be expected to give rise to CR hybrids. Gehring *et al.* (1972) were the first to approach this question experimentally. Corticoid-resistant EL-4 lymphoma cells were fused with CS mouse myeloma cells. Both parent lines contained about 6500 [^{3}H]dexamethasone-binding sites per cell. Two hybrid clones, each with close to 9000 binding sites per cell, were tested for sensitivity to glucocorticoids. Both clones were killed by dexamethasone in a time- and dose-dependent manner that was indistinguishable from the kinetics of the lethal effect of dexamethasone on the CS myeloma parent. This experiment suggested that resistance was not due to an inhibitor of lymphocytolysis and that sensitivity was a dominant trait. However, in later work, Gehring (1980) determined that EL-4 was an nt$^-$ (nuclear transfer negative) variant since its HR complexes bound only minimally to isolated DNA.

Fusion of EL-4 cells with wild-type S49 lymphocytes also gave rise to CS hybrids (Gehring, 1980). In this instance, the hybrids were two orders of magnitude less sensitive to 1 μM dexamethasone than the CS S49 parent as judged by their cloning efficiency in soft agar. Sensitivity, therefore, appeared to be codominant. Fusion of cells with two different types of resistance [EL-4 nt$^-$ × S49 r(−) (receptor negative) or EL-4 nt$^-$ × S49 nt$^-$] did not give rise to CS hybrids. Hybridization of r(−) CR lymphocytes with nt^i (nuclear transfer increased) CR variants also failed to give rise to CS progeny (Yamamoto *et al.*, 1976). These results make it unlikely that resistance of one of the cell lines was due to lack of a diffusible factor that was conserved in the other CR parent. Although sensitivity to glucocorticoid appears to be dominant or codominant in hybrids between CS and CR lymphoma cells, CS lymphoma S49 × L cell fibroblast hybrids were not lysed by glucocorticoids in spite of the fact that one parent (S49) was killed by steroid and the other (L cell) was growth inhibited (unpublished results of Gehring, cited in Gehring and Thompson, 1979).

Yamamoto *et al.* (1976) examined the DNA-binding properties of glucocorticoid receptors in the hybrid clones. In all cases, the properties of receptors isolated from hybrid cells were exactly those predicted from the behavior of the receptors in each parent. For example, wt × nt^i hybrids contained two discrete populations of HR complexes: one eluted from DNA–cellulose at the same ionic strength as receptors from wild-type CS cells, and the other eluted at the higher salt concentration previously shown to be required for eluting HR complexes from CR nt^i variants. Hormone–receptor complexes from wt × wt or $r(-)$x nt^i hybrids eluted from DNA as single peaks at the ionic strength required to elute wt and nt^i HR complexes, respectively. Therefore, ability to synthesize one type of receptor did not interfere, qualitatively, with the ability to synthesize another type. No new types of receptor molecule were detected in the hybrids.

Pfahl and Bourgeois (1980) examined steroid resistance in heterologous lymphoid cell hybrids in considerable detail. The CR lymphocytes were either $r(-)$ or nt^-. The CS lines were either functionally diploid (r^+/r^+) or functionally hemizygous (r^+/r^-) for the steroid receptor gene. These authors confirmed the observations of Gehring and Thompson (1979) and of Yamamoto *et al.* (1976) that no positive complementation took place (i.e., no CS clones were generated) when $r(-)$ cells were fused with $r(-)$ or nt^- lymphocytes. The frequency of resistance in pseudotetraploid hybrids containing only one positive receptor allele $[r^-/r^+(nt^-) \times r^-/r^+; r^-/r^- \times r^-/r^+]$ was quite high (0.03–0.09) compared to the frequency of steroid resistance found previously in heterozygous (r^+/r^-) pseudodiploid lines $(10^{-5}–10^{-6})$. These results are in agreement with the earlier work of Gehring and Thompson (1979). Two positive alleles had to be present for the pseudotetraploid hybrids to exhibit a comparable frequency of resistance to dexamethasone. Even so, this frequency of resistance was still orders of magnitude higher than that displayed by CS clones with the genotype r^+/r^+ ($<2 \times 10^{-9}$). Therefore, the emergence of steroid resistance in pseudotetraploid hybrids may obey mechanisms different from those that operate in pseudodiploid cell lines. The higher than expected frequency of resistance in pseudotetraploid hybrids with one or two positive alleles could be due to partial dominance of the resistant alleles or to loss or rearrangement of genetic material coding for receptor. The experimental results of Pfahl and Bourgeois (1980) are consistent with the second possibility. Thus, most CR pseudotetraploid clones that arose from CS hybrids with genotype $[r^-/r^+(nt^-) \times r^-/r^+]$ or $[r^-/r^+(nt^-) \times r^+/r^+]$ contained diminished amounts of steroid-binding activity and displayed reduced nuclear transfer. However, when the parental hybrids produced "normal" receptor, $(r^-/r^+ \times r^-/r^+)$,

$(r^-/r^- \times r^-/r^+)$, or $(r^-/r^- \times r^+/r^+)$ the CR hybrids derived from them exhibited complete loss of specific glucocorticoid binding.

Another mechanism of resistance, suggested by Yamamoto *et al.* (1976), could involve a nonreceptor component, present in limiting amounts, that must interact with normal receptor for killing to take place. Interaction of this hypothetical component with defective receptor in the hybrids would make it unavailable for association with wild-type receptor, thereby reducing the magnitude of cell kill. To test this type of negative complementation, it will be necessary to determine if $r(-)$ CR lymphocytes are completely devoid of receptor protein, or whether they contain defective receptors that are incapable of binding steroid or only do so with very low affinity. The availability of antibodies against glucocorticoid receptor might help to clarify this issue (see Section III,G). Yet another possibility is that the reduced *concentration* of wild-type receptors in the hybrids (which are about twice the size of the parent cells) is the causal factor in reducing the killing efficiency of the steroid.

Francke and Gehring (1980) used the technique of intraspecies somatic cell hybridization in an attempt to map the chromosomal localization of the gene for glucocorticoid receptor. Wild-type CS S49 lymphoma cells were fused with CR EL-4 lymphocytes. As mentioned earlier, EL-4 glucocorticoid receptors are of the nt$^-$ class. Receptor analysis indicated that the CS hybrids produced a mixture of wt and nt$^-$ receptor whereas only the nt$^-$ form was detectable in the CR variants. Both parent lines, three CS, and three CR hybrids were karyotyped. Of 32 metaphase spreads from CS hybrid clone 39.4N, 18 contained 79 chromosomes, equal to the sum of chromosomes in the two parent lines. Random losses or gains were observed in the other 14 metaphases. All 32 spreads had three normal chromosomes 18: two from the S49 parent (S49.1-18[1] and S49.1-18[2]) and 1 from the EL-4 parent (EL-4-18). The chromosomes 18 from S49 could be easily distinguished from each other and also from EL-4-18. The other two CS hybrids, one with 79 chromosomes, the other containing 78, also had the same three chromosomes 18. In contrast, 27 metaphase spreads of CR hybrid clone 39.4 D, which displayed the karyotype expected from the addition of S49 and EL-4 chromosomes, contained two instead of three chromosomes 18. One was derived from EL-4; the other was S49.1-18[2]. Chromosome S49-18[1] was consistently missing. Metaphases that deviated from the modal karyotype also lacked chromosome S49.1-18[1], but EL-4-18 and S49.1-18[2] were always present. Karyotypic analysis of two additional CS and two additional CR hybrids also indicated the consistent presence of 3 chromosomes 18 in the CS hybrids and the absence of S49.1-18[1] in all metaphase spreads from the CR hybrids.

An attractive interpretation of these results is that chromosome S49.1-

18^1 contained the gene that coded for wild-type glucocorticoid receptor in CS S49.1 lymphoma cells. On the other hand, the receptor gene may have been located on another chromosome but subject to regulation by a locus on chromosome 18^1. A third possibility is that chromosome S49.1-18^2 contained the functional gene for receptor but its expression was extinguished by an unknown mechanism in the hybrids.

C. Interaction of Glucocorticoid–Receptor Complexes with Nuclei and DNA

As pointed out earlier, glucocorticoid binding levels in several of the CR clones of S49 lymphoma isolated by Sibley and Tomkins (1974b) were comparable to the levels of binding in wild-type CS S49 cells. Sibley and Tomkins (1974b), Yamamoto et al. (1974), and Gehring and Tomkins (1974) found that these receptor-positive CR clones could be divided into three categories: (1) Clones with significantly less nuclear binding of [^{3}H]dexamethasone at 37°C than wild-type cells; these clones were designated nuclear transfer minus, $S^R[r(+) \ nt^-]$. (2) Clones with significantly more nuclear binding of [^{3}H]dexamethasone at 37°C than wild-type cells; these clones were designated nuclear transfer increased, $S^R[r(+) \ nt^i]$. (3) Clones in which the level of nuclear binding of [^{3}H]dexamethasone at 37°C was similar to that in wild-type lymphocytes; these clones were designated nuclear transfer positive, deathless (d^-), $S^R[r(+) \ nt^+ \ d^-]$. There was no difference in the number of [^{3}H]dexamethasone-binding sites per milligram cytosol protein or in the dissociation constant of binding (measured in cell-free extracts) between $4[r(+) \ nt^-]$ clones and wild-type lymphocytes. However, two $[r(+) \ nt^i]$ clones (55R and 57R) displayed considerably higher concentrations of glucocorticoid–receptor complexes than wild-type cells in the cell-free binding assay. Furthermore, the receptors in the extracts from the resistant mutants appeared to have a somewhat higher affinity for the ligand. The results of Pfahl et al. (1978b) suggest that the $[r(+) \ nt^i]$ mutation is a rather rare event. These workers screened 271 CR variants of S49 and W7 lymphoma and failed to detect a single $[r(+) \ nt^i]$ variant among the 27 $r(+)$ CR clones that were identified. All 27 CR clones were classified as $[r(+) \ nt^-]$. Most but not all of these 27 variants contained fewer glucocorticoid-binding sites per cell (whole cell assay at 37°C) than the corresponding wild-type parent lines. As noted earlier, the CR strain of transplantable mouse lymphoma P1798 also contains diminished levels of cytosolic glucocorticoid receptor (Hollander and Chiu, 1966; Kirkpatrick et al., 1971, 1972). However, no difference was found between CS and CR P1798 lymphocytes in terms of the partition of bound steroid between the nucleus and cytoplasm in whole cells at 37°C, with 80% nuclear localization of [³H]triamcinolone acetonide–receptor complexes in both strains of tumor (Stevens and Stevens, 1979).

Gehring and Tomkins (1974) and Yamamoto *et al*. (1974) attempted to establish the molecular basis for the nt⁻ and ntⁱ phenotypes. As shown in Table II, Gehring and Tomkins (1974) found that when cytosol from CS S49 cells was charged with [³H]dexamethasone and incubated with homologous nuclei at 20°C, a high level of HR complex uptake by the nuclei was achieved. In contrast, only low levels of nuclear uptake were observed when CR nuclei were presented with CR S49 cytosol. The concentration of [³H]dexamethasone–receptor complexes was similar in both types of cytosol. However, incubation of CS cytosol with CR nuclei resulted in a pronounced degree of nuclear transfer whereas only minimal nuclear uptake was observed when CS nuclei were combined with CR cytosol. The presence of a diffusible inhibitor in CR cytosol that might prevent CR receptors from binding to CS or to CR nuclei was ruled out in control mixing experiments. These results are consistent with the idea that the nt⁻ phenotype may be due to a defect in the receptor molecules themselves rather than to an alteration in the nuclear acceptor sites. The failure of heat-activated nt⁻ dexamethasone–receptor complexes to bind to either CS or CR nuclei in the cell-free system correlated with the inability of these complexes to bind DNA isolated from lymphoma cells or calf thymus. Gehring and Tomkins (1974) also showed that the lymphoma HR complexes had to be activated (which was achieved either by warming the charged cytosol or by exposure to high ionic strength, or both) in order for them to bind to nuclei or DNA. At the time these studies were performed, no procedure had been developed for examining the activation process separately from the nuclear- or DNA-binding step. However, Gehring and Tomkins recognized that lack of nuclear

TABLE II

BINDING OF RECEPTOR–DEXAMETHASONE COMPLEXES TO NUCLEI FROM SENSITIVE AND RESISTANT CELLS[a]

Cytosol from	Nuclei from	Specifically bound dexamethasone (molecules/nucleus)
Sensitive cells	Sensitive cells	4170
Resistant cells	Resistant cells	305
Sensitive cells	Resistant cells	4680
Resistant cells	Sensitive cells	365

[a] Cytosols were pretreated with [³H]dexamethasone and incubated for 60 minutes at 20°C with 10⁸ nuclei. The incubations contained 3.8 mg cytosol protein of the sensitive and resistant cell lines, corresponding to 0.87 and 0.63 pmol specifically bound dexamethasone per milligram protein, respectively. From Gehring and Tomkins (1974) with permission.

binding of the nt⁻ HR complexes could have been due to a defect in
activation rather than to impairment of nuclear binding itself. More recently,
Parchman and Litwack (1977) and Sakaue and Thompson (1977) described
procedures for separating activated and unactivated glucocorticoid–receptor
complexes. It would be interesting to reexamine the [r(+) nt⁻] clones using
this methodology. Indeed, a human CR[r(+) nt⁻] variant that appears to
be deficient in the activation step has been isolated (Schmidt *et al.*, 1980)
(Section IV,B).

Yamamoto *et al.* (1974) compared the DNA-binding properties of dexamethasone–receptor complexes from the [r(+) ntⁱ] CR S49 variants to those
of wild-type and [r(+) nt⁻] CR cells. Whereas heat-activated CS S49 and
heat-activated CR[r(+) ntⁱ] complexes were retained almost quantitatively
on columns of DNA–cellulose, less than 25% of HR complexes in heat-
activated cytosol from two nt⁻ clones bound to DNA–cellulose. Mixing
experiments showed that nt⁻ cytosol did not inhibit binding of wild-type
HR complexes to DNA, and wild-type cytosol did not increase the binding
to DNA of HR complexes derived from nt⁻ lymphocytes. More strikingly,
the small amount of nt⁻ receptor that was retained by DNA–cellulose
eluted from the column at a much lower salt concentration than that required
to elute wild-type receptors. In contrast, receptors from the ntⁱ variants
eluted at significantly higher salt concentrations than wild-type receptors.
In other experiments, Yamamoto *et al.* (1976) found that the DNA-binding
and elution properties of [³H]dexamethasone–receptor complexes from two
"deathless" CR clones were indistinguishable from wild-type, suggesting
the presence of unaltered cytoplasmic glucocorticoid receptors in these
cells. Based on analysis by sedimentation partition chromatography, Yamamoto
et al. (1976) estimated that the affinity of nt⁻ HR complexes for DNA was
about 70 times lower than that of wild-type complexes whereas ntⁱ HR
complexes bound 10–100 times more tightly to DNA than complexes from
CS lymphocytes. Although Yamamoto *et al.* (1976) recognized that the
DNA-binding properties of HR complexes in an *in vitro*, cell-free system
were not necessarily a faithful measure of HR complex interaction with the
nucleus in whole cells under physiological conditions, the simplest interpretation of the above results [and the one favored by Yamamoto *et al.*
(1976)] was that the nt⁻ and ntⁱ variants contained glucocorticoid receptors
with altered nuclear-binding domains and that the degree of HR complex
retention in the nucleus was probably determined by the affinity of the
complexes for nuclear DNA.

In studies on the kinetics of [³H]dexamethasone interaction with cytosolic
receptors from wild-type and steroid-resistant (ntⁱ and nt⁻) S49 lymphoma
cells, Spindler-Barth and Gehring (1982) observed that the rate constant
of dissociation of the hormone from receptors of a CR nt⁻ clone was several-

fold faster (4×10^{-3} min^{-1}) than in wild-type lymphocytes or than in the other CR clones that were tested (1×10^{-3} min^{-1}). In contrast, the association rate constant was similar for all the clones regardless of their phenotype (1×10^{6} min^{-1} M^{-1}). The increased rate constant of dissociation does not seem to be a causal determinant of the inability of nt$^-$ receptor complexes to bind tightly to DNA or nuclei, inasmuch as another nt$^-$ variant contained receptors with a dissociation rate constant comparable to that of wild-type and nt^i mutants. Spindler-Barth and Gehring (1982) suggested that a single genetic event might have affected the nuclear-binding domain and the steroid-binding site in the nt$^-$ clone with altered dissociation kinetics.

Stevens *et al.* (1978a) recently examined the interaction of [^{3}H]TA–receptor complexes with the nucleus in the CS and CR strains of mouse lymphoma P1798.* In these experiments intact cells were incubated for 60 minutes at 37°C with a near-saturating level of [^{3}H]TA after which highly purified nuclei were prepared by homogenizing the labeled cells in buffered 2 *M* sucrose containing 0.1% Triton X-100. As shown in Fig. 2, low concentrations of KCl (0.1 *M*) extracted a significantly higher percentage of [^{3}H]TA from CS P1798 nuclei than from CR P1798 nuclei. The same result was obtained whether or not the protease inhibitor carbobenzoxy (CBZ)-L-phenylalanine was included in the extraction buffer, except that the combination of 0.1 *M* KCl and CBZ-L-phenylalanine was twice as effective as 0.1 *M* KCl alone in extracting [^{3}H]TA from either type of nucleus. No difference was observed between the two strains of tumor when the extraction was performed with 0.2 *M* KCl. This concentration of salt was nearly as effective as 0.6 *M* KCl, which extracted about 90% of [^{3}H]TA from both CS and CR nuclei.

An even more striking difference was discovered when sensitive and resistant P1798 nuclei were extracted with divalent (MgCl$_2$ or CaCl$_2$) or trivalent (spermidine) cations. The ability of millimolar concentrations of MgCl$_2$ to extract [^{3}H]TA from CS P1798 but not from CR P1798 nuclei is illustrated in Fig. 3. This was not due to dissociation of free [^{3}H]TA from the nuclear acceptor sites, inasmuch as 60% of the radioactivity in the MgCl$_2$ extracts was associated with macromolecules (excluded from Sephadex G-25). This percentage was increased to 90% or more by including bovine serum albumin in the extraction buffer (Stevens and Stevens, 1979). For these experiments, nuclei were purified in the presence of Ca^{2+} and then exposed to MgCl$_2$ in the presence of EGTA, which binds Ca^{2+} 10^6 times more tightly than it binds Mg^{2+} (Boyd *et al.*, 1965). The results obtained

---

*The CS and CR strains of mouse lymphoma P1798 used by Stevens *et al.* (1978a) in these and subsequent experiments can be obtained by writing to Ms. Wendy L. Grant, Supervisor, DCT Tumor Bank, E.G. and G. Mason Research Institute, 57 Union Street, Worcester, Massachusetts 01608. They are designated CS lymphoma P1798/JS and CR lymphoma P1798/JS and were cryopreserved in June, 1981.

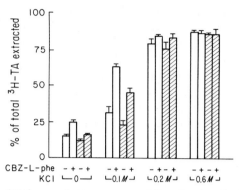

FIG. 2. Influence of KCl concentration on extractability of nuclear [³H]TA. Nuclei from CS (open bars) and CR (hatched bars) P1798 tumor lymphocytes were extracted with the indicated concentrations of KCl in the absence or presence of 10 mM CBZ-L-phenylalanine. Each bar represents the mean ± SD of three to five experiments. Total radioactivity (salt-extractable plus ethanol-extractable) was 114,900 ± 22,500 dpm/10⁸ CS nuclei and 58,950 ± 12,900 dpm/10⁸ CR nuclei. From Stevens *et al.* (1978a).

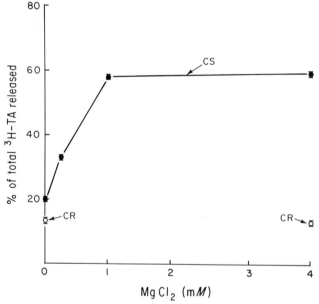

FIG. 3. MgCl₂-induced release of [³H]TA from P1798 tumor nuclei. CS (●) and CR (○) nuclei were extracted with the indicated concentrations of MgCl₂. The sum of bound and free [³H]TA in the extracts is expressed as a percentage of total nuclear-associated [³H]TA (MgCl₂ plus ethanol-extractable counts). Each point represents the mean ± SD of three experiments with each strain of tumor. Total nuclear-associated radioactivity was 82,500 ± 10,200 dpm/10⁸ CS nuclei and 57,000 ± 900 dpm/10⁸ CR nuclei. From Stevens *et al.* (1978a).

with spermidine are illustrated in Fig. 4. While the ability of spermidine to release [³H]TA from CS nuclei was nearly maximal at 1 mM, this level of polyamine had only a small effect on CR nuclei. The difference between the two strains of tumor was also observed with 2 mM spermidine, but was no longer apparent with 5 mM spermidine. As in the case of the MgCl$_2$ extractions, 90% or more of radioactivity released with spermidine was in the form of a macromolecular complex when the extraction buffer was supplemented with bovine serum albumin (Stevens and Stevens, 1979).

The ability of low concentrations of divalent and trivalent cations to release glucocorticoid–receptor complexes from highly purified nuclei was not limited to the CS strain of mouse lymphoma P1798. Virtually identical results were obtained with nuclei that were isolated from [³H]TA-labeled (1 hour at 37°C) peripheral blood lymphocytes of patients with chronic lymphatic leukemia by the hypertonic sucrose–Triton X-100 technique (Stevens *et al.*, 1979b). The lymphocytes from all 10 patients were glucocorticoid responsive as judged by the inhibitory effect of TA on the uptake and incorporation of [³H]uridine into acid-insoluble material.

Stevens and Stevens (1981) also examined the DNA-binding properties of cytosolic [³H]TA–receptor complexes from CS and CR P1798 tumor lymphocytes. Both CS and CR [³H]TA complexes bound efficiently to DNA–cellulose. As shown in Fig. 5, close to maximal binding was achieved by incubating heat-activated, labeled cytosol with 10–20 μg of DNA. Optimal binding was achieved after 90 minutes incubation at 15°C (Fig. 6). Figure 7 shows that 40 to 50% of CS P1798 complexes could be extracted from DNA–cellulose with 2–4.5 mM MgCl$_2$ and 50–60% with 1 mM spermidine. In contrast, these concentrations of divalent and trivalent cation were in-

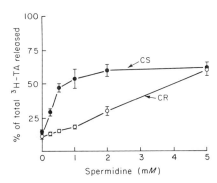

FIG. 4. Spermidine-induced release of [³H]TA from P1798 tumor nuclei. CS (●) and CR (○) nuclei were extracted with the indicated concentrations of spermidine. Results are expressed as in Fig. 3. Total nuclear-associated radioactivity was 89,700 ± 25,500 dpm/10⁸ CS nuclei and 47,400 ± 9300 dpm/10⁶ CR nuclei. From Stevens *et al.* (1978a).

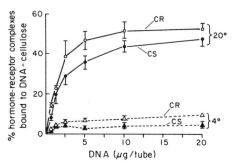

Fig. 5. Relationship between DNA concentration and binding of P1798 HR complexes. After incubation of [³H]TA-labeled cytosol with the indicated amounts of DNA–cellulose for 1 hour at 4° or 20°C, the samples were washed with buffer, and radioactivity was extracted from the pellets with ethanol. Results are expressed as the percentage of input bound counts that became attached to DNA–cellulose. Points, mean of three experiments; bars, SE. Average input was 13,164 dpm for CS cytosol and 6813 dpm for CR cytosol. The lower input with CR cytosol is a reflection of the lower level of glucocorticoid binding in the CR lymphocytes. From Stevens and Stevens (1981) with permission.

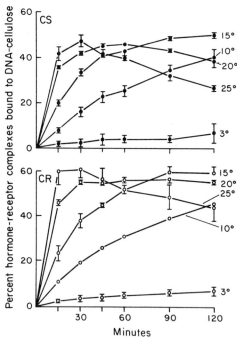

Fig. 6. Temperature dependence and time course of P1798 HR complex binding to DNA–cellulose. All tubes contained 10 μg of DNA. Points, average of two experiments, except for the CR cytosol at 10°C (1 experiment); bars, range. Other details as in Fig. 5. Average input was 10,203 dpm for CS cytosol and 6466 dpm for CR cytosol. From Stevens and Stevens (1981) with permission.

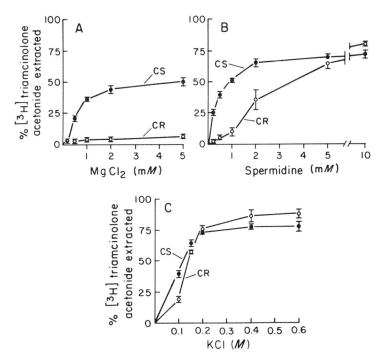

FIG. 7. Extractability of P1798 HR complexes from DNA–cellulose. Points, mean of three experiments; bars, SE. The amount of radioactivity extracted from DNA–cellulose in the absence of added cation has been subtracted from all values (5–10% of the initially bound radioactivity). Average binding of input HR complexes to DNA–cellulose was 54% for CS cytosol and 63% for CR cytosol. From Stevens and Stevens (1981) with permission.

effective in extracting CR P1798 [³H]TA–receptor complexes from DNA–cellulose. A similar, though less dramatic difference between the two strains of tumor was observed when DNA–cellulose was extracted with 0.1 M KCl. Comparison of these results with the experiments in Figs. 2–4 indicates that there is a remarkable similarity between MgCl₂, spermidine, and KCl extractability of HR complexes from DNA–cellulose and the ability of these agents to release [³H]TA–receptor complexes from homologous P1798 tumor nuclei. In all instances, 80–90% of radioactivity in the extracts was bound to macromolecules, demonstrating that the greater release of [³H]TA in the case of CS cytosol was not due to a difference in stability of steroid–receptor interaction in CS versus CR complexes. The mixing experiments, summarized in Table III, appear to rule out the possibility that CS cytosol might have contained a component that promoted release of [³H]TA complexes from DNA–cellulose, or that CR cytosol might have lacked this component or contained an inhibitory factor.

TABLE III
EXTRACTABILITY OF "MIXED" CYTOSOLS FROM DNA–CELLULOSE[a]

Cytosol	[³H]TA bound to DNA–cellulose (% of input)	Percentage (%) of DNA-associated [³H]TA extracted with	
		MgCl₂ (4.5 mM)	Spermidine (1 mM)
Labeled CS + unlabeled CS			
Experiment 1	50	50	56
Experiment 2	54	48	51
Labeled CR + unlabeled CR			
Experiment 1	60	8	13
Experiment 2	62	8	12
Labeled CS + unlabeled CR			
Experiment 1	53	51	52
Experiment 2	54	48	51
Labeled CR + unlabeled CS			
Experiment 1	61	7	14
Experiment 2	68	8	12

[a] The indicated mixtures of cytosol were incubated for 90 minutes at 15°C with DNA–cellulose, after which the DNA–cellulose was washed and then extracted with 4.5 mM MgCl₂ or 1 mM spermidine. Input varied from 5000 to 7000 dpm for CS cytosol and from 3200 to 3400 dpm for CR cytosol. From Stevens and Stevens (1981) with permission.

Taken together, the nuclear and DNA extraction experiments are consistent with the idea that binding to DNA may be a major factor in determining the mode of hormone–receptor complex interaction with the nucleus in intact P1798 tumor lymphocytes. However, participation of other intranuclear components is not excluded by these data. In this context, it should be kept in mind that in addition to DNA, practically every nuclear structure has been proposed as a possible "acceptor" site for steroid hormone–receptor complexes, including the nuclear membrane (Jackson and Chalkley, 1975), ribonucleoprotein particles (Liao, 1976), chromosomal proteins (Spelsberg *et al.*, 1977), the nuclear matrix (Barrack *et al.*, 1977), or combinations of these (Schrader *et al.*, 1977). The above results also suggest that the differences in nuclear glucocorticoid interactions between CS and CR P1798 tumor cells probably stem from an alteration in the properties of the CR P1798 receptor molecule, rather than from a gross difference in nuclear structure between the sensitive and resistant tumors. Evidence for this is presented later.

In the S49 lymphoma system, tighter binding of HR complexes to DNA–cellulose correlated with increased nuclear localization of bound steroid in the intact cell (Yamamoto *et al.*, 1974). However, this was not the case in mouse lymphoma P1798 since there was no difference in the partitioning of [^{3}H]TA–receptor complexes between nucleus and cytoplasm (80% nuclear, 20% cytoplasmic) between the CS and CR strains of tumor (Stevens and Stevens, 1979). Thus, the intracellular distribution of steroid HR complexes in whole cells at 37°C may not be determined exclusively by the affinity of the complexes for nuclei or DNA.

Pfahl *et al.* (1978a,b) examined glucocorticoid–receptor complex interaction with the nucleus in a large number of CR variants of the S49 lymphoma and W7 thymoma cell lines. All the variants were nt$^-$ mutants. A crude nuclear fraction was isolated from intact cells that had been incubated with [^{3}H]dexamethasone at 37°C and the percentage of nuclear-associated steroid that could be extracted with increasing concentrations of NaCl was determined. In some cases, a greater fraction of radioactivity was released from the nuclei of the CR clones than from the nuclei of the CS parental line. In other cases, the opposite was true. With only a single exception, all the CR variants could be distinguished from wild-type cells based on the altered interaction of their HR complexes with the nucleus. As mentioned earlier, no nt^i mutants were detected. McPartland *et al.* (1977) described a receptor(+) CR variant of mouse lymphoma P1798 in which glucocorticoid–receptor complexes displayed reduced affinity for their nuclear acceptor sites, based on increased extractability with NaCl compared to CS P1798.

In general, it appears that steroid resistance of receptor(+) murine lymphoma cells is associated with either tighter or weaker (but rarely unchanged) binding of glucocorticoid–receptor complexes to the nucleus. These mutants hold the promise of being powerful tools not only for the study of steroid-resistant leukemias and lymphomas, but also for examining aberrations in the regulation of gene expression in mammalian cells in general.

D. PHYSICOCHEMICAL PROPERTIES OF GLUCOCORTICOID RECEPTORS

As indicated in the previous section, the anomalous interaction of glucocorticoid–receptor complexes from CR mouse tumor lymphocytes with the nucleus appears to be due, at least in part, to alterations in the properties of the HR complexes themselves. This supposition is supported by the results of physicochemical studies on glucocorticoid–receptor complexes from CR S49 and P1798 lymphoma mutants.

Yamamoto *et al.* (1974) and Sibley and Yamamoto (1979) found that under high salt conditions (250 mM NaCl), crude [^{3}H]dexamethasone–receptor complexes from two S49 nt^i CR variants sedimented more slowly on 5 to 20% sucrose gradients (sedimentation coefficient of 3.5 S) than crude [^{3}H] dexamethasone–receptor complexes from wild-type cells which sedimented at 4.0 S. A similar difference was observed when partially purified nt^i and wild-type HR complexes were analyzed under low salt conditions (50 mM NaCl). HR complexes from some nt^- and d^- CR mutants sedimented at the same rate as receptors from CS cells, whereas with other nt^- and d^- clones, small differences were observed depending on the ionic strength of the buffer used for ultracentrifugation.

Gel filtration on columns of agarose BioGel A-0.5m equilibrated with 0.5 M NaCl revealed further differences between $[^3H]$dexamethasone–receptor complexes from nt^i variants and wild-type lymphocytes. Whereas HR complexes from CS cells eluted ahead of the catalase standard, the nt^i receptors were significantly more retarded and eluted slightly after human hemoglobin. Based on the sucrose gradient centrifugation and gel filtration data, the CS receptor was found to be a rather asymmetric molecule with an axial ratio (prolate ellipsoid) of 8:1 and an apparent molecular weight of 90,000, compared to an axial ratio of 4:1 and a molecular weight of about 50,000 for the nt^i receptor. In contrast, HR complexes from d^- mutants did not differ from wild-type receptors with regard to these parameters. Receptors from nt^- cells were reported to be only "slightly altered."

Ultracentrifugal studies by Kaiser *et al.* (1974) suggested that $[^3H]$TA–receptor complexes from CR mouse lymphoma P1798 cells might be smaller than CS P1798 receptors. However, interpretation of the data was complicated by the fact that the CR P1798 tumors utilized by Kaiser *et al.* (1974) may have contained a mixed population of CS and CR lymphocytes.

More recently, Stevens and Stevens (1979) carried out a detailed comparison of the physicochemical properties of glucocorticoid receptors in the CS and CR strains of mouse lymphoma P1798. Nuclear and cytosolic receptors were examined in this study. In order to prevent possible emergence of CS cells in the CR tumors, the donor mice whose CR tumors were to be used for passaging into new recipients were always injected with 25 mg/kg of 9α-fluoroprednisolone 48 and 24 hours prior to using the tumors for transplantation (Stevens *et al.*, 1978a). Corticoid-resistant P1798 is completely refractory to this dose of steroid, both *in vivo* (Stevens *et al.*, 1974) and *in vitro* (Stevens and Stevens, 1975a), whereas CS P1798 undergoes prompt regression with the same regimen of steroid administration (Stevens *et al.*, 1974).

Purified nuclei were isolated from CS and CR P1798 tumor lymphocytes that had been incubated with 30 nM $[^3H]$TA for 1 hour at 37°C. The CS nuclei were extracted with 0.6 M KCl, 10 mM spermidine, or 4.5 mM $MgCl_2$. The CR nuclei were extracted with KCl or spermidine but not with $MgCl_2$. As discussed earlier, nuclear-associated $[^3H]$TA–receptor complexes in CR P1798 lymphocytes were resistant to extraction with divalent cations. In order for the comparison between the two strains of tumor to be valid, it was essential to isolate HR complexes under conditions of maximal stability and minimal degradation. When nuclei were extracted with 0.6 M KCl, degradation of receptor and/or dissociation of bound [³H]TA was prevented by including CBZ-L-phenylalanine, bovine serum albumin, and glycerol in the extraction buffer. Under these conditions, 90% of [³H]TA in the salt extract from nuclei of either strain of tumor was bound to macromolecules. However, it was not necessary to include CBZ-L-phenylalanine or glycerol during extraction of nuclei with MgCl₂ or spermidine, since 90% or more of the [³H]TA was recovered in the form of a macromolecular complex as long as the extraction buffers were supplemented with bovine serum albumin. Analysis of CS and CR P1798 nuclear extracts by agarose gel filtration on columns equilibrated with 0.6 M KCl revealed striking differences between the two strains of tumor.

Whereas [³H]TA–receptor complexes extracted from CS nuclei with KCl, spermidine, or MgCl₂ eluted coincidentally with, or slightly after, the ferritin standard (Fig. 8), [³H]TA–receptor complexes in KCl and spermidine extracts from CR nuclei were much smaller and they eluted after the ovalbumin standard (Fig. 9). The Stokes radius of CS complexes was approximately 57–60 Å compared to 28–29 Å for CR complexes. As shown in Fig. 10,

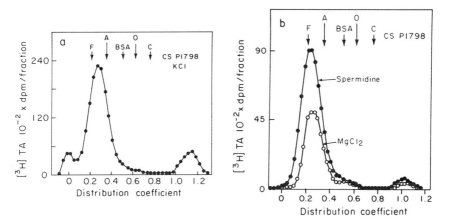

FIG. 8. Agarose gel filtration of [³H]TA–receptor complexes extracted from CS P1798 tumor nuclei with 0.6 M KCl (a) or 4.5 mM MgCl₂ or 10mM spermidine (b) on columns of BioGel A-1.5m. Even though 10 mM spermidine and 0.6 M KCl extracted similar percentages of nuclear-associated [³H]TA, radioactivity in the spermidine sample was considerably lower than in KCl samples because of greater dilution during extraction of the nuclei (2 ml of spermidine-containing buffer were used as opposed to 1.3 ml of 0.6 M KCl buffer). The spermidine extract was further diluted by addition of 0.2 volume of 3 M KCl to adjust the salt concentration to 0.6 M KCl before analysis by gel filtration or gradient centrifugation. The same applies to the MgCl₂ extract. Furthermore, MgCl₂ extracted less [³H]TA than did spermidine or KCl. Arrows, position of protein standards used to calibrate the columns. F, ferritin; A, aldolase; BSA, bovine serum albumin; O, ovalbumin; C, chymotrypsinogen A. From Stevens and Stevens (1979) with permission.

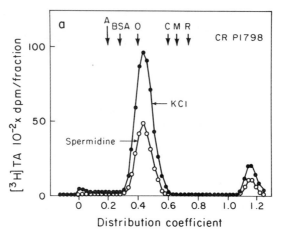

Fig. 9. Agarose gel filtration of [³H]TA–receptor complexes extracted from CR P1798 tumor nuclei with 0.6 M KCl or 10 mM spermidine on columns of BioGel A-0.5m. Profiles from two runs are superimposed. See Fig. 8 for explanation of lower level of radioactivity in the spermidine extract. Arrows, position of protein standards used to calibrate the columns. M, myoglobin; R, RNase A; other abbreviations as in Fig. 8. From Stevens and Stevens (1979) with permission.

HR complexes from CS P1798 nuclei had a sedimentation coefficient of 3.6–3.7 S on 8–35% glycerol density gradients under high salt conditions whereas CR P1798 nuclear [³H]TA–receptor complexes had a sedimentation coefficient of only 3.2–3.3 S. Based on these data and assuming a partial specific volume of 0.74 ml/gm (Smith, 1968) and a solvation factor of 0.2 gm of solvent per gram of protein (Tanford, 1961), the apparent molecular

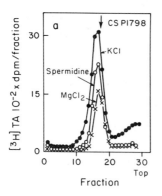 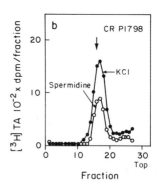

Fig. 10. Glycerol gradient profiles of [³H]TA–receptor complexes extracted from CS (a) and CR (b) P1798 nuclei. Arrow, position of the 3.53 S [¹⁴C]ovalbumin internal marker. From Stevens and Stevens (1979) with permission.

weight of the CS P1798 [³H]TA–receptor complex was estimated to be about 90,000 with a frictional ratio (f/f_0) due to shape of 1.8 and an axial ratio (prolate ellipsoid) of about 15. Thus, the CS P1798 receptor appears to be much larger and more asymmetrical than the CR P1798 receptor which had an apparent molecular weight of 40,000, a (f/f_0) shape of 1.25, and an axial ratio (prolate ellipsoid) of about 5. Moreover, the molecular weight of the CS P1798 nuclear [³H]TA–receptor complex is comparable to that of the cytosolic [³H]dexamethasone complex in CS S49 lymphoma cells. The molecular weight of the nuclear [³H]TA–receptor complex from CR P1798 tumor lymphocytes appears to be somewhat lower than that of cytosolic [³H]dexamethasone–receptor complexes isolated from nt^i CR S49 variants. However, when cytosolic glucocorticoid receptors from nt^i CR S49 cells were photoaffinity-labeled with R5020 (17α,21 dimethyl-19-nor-pregna-4,9-diene-3,20-dione) or triamcinolone acetonide and then analyzed on SDS–polyacrylamide gels, a molecular weight of 39,000 to 42,000 was obtained (Nordeen *et al.*, 1981; Dellweg *et al.*, 1982). Cytosolic HR complexes from CS P1798 lymphocytes that had been incubated for 2 hours at 4°C with [³H]TA were identical in size to CS nuclear complexes. Similarly, the physicochemical properties of CR P1798 cytosolic [³H]TA–receptor complexes were comparable to those present in the CR nuclear extracts.

These data should not be interpreted to mean that unactivated lymphoid glucocorticoid receptors (i.e., HR complexes present in cytosol that was kept at 4°C throughout) are similar in size to activated HR complexes (i.e., receptors extracted from nuclei of cells that were labeled with [³H]TA at 37°C). In all the experiments described above, cytosolic and nuclear HR complexes were analyzed by gel filtration and density gradient centrifugation in high-ionic-strength buffers. It is well established that glucocorticoid– and other steroid hormone–receptor complexes become activated under these conditions (Milgrom, 1981). Therefore, it is likely that the cytosolic [³H]TA–receptor complexes were activated during gel permeation and ul-tracentrifugation. Indeed, as discussed in more detail later on (Section III,F), Stevens *et al.* (1981a) recently showed that unactivated CS and CR P1798 [³H]TA–receptor complexes are probably much larger than their activated counterparts.

Several lines of evidence suggest that the small CR P1798 nuclear [³H] TA–receptor complex did not arise by cleavage of a larger, CS-like complex during the extraction procedure. (1) All the extraction buffers were sup-plemented with bovine serum albumin (and in the case of the 0.6 *M* KCl extractions, with glycerol and CBZ-L-phenylalanine) to maximally stabilize binding activity. (2) No increase in size of the CR [³H]TA complex was achieved by extracting nuclei in the presence of concentrations of leupeptin that are known to block degradation of glucocorticoid and other steroid

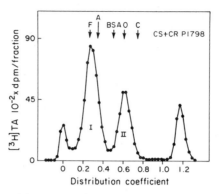

FIG. 11. Gel filtration of the 0.6 *M* KCl extract from a mixture of CS and CR P1798 nuclei. CS and CR cells were labeled separately with [³H]TA and mixed in equal proportions. Nuclei were isolated from the mixture of cells and extracted with 0.6 *M* KCl. Extract (3 ml) was applied to the agarose A-1.5m column. Arrows, position of standard proteins. Abbreviations as in Fig. 8. From Stevens and Stevens (1979) with permission.

receptors (Sherman *et al.*, 1978, 1979). (3) Extraction of nuclei with low-ionic-strength buffers containing spermidine (CS and CR nuclei) or MgCl₂ (CS nuclei) yielded HR complexes identical in size to HR complexes extracted with high salt. Low-ionic-strength buffers are unlikely to release chromatin-associated proteases (Chauvière, 1977). (4) Finally, the experiment in Fig. 11 shows that when the 0.6 *M* KCl extract from a mixture of CS and CR nuclei was chromatographed on a BioGel A-1.5m column, there appeared to be no activity in the CR extract capable of converting the large CS [³H] TA–receptor complex (peak I) to the small CR form (peak II). Thus, the amount of radioactivity under each peak was exactly what was predicted from the number of CS and CR lymphocytes in the initial mixture of cells from which the nuclei were prepared. These experiments also indicate that the larger size of the CS nuclear receptor was not due to interaction of the complex with constituents present in CS, but not in CR extracts. This possibility is made even more unlikely by the fact that all these studies were performed in high-ionic-strength buffers. Thus, CR lymphoma P1798 contains a markedly smaller and more globular nuclear glucocorticoid receptor than the one present in CS P1798 tumor lymphocytes.

These alterations in physicochemical properties may be responsible, at least in part, for the previously described ability of CR P1798 [³H]TA–receptor complexes to bind more tightly to nuclei and to DNA–cellulose than CS P1798 [³H]TA complexes. Stevens and Stevens (1979) found that purified mouse thymocyte nuclei also contained predominantly a 59-Å form of glucocorticoid receptor, as did nuclei from CS lymphocytes of patients with chronic lymphatic leukemia (Stevens *et al.*, 1979b). We have isolated a similar form from the nuclei of CS human acute leukemic lymphoblasts in tissue culture (clone CH6 of CCRF-CEM cells; Section IV,D). Furthermore, other glucocorticoid-responsive tissues such as rat liver (Wrange and Gustafsson, 1978) and corticoid-responsive Novikoff hepatoma cells (Liu and Webb, 1977) also contain a 90,000- to 100,000-dalton glucocorticoid binder.

The presence of glucocorticoid receptors with a molecular weight of 90,000 in CS S49 lymphoma cells was mentioned earlier. These results are consistent with the idea that expression of glucocorticoid sensitivity by normal and malignant lymphocytes and other glucocorticoid target tissues requires the presence of the large nuclear glucocorticoid-binding component. However, possession of such a binder does not suffice to guarantee responsiveness inasmuch as the [³H]dexamethasone–receptor complex from CR "deathless" S49 mutants was reported to be similar in size to the glucocorticoid receptor of CS S49 lymphocytes (Yamamoto et al., 1976). Moreover, we have found that CR clone E10 derived from the human acute lymphoblastic leukemia cell line CCRF-CEM also contained appreciable levels of [³H]TA–receptor complexes which under high salt conditions had a Stokes radius of 58–60 Å (Section IV,B). In such instances, resistance may be due to a postreceptor defect or the receptors in nonresponsive cells may differ from wild-type receptors in subtle ways that are undetectable with currently available techniques.

Before concluding that a given population of lymphocytes contains altered glucocorticoid-binding components, it is essential to rule out artifacts that can easily arise if proper measures are not taken to prevent receptor degradation during preparation and analysis of subcellular fractions. This was particularly well illustrated in a study of nuclear glucocorticoid binding in chronic lymphatic leukemia lymphocytes by Stevens et al. (1979b): Extraction of nuclei with 0.6 M KCl and CBZ-L-phenylalanine or leupeptin consistently yielded preparations that contained a mixture of 57- to 60-Å and approximately 35-Å [³H]TA–receptor complexes. The amount of 35-Å material in these extracts varied from patient to patient and sometimes accounted for more than 50% of total nuclear-bound [³H]TA. In contrast, when nuclei were extracted with spermidine and leupeptin, little or no 35-Å [³H]TA–receptor complex was observed and 90% or more of the radioactivity extracted from the nuclei eluted with a Stokes radius of 58–60 Å. It should be noted that 10 mM spermidine and 0.6 M KCl were equally efficient in extracting [³H]TA from the nuclei: 90% of total nuclear-associated [³H]TA in both cases. Therefore, the nearly complete absence of the 35-Å peak in the spermidine:leupeptin extracts was not attributable to selective retention of this species in the nucleus due to inefficiency of the extraction procedure. Rather, the 35-Å material probably arose by artifactual cleavage of the 58- to 60-Å complex.

John Stevens et al.

E. Structural Analysis of Glucocorticoid Receptors

Wrange *et al*. (1979) reported that purified rat liver glucocorticoid receptors had a Stokes radius of 60 Å and a sedimentation coefficient of 3.4 S in 0.15 M KCl, with an apparent molecular weight of 89,000. Chymotryptic digestion of crude cytosolic rat liver [³H]dexamethasone–receptor complexes converted the 61-Å complex to a smaller form with a Stokes radius of 30 to 36Å (Wrange and Gustafsson, 1978). After heat activation, the 30- to 36-Å chymotryptic fragment bound more tightly to DNA than the undigested 61-Å receptor. Clearly, there is a striking similarity between the physicochemical and DNA-binding properties of CS P1798 and undigested rat liver glucocorticoid receptors, and also between the physicochemical and DNA-binding properties of undigested CR P1798 and chymotrypsin-treated rat liver glucocorticoid receptors. Based on these observations, Stevens and Stevens (1979) speculated that the large, asymmetrical CS P1798 glucocorticoid receptor might consist of a portion similar or identical in size to the smaller, more globular CR P1798 receptor, plus another portion that enabled it to interact "normally" with its nuclear acceptor sites, perhaps initiating the events that ultimately result in cell death. If this were the case, limited proteolysis of P1798 glucocorticoid–receptor complexes should give rise to a smaller form with physicochemical and DNA-binding properties comparable to those of undigested CR P1798 receptors.

As shown in Fig. 12, incubation of [³H]TA-labeled CS P1798 cytosol with 0.12 units of chymotrypsin per milligram of cytosol protein resulted in quantitative conversion of the ~60-Å complex to a discrete new form that eluted slightly after the internal [¹⁴C]ovalbumin standard with a Stokes radius of 28 Å (Stevens and Stevens, 1981). As documented earlier, this is exactly the Stokes radius of cytosolic CR P1798 [³H]TA–receptor complexes. Digestion with chymotrypsin did not change the elution profile of CR P1798 glucocorticoid receptors. In contrast, digestion with trypsin converted both CS and CR P1798 cytosolic [³H]TA–receptor complexes to discrete 21- to 22-Å forms (Fig. 13). Due to an error the Stokes radius of the trypsin fragment was previously reported to be 19 Å (Stevens and Stevens, 1981). The possibility that CR P1798 lymphocytes might contain activity that could artifactually give rise to the 28-Å complex by cleavage of a putative CS-like 60-Å form during homogenization of the cells and subsequent incubation of the cytosol with [³H]TA was ruled out by performing mixing experiments comparable in design to those described earlier for nuclear extracts.

In addition to the physicochemical similarity between the 28-Å CR P1798 [³H]TA–receptor complex and the chymotrypsin fragment of the CS P1798 receptor, these two forms of receptor also displayed functional similarities (Stevens and Stevens, 1981). Table IV shows that the chymotrypsin fragment

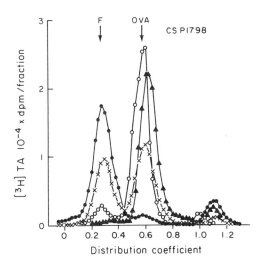

FIG. 12. Influence of chymotrypsin on CS P1798 [³H]TA–receptor complexes. Cytosol was incubated without (●) or with 0.015 (X), 0.06 (○), or 0.12 (▲) unit of chymotrypsin per milligram of cytosol protein and then analyzed by agarose gel filtration on columns of BioGel A-1.5m (100–200 mesh). Free [³H]TA eluted with a distribution coefficient > 1. Arrows, position of standard proteins; F, ferritin; OVA, [¹⁴C]ovalbumin. From Stevens and Stevens (1981) with permission.

of heat-activated CS receptor bound to DNA–cellulose to about the same extent as heat-activated, chymotrypsin-treated, CR P1798 HR complexes. As described earlier, 4.5 mM MgCl$_2$ and 1 mM spermidine were practically ineffective in extracting CR P1798 [³H]TA–receptor complexes from DNA–cellulose. Table IV clearly shows that the chymotrypsin fragment of CS P1798 HR complexes was also resistant to extraction from DNA–cellulose with these concentrations of divalent and trivalent cation. In contrast, 4.5 mM MgCl$_2$ and 1 mM spermidine readily released undigested (~60 Å) CS P1798 [³H]TA–receptor complexes. Neither CS nor CR trypsin fragments bound appreciably to DNA–cellulose.

These data are consistent with the idea that the large ~60-Å CS P1798 complex may contain a region similar, if not identical, to the small 28-Å CR P1798 receptor. The results also support the notion that the 60 → 28-Å domain of the CS P1798 [³H]TA–receptor complex (i.e., that portion of the CS receptor that is removed by chymotrypsin thereby reducing the Stokes radius of the complex from ~60 to 28 Å), or a subregion of this domain, may play an important role in giving rise to a glucocorticoid response.

Wrange and Gustafsson (1978) suggested that rat liver glucocorticoid receptor may consist of three regions: (1) the steroid-binding site present on the trypsin fragment; (2) the DNA-binding site present on the chymotrypsin

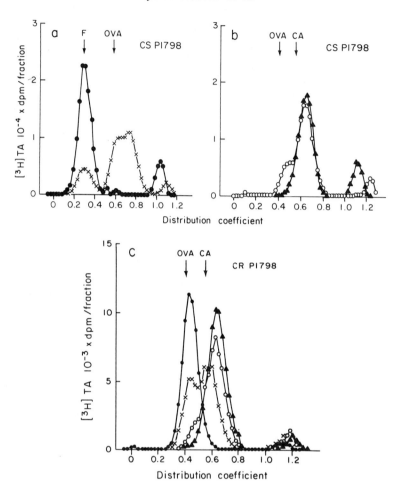

FIG. 13. Influence of trypsin on CS and CR [³H]TA–receptor complexes. Cytosol was incubated without (●) or with 0.34 (X), 1.36 (○), and 2.72 (▲) units of trypsin per milligram of cytosol protein and analyzed by agarose gel filtration. (a) CS cytosol, BioGel A-1.5m (100 to 200 mesh). (b) CS cytosol, BioGel A-0.5m (100 to 200 mesh). (c) CR cytosol BioGel A-0.5m (100 to 200 mesh). Arrows, position of standard proteins; OVA, [¹⁴C]ovalbumin; CA, [¹⁴C]carbonic anhydrase. From Stevens and Stevens (1981) with permission.

fragment but absent from the trypsin fragment, and (3) a region of unknown function present only on the undigested 61-Å receptor. As suggested above, the presence of this region may be essential in eliciting a phenotypic response to glucocorticoids. It is not known whether the 60 → 28-Å region itself contains a low-affinity DNA-binding domain or if it in some way modulates interaction of the 28-Å portion of the receptor with DNA. Also, it is not

TABLE IV

BINDING TO AND EXTRACTABILITY FROM DNA–CELLULOSE OF PROTEASE-TREATED
LYMPHOMA P1798 [^{3}H]TA–RECEPTOR COMPLEXES[a]

| | [^{3}H]TA bound to DNA–cellulose (% of input) | Percentage (%) of DNA-associated [^{3}H]TA extracted with | | |
| | | MgCl$_2$ (4.5 mM) | Spermidine | |
			1 mM	10 mM
CS P1798				
DFP–chymotrypsin	48	55	48	76
Active chymotrypsin	48	6	5	84
SBTI + TPCK–trypsin	46	ND[b]	ND	ND
Active TPCK–trypsin	0.3	ND	ND	ND
CR P1798				
DFP–chymotrypsin	52	8	10	86
Active chymotrypsin	51	10	10	86
SBTI + TPCK–trypsin	54	ND	ND	ND
Active TPCK–trypsin	0.1	ND	ND	ND

[a] Activated (20°C, 60 minutes) [^{3}H]TA-labeled cytosol was incubated for 30 minutes at 10°C with *p*-tosyl-L-lysine chloromethyl ketone (TLCK)–chymotrypsin (0.12 unit/mg cytosol protein), inactive diisopropyl fluorophosphate (DFP)–chymotrypsin, L-tosylamide-2-phenylethyl chloromethyl ketone (TPCK)–trypsin alone (2.72 units/mg cytosol protein), or the same amount of TPCK–trypsin plus fivefold excess, by weight, of soy bean trypsin inhibitor (SBTI). The enzyme-treated cytosol (50 µl; 4 mg protein/ml) was incubated with DNA–cellulose or plain cellulose for 30 minutes at 4°C, after which the samples were washed and extracted. Each value is the average of two closely agreeing experiments. Results have been corrected for the amount of radioactivity bound to plain cellulose and for the amount of [^{3}H]TA extracted in the absence of MgCl$_2$ or spermidine (2–8% of the [^{3}H]TA taken up by DNA–cellulose). Input varied from 9150 to 10,300 dpm for CS cytosol and from 5800 to 7000 dpm for CR cytosol. From Stevens and Stevens (1981) with permission.
[b] ND, not done.

known whether the ~60-Å CS P1798 HR complex recognizes the same nucleotide sequence on DNA as the 28-Å CR P1798 HR complex.

If steroid effects are indeed triggered by interaction of HR complexes with a limited number of specific acceptor sites on the chromatin (Yamamoto and Alberts, 1976), one explanation for the resistance of CR P1798 to the lympholytic action of glucocorticoids could be the inability of the tightly binding 28-Å HR complexes to conduct a "search" for these sites.

At present one can only speculate on the origin of the 28-Å receptor characteristic of CR P1798 tumor lymphocytes. The "mixing" experiments described earlier argue against it being a proteolytic cleavage product of a 60-Å, CS-like complex. However, it could arise by processing of a larger precursor that is more susceptible to proteolysis than the CS receptor. On the other hand, the CR P1798 receptor may be synthesized directly as a 28-Å polypeptide because of a genetic defect that only permits transcription of "small" receptor mRNA. Abnormal processing or defective translation of "large" receptor mRNA could also give rise to the 28-Å form. Another possibility is that the 60 → 28-Å region is synthesized as a separate polypeptide chain, but it fails to link up with the steroid- and DNA-binding (28 Å) portion of the molecule. If this were the case, CR P1798 cytosol should contain immunoactive material capable of being recognized by antigluco-corticoid receptor antibodies that interact with the 60 → 28-Å region of the receptor. Such antibodies have been described by Okret *et al.* (1981) and by Eisen (1982). (See Section I,G). However, recent studies by Carlstedt-Duke *et al.* (1983) and by Okret and co-workers (1982) are not consistent with this explanation. Thus, no immunoactivity was found in CR P1798 cytosol that had been fractionated by gel filtration or DNA–cellulose chro-matography. In contrast, CS P1798 cytosol that had been digested with chymotrypsin to generate the 60 → 28-Å fragment contained appreciable amounts of immunoreactive material. These results do not exclude the possibility that CR P1798 cytosol might contain a "free" 60 → 28-Å domain with altered antigenic determinants that are not recognized by currently available antibodies.

Clearly, it will be very important to isolate and characterize the 60 → 28-Å portion of the CS receptor, a challenging task that should be greatly aided by the purification (Eisen and Glinsmann, 1978; Govindan, 1979; Wrange *et al.*, 1979), immunoaffinity (Eisen, 1982; Govindan, 1979; Okret *et al.*, 1981), and affinity-labeling techniques (Simons and Thompson, 1979; Eisen *et al.*, 1981) that are becoming available for the study of glucocorticoid receptors. Indeed, Carlstedt-Duke *et al.* (1982) have successfully used an antiglucocorticoid receptor antibody to identify this particular domain of the glucocorticoid receptor. Rat liver cytosol was labeled with [³H]TA, digested with chymotrypsin, and passed through a column of BioGel A-0.5m in buffer containing 0.15 M NaCl. The column fractions were assayed for radioactivity and immunoactivity. As expected, all the bound [³H]TA eluted as a single peak with a Stokes radius of 33 Å. No immunoactive material was associated with this peak. This receptor fragment probably corresponds to the 28-Å species described by Stevens and Stevens (1981). The difference in size is most likely attributable to the use of buffers containing 0.6 M KCl by these workers. In contrast, all the immunoactivity eluted as two peaks with Stokes radii of 26 and 14 Å. No radioactivity was associated with either of these peaks. More extensive digestion with chy-motrypsin increased the amount of the 14-Å peak at the expense of the 26-Å peak. With undigested cytosol, all the immunoactivity cochromato-graphed with bound [³H]TA close to the void volume of the column. In other experiments, it was shown that the 26-Å immunoactive fragment of rat liver glucocorticoid receptor bound to DNA–cellulose with much lower affinity than the 33-Å portion of the receptor containing the steroid-binding site.

F. Sodium Molybdate and Unactivated Glucocorticoid Receptors

As indicated earlier (Section III,D), CS P1798 tumor lymphocytes contain $\sim$60-Å, 3.7 S glucocorticoid receptors, whereas CR P1798 tumor cells contain much smaller, $\sim$28-Å, 3.3 S HR complexes. Since these parameters were measured in high-ionic-strength buffers containing 0.6 M KCl, they probably correspond to activated forms of the glucocorticoid receptor. Taking advantage of the ability of Na_2MoO_4 to prevent activation (transformation) of steroid HR complexes to the nuclear or DNA-binding form (Leach *et al.*, 1979; Nishigori and Toft, 1980; Shyamala and Leonard, 1980), Stevens *et al.* (1981b) examined the physicochemical properties of unactivated glucocorticoid–receptor complexes from the CS and CR strains of mouse lymphoma P1798. Cytosol was labeled with [^{3}H]TA at 4°C in the presence of Na_2MoO_4 and analyzed on columns of BioGel A-1.5m equilibrated with low-ionic-strength buffer containing 50 mM KCl plus 20 mM Na_2MoO_4 or with 50 mM KCl plus 30 mM NaCl. The conductivity of this buffer is identical to that of 50 mM KCl plus 20 mM Na_2MoO_4. The cytosol was kept at 4°C at all times. Figure 14a shows that when chromatographed in low-salt buffer containing Na_2MoO_4, unactivated CS P1798 [^{3}H]TA–receptor complexes eluted as a single peak with a Stokes radius of $\sim$81 Å, slightly smaller than the 85-Å thyroglobulin standard (T) and considerably larger than the 61.5-Å ferritin standard (F). In the absence of Na_2MoO_4 the CS HR complexes eluted slightly after ferritin with a Stokes radius of $\sim$60 Å (Fig. 14b). In sharp contrast, unactivated CR P1798 [^{3}H]TA–receptor complexes eluted with a Stokes radius of $\sim$70 Å in the presence of Na_2MoO_4 (Fig. 15a) compared to a Stokes radius of 34 Å in its absence (Fig. 15b). This result has been obtained consistently. Therefore, the Stokes radius of unactivated CS P1798 tumor lymphocyte cytosolic [^{3}H]TA–receptor complexes (81 $\pm$ 1 Å; mean $\pm$ SD; $n = 13$) was significantly larger ($p < 0.001$) than that of unactivated CR P1798 [^{3}H]TA–receptor complexes (70 $\pm$ 1 Å; mean $\pm$ SD; $n = 11$). In order to detect the 81- and 70-Å forms of CS and CR P1798 complexes, respectively, it was only necessary for the columns to have been equilibrated and eluted with low-ionic-strength buffer containing Na_2MoO_4. Thus, results identical to those just described were obtained whether or not the cytosol itself had been prepared with buffer containing molybdate. This suggests that conversion of the 81- and 70-Å forms to the 60- and 34-Å species, respectively, took place in the course of gel filtration and not during preparation and labeling of the cytosol.

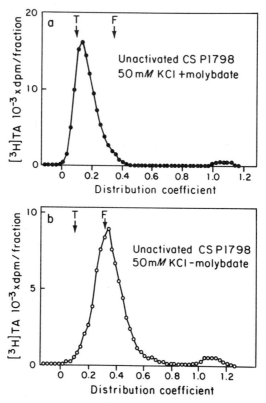

Fɪɢ. 14. Influence of Na_2MoO_4 on the size of CS P1798 cytosolic [³H]TA–receptor complexes. Agarose gel filtration of [³H]TA-labeled cytosol on a column of BioGel A-1.5m equilibrated with 50 mM KCl plus 20 mM Na_2MoO_4 in 10 mM tris(hydroxymethyl)methyl-2-aminoethane sulfonic acid (TES):4 mM EDTA:10% (w/v) glycerol:0.5 mM dithiothreitol (pH 7.4 at 4°C) (a), or with 50 mM KCl minus Na_2MoO_4 in the same buffer (b). Arrows, position of standard proteins; T, thyroglobulin; F, ferritin.

As shown in Fig. 16, when molybdate-free [³H]TA-labeled CS P1798 cytosol was activated by warming for 1 hour at 20°C and then analyzed on columns of BioGel A-1.5m equilibrated with low-salt buffer plus Na_2MoO_4, the HR complexes eluted in two distinct peaks with Stokes radii of ∼81 and 60 Å. Figure 17 shows that similar treatment of CR P1798 cytosol caused a reduction in the amount of 70-Å [³H]TA–receptor complexes and the concomitant appearance of complexes with a Stokes radius of 26 Å. Figures 16 and 17 also show that the magnitude of the shift from larger to smaller Stokes radius was more pronounced in cytosols containing 5 mg protein/ml than in preparations containing 10 mg protein/ml. This was true

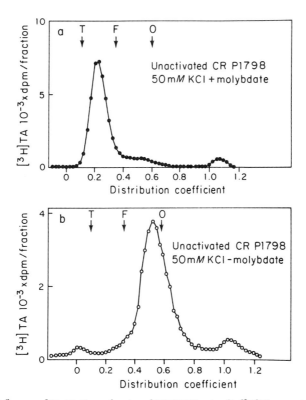

FIG. 15. Influence of Na_2MoO_4 on the size of CR P1798 cytosolic [³H]TA–receptor complexes. Conditions as in Fig. 14. Arrows, position of standard proteins; T, thyroglobulin; F, ferritin; O, [¹⁴C]ovalbumin.

for both CS and CR cytosols and may be due to dilution of inhibitors that are known to be present in crude receptor preparations (Milgrom, 1981).

In these experiments, Na_2MoO_4 (final concentration, 20 mM) was added to the cytosol immediately after the 1-hour warming period following which the cytosol was held at 4°C for an additional 2 hours prior to chromatographic analysis. Therefore, the larger fraction of 81- or 70-Å material in the more concentrated cytosol could have been due to the ability of molybdate to cause reaggregation of putative subunits more easily in cytosols with higher amounts of protein. This possibility was tested by warming a concentrated cytosol (8 mg protein/ml) and then dividing it into two portions, one of which was immediately diluted more than threefold to 2.5 mg protein/ml. Molybdate was added to the diluted and undiluted samples and after an additional 2 hours at 4°C, both kinds of cytosol were analyzed by gel filtration in the presence of molybdate. If molybdate were acting by a

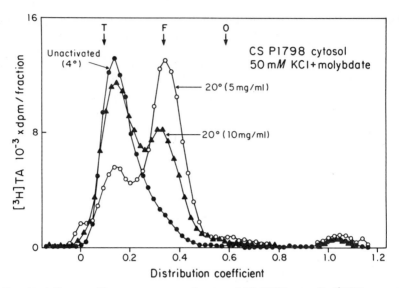

FIG. 16. Influence of heat activation on the size of CS P1798 cytosolic [³H]TA–receptor complexes. Agarose gel filtration of [³H]TA-labeled cytosol on a column of BioGel A-1.5m equilibrated with 50 m*M* KCl plus 20 m*M* Na₂MoO₄ in the same buffer as in Fig. 14a. Arrows and abbreviations as in Fig. 15.

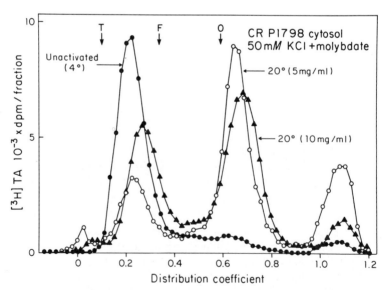

FIG. 17. Influence of heat activation on the size of CR P1798 cytosolic [³H]TA–receptor complexes. See legend to Fig. 16 for experimental details.

process of reaggregation, the cytosol that received molybdate subsequent to heat activation and dilution should have contained considerably more ~60-Å (CS P1798) or ~26-Å (CR P1798) HR complexes than cytosol that was not diluted after heat activation. However, this was not the case. Therefore, in this system, Na_2MoO_4 appears to act by stabilizing preexisting large (81- and 70-Å) forms of the [^{3}H]TA–receptor complex. It is not known if these large forms exist as such in whole cells or whether they are generated as a result of cell disruption and subsequent labeling procedures.

Ultracentrifugal analysis of unactivated P1798 [^{3}H]TA–receptor complexes on low-ionic-strength glycerol gradients containing 20 mM Na_2MoO_4 also revealed much larger forms of HR complex than detected previously under "activating" conditions (Section III,D). In these experiments, [^{14}C]ovalbumin (3.53 S), [^{14}C]bovine serum albumin (4.4 S), [^{14}C]IgG (6.6 S), or catalase (11.3 S) were used as internal standards on the gradients. Figure 18a shows that unactivated CS P1798 [^{3}H]TA–receptor complexes had a sedimentation coefficient of 9.2 ± 0.1 S (mean ± SD; $n = 3$), which was significantly smaller ($p < 0.001$) than the sedimentation coefficient (9.9 ± 0.1 S) (mean ± SD; $n = 3$) of unactivated cytosolic CR P1798 [^{3}H]TA–receptor complexes (Fig. 18b). After heat activation (1 hour at 20°C; 5 mg protein/ml), the sedimentation coefficient of CS P1798 [^{3}H]TA–receptor complexes decreased to 4.0 ± 0.04 S (mean ± SD; $n = 3$) on low-salt gradients with molybdate

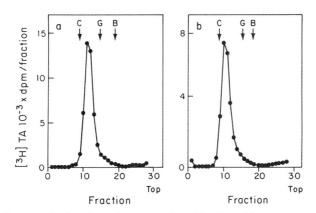

FIG. 18. Ultracentrifugal analysis of unactivated CS (a) and CR (b) P1798 cytosolic [^{3}H]TA–receptor complexes. Linear 8–35% (w/v) glycerol gradients containing 50 mM KCl and 20 mM Na_2MoO_4 in 10 mM TES:4 mM EDTA:0.5 mM dithiothreitol (pH 7.4 at 4°C) were centrifuged for 17 hours at 40,000 rpm in an SW 50.1 rotor (Beckman Instruments, Inc.). Each sample contained 1 mg of protein in a total volume of 0.4 ml. The gradients were fractionated and analyzed according to Stevens and Stevens (1979). Arrows, position of the internal marker proteins; C, catalase (assayed spectrophotometrically as described in the Worthington Enzyme Manual, 1977); G, [^{14}C]IgG; B, [^{14}C]bovine serum albumin.

(Fig. 19a). Surprisingly, the sedimentation coefficient of heat-activated CR P1798 complexes that were analyzed under identical conditions (4.1 ± 0.05 S; mean ± SD, $n = 3$) was not significantly different from that of the CS complexes (Fig. 19b). The small peak near the bottom of the tube probably corresponds to residual unactivated complex. Portions of activated cytosol were also centrifuged through glycerol gradients containing 0.6 M KCl with or without Na_2MoO_4. In this high-ionic-strength environment and in agreement with earlier results (Section III,D) CS complexes had a sedimentation coefficient of 3.7 ± 0.02 S whereas that of CR complexes was 3.4 ± 0.04 S ($p < 0.001$), regardless of whether the gradients contained molybdate or not (not shown).

In other studies we found that after warming [³H]TA-labeled CS or CR P1798 cytosol (5 mg protein/ml; no molybdate) for 1 hour at 20°C, 60–70% of HR complexes were retained on a column of DNA–cellulose (equilibrated with 20 mM Na_2MoO_4) compared to less than 5% of HR complexes in unwarmed cytosol. These values are in good agreement with the proportion of complexes undergoing a shift in Stokes radius from 81 to ~60 Å (CS cytosol) and from 70 to ~26 Å (CR cytosol) detected by gel filtration in low-salt buffer plus molybdate on columns of BioGel A-1.5m. These results and the data presented in previous sections are consistent with the idea that the Stokes radius of activated (DNA-binding form) CS P1798 [³H]TA–receptor complexes is ~60 Å whereas that of CR P1798 glucocorticoid–receptor complexes is considerably smaller (26–28 Å). Furthermore, the experiments show that heat activation of tumor lymphocyte glucocorticoid receptors causes a pronounced change in their physicochemical properties

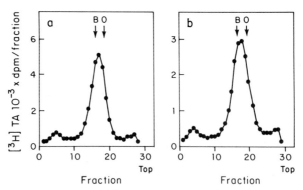

FIG. 19. Ultracentrifugal analysis of heat-activated CS (a) and CR (b) P1798 cytosolic [³H] TA–receptor complexes. Conditions as in Fig. 18 except that the gradients contained 4–17.5% (w/v) glycerol. Arrows, position of the internal marker proteins; B, [¹⁴C]bovine serum albumin; O, [¹⁴C]ovalbumin.

that can be readily detected by gel filtration and ultracentrifugal analysis. Thus, the alteration in surface charge that appears to be responsible, at least in part, for the difference in affinity between unactivated and activated HR complexes for polyanions (e.g., DNA) (DiSorbo *et al.*, 1980, Milgrom, 1981) takes place on a background of profound modifications of the physicochemical properties of the receptor molecule. Although several hypotheses have been advanced to explain how these changes take place (Sando *et al.*, 1979; Barnett *et al.*, 1980; Milgrom, 1981), the actual mechanisms involved and how molybdate influences them remain to be established.

It has not been unequivocally determined whether unactivated glucocorticoid receptors consist exclusively of polypeptide chains or whether they contain nonprotein components or are modified in other ways that could influence their hydrodynamic behavior. For example, although the Stokes radius of unactivated CS P1798 [^{3}H]TA–receptor complexes is larger than that of CR P1798 complexes (81 versus 70 Å), the CS complexes sediment more slowly than the CR complexes (9.2 versus 9.9 S). Based on conventional assumptions (Sherman, 1975) this would imply that the molecular weights of unactivated CS and CR P1798 [^{3}H]TA–receptor complexes are ~325,000 and ~300,000, respectively.

It was shown earlier (Section III, E) that limited digestion with chymotrypsin converted activated CS P1798 [^{3}H]TA–receptor complexes to a smaller form, the physicochemical and DNA-binding properties of which were indistinguishable from those of CR P1798 [^{3}H]TA–receptor complexes. In addition, it was shown that mild trypsinization reduced both activated CS and CR HR complexes to a much smaller form (meroreceptor?) that did not bind to DNA. Therefore, it was of interest to examine the effect of similar enzymatic treatment on unactivated CS and CR glucocorticoid receptors. Incubation with chymotrypsin (0.12 unit per milligram of cytosol protein) was carried out for 30 minutes at 10°C in the absence of molybdate. This resulted in little or no activation of the complexes. The digestion products were analyzed under low salt conditions in the presence of Na$_2$MoO$_4$. As shown in Fig. 20, digestion of [^{3}H]TA-labeled CS cytosol with chymotrypsin caused the CS complexes to elute about halfway between thyroglobulin and ferritin with a Stokes radius of ~70 Å, identical to the Stokes radius of unactivated, undigested CR complexes. Chymotrypsin had no effect on the Stokes radius of unactivated CR HR complexes which, therefore, remained at ~70 Å (not shown). In contrast, as shown in Figs. 21 and 22, digestion with trypsin (2.72 units per milligram of cytosol protein) converted both unactivated CS and CR P1798 [^{3}H]TA–receptor complexes to a much smaller form that eluted between [^{14}C]carbonic anhydrase and myoglobin with a Stokes radius of 21–22 Å. Thus, after digestion with chymotrypsin, unactivated CS and CR glucocorticoid–receptor complexes were still larger than their

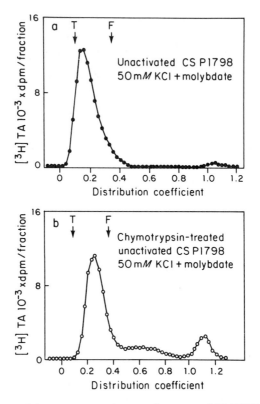

FIG. 20. Influence of chymotrypsin on the size of unactivated CS P1798 cytosolic [³H]TA–receptor complexes. Gel filtration was performed as in Fig. 14a. (a) Undigested cytosol. (b) Chymotrypsin-treated cytosol. Arrows, position of the standard proteins; abbreviations as in Fig. 14.

activated counterparts whereas there appeared to be no difference in size between the trypsin fragments generated from unactivated or activated complexes.

The influence of molybdate on glucocorticoid receptors from CS and CR human leukemic lymphoblasts is discussed in Section IV,C.

Sherman *et al*. (1981) showed that in the presence of Na₂MoO₄, fresh, unactivated rat liver cytosolic glucocorticoid receptors had a Stokes radius of 82 ± 4 Å and a sedimentation coefficient of 9.2 ± 0.1 S. In contrast, rat kidney cytosolic [³H]TA–receptor complexes had a Stokes radius of 71 ± 3 Å and a sedimentation coefficient of 9.9 ± 0.3 S under identical conditions. Markovic *et al*. (1980) reported that the Stokes radius of activated kidney cortex glucocorticoid receptor was 20–26 Å and showed that this

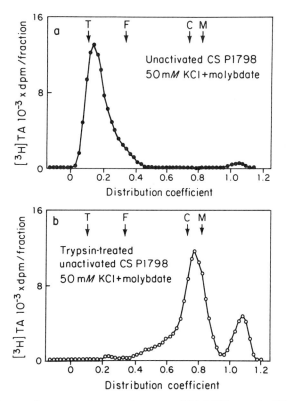

FIG. 21. Influence of trypsin on the size of unactivated CS P1798 cytosolic [³H]TA–receptor complexes. Other conditions as in Fig. 14a. (a) Undigested cytosol. (b) Trypsin-treated cytosol (2.72 units per milligram of protein for 30 minutes at 10°C). Arrows, position of the standard proteins; C, [¹⁴C]carbonic anhydrase; M, myoglogin. The small peak after myoglobin is free [³H]TA.

form was a DNA-binding protein. The appearance of this form of receptor, designated corticosteroid binder IB by analogy to a similar protein described by Litwack and Rosenfield (1975) in rat liver, was not prevented by 5 mM leupeptin. Rat liver glucocorticoid binder II (~60 Å) was not converted to IB by warming a mixture of liver and kidney cytosol for 30 minutes at 25°C. Clearly, there is a certain degree of similarity between the physicochemical characteristics of CR mouse lymphoma P1798 and rat kidney cortex [³H]TA–receptor complexes. Furthermore, neither CR P1798 nor kidney cortex HR complexes were recognized by antibody raised against rat liver 60-Å glucocorticoid receptor (Markovic *et al.*, 1980; Section III,G).

Administration of dexamethasone is known to increase the activity of rat kidney cortex tyrosine aminotransferase (Elam and Barnett, 1981). If it can

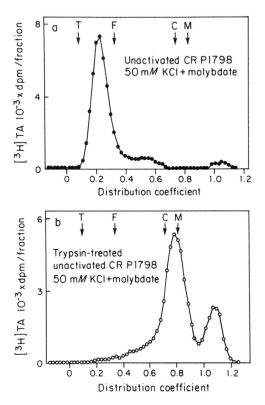

FIG. 22. Influence of trypsin on the size of unactivated CR P1798 cytosolic [³H]TA–receptor complexes. (a) Undigested cytosol. (b) Trypsin-treated cytosol. See Fig. 21 for other details. The small peak after myoglobin is free [³H]TA.

be shown that this is a direct, receptor-mediated effect of the steroid, this would imply that HR complexes with altered physicochemical properties, such as those present in kidney cortex, the CR strain of mouse lymphoma P1798 and the CR [r(+) nt^i] mutant of lymphoma S49 may be functional. In this case, resistance of malignant lymphocytes with "small" glucocorticoid receptors to steroid-induced cell killing might not be entirely attributable to "defective" receptor.

The possibility still remains that CR P1798, CR S49 [r(+) nt^i], and rat kidney cortex glucocorticoid receptors are cleaved instantaneously upon rupture of the cells by extremely labile, molybdate-insensitive, leupeptin-insensitive enzymes that lose activity very rapidly in broken cell preparations. It may be possible to shed light on this problem by incubating intact cells with steroidal affinity labels such as [³H]dexamethasone-21-mesylate (Eisen *et al.*, 1981) followed by isolation and analysis of glucocorticoid–receptor complexes under conditions that prevent all degradative activity without dissociation of the covalently bound radioactive ligand. It is clear that resolution of this problem is of utmost importance for understanding the mechanism of resistance to steroid action in CR mutants in which glucocorticoid receptors appear to have altered physicochemical properties.

G. Immunochemical Studies

The pioneering work of Eisen (1982), Okret *et al.* (1981), and Govindan (1979) in developing antibodies against glucocorticoid receptors has opened new avenues of inquiry into the properties of these important regulatory proteins. The antibody described by Eisen was raised against highly purified, 60-Å Stokes radius, rat liver [^{3}H]TA–receptor complex. The immune IgG was purified and an immunoaffinity column was prepared by covalently linking it to Sepharose CL-4B. The antiserum did not cross-react with rat serum cortisol-binding globulin, rat liver glucocorticoid binder 1B, or with rat liver estrogen-binding protein (Eisen, 1982). This antiserum was used to investigate the immunochemical properties of glucocorticoid receptors from CS and CR malignant lymphocytes (Stevens *et al.* 1981b). Figure 23 shows that more than 80% of CS P1798 [^{3}H]TA–receptor complexes were retained by the immunoaffinity column compared to only 1% retention by a column prepared with nonimmune IgG. The inability of the nonimmune column to retain bound [^{3}H]TA was not due to dissociation or degradation of the HR complexes since 85% of the radioactivity that was recovered in the drop-through fractions chromatographed as the typical ~60-Å CS P1798 [^{3}H]TA–receptor complex on BioGel A-1.5m. In contrast, CR P1798 [^{3}H]TA–receptor complexes behaved very differently from CS P1798 complexes on the immune IgG column.

Only 1% of CR complexes were adsorbed onto the immune column (Fig. 24) and most of the nonretained radioactivity was recovered in the form of the characteristic 28-Å CR P1798 HR complex in the drop-through fractions. Therefore, failure of the immune IgG–Sepharose to recognize CR P1798 receptor was not attributable to dissociation of the [^{3}H]TA or degradation of HR complexes on the column. Similar results were obtained independently by Carlstedt-Duke *et al.* (1982) and Okret *et al.* (1982) also using antisera raised against highly purified, 60-Å rat liver glucocorticoid receptor.

In other experiments it was established that the immune IgG affinity gel also recognized [^{3}H]TA–receptor complexes from normal CS mouse lymphocytes (thymus) as well as from CS human acute (CH6) and chronic leukemic lymphocytes (CLL) (Table V). In all cases, the Stokes radius of

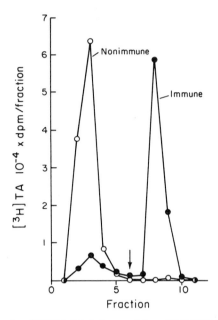

FIG. 23. Chromatography of [³H]TA-labeled cytosol from CS P1798 tumor lymphocytes on "immune" (●) and "nonimmune" (○) IgG–Sepharose CL-4B. Radioactivity from HR complexes that were retained on the column after extensive washing with equilibrating buffer (10 m*M* TES:4 m*M* EDTA:0.5 *M* NaCl:10% (v/v) glycerol:0.5 m*M* dithiothreitol; pH 7.5 at 4°C) was eluted with 0.1 *M* acetic acid. Arrow, start of elution with acetic acid. From Stevens *et al.* (1981a) with permission. This reference should be consulted for details.

cytosolic [³H]TA–receptor complexes from these cells was 58 to 61 Å in high-ionic-strength buffer. It is interesting that Eisen's anti-rat glucocorticoid receptor antibody was unable to recognize the 20- to 26-Å glucocorticoid binder in rat kidney cortex (Markovic *et al.*, 1980).

As indicated earlier, the antibody used in the above studies was raised against 60-Å rat liver [³H]TA–receptor complexes (Eisen, 1982). All the [³H]TA–receptor complexes it recognized had a Stokes radius of 58–62 Å. The inability of the antibody to react with the 28-Å CR P1798 receptor suggests that the antigenic recognition site(s) may be located on the 61 → 28-Å portion of the receptor molecule. Another explanation is that the 28-Å fragment obtained by chymotrypsin digestion of the 60-Å CS P1798 receptor may be immunochemically distinct from the 28-Å CR P1798 [³H] TA–receptor complex. Finally, it is possible that both regions of the receptor molecule must be present for the antibody to bind. In any event, these results suggest that rat liver glucocorticoid receptor and lymphoid [³H]TA– receptor complexes from species as diverse as mouse and humans may

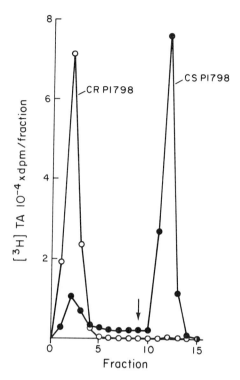

FIG. 24. Chromatography of [³H]TA-labeled cytosol from CS (●) and CR (○) P1798 tumor lymphocytes on "immune" IgG–Sepharose CL-4B. Other details as in Fig. 23. From Stevens *et al.* (1981a) with permission.

share antigenic determinants. However, the cross-reactivity is probably incomplete, as indicated by the fact that an immunoaffinity column capable of retaining more than 200 pmol of 60-Å rat liver glucocorticoid receptor adsorbed only 9% of an equivalent input load of 60-Å mouse liver [³H]TA–receptor complexes (Eisen, 1980). In our experiments with mouse and human lymphoid glucocorticoid receptors, the input loads were kept between 1 and 2 pmol.

Another conclusion to be drawn from these experiments is that it may be feasible to distinguish between CS and r(+) CR leukemias and lymphomas on the basis of differences in immunochemical properties of their glucocorticoid receptors. In the particular case described here, CS and CR HR complexes were not only immunochemically different but also physicochemically distinct. As more antisera become available, and with the development of monoclonal antibodies, it may be possible to detect immunochemical differences between

TABLE V

IMMUNOAFFINITY CHROMATOGRAPHY OF MOUSE AND HUMAN
LYMPHOID GLUCOCORTICOID–RECEPTOR COMPLEXES[a]

| Cytosol | Input dpm absorbed (%) | |
	Immune gel	Nonimmune gel
CS P1798		
1	78	ND[b]
2	84	1
CR P1798		
1	2.4	ND
2	1.0	ND
Mouse thymus		
1	72	ND
2	68	0.8
CH6		
1	67	ND
2	69	1
CLL		
J.M.	70	1
L.C.	70	1

[a] The amount of protein applied varied from 1.54 to 3.32 mg. Input dpm varied from 55,000 to 156,000. From Stevens *et al.* (1981b) with permission.
[b] ND, not done.

CS and CR glucocorticoid receptors that are indistinguishable by the classic techniques of protein biochemistry.

The availability of antibodies directed against purified glucocorticoid receptors may also help to clarify whether so called r(−) CR lymphocytes actually lack receptor protein or whether they contain defective glucocorticoid-binding components that cannot bind steroid or only do so with very low affinity.

H. THE "FREE FATTY ACID" HYPOTHESIS OF RESISTANCE

Turnell *et al.* (1973) noted the existence of a parallelism between the ability of free fatty acids to lyse malignant lymphocytes and the sensitivity of the cells to corticosteroids. Exposure of CS P1798 tumor lymphocytes to 78 μM palmitic acid or 53 μM azelaic acid caused a 35–40% reduction in the number of viable (eosin-excluding) cells after 4 hours at 38°C. All the CS cells were lysed after 5.5 hours incubation with 53 μM azelaic acid. In contrast, 10-fold higher concentrations of azelaic acid lysed only 10% of

CR P1798 lymphocytes. Normal thymocytes, which are exquisitely sensitive to corticosteroids, were lysed by the same concentrations of free fatty acids that were toxic to CS P1798 lymphocytes. Electron microscopic studies showed that the changes in nuclear structure caused by exposure of CS cells to free fatty acids were strikingly similar to those usually observed after treatment with cortisol. Although free fatty acids were toxic to intact CS P1798 lympohcytes but not to CR P1798 lymphocytes, isolated nuclei from both strains of tumor were equally sensitive to damage by 50 μM sodium oleate. Therefore, the CR cells appeared to have an extranuclear mechanism that protected them from free fatty acid-induced cytolysis. Turnell *et al.* (1973) suggested that this may be related to the greater capacity of the CR cells to oxidize free fatty acids, thereby preventing intracellular levels from reaching concentrations capable of damaging the nucleus. When three tumor lines that were resistant both to cortisol and 500 μM free fatty acids (CR P1798, L1210, and L5178Y) were incubated with 80 μM oleic acid plus 132 μM citral (a branched C_8 aldehyde that may block β-oxidation), 90–100% of the cells were lysed after 5 hours incubation at 37°C, compared to only 15–30% when the cells were exposed to citral alone (Turnell and Burton, 1974).

If glucocorticoid-induced lymphocytolysis is mediated by increased intracellular free fatty acids, it should be possible to demonstrate this increase in CS cells that were exposed to steroid. Indeed, Turnell *et al.* (1973) found a 76% increase in free fatty acid concentration in thymocytes from mice injected 2 hours previously with 1 mg of dexamethasone. However, CS P1798 lymphocytes showed only a 14% increase; there was a 22% decrease in CR P1798 lymphocytes. It is not clear whether these changes were due to direct effects of the steroid on the lymphocytes or whether they resulted from systemic actions of the hormone. Zyskowski *et al.* (1979) were unable to demonstrate increased intracellular accumulation of nonesterified fatty acids after incubating thymocytes for 2 hours with 1.3 μM cortisol. These results were confirmed by Seillan *et al.* (1981). Since Burton *et al.* (1967) had previously reported that cortisol-induced alterations in the nuclear structure of mouse thymocytes were clearly visible by 2 hours, it seems unlikely that the nuclear damage was caused by an accumulation of free fatty acids. On the other hand, the ability of CR lymphocytes to withstand higher extracellular concentrations of free fatty acids than CS lymphocytes may be a manifestation of the hardier nature of CR cells described by Nicholson and Young (1978) (see below). Liver tumor cells displayed enhanced sensitivity to killing by antibody plus complement when their lipid and fatty acid composition was modified by growth in medium enriched with certain phospholipids or free fatty acids (Schlager *et al.*, 1979; Schlager and Ohanian, 1980; You *et al.*, 1980).

Would it be possible to sensitize CR lymphocytes to glucocorticoid by altering their lipid composition?

I. Nuclear Fragility, Resistance, and the Cell Membrane

Giddings and Young (1974) found that hypotonic lysis of rat thymocytes was accompanied by significantly greater release of DNA from nuclei of cortisol-treated cells than from nuclei of untreated thymocytes. This was attributed to increased nuclear fragility of the steroid-treated cells. Recent studies by Wyllie (1980) suggest that the enhanced release of DNA may be due to chromatin cleavage at multiple sites by glucocorticoid-induced endonuclease activity. Nicholson and Young (1978) then investigated the ability of glucocorticoids to cause increased nuclear fragility in the CS and CR strains of mouse lymphoma P1798. Incubation of CS cells with micromolar concentrations of cortisol caused a significant increase in nuclear fragility by 2–3 hours. Surprisingly, exposure of CR P1798 lymphocytes to 1 μM cortisol also resulted in a pronounced increase in nuclear fragility, except that development of the effect was delayed by approximately 3 hours compared to its appearance in CS cells. Untreated CR P1798 cell suspensions deteriorated more slowly under conditions of *in vitro* incubation than untreated CS P1798 lymphocytes, as indicated by the fact that spontaneous release (prior to hypotonic lysis) of DNA into the medium after 3 hours incubation in the absence of steroid was somewhat lower for CR than for CS lymphocytes. By 6 hours, there was further deterioration of the untreated CR tumor cells as reflected by an increase in the amount of DNA spontaneously released into the medium. Emergence of the cortisol-induced increase in nuclear fragility of the CR lymphocytes coincided with the increase in deterioration of the cells. Control experiments were performed to rule out the possibility that this was caused by the presence of a small population of more fragile CS cells in the CR tumor.

Nicholson and Young (1978) interpreted these results to mean that the events leading to cell death were initiated by glucocorticoids in both CS and CR lymphoma P1798 cells. Because of their hardier membranes (i.e., they underwent less spontaneous destruction than CS cells when incubated *in vitro*), CR P1798 tumor lymphocytes were able to withstand steroid action and were not killed by the hormone. However, when placed in an adverse environment (in this case, prolonged incubation *in vitro*), the CR lymphocytes were sufficiently "weakened," thereby enabling the underlying cortisol effect to emerge. It would be of great interest to know whether the CR strain of mouse lymphoma P1798 used by Nicholson and Young

(1978) had glucocorticoid receptors with altered physicochemical characteristics (Stevens and Stevens, 1979) since this might help to clarify whether mutant receptors are able to mediate specific glucocorticoid effects.

Behrens *et al.* (1974) reported that another CR variant of mouse lymphoma P1798 had reduced levels of sialic acid on the cell surface. It is not known whether the CR P1798 lymphocytes used by Nicholson and Young (1978) had lower levels of exposed sialic acid, and if so, whether this would have contributed to the difference in "hardiness" between CS and CR strains. Nicholson *et al.* (1981a) analyzed the proteins of CS and CR P1798 lymphocytes by two-dimensional gel electrophoresis and discovered that of approximately 700 proteins visualized, a few differed consistently between the two tumor lines. It will be interesting to see whether these proteins can be used as specific markers for steroid-resistant lymphoma cells and whether they are in some way responsible for the increased "hardiness" of CR P1798 lymphocytes. In further studies, Nicholson *et al.* (1981b) found that glucocorticoid-resistant thymocytes (obtained from rats treated for 3 days with 10 mg dexamethasone/kg body weight) contained a new 36,000-dalton protein that corresponded to a similar protein present in CR P1798 lymphocytes. However, a recent report suggests that, at least in mice, thymocytes that survive a 41-hour treatment with cortisone *in vivo* are not necessarily resistant to glucocorticoid *in vitro*. In this case, *in vivo* resistance to steroid may be a function of the microenvironment of the cells rather than an intrinsic property of the thymocytes themselves (Triglia and Rothenberg, 1981).

J. OTHER MECHANISMS OF RESISTANCE

Davis *et al.* (1980) have described what appears to be a reversible form of resistance to glucocorticoids in mouse lymphoma P1798 which apparently depends on the age or size of the tumor. Cells obtained from ascites tumors or from small subcutaneous masses were sensitive to cortisol as judged by the inhibitory effect of the steroid on thymidine incorporation into acid-insoluble material. In contrast, cortisol did not suppress thymidine incorporation by cells derived from large subcutaneous tumors. Administration of 2 mg cortisol/day up to 10 days after inoculation of 10^6 tumor cells either prevented outgrowth of the tumor or made it regress completely. However, if cortisol treatment was begun after 14 days, only partial regression was obtained followed by rapid regrowth of the tumor. Further delay rendered the treatment ineffective. The number of specific binding sites for [³H] dexamethasone was virtually identical in sensitive ascites cells and in resistant cells derived from large subcutaneous tumors, although binding affinity in the CR cells was about half that of the CS cells. Administration of nonradioactive dexamethasone to animals bearing large (CR) subcutaneous tumors decreased binding of [³H]dexamethasone in the cell-free assay by 85%. Therefore, lack of regression was not due to inability of the steroid to penetrate the large tumor mass. Other experiments revealed that the resistant state of cells obtained from large, subcutaneous tumors was fully reversible. When lymphocytes from such tumors were injected intraperitoneally, thymidine incorporation by the resultant progeny of ascites cells was inhibited more than 90% 15 hours after administration of a single 2-mg dose of cortisol. The abrupt appearance of resistance when the subcutaneous tumors reached a certain age (14 days) or size (2–3 gm) led Davis *et al.* (1980) to suggest that a nonmutational mechanism may be involved, possibly analogous to the differentiation of immature, CS cortical thymocytes to more mature medullary thymocytes which appear to be resistant to glucocorticoid-induced lymphocytolysis (Claman, 1972). Another possibility is that the large subcutaneous tumors were very hypoxic and that the normal sequence of steps in steroid hormone action was blocked under those conditions. For example, Munck *et al.* (1972) found that glucocorticoid–receptor complexes did not translocate to the nucleus in O_2-deprived, intact thymocytes at 37°C.

The influence of extracellular factors on responsiveness of lymphocytes to glucocorticoids was clearly demonstrated by Johnson *et al.* (1979). These authors found that exposure of CS mouse lymphoma S49 cells to 1 μM dexamethasone in fresh tissue culture medium for 20 hours resulted in a 50% killing effect (trypan blue exclusion test). In contrast, 90% of the cells were unable to exclude trypan blue when the lymphocytes were exposed to dexamethasone in depleted medium (i.e., the same medium in which the cells had been grown for 4 days prior to addition of steroid). Incubation of CR S49 lymphocytes with dexamethasone in depleted medium did not render the CR mutants sensitive. These results should be interpreted with caution because of the well-known limitations of dye exclusion tests for assessing cell viability (Roper and Drewinko, 1976). Another example of modulation of the cytotoxic effect of glucocorticoids by extracellular factors was reported by Kido *et al.* (1978). These authors found that the cytotoxic action of 10^{-10}–10^{-6} M TA on mouse L5178Y lymphoblasts was enhanced considerably when cells were exposed to steroid plus an amplifier isolated from the enteric bacterium *Proteus mirabilis*. The amplifier by itself was not cytotoxic and appeared to require an intact carbohydrate portion for its activity.

Kido *et al.* (1977) suggested that the amplifier might exert its effects by increasing steroid binding and decreasing decay of the HR complexes. It would be interesting to determine whether the amplifier could overcome the resistance to steroid of lymphocytes with low levels of what, by all available criteria, appear to be normal glucocorticoid receptors. Lymphocyte proliferation may also be influenced by glucocorticoidal regulation of the synthesis and/or release of specific growth-promoting factors (Smith *et al.*, 1980). For example, continuous proliferation of antigen- or lectin-activated T lymphocytes was found to be dependent on the presence of interleukin 2 (T cell growth factor). Glucocorticoids suppressed the generation of cytotoxic T cells in a mixed lymphocyte culture probably by blocking the production of interleukin 2 directly, or via inhibition of the release of a monokine that was required for interleukin 2 production. Glucocorticoids did not lyse proliferating murine T cells in medium containing interleukin 2, but caused rapid lymphocytolysis of cells in nonsupplemented medium. It is conceivable that the beneficial effects of glucocorticoids in certain types of leukemia/lymphoma might be exerted indirectly via suppression of growth factor(s) that support the proliferation of the malignant cells. In such cases, resistance could be due to the emergence of cells that are no longer dependent on the growth factor(s) for their capacity to multiply indefinitely.

IV. RESISTANCE TO GLUCOCORTICOIDS IN HUMAN LEUKEMIA AND LYMPHOMA

A. CLINICAL RESPONSE AND GLUCOCORTICOID BINDING LEVELS

Early studies on CR human leukemias and lymphomas suggested that, as in most CR murine lymphoma cell lines, steroid resistance was associated with lack of specific glucocorticoid receptors. Thus, Lippman *et al.* (1973) found that cytosol from lymphoblasts of patients with untreated acute lymphoblastic leukemia (ALL) contained appreciable levels of specific glucocorticoid-binding activity whereas cytosol from lymphoblasts of patients who no longer responded to chemotherapy schedules that included glucocorticoid was virtually devoid of specific glucocorticoid binding. Gailani *et al.* (1973) reported appreciable levels of specific glucocorticoid binding in cytosol from four lymphosarcomatous lymph nodes and also in cytosol from leukemic lymphocytes of three patients with ALL. In contrast, relatively low levels of glucocorticoid binding were detected in cytosol from a tissue culture line of lymphoblasts (MOLT-4) derived from a patient who had relapsed after receiving combination chemotherapy that included prednisone. However, more recent studies by Crabtree *et al.* (1978), Kontula *et al.* (1980), and Barrett *et al.* (1981) suggest that cells of most, if not all, hematological malignancies will be found to contain glucocorticoid receptors, regardless of the clinical response to glucocorticoids. These authors used a whole-cell binding assay in which formation of HR complexes took place within the intact cell. In the previously mentioned experiments of Lippman *et al.* (1973) and Gailani *et al.* (1973), a cytosol assay was used in which the cells were homogenized and subjected to high-speed centrifugation prior to the steroid-binding step. Whole cell binding may be more reliable than the cytosol assay under some circumstances. For example, specific glucocorticoid binding was readily demonstrated in normal human lymphocytes with the whole cell assay (Lippman and Barr, 1977; Smith *et al.*, 1977; Homo *et al.*, 1978) whereas little or no specific binding was apparent when the cytosol assay was used (Lippman *et al.*, 1973). Similarly, whole-cell assay of peripheral blood lymphocytes of most patients with CLL revealed appreciable levels of glucocorticoid binding (Terenius *et al.*, 1976; Homo *et al.*, 1978; Stevens *et al.*, 1978b, 1979b) whereas no binding was detected with the cell-free, cytosol assay (Gailani *et al.*, 1973).

When administered as a single agent, glucocorticoid induced complete remission in 45–65% of children with ALL (Cline, 1974). With modern combination chemotherapy, including glucocorticoid, over 90% of children with ALL achieve complete remission (Simone, 1979). The results of Yarbro *et al.* (1977) and Lippman (1980) suggest that the number of glucocorticoid-binding sites in the leukemic cells may be an important determinant of patient survival, regardless of the cell type involved (T, B, or null).

In general, children with greater than 6000 sites per cell remained longer in complete remission and had a longer median survival than children whose lymphoblasts had less than 6000 glucocorticoid-binding sites per cell. It is not known whether this correlation is related to the role of glucocorticoid receptors in mediating a steroid response. Bloomfield and associates (1980) reported that the median number of glucocorticoid-binding sites in lymphoma cells from a group of patients with adult malignant lymphoma who responded to single agent glucocorticoid therapy ($\geq$50% decrease in size of all tumor masses) was significantly higher than in lymphoma cells from a group of nonresponders (5600 versus 3200, $p < 0.01$). In addition, lymphoma cells from responders were more sensitive to *in vitro* inhibition of leucine and uridine (but not of thymidine) incorporation by dexamethasone than cells from nonresponders. However, on an individual basis there was considerable overlap both of receptor levels and in the degree of inhibition of precursor uptake between responding and nonresponding patients. It is important to note that readily detectable levels of specific glucocorticoid binding were present in the nonresponders' lymphoma cells, indicating that resistance was not attributable to complete absence of steroid-binding activity. The data of Marchetti *et al.* (1981) on glucocorticoid receptor levels and response to chemotherapy in patients with ALL (age 2–48 years) are in general agreement with the results of Lippman (1980) and Bloomfield and associates (1980).

Other workers have not observed a correlation between number of glucocorticoid-binding sites and *in vitro* response of human lymphoblastoid cell lines or freshly isolated human leukemic lymphocytes to glucocorticoid (Crabtree *et al.*, 1978; Homo *et al.*, 1980; Kontula *et al.*, 1980; Barrett *et al.*, 1981; Burrow *et al.*, 1981). Homo *et al.* (1980) subjected 11 patients (ages 5 to 15) with ALL to a short course of prednisone treatment prior to initiation of conventional combined chemotherapy. Six patients responded to steroid with more than 50% decrease in white blood cell count and a marked reduction in circulating blasts. However, there was no difference between responders and nonresponders in number of glucocorticoid-binding sites per cell or inhibition of thymidine incorporation *in vitro* by dexamethasone. From a similar type of study involving 19 children with ALL, Mastrangelo *et al.* (1980) likewise concluded that high concentrations of glucocorticoid receptor did not guarantee a clinical response. Furthermore, there was no correlation between *in vitro* sensitivity of the cells to dexamethasone suppression of [^{3}H]thymidine incorporation into DNA and number of binding sites per cell or clinical response to glucocorticoid.

B. Steroid Resistance in Established Human Acute Lymphoblastic Leukemia Cell Lines

Recent studies with a human ALL cell line have revealed a new form of resistance to glucocorticoid action. The original culture (CCRF-CEM) was established in the mid-1960s from a child with ALL who had been treated with a variety of chemotherapeutic agents, including prednisone (Foley *et al.*, 1965). Thompson *et al.* (1980) isolated CS and CR lines by cloning the CCRF-CEM cells in the absence or presence of 1 μM dexamethasone. The CS clone CEM-C7 contained about 20,000 [^{3}H]dexamethasone-binding sites per lymphoblast. C7 cells were killed by concentrations of dexamethasone greater than $1 \times 10^{-8} M$ with maximal effects at $5 \times 10^{-7} M$ (Norman and Thompson, 1977; Harmon *et al.*, 1979). The CR clone 4R4 contained only 5900 [^{3}H]dexamethasone-binding sites per cell and was completely refractory to the lethal action of glucocorticoids. Schmidt *et al.* (1980) compared nuclear binding in C7 and 4R4 cells. Whereas 40% of intracellular glucocorticoid–receptor complexes were associated with the nucleus after incubating C7 cells for 1 hour at 37°C with [^{3}H]steroid, no nuclear binding was observed in 4R4 cells under identical conditions. Thus, clone 4R4 is a r(+) nt$^-$ CR mutant. About 60 CR clones were isolated and all displayed the nt$^-$ phenotype.

Further characteriziation of C7 and 4R4 HR complexes revealed that CS C7 cytosolic [^{3}H]TA–receptor complexes could be activated in a cell-free system by warming the charged cytosol at 20°C in the presence of 0.2 M KCl. Activation was monitored by the change in elution profile of HR complexes from a column of DEAE–cellulose. (Sakaue and Thompson, 1977). In contrast, similar treatment of [^{3}H]TA-labeled cytosol from CR 4R4 cells resulted in rapid loss of bound [^{3}H]TA with only transient appearance of a small amount of activated complex. Thus, failure to detect nuclear-associated glucocorticoid–receptor complexes in intact 4R4 lymphoblasts at 37°C may be due to instability of the CR HR complexes under conditions that promote activation. This new form of resistance was termed "activation labile." It would be interesting to determine whether the r(+) nt⁻ CR variants of mouse lymphoma S49 belong to the activation labile category or whether this form of resistance to steroid is peculiar to human leukemic lymphoblasts. Furthermore, it might be revealing to compare the stability, charge, and physicochemical characteristics of glucocorticoid–receptor complexes from C7 and 4R4 cells that were first incubated with [^{3}H]TA at 4°C and then warmed for an appropriate period of time at 37°C, thereby allowing activation to occur in whole cells under physiological conditions.

In other studies, Harmon and Thompson (1981) found that acquisition of steroid resistance by the CS C7 cells in the absence of selective pressure was a random process that occurred at the relatively high frequency of 2–3×10^{-5} cells per generation. This rate is about 10-fold higher than that observed with mouse lymphoma cells (see Section III,B). Fifty-four spontaneously arising CR clones (among them 4R4) were examined for glucocorticoid receptor content. In most CR clones, glucocorticoid-binding activity was 10 to 30% of the level in the CS C7 parent line. The range was 5 to 104%. In this respect, the spontaneously arising human CR lymphoblasts differed from most murine CR lymphocytes, which, as described previously (Section III,C), were usually receptor negative. However, induction of steroid resistance with mutagens such as ICI 191 or MNNG resulted in CR clones which frequently contained lower levels of glucocorticoid receptor than spontaneously arising resistant mutants.

Not all CR CCRF-CEM cell lines are unresponsive to steroid because of a defect in receptor activation. In earlier experiments, Lippman *et al.* (1974) found that cytosolic [^{3}H]dexamethasone–receptor complexes from resistant CCRF-CEM cells were taken up very efficiently in a temperature-dependent manner by homologous nuclei in a cell-free nuclear binding assay. A similar observation was made with cytosolic receptors from another CR human ALL cell line, CCRF-SB. In these experiments, resistance was defined as the inability of 1 μM dexamethasone to suppress proliferation of uncloned CCRF-CEM and CCRF-SB cells in mass culture over a 2-day period. However, the results of Norman and Thompson (1977) indicate that growth inhibition may only become apparent after 3 days under these conditions. Since no companion CS cell line was examined, it could not be determined whether the putative CR cells studied by Lippman *et al.* (1974) contained normal or reduced levels of glucocorticoid-binding activity.

These observations suggested that it might be possible to obtain r(+) CR CCRF-CEM variants in which nuclear transfer of HR complexes was unimpaired. The experiments described below bear out this prediction. We cloned the commercially available CCRF-CEM cell line (American Type Culture Collection CCL 119; frozen September 1975, identifying label F-953) in RPMI 1640 medium with or without 1 μM TA by the limiting dilution technique. The resulting clones were tested for resistance or sensitivity to glucocorticoid. One resistant (CEM-E10) and one sensitive (CEM-CH6) clone were selected for further study.

In the presence of 10^{-7} M TA, the CR CEM-E10 cells cloned with 95 ± 25% (mean ± SD of five experiments) of the cloning efficiency of E10 cells that were not exposed to steroid. In contrast, the cloning efficiency of the CS CEM CH6 cells was 0.8 ± 0.1% (mean ± SD of three experiments) in the presence of 1×10^{-7} M TA compared to 78 ± 6% (mean ± SD of five experiments) in the absence of TA.

Scatchard (1949) analysis of whole-cell binding of [^{3}H]TA at 37°C indicated that CH6 cells contained 12,678 ± 3462 binding sites per cell (mean ± SD of three experiments) with an apparent dissociation constant for binding of 5.2 ± 0.5 nM compared to 6943 ± 2191 (mean ± SD of three experiments) sites per cell for E10 and an apparent dissociation constant for binding of 4.9 ± 1.0 nM. The difference in sites per cell between clone CH6 and clone E10 was not statistically significant ($0.1 > p > 0.05$) because of the rather large variability from experiment to experiment. As expected, the CS CH6 lymphoblasts displayed a considerable degree of nuclear binding at 37°C: 60% of total intracellular [^{3}H]TA–receptor complexes were associated with purified nuclei of cells incubated previously with a near-saturating concentration of [^{3}H]TA. Moreover, a similar degree of nuclear transfer was observed in the CR E10 cells. Therefore, clone E10 appears to be a bona fide r(+), nuclear transfer (+) CR human acute lymphoblastic leukemia cell line. In this respect, it differs from the CR clones isolated by Schmidt *et al.* (1980) which were r(+), nt⁻. Whole cell competition experiments at 37°C with cortisol, deoxycorticosterone, progesterone, estradiol, and testosterone (incubation with 10 nM [^{3}H]TA alone or with 10 nM [^{3}H]TA plus 25-fold molar excess of each competing steroid) indicated that the binding sites in the CH6 and E10 lymphoblasts were glucocorticoid specific.

C. PHYSICOCHEMICAL PROPERTIES OF GLUCOCORTICOID RECEPTORS

As discussed earlier, the physicochemical properties of glucocorticoid receptors in certain classes of CR murine lymphoma cells were quite different from those of HR complexes in CS lymphocytes. If similar differences existed between CS and CR human malignant lymphocytes, it would be possible to identify responsive and nonresponsive patients using relatively straightforward analytical techniques. Stevens *et al.* (1979b) characterized nuclear and cytosolic glucocorticoid–receptor complexes from peripheral lymphocytes of patients with stage 0, I, or II CLL. In the presence of high salt (0.6 M KCl) the physicochemical properties of HR complexes from these cells were very similar to those of HR complexes from CS mouse lymphoma P1798 (Stokes radius 57–61 Å; sedimentation coefficient 3.7– 3.8 S), provided adequate precautions were taken to prevent degradation of the complexes during the extraction procedure.

Although the CLL lymphocytes were responsive to glucocorticoids *in vitro*, as judged by inhibition of precursor uptake and incorporation into macromolecules (Stevens *et al.*, 1979b), it is not known whether the ability of glucocorticoids to reduce lymphoid mass in patients with CLL is due to a direct lethal effect of the steroid on the abnormal lymphocytes (Stevens *et al.*, 1979a). Gel filtration on columns of agarose A-1.5m and glycerol gradient centrifugation (both in the presence of 0.6 M KCl) of cytosolic [³H]TA–receptor complexes from CS CEM-CH6 lymphoblasts also revealed a 58- to 61-Å (Stokes radius) species that had a sedimentation coefficient of 3.6–3.7 S. Since CR mouse P1798 tumor lymphocytes and CR S49 nt^i lymphoma cells had previously been shown to contain smaller glucocorticoid receptors than the corresponding wild-type CS cells, it was of interest to determine whether a similar situation might prevail in the r(+) nuclear transfer (+) CR E10 human lymphoblasts. However, this was not the case, inasmuch as E10 cytosolic [³H]TA–receptor complexes, like CS P1798, CLL, and CH6 receptors, had a Stokes radius of 58–59 Å and a sedimentation coefficient of 3.6–3.7 S when analyzed in buffers containing 0.6 M KCl.

As discussed earlier (Section III,D), the HR complexes in the above experiments were probably activated during the analytical procedures. Indeed, we found that the Stokes radius and sedimentation coefficient of unactivated cytosolic CH6 and E10 [³H]TA–receptor complexes that were prepared and analyzed in low-ionic-strength buffers containing 20 mM Na₂MoO₄ were quite different from those of HR complexes prepared in buffers without molybdate and analyzed under high salt conditions. Thus, molybdate-stabilized CH6 complexes had a Stokes radius of 80–82 Å and a sedimentation coefficient of 9.2–9.3 S. These values were not significantly different from the phys-icochemical parameters of molybdate-stabilized E10 [³H]TA–receptor complexes (J. Stevens, Y.-W. Stevens, and H. Haubenstock, unpublished results). Niu *et al.* (1981) reported that molybdate-stabilized cytosolic glucocorticoid receptors from normal human lymphocytes and from leukocytes of children with ALL or acute nonlymphocytic leukemia were similar in size to those present in CS P1798 mouse tumor lymphocytes (Section III,F), in CS CH6, and in CR E10 human lymphoblasts. No information was provided concerning the response of these leukemic patients to glucocorticoid alone or to multidrug regimens that included steroid.

One conclusion to be drawn from the above studies is that resistance of E10 lymphoblasts to the cytotoxic action of triamcinolone acetonide cannot be due to gross alterations in the physicochemical properties of the glucocorticoid receptor or to inability of the HR complexes to be activated and bind to the nucleus in whole cells at 37°C. Whether the reduced number of binding sites might contribute to resistance has not been determined. At the present time it is not known whether the glucocortoid receptor system in E10 cells is functional or nonfunctional. The direction of future research on the mechanism of resistance of clone E10 and of others like it, which may be identified in the future, depends strongly on the outcome of experiments designed to answer this important question.

McCaffrey *et al.* (1982) have used the DEAE–cellulose technique of Sakaue and Thompson (1977) to examine the properties of glucocorticoid receptors in human acute leukemia cells. These studies were performed in the absence of molybdate. Unactivated cytosolic receptors from normal human thymus, normal human peripheral blood mononuclear cells, and from 14/14 childhood ALL samples eluted predominantly as a single component from DEAE–cellulose with 0.22 M salt, with only a minor component present in the 0.04 M salt eluate. This normal profile is comparable to the results obtained by Sakaue and Thompson with normal rat tissues, hepatoma tissue culture cells, and LA9 cells. In contrast, 10/12 adult ALL samples, 12/20 AML cases (19 adults, 1 child), and 12/16 adult CML cases in blast crisis displayed a predominant 0.04 M salt peak or a multiple-peak pattern (abnormal profile). Mixing experiments (normal profile ALL plus abnormal AML; normal AML plus abnormal AML) did not result in conversion of the normal profile to the abnormal one. This suggested that the abnormal profile was not generated artifactually during the analytical procedures.

Heat activation of cytosol from leukemic cells with the normal profile caused the expected appearance of the 0.04 M peak at the expense of the 0.22 M peak. The 0.04 M peak obtained in this fashion showed substantial binding to DNA–cellulose. In contrast, the predominant 0.04 M component in leukemic cytosol with the abnormal profile bound minimally to DNA–cellulose before or after heat activation. Finally, the 0.04 M peak from cytosols with abnormal profile sedimented more slowly (2.5 S) than the 0.04 M peak from cytosols with normal profile (3.5 S). Of the 62 cases that were studied, none were found to have activation-labile hormone–receptor complexes of the kind described by Schmidt *et al.* (1980) in steroid-resistant CEM cells.

Since all the patients studied by McCaffrey *et al.* (1982) had received multiple-agent therapy, these authors were unable to correlate receptor phenotype with steroid responsiveness. Also, as pointed out by these workers, with the exception of two cases, all the analyses were performed on samples that had been stored frozen at $-90°C$. A normal DEAE profile was obtained in the two instances in which fresh (unfrozen) cytosol was used. Lee *et al.* (1981) have shown that the Stokes radius of rat liver glucocorticoid receptor is smaller in frozen than in fresh cytosol.

V. CONCLUSIONS

Available evidence overwhelmingly favors the view that nuclear binding of HR complexes is a necessary, but not sufficient, step for steroid hormones to exert their effects on target cells, including lymphocytes. Therefore, it is not surprising that most studies on the mechanism of resistance of malignant lymphocytes to glucocorticoids have focused on the glucocorticoid–receptor complex and its interaction with the nucleus or nuclear components. However, it should be kept in mind that no direct evidence for involvement of a specific gene product capable of mediating glucocorticoid-induced cell death has been identified so far. Indeed, much pertinent information on the mechanism of resistance of certain classes of lymphocytes to the cytolytic effects of glucocorticoids has been derived from studies that are not directly concerned with receptor structure and function.

Introduction of specific DNA fragments into mammalian cells with apparent conservation of hormonal regulation of the expression of the transfected genes has recently been achieved by Hynes *et al.* (1981), Kurtz (1981), and Doehmer *et al.* (1982). Another promising development is the demonstration by Lee *et al.* (1981) and Huang *et al.* (1981) that when genes which are not normally inducible by dexamethasone are linked to DNA containing the long terminal repeat of glucocorticoid-inducible mouse mammary tumor virus (MMTV) and transfected into host cells either lacking or not inducible for the gene of interest, the transfected gene becomes steroid responsive. It can be shown that acquisition of glucocorticoid regulation most probably depends on the presence of promoter sequences within the MMTV long terminal repeat. Equally promising are the results of Payvar *et al.* (1981), who showed that highly purified (40–60% pure) rat liver glucocorticoid–receptor complexes specifically recognized certain restriction fragments of cloned MMTV DNA. At least one of these sequences was clearly not in the long terminal repeat. However, it is likely that regulation of gene expression by glucocorticoids (and other hormones) will be considerably more complex than might be inferred from the above experiments. For example, Ucker *et al.* (1981) and Feinstein *et al.* (1982) have reported that the site of integration of MMTV DNA into the genome may determine the degree to which the viral sequences can be induced by dexamethasone.

It is hoped that these advances will spur rapid progress in the understanding of the mechanisms that control glucocorticoid action in CS lymphocytes. This, in turn, should make it possible to pinpoint the defects that underlie the lack of response to steroid in CR leukemias and lymphomas.

ACKNOWLEDGMENTS

Work by J. S., Y.-W. S. and H. H. was performed in the Section on Leukemia Studies of the Research Institute of the Hospital for Joint Diseases and Medical Center, Mount Sinai School of Medicine of the City University of New York, and was generously supported by Grant CA 14987 from the National Cancer Institute and Grant BC 327 from the American Cancer Society, Inc. J. S. was the recipient of a Special Fellowship (1974 to 1976) and a Scholar Award (1976–1981) from the Leukemia Society of America, Inc. The authors are most grateful to Ms. Pauline Thomas for preparing all the figures, to Ms. Mary Kerins for typing the manuscript, and to Dr. Merry Sherman for her constructive criticism. Last, but not least, we wish to express our deep appreciation to Dr. Vincent P. Hollander for the advice and encouragement he gave us over the many years we spent together at the Research Institute.

REFERENCES

Baran, D. T., Lichtman, M. A., and Peck, W. A. (1972). *J. Clin. Invest.* **51**, 2181–2189.

Barnett, C. A., Schmidt, T. J., and Litwack, G. (1980). *Biochemistry* **19**, 5446–5455.

Barrack, E. R., Hawkins, E. F., Allen, S. L., Hicks, L. L., and Coffey, D. S. (1977). *Biochem. Biophys. Res. Commun.* **79**, 829–836.

Barrett, I. D., Panesar, N. S., Bird, C. C., Abbot, A. C., Burrow, H. M., and Steel, C. M. (1981). *Diagn. Histopathol.* **4**, 189–198.

Baxter, J. D., Harris, A. W., Tomkins, G. M., and Cohn, M. (1971). *Science* **171**, 189–191.

Behrens, U. J., Mashburn, L. T., Stevens, J., Hollander, V. P., and Lampen, N. (1974). *Cancer Res.* **34**, 2926–2932.

Bell, P. A., and Borthwick, N. M. (1979). *J. Steroid Biochem.* **11**, 381–387.

Bloomfield, C. D., Smith, K. A., Hildebrandt, L., Zaleskas, J., Gajl-Peczalska, K., Frizzera, G., Peterson, B. A., Kersey, J. H., Crabtree, G. R., and Munck, A. (1980). *Prog. Cancer Res. Ther.* **14**, 345–359.

Bourgeois, S., and Newby, R. F. (1977). *Cell* **11**, 423–430.

Bourgeois, S., and Newby, R. F. (1979). *Cancer Res.* **39**, 4749–4751.

Boyd, S., Bryson, A., Nancollas, G. H., and Torrance, K. (1965). *J. Chem. Soc.* 7353–7358.

Burrow, H. M., Bird, C. C., Waren, J. V., Steel, C. M., Barrett, I. D., and Panesar, N. S. (1981). *Diagn. Histopathol.* **4**, 175–188.

Burton, A. F., Storr, J. M., and Dunn, W. L. (1967). *Can. J. Biochem.* **45**, 289–297.

Carlstedt-Duke, J., Okret, S., Wrange, O., and Gustafsson, J.-A. (1982). *Proc. Natl. Acad. Sci. U.S.A.* **79**, 4260–4264.

Carlstedt-Duke, J., Wrange, O., Okret, S., Stevens, J., Stevens, Y.-W., and Gustafsson, J.-A. (1983). *In* "Gene Regulation by Steroid Hormones" (A. K. Roy and J. H. Clark, eds.), Vol II. Springer-Verlag, New York (in press).

Chauvière, M. (1977). *Exp. Cell Res.* **108**, 127–138.
Claman, H. N. (1972). *N. Engl. J. Med.* **287**, 388–397.
Cline, M. J. (1974). *Cancer Chemother. Rep., Part 1* **58**, 521–525.
Crabtree, G. R., Smith, K. A., and Munck, A. (1978). *Cancer Res.* **38**, 4268–4272.
Davis, J. M., Chan, A. K., and Thompson, E. A., Jr. (1980). *J. Natl. Cancer Inst.* **64**, 55–62.
Dellweg, H.-G., Hotz, A., Mugele, K., and Gehring, U. (1982). *EMBO J.* **1**, 285–289.
DiSorbo, D. M., Phelps, D. S., and Litwack, G. (1980). *Endocrinology (Baltimore)* **106**, 922–929.
Doehmer, J., Barinaga, M., Vale, W., Rosenfeld, M. G., Verma, I. M., and Evans, R. M. (1982). *Proc. Natl. Acad. Sci. U.S.A.* **79**, 2268–2272.
Eisen, H. J. (1980). *Proc. Natl. Acad. Sci. U.S.A.* **77**, 3893–3897.
Eisen, H. J., and Glinsmann, W. H. (1978). *Biochem J.* **171**, 177–183.
Eisen, H. J., Schleenbaker, R. E., and Simons, S. S., Jr. (1981). *J. Biol. Chem.* **256**, 12920–12925.
Eisen, H. J. (1982). *In* "Biochemical Actions of Hormones" (G. Litwack, ed.), Vol. IX, pp. 255–270. Academic Press, New York.
Elam, L., and Barnett, C. A. (1981). *Biochem. Biophys. Res. Commun.* **100**, 1143–1147.
Feinstein, S. C., Ross, S. R., and Yamamoto, K. R. (1982). *J. Mol. Biol.* **156**, 549–565.
Foley, G. E., Lazarus, H., Farber, S., Uzman, B. G., Boone, B. A., and McCarthy, R. E. (1965). *Cancer (Philadelphia)* **18**, 522–529.
Foley, J. E., Jeffries, M., and Munck, A. (1980). *J. Steroid Biochem.* **12**, 231–243.
Francke, U., and Gehring, U. (1980). *Cell* **22**, 657–664.
Gailani, S., Minowada, J., Silvernail, P., Nussbaum, A., Kaiser, N., Rosen, F., and Shimaoka, K. (1973). *Cancer Res.* **33**, 2653–2657.
Gehring, U. (1980). *Prog. Cancer Res. Ther.* **14**, 79–88.
Gehring, U., and Thompson, E. B. (1979). *In* "Glucocorticoid Hormone Action" (J. D. Baxter and G. G. Rousseau, eds.), pp. 399–421. Springer-Verlag, Berlin and New York.
Gehring, U., and Tomkins, G. M. (1974). *Cell* **3**, 301–306.
Gehring, U., Mohit, B., and Tomkins, G. M. (1972). *Proc. Natl. Acad. Sci. U.S.A.* **69**, 3124–3127.
Giddings, S. J., and Young, D. A. (1974). *J. Steroid Biochem.* **5**, 587–595.
Govindan, M. V. (1979). *J. Steroid Biochem.* **11**, 323–332.
Harmon, J. M., and Thompson, E. B. (1981). *Mol. Cell. Biol.* **1**, 512–521.
Harmon, J. M., Norman, M. R., Fowlkes, B. J., and Thompson, E. B. (1979). *J. Cell. Physiol.* **98**, 267–278.
Hollander, N., and Chiu, Y.-W. (1966). *Biochem. Biophys. Res. Commun.* **25**, 291–297.
Homo, F., Duval, D., Meyer, P., Belas, F., Debre, P., and Binet, J.-L. (1978). *Br. J. Haematol.* **38**, 491–499.
Homo, F., Duval, D., Harousseau, J. L., Marie, J. P., and Zittoun, R. (1980). *Cancer Res.* **40**, 2601–2608.
Huang, A. L., Ostrowski, M. C., Berard, D., and Hager, G. L. (1981). *Cell* **27**, 245–255.
Hynes, N. E., Kennedy, N., Rahmsdorf, U., and Groner, B. (1981). *Proc. Natl. Acad. Sci. U.S.A.* **78**, 2038–2042.
Jackson, V., and Chalkley, R. (1975). *J. Biol. Chem.* **249**, 1615–1626.
Johnson, L. K., Lan, N. C., and Baxter, J. D. (1979). *J. Biol. Chem.* **254**, 7785–7794.
Kaiser, N., Milholland, R. J., and Rosen, F. (1974). *Cancer Res.* **34**, 621–626.
Kido, H., Higashi, T., and Katanuma, N. (1977). *Eur. J. Biochem.* **78**, 541–546.
Kido, H., Nakanishi, T., and Katanuma, N. (1978). *Cancer Res.* **38**, 3100–3103.
Kirkpatrick, A. F., Milholland, R. J., and Rosen, F. (1971). *Nature (London), New Biol.* **232**, 216–218.

Kirkpatrick, A. F., Kaiser, N., Milholland, R. J., and Rosen, F. (1972). *J. Biol. Chem.* **247**, 70–74.

Kontula, K., Andersson, L. C., Paavonen, T., Myllyla, G., Teerenhovi, L., and Vuopio, P. (1980). *Int. J. Cancer* **26**, 177–183.

Kurtz, D. T. (1981). *Nature (London)* **291**, 629–631.

Leach, K. L., Dahmer, M. K., Hammond, N. D., Sando, J. J., and Pratt, W. B. (1979). *J. Biol. Chem.* **254**, 11884–11890.

Lee, F., Mulligan, R., Berg, P., and Ringold, G. (1981). *Nature (London)* **294**, 228–232.

Lee, H. J., Bradlow, H. L., Moran, M. C., and Sherman, M. R. (1981). *J. Steroid Biochem.* **14**, 1325–1335.

Liao, S. (1976). *In* "Receptors and Mechanism of Action of Steroid Hormones" (J. R. Pasqualini, ed.), Vol. I, pp. 159–214. Dekker, New York.

Lippman, M. E. (1980). *In* "Steroid Receptors and Hormone-Dependent Neoplasia" (J. L. Wittliff and O. Dapunt, eds.), pp. 167–176. Masson, New York.

Lippman, M. E., and Barr, R. (1977). *J. Immunol.* **118**, 1977–1981.

Lippman, M. E., Halterman, R. H., Leventhal, B. G., Perry, S., and Thompson, E. B. (1973). *J. Clin. Invest.* **52**, 1715–1725.

Lippman, M. E., Perry, S., and Thompson, E. B. (1974). *Cancer Res.* **34**, 1572–1576.

Litwack, G., and Rosenfield, S. A. (1975). *J. Biol. Chem.* **250**, 6799–6805.

Liu, S.-L., and Webb, T. E. (1977). *Arch. Biochem. Biophys.* **184**, 141–148.

McCain-Lampkin, J., and Potter, M. (1958). *J. Natl. Cancer Inst.* **20**, 1091–1108.

McCaffrey, R., Lillquist, A., and Bell, R. (1982). *Blood* **59**, 393–400.

MacDonald, R. G., Martin, T. P., and Cidlowski, J. A. (1980). *Endocrinology (Baltimore)* **107**, 1512–1524.

McPartland, R. P., Milholland, R. J., and Rosen, F. (1977). *Cancer Res.* **37**, 4256–4260.

Makman, M. H., Dvorkin, B., and White, A. (1968). *J. Biol. Chem.* **243**, 1485–1497.

Makman, M. H., Dvorkin, B., and White, A. (1971). *Proc. Natl. Acad. Sci. U.S.A.* **68**, 1269–1273.

Marchetti, P., Natoli, V., Ranelletti, F. O., Mandelli, F., De Rossi, G., and Iacobelli, S. (1981). *J. Steroid Biochem.* **15**, 261–268.

Markovic, R. D., Eisen, H. J., Parchman, G., Barnett, C. A., and Litwack, G. (1980). *Biochemistry* **19**, 4556–4564.

Mastrangelo, R., Malandrino, R., Riccardi, R., Longo, P., Ranelletti, F. O., and Iacobelli, S. (1980). *Blood* **56**, 1036–1040.

Melby, J. C. (1977). *Annu. Rev. Pharmacol. Toxicol.* **17**, 511–527.

Milgrom, E. (1981). *In* "Biochemical Actions of Hormones" (G. Litwack, ed.), Vol. VIII, pp. 465–492. Academic Press, New York.

Mosher, K. M., Young, D. A., and Munck, A. (1971). *J. Biol. Chem.* **246**, 654–659.

Munck, A. (1968). *J. Biol. Chem.* **243**, 1039–1042.

Munck, A., and Brinck-Johnsen, T. (1968). *J. Biol. Chem.* **243**, 5556–5565.

Munck, A., and Crabtree, G. R. (1981). *In* "Cell Death in Biology and Pathology" (I. D. Bowen and R. A. Lockshin, eds.), pp. 329–359. Chapman and Hall, New York.

Munck, A., Wira, C., Young, D. A., Mosher, K. M., Hallahan, C., and Bell, P. A. (1972). *J. Steroid Biochem.* **3**, 567–578.

Nicholson, M. L., and Young, D. A. (1978). *Cancer Res.* **38**, 3673–3680.

Nicholson, M. L., Voris, B. P., and Young, D. A. (1981a). *Cancer Res.* **41**, 3530–3537.

Nicholson, M. L., Voris, B. P., Wood, I. E., and Young, D. A. (1981b). *63rd Annu. Meet. Endocr. Soc., Cincinnati, Ohio* Abstract 672.

Nielsen, C. J., Sando, J. J., and Pratt, W. B. (1977). *Proc. Natl. Acad. Sci. U.S.A.* **74**, 1398–1402.

Nishigori, H., and Toft, D. (1980). *Biochemistry* **19**, 77–83.

444   *John Stevens* et al.

Niu, E.-M., Neal, R. M., Pierce, V. K., and Sherman, M. R. (1981). *J. Steroid Biochem.* **15**, 1–10.

Nordeen, S. K., Lan, N. C., Showers, M. O., and Baxter, J. D. (1981). *J. Biol. Chem.* **256**, 10503–10508.

Norman, M. R., and Thompson, E. B. (1977). *Cancer Res.* **37**, 3785–3791.

Okret, S., Carlstedt-Duke, J., Wrange, O., Carlstrom, K., and Gustafsson, J.-A. (1981). *Biochim. Biophys. Acta* **677**, 205–219.

Okret, S., Stevens, Y.-W., Carlstedt-Duke, J., Wrange, Ö., Gustafsson, J.-A., and Stevens, J. (1983). *Cancer Res.* (submitted for publication).

Parchman, L. G., and Litwack, G. (1977). *Arch. Biochem. Biophys.* **183**, 374–382.

Payvar, F., Wrange, O., Carlstedt-Duke, J., Okret, S., Gustafsson, J.-A., and Yamamoto, K. R. (1981). *Proc. Natl. Acad. Sci. U.S.A.* **78**, 6628–6632.

Pfahl, M., and Bourgeois, S. (1980). *Somatic Cell Genet.* **6**, 63–74.

Pfahl, M., Sandros, T., and Bourgeois, S. (1978a). *Mol. Cell. Endocrinol.* **10**, 175–191.

Pfahl. M., Kelleher, R. J., Jr., and Bourgeois, S. (1978b). *Mol. Cell. Endocrinol.* **10**, 193–207.

Picard, F., Homo, F., and Duval, D. (1980). *J. Steroid Biochem.* **12**, 253–258.

Roper, P. R., and Drewinko, B. (1976). *Cancer Res.* **36**, 2182–2188.

Rosen, J. M., Fina, J. J., Milholland, R. J., and Rosen, F. (1972). *Cancer Res.* **32**, 350–355.

Rosenau, W., Baxter, J. D., Rousseau, G. G., and Tomkins, G. M. (1972). *Nature (London), New Biol.* **237**, 20–24.

Sakaue, Y., and Thompson, E. B. (1977). *Biochem. Biophys. Res. Commun.* **77**, 533–541.

Sando, J. J., Hammond, N. D., Stratford, C. A., and Pratt, W. B. (1979). *J. Biol. Chem.* **254**, 4779–4789.

Scatchard, G. (1949). *Ann. N. Y. Acad. Sci.* **51**, 660–672.

Schlager, S. I., and Ohanian, S. H. (1980). *J. Immunol.* **125**, 1196–1200.

Schlager, S. I., Ohanian, S. H., and Borsos, T. (1979). *J. Immunol.* **122**, 108–114.

Schmidt, T. J., Harmon, J. M., and Thompson, E. B. (1980). *Nature (London)* **286**, 507–510.

Schrader, W. T., Coty, W. A., Smith, R. G., and O'Malley, B. W. (1977). *Ann. N. Y. Acad. Sci.* **286**, 64–80.

Seillan, C., Duval, D., and Homo, F. (1981). *J. Steroid Biochem.* **14**, 829–833.

Sherman, M. R. (1975). *In* "Methods in Enzymology" (B. W. O'Malley and J. G. Hardman, eds.), Vol. XXXVI, pp. 211–234. Academic Press, New York.

Sherman, M. R., Pickering, L. A., Rollwagen, F. M., and Miller, L. K. (1978). *Fed. Proc., Fed. Am. Soc. Exp. Biol.* **37**, 167–173.

Sherman, M. R., Barzilai, D., Pine, P. R., and Tuazon, F. B. (1979). *Adv. Exp. Med. Biol.* **117**, 357–375.

Sherman, M. R., Moran, M. C., Neal, R. M., Niu, E.-M., and Tuazon, F. B. (1981). *In* "Progress in Research and Clinical Applications of Corticosteroids" (H. J. Lee and T. J. Fitzgerald, eds.), pp. 45–66. Heyden and Son, Philadelphia.

Shyamala, G., and Leonard, L. (1980). *J. Biol. Chem.* **255**, 6028–6031.

Sibley, C. H., and Tomkins, G. M. (1974a). *Cell* **2**, 213–220.

Sibley, C. H., and Tomkins, G. M. (1974b). *Cell* **2**, 221–227.

Sibley, C. H., and Yamamoto, K. R. (1979). *In* "Glucocorticoid Hormone Action" (J. D. Baxter and G. G. Rousseau, eds.), pp. 357–376. Springer-Verlag, Berlin and New York.

Simone, J. V. (1979). *Cancer Res.* **39**, 4301–4307.

Simons, S. S., Jr., and Thompson, E. B. (1979). *Biochemistry* **18**, 4915–4922.

Smith, K. A., Crabtree, G. R., Kennedy, S. J., and Munck, A. (1977). *Nature (London)* **267**, 523–526.

Smith, K. A., Crabtree, G. R., Gillis, S., and Munck, A. (1980). *Prog. Cancer Res. Ther.* **14**, 125–134.

Smith, M. H. (1968). *In* "Handbook of Biochemistry" (H. A. Sober, ed.), p. C3. Chemical Rubber Co., Cleveland, Ohio.

Spelsberg, T. C., Thrall, C., Webster, R., and Pikler, G. (1977). *J. Toxicol. Environ. Health* **3**, 309–337.

Spindler-Barth, M., and Gehring, U. (1982). *FEBS Lett.* **138**, 91–94.

Stevens, J., and Stevens, Y.-W. (1975a). *J. Natl. Cancer Inst.* **54**, 1493–1494.

Stevens, J., and Stevens, Y.-W. (1975b). *Cancer Res.* **35**, 2145–2153.

Stevens, J., and Stevens, Y.-W. (1979). *Cancer Res.* **39**, 4011–4021.

Stevens, J., and Stevens, Y.-W. (1981). *Cancer Res.* **41**, 125–133.

Stevens, J., Stevens, Y.-W., and Hollander, V. P. (1973). *Cancer Res.* **33**, 370–374.

Stevens, J., Stevens, Y.-W., and Hollander, V. P. (1974). *Cancer Res.* **34**, 2330–2337.

Stevens, J., Stevens, Y.-W., Rhodes, J., and Steiner, G. (1978a). *J. Natl. Cancer Inst.* **61**, 1477–1485.

Stevens, J., Stevens, Y.-W., Sloan, E., Rosenthal, R., and Rhodes, J. (1978b). *Endocr. Res. Commun.* **5**, 91–108.

Stevens, J., Stevens, Y.-W., and Hollander, V. P. (1979a). *In* "Influences of Hormones in Tumor Development" (J. A. Kellen and R. Hilf, eds.), Vol. II, pp. 85–109. CRC Press, Boca Raton, Florida.

Stevens, J., Stevens, Y.-W., and Rosenthal, R. L. (1979b). *Cancer Res.* **39**, 4939–4948.

Stevens, J., Stevens, Y.-W., and Haubenstock, H. (1981a). *63rd Annu. Meet. Endocr. Soc., Cincinnati* Abstract 483.

Stevens, J., Eisen, H. J., Stevens, Y.-W., Haubenstock, H., Rosenthal, R. L., and Artishevsky, A. (1981b). *Cancer Res.* **41**, 134–137.

Story, T. M., Standaert, M. M., and Melnykovych, G. (1973). *Cancer Res.* **33**, 2872–2877.

Sutherland, E. W., III. and Haynes, R. C., Jr. (1967). *Endocrinology (Baltimore)* **80**, 288–296.

Tanford, C. (1961). *In* "Physical Chemistry of Macromolecules" (C. Tanford, ed.), pp. 317–456. Wiley, New York.

Terenius, L., Simonsson, B., and Nilsson, K. (1976). *J. Steroid Biochem.* **7**, 905–909.

Thompson, E. B., Harmon, J. M., Norman, M. R., and Schmidt, T. J. (1980). *Prog. Cancer Res. Ther.* **14**, 89–98.

Triglia, D., and Rothenberg, E. (1981). *J. Immunol.* **127**, 64–68.

Turnell, R. W., and Burton, A. F. (1974). *Cancer Res.* **34**, 39–42.

Turnell, R. W., and Burton, A. F. (1975). *Mol. Cell. Biochem.* **9**, 175–189.

Turnell, R. W., Clarke, L. H., and Burton, A. F. (1973). *Cancer Res.* **33**, 203–212.

Ucker, D. S., Ross, S. R., and Yamamoto, K. R. (1981). *Cell* **27**, 257–266.

Voris, B. P., and Young, D. A. (1981). *J. Biol. Chem.* **256**, 11319–11329.

Wheeler, R. H., Leach, K. L., LaForest, A. C., O'Toole, T. E., Wagner, R., and Pratt, W. B. (1981). *J. Biol. Chem.* **256**, 434–441.

Wrange, Ö., and Gustafsson, J.-Å. (1978). *J. Biol. Chem.* **253**, 856–865.

Wrange, Ö., Carlstedt-Duke, J., and Gustafsson, J.-Å. (1979). *J. Biol. Chem.* **254**, 9284–9290.

Wyllie, A. H. (1980). *Nature (London)* **284**, 555–556.

Yamamoto, K. R., and Alberts, B. (1976). *Annu. Rev. Biochem.* **45**, 721–746.

Yamamoto, K. R., Stampfer, M. R., and Tomkins, G. M. (1974). *Proc. Natl. Acad. Sci. U.S.A.* **71**, 3901–3905.

Yamamoto, K. R., Gehring, U., Stampfer, M. R., and Sibley, C. H. (1976). *Recent Prog. Horm. Res.* **32**, 3–32.

Yarbro, G. S. K., Lippman, M. E., Johnson, G. E., and Leventhal, B. G. (1977). *Cancer Res.* **37**, 2688–2695.

Yoo, T.-J., Chiu, H. C., Spector, A. A., Whiteaker, R. S., Denning, G. M., and Lee, N. F. (1980). *Cancer Res.* **40**, 1084–1090.

Young, D. A., Barnard, T., Mendelsohn, S., and Giddings, S. (1974). *Endocr. Res. Commun.* **1**, 63–72.

Zyskowski, L. P., Cushman, S. W., and Munck, A. (1979). *J. Steroid Biochem.* **11**, 1639–1640.

Index

A

Acetylcholine palate elevation and, 358–359

N-Acetyl-N'-formyl-5-methoxykynuren-amine, formation from melatonin, 202

N-Acetylglucosamine, α_{2u} globulin and, 9

N-Acetylserotonin, melatonin and, 191

Acid phosphatase
neuraminidase and, 366
palatal shelf and, 359

Actinomycin D
phospholipase A_2 inhibitor and, 372
progesterone action on estrogen receptor, 342
steroid receptor binding to DNA and, 271–272

Activation of glucocorticoid receptors, 407
in CR lines, 436

Acute leukemic lymphoblasts, human, glucocorticoid receptors of, 409

Acute lymphoblastic leukemia cell lines, human, steroid resistance in, 435–437

Adenosine triphosphate, cortisol binding and, 387

Adrenal chromaffin cells, NGF and, 98

Adrenocorticotropin, OIR and, 310

Age
α_{2u} globulin excretion and, 2
melatonin levels and, 212–214

Agents, hormone-like, 91–92

Ah locus
evidence for possible temporal genes, 237
history, 230–234
regulatory genes, 234–236
structural genes, 236–237

Ah receptor
characteristics of
cytosolic receptor, 238–244
nuclear receptor, 244–247

Ah receptor, characteristics of (contd.)
receptor in tissue culture, 248–250
future directions
receptors inducing other drug-metabolizing enzymes, 252
recombinant DNA and ancillary techniques, 252
structure–activity relationships, 251
transformation of cytosolic to nuclear form of receptor, 250–251
purification of, 235
speculation on origin and function of, 252–254

Aldehyde dehydrogenase, cytosolic, Ah receptor and, 254

Aldosterone, mammary growth and, 167, 173, 179

Alkaline phosphatase, glucocorticoid binding capacity and, 387–388

α-Amatin, α_{2u} globulin excretion and, 2

Amino acid(s) derivatives
as hormones, 94
incorporation, dexamethasone and, 385

Amino acid sequence
of β subunit of NGF, 102
of γ subunit of NGF, 101

9-Aminoacridine, glucocorticoid resistance and, 388

γ-Aminobutyric acid, palate elevation and, 358–359

δ-Aminolevulinic acid synthetase, induction by TCDD, 232–233

Anaerobiosis, cortisol binding by thymocytes and, 387, 432

Androgen
α_{2u} globulin excretion and, 1–2
identification and characterization of binding sites on nuclear matrix of rat prostate, 58–61

447

Contents of Previous Volumes